FAST FRACTURE AND CRACK ARREST

A symposium
sponsored by ASTM
Committee E-24 on
Fracture Testing of Metals
AMERICAN SOCIETY FOR
TESTING AND MATERIALS
Chicago, Ill., 28–30 June 1976

ASTM SPECIAL TECHNICAL PUBLICATION 627
G. T. Hahn and M. F. Kanninen
Battelle Columbus Laboratories
editors

List price $42.50
04-627000-30

AMERICAN SOCIETY FOR TESTING AND MATERIALS
1916 Race Street, Philadelphia, Pa. 19103

Library of Congress Catalog Card Number: 76-58595

NOTE

The Society is not responsible, as a body,
for the statements and opinions
advanced in this publication.

Printed in Baltimore, Md.
July 1977

Foreword

The symposium on Fast Fracture and Crack Arrest was presented at Chicago, Ill., 28–30 June 1976. ASTM Committee E-24 on Fracture Testing of Metals sponsored the symposium. G. T. Hahn, Battelle Columbus Laboratories, presided as symposium chairman. G. T. Hahn and M. F. Kanninen, Battelle Columbus Laboratories, are editors of this publication.

Related ASTM Publications

Resistance to Plane-Stress Fracture (R-Curve Behavior) of A572 Structural Steel, STP 591 (1976), $5. 25, 04-591000-30

Cracks and Fracture, STP 601 (1976) $51.75, 04-601000-30

Properties Related to Fracture Toughness, STP 605 (1976), $15.00, 04-605000-30

A Note of Appreciation to Reviewers

This publication is made possible by the authors and, also, the unheralded efforts of the reviewers. This body of technical experts whose dedication, sacrifice of time and effort, and collective wisdom in reviewing the papers must be acknowledged. The quality level of ASTM publications is a direct function of their respected opinions. On behalf of ASTM we acknowledge with appreciation their contribution.

ASTM Committee on Publications

Editorial Staff

Contents

Introduction

Structural integrity can be normally assured by preventing the *onset* of unstable crack extension. With fracture mechanics, this is done by designing structural components so that the stresses will not exceed limits imposed by flaw size and material toughness considerations. However, designs which preclude crack instablility under all conditions can be far too costly. There are, in addition, applications where the large-scale extension of a crack would have catastrophic consequences. In particular, in structures like LNG ships, arctic pipelines, and nuclear pressure vessels, unchecked crack propagation would be intolerable. Provisions for the timely arrest of an unstable crack can at the very least represent an economical second line of defense and may be a practical necessity.

It is interesting to recognize that, in giving direct consideration to the arrest of unstable crack propagation, fracture mechanics is returning to an initial focal point of the subject. Present day fracture mechanics has largely evolved from the failures of World War II all-welded merchant ships. Attempts to control these were made by installing flame-cut longitudinal slots covered with riveted straps where unstable cracks were anticipated. But, while many cases are on record of cracks being arrested by these devices and ships saved by their presence, this approach was quickly abandoned after the war in favor of designing against the initiation of crack growth. This work was spearheaded by G. R. Irwin, the author of the first paper in this volume, and his colleagues at the Naval Research Laboratory. Their work laid the foundations of present day linear elastic fracture mechanics which is now the basis for a more rational approach to crack-arrest design.

Since World War II, the crack-arrest strategy has found application in welded ships, aircraft structures, transmission pipelines, and nuclear pressure vessels. Taking linear elastic fracture mechanics concepts as the starting point, design guidelines for arresters integral with ship hulls were developed in Japan in the 1960s. An excellent review of the Japanese research by Professor T. Kanazawa can be found in *Dynamic Crack Propagation,* G. S. Sih, Ed., Noordhoff, 1972, the proceedings of the last major conference devoted entirely to this topic. As a more specialized example, fracture mechanics applications to crack arrest in gas transmission pipelines have also been made. These are reported in *Crack Propagation in Pipelines,* published by the Institute of Gas Engineers, London, 1974.

The present symposium was sponsored by ASTM Committee E-24 on Fracture Testing of Metals. It reflects the recent expansion of interest in crack-arrest technology. This interest has been stimulated both by the availability of *dynamic* fracture mechanics analyses—calculations, which account for the effects of kinetic energy and inertia—and the importance of the technological applications. The analyses have raised serious questions about the conventional interpretation of laboratory procedures for measuring and applying the arrest toughness property. Concurrently, research has been prompted by the assessments of crack arrest in nuclear pressure vessels required by the ASME Code. A study of this problem by a joint PVRC/MPC Working Group, in 1973 and 1974, has led to several large research programs under U.S. Nuclear Regulatory Commission (USNRC) and the Electric Power Research Institute (EPRI) auspices. All of these activities have generated interest in a test practice for measuring the crack-arrest material properties. Work leading to a test method was begun in 1975 within ASTM E24.03.04. This symposium represents an initial step in the subcommittee's work.

The symposium was organized with the specific aim of collecting and disseminating recent research findings that have a bearing on the definition and measurement of the material properties involved in crack arrest. Owing to the growing interest in this subject in the United States and abroad, efforts made to obtain the widest possible representation were quite successful. The symposium attracted 15 technical papers from this country and 12 papers from abroad. Over 70 specialists participated in the three-day program. The papers themselves describe new methods of analyzing run-arrest events, evaluations of the effects of rapid acceleration and deceleration, new techniques for measuring crack speed, new procedures for evaluating the stress intensity of a fast propagating crack up to and beyond arrest, as well as data for nuclear grades of steel and other materials. This volume therefore offers an up-to-date account of all phases of the fast fracture arrest problem.

The symposium was organized by a committee drawn principally from E24.03.04: G. T. Hahn, Battelle's Columbus Laboratories (Chairman), H. T. Corten, University of Illinois, L. B. Freund, Brown University, G. R. Irwin, University of Maryland, M. F. Kanninen, Battelle's Columbus Laboratories (Secretary), A. S. Kobayashi, University of Washington, J. G. Merkle, Oak Ridge National Laboratories, and E. T. Wessel, Westinghouse Research Laboratory. Assistance and encouragement were also received from K. Stahlkopf and T. U. Marston, EPRI, and E. K. Lynn, USNRC. The editors would also like to express their appreciation to G. Kaufman, Aluminum Company of America, who served as a technical consultant, and J. Scott, the Chairman of E24.03. The nuts and bolts of assembling the manuscript for the printer was, as always, admirably performed by Jane Wheeler and the Staff of ASTM.

G. T. Hahn

Manager, Metal Science Section, Battelle's Columbus Laboratories, Columbus, Ohio; symposium chairman and editor

M. F. Kanninen

Senior Research Scientist, Applied Solid Mechanics Section, Battelle's Columbus Laboratories, Columbus, Ohio; editor

Analyses of the Crack Arrest Problem

G. R. Irwin[1]

Comments on Dynamic Fracturing

REFERENCE: Irwin, G. R., "**Comments on Dynamic Fracturing,**" *Fast Fracture and Crack Arrest, ASTM STP 627,* G. T. Hahn and M. F. Kanninen, Eds., American Society for Testing and Materials, 1977, pp. 7–18.

ABSTRACT: A brief review is given of basic definitions and concepts applicable to linear elastic analysis of dynamic fracturing. It is noted that determinations of the crack-extension force, $\mathcal{G}$, based upon conservation of energy may require adjustment for energy losses elsewhere than at the crack tip. From direct observation of running crack stress fields, crack speed increases rapidly with K toward a limiting speed which is maintained until K becomes large enough to cause crack division. The minimum K value of this relationship is termed K_{Im}. Estimates of K_{Im} by use of the test methods termed K_{Id} (dynamic initiation) and K_{Ia} (crack arrest) are of practical interest. The uncertainties associated with such estimates as well as testing difficulties are restricted mainly to the region above nil-ductility transition temperature where toughness increases rapidly with test temperature. Use of deep face grooves to overcome testing problems in the high toughness range introduces serious questions as to applicability of test results to natural cracks in heavy section structures.

KEY WORDS: crack propagation, dynamic fracturing, fracture (materials), fracture strength, fracture properties

Nomenclature

K	Stress intensity factor
$\mathcal{G}$	Crack extension force
x, y, z	Cartesian coordinates at a crack front point
r, θ	Polar coordinates at the crack tip
σ_y	Extensional stress normal to the crack plane
τ_{xy}, τ_{yz}	Shear stresses
α	Small segment of the x-axis at the crack tip
μ	Shear modulus
ν	Poisson's ratio
c	Crack velocity
c_1	A longitudinal wave velocity
c_2	Shear wave velocity
β_1, β_2	Dimensionless functions of c/c_1 and c/c_2

[1]Visiting professor of mechanical engineering, University of Maryland, College Park, Md. 20742.

$f(c)$	Dimensionless function of β_1 and β_2
ρ	Density
σ_Y	Tensile stress governing plastic strains
$2r_Y$	Nominal plastic zone size
δ	Crack (tip) opening displacement
E	Young's modulus
dA	Increment of separational area
dt	Increment of time
U_T	Total stress field energy
T	Total kinetic energy
P	Loading force
Δ_p	Loading force displacement
K_{Im}	Minimum value of K versus crack speed graph
NDT	Nil-ductility transition
K_{Id}	Rapid load initiation toughness
K_{Ia}	Crack arrest toughness
J, J-integral	Computation of crack tip energy loss rate from a path independent integral
DCB	Double cantilever beam (specimen type)

Definitions and Concepts

In the case of isotropic and orthotropic materials the same definitions of the characterization parameters, K and $\mathcal{G}$, may be used for the leading edge region of either a stationary or a running crack. The basic analysis assumes that the stress-strain relationship is linear-elastic, each segment of the leading edge is a portion of a straight line or simple (continuous) curve, the separational area adjacent to and behind the leading edge is flat, and the progressive fracturing characterized consists of infinitesimal increments of new separational area each of which is coplanar with plane of fracture adjacent to the leading edge. A summary of situations for which characterization in terms of K and $\mathcal{G}$ may not be appropriate, even when the foregoing assumptions are adequately representational, is given later. The influences of representational inaccuracies of the analysis model (for physical reasons) are also discussed at a later point.

For purposes of analytical discussion assume Cartesian coordinates, x,y,z, always positioned at the leading edge of the crack with y normal to the crack plane, z coincident with leading edge segment (which is of characterization interest), and x (positive) directly forward from the crack tip. In addition, assume polar coordinates, r, θ, in the plane, $z = 0$, and from the same coordinate origin such that r coincides with x (positive) when $\theta = 0$. In the special case of a two-dimensional generalized plane-stress analysis, the leading edge of the crack becomes a point, the crack plane adjacent to the leading edge becomes a line segment, and the small increment of new separational area becomes an infinitesimal line segment colinear with the crack line adjacent to the crack tip. A similar pictorial view is applicable to each segment of the leading edge of a crack in a state of generalized plane strain because, in the three-dimensional perspective, an infinitesimal increment of new separational area is always thought of as a strip parallel to the leading edge (having a dimension forward from the leading edge which is very small relative to the dimension parallel to the leading edge). For a running crack, the preceding comments imply that the coordinate origin moves with the leading edge of the crack.

The Mode 1 (opening mode) stress intensity factor, K, is defined as

$$K = \text{limit}\ (\sigma_y \sqrt{2\pi r}) \quad \text{as } r = 0 \text{ on } \theta = 0 \tag{1}$$

where σ_y is the extensional stress normal to the crack at the position, r, ahead of the crack tip. Definitions of K for Modes 2 and 3 stress fields are obtained by replacing σ_y, respectively, by the shear stresses τ_{xy} and τ_{yz} in Eq 1.

The Mode 1 crack-extension force, $\mathcal{G}$, is defined as

$$\mathcal{G} = \text{limit} \left\{ \frac{1}{\alpha} \int_0^\alpha (v)_{\alpha - r}\, \sigma_y\, dr \right\} \quad \text{as } \alpha \rightarrow 0 \tag{2}$$

where $(v)_{\alpha - r}$ is the y-direction (positive) displacement of a point on the crack plane at a distance, $\alpha - r$ behind the crack tip, and σ_y has the same meaning as in Eq 1. Definitions of $\mathcal{G}$ for Modes 2 and 3 stress fields can be obtained by replacing the integrand of Eq 2, respectively, by $(u)_{\alpha - r}\, \tau_{xy}$ and $(w)_{\alpha - r}\tau_{yz}$ where u and w are displacements in the x and z directions.

In the verbal terms, $\mathcal{G}$ is the rate of loss of energy from the stress-strain field at the crack tip singularity per unit of new separational area. The increment of new separational area used in computation of $\mathcal{G}$ is infinitesimal and virtual.

In Eq 2, as α becomes small enough, σ_y approaches the value

$$\sigma_y = K/\sqrt{2\pi r} \tag{3}$$

and $(v)_{\alpha - r}$ approaches the value

$$2\mu\, (v)_{\alpha - r} = f(c)\, \frac{2K}{\pi} \sqrt{(\alpha - r)\, 2\pi} \tag{4}$$

where μ is the modulus of shear and $f(c)$ is a dimensionless function of the crack speed, c. Carrying out the integration indicated in Eq 2 gives

$$\mathcal{G} = \frac{f(c)}{2\mu} K^2 \tag{5}$$

The corresponding proportionalities of $\mathcal{G}$ to K^2 for Modes 2 and 3 and nonisotropic materials will be omitted here. For isotropic materials and Mode 1, the proportionality factor $f(c)$ is given by

$$f(c) = \frac{\beta_1(1 - \beta_2^2)}{4\beta_1\beta_2 - (1 + \beta_2^2)^2} \tag{6}$$

where

$$\beta_1^2 = 1 - (c/c_1)^2 \tag{7}$$

and

$$\beta_2 = 1 - (c/c_2)^2 \tag{8}$$

The velocities, c_1 and c_2 are given by

$$c_1^2 = \frac{2\mu}{\rho} \frac{(1 - \nu)}{(1 - 2\nu)} \qquad \text{plane strain}$$

$$c_1^2 = \frac{2\mu}{\rho} \frac{1}{1 - \nu} \qquad \text{plane stress} \tag{9}$$

$$c_2^2 = \frac{\mu}{\rho} \quad \text{plane strain or plane stress} \tag{10}$$

where
ν = Poisson's ratio and
ρ = density of the material.

In the limit, as c approaches zero, the factor $f(c)$ approaches the values

$$f(c) = 1 - \nu \qquad \text{plane strain}$$

$$f(c) = \frac{1}{1 + \nu} \qquad \text{plane stress} \tag{11}$$

Table 1 shows the approach of $(1 + \nu)\,f(c)$ toward unity as c decreases toward zero. The computations assume plane stress and $\nu = 0.3$.

TABLE 1—*Results of experiments.*

Crack Speed	$0.5c_2$	$0.4c_2$	$0.3c_2$	$0.2c_2$	$0.1c_2$
$(1 + \nu) f(c)$	1.26	1.15	1.075	1.032	1.008

Essentially the values of $(1 + \nu) f(c)$ in Table 1 represent the increase factor of near-crack-tip opening displacements relative to static values for a given K. Actually, in the case of certain illustrative problems such as that treated by Broberg [*1*],[2] this increase of opening displacements is offset by a decrease of K below the value predicted by static analysis.

Although the crack speeds of practical interest are at or below $0.5c_2$, it can be noted that the Raleigh wave velocity (about $0.9c_2$) where

$$4\beta_1\beta_2 = (1 + \beta_2^2)^2 \tag{12}$$

represents the inertial limitation on the propagation of an undamped perfect crack disturbance.

Representational Aspects of the Linear-Elastic Model

Certain conditions of continuity are required by the linear-elastic perfect crack model previously discussed. The K and $\mathcal{G}$ characterizations are not appropriate in the close neighborhood of the intersection of the leading edge of a crack with a free surface. In addition, the increment of infinitesimal crack extension basic to the definition of $\mathcal{G}$ cannot be inclined at a finite angle with the crack plane adjacent to and behind the crack tip. Thus K and $\mathcal{G}$ must be used with caution in the close neighborhood of a finite angle change in trajectory of a crack. In many structural metals onset of rapid fracturing tends to be abrupt, and the most convenient analysis model may be one in which rapid fracturing begins with a step increase of velocity from zero or very small crack speed. Although the definitions of K and $\mathcal{G}$ are applicable before and after the abrupt change of crack speed, their values during this event are ambiguous. A similar situation occurs when arrest of a running crack appears to happen abruptly from a finite crack speed [*2*].

In structural metals, the analytical model stress field loses accuracy close to and within the crack-tip plastic zone. In response, one can simply regard K (or $\mathcal{G}$) as a parameter indicative of the stress intensity acting across the crack-tip plastic zone. The energy loss rate, concentrated in the analysis model at the crack tip, obviously occurs throughout the plastic

[2]The italic numbers in brackets refer to the list of references appended to this paper.

zone. As a rough measure of the lateral size of the plastic zone, one can use the value, $2r_Y$ given by

$$2r_Y = \frac{1}{\pi}(K/\sigma_Y)^2 \tag{13}$$

where σ_Y is a judgment choice of the average tension which accompanies yielding in the plastic zone. The progressive fracturing process consists in formation and joining of advance separations within a region adjacent to the crack tip termed the fracture process zone. The size of this zone varies with temperature, fracture mode, and material properties. With structural steels, cleavage fracturing at low temperatures may have a process zone larger than $2r_Y$. However, in the temperature regions of common interest near or above the NDT temperature, one would expect the size of the fracture process zone to be about 5δ where

$$5\delta = \frac{5K^2}{E\sigma_Y} \tag{14}$$

From Eqs 13 and 14, the fracture process zone then occupies only a small fraction of the crack-tip plastic zone. For various reasons, the irregularities characteristic of a running crack fracture surface are considerably larger than 5δ.

The formation and joining of advance separations in the fracture process zone tends to produce locally discontinuous increments of crack extension. The crack speed has no significance other than as an average of such events along the leading edge and across a forward motion substantially larger than the leading edge contour irregularities.

It is helpful to recognize that the separational behaviors in the fracture process zone are controlled by the local environmental strain across the fracture process zone. In order to produce a running crack, the surrounding elastic field must produce plastic strains continually near the advancing crack tip adequate for the separational process. Introduction of a device which would clamp or fix the displacements above and below the fracture process zone would stop the fracturing process immediately. An increase of K can enlarge the plastic strain field, increase the size of segments of crack extension, and produce a higher crack speed. Although there are complications, such as unsuccessful attempts at branching of the crack, it seems likely that limitations on the speed of propagation of the crack-tip plastic zone are a major factor in fixing the upper limiting velocity of a running crack in a structural metal. For example, velocities in the range of 1500 to 1800 m/s have been observed during brittle fracturing of wide steel plates, 25 mm thick. In comparison, observations of running cracks in gas transmission line pipe, about 10 mm thick, showed that when the plastic zone was relatively large (50 percent or more oblique shear on the fracture surface) the limiting crack speed was usually less than 400 m/s [3].

Branching of a running crack in a large plate, or hackle for a deeply embedded running crack, appears to be related closely to the attainment of a limiting crack speed. In steel plates, branching has been observed at limiting crack speeds as low as $0.17c_2$. This speed is much too low to cause a significant difference between the static and dynamic elastic stress field patterns around the crack tip. Many instances of branching have been observed which cannot be explained by dynamic warping of the crack-tip stress field, the explanation proposed by Yoffe [4]. On the other hand the association of branching with the attainment of a limiting crack speed has been consistently found.

In the case of a static crack, Eq 2 for $\mathcal{G}$ can be replaced by a path independent line-integral termed J [5]. If one extends the line-integral path to the specimen boundaries and in a manner that encircles the loading points, the equivalence of the J-integral to a compliance calibration method for $\mathcal{G}$ becomes clear. In the case of a specimen which contains a running crack, certain precautions are necessary when $\mathcal{G}$ is determined from a "total specimen" method. For example, it has been suggested that $\mathcal{G}$ can be determined from the equation

$$\mathcal{G}\frac{dA}{dt} + \frac{dU_T}{dt} + \frac{dT}{dt} - \frac{Pd\Delta p}{dt} = 0 \tag{15}$$

where

dt = small increment of time,
dA = small increment of new separational area,
U_T = total strain energy in the stress field,
T = total kinetic energy in the stress field,
P = loading force (we assume only one nonstationary loading point, and
Δ_P = load point displacement parallel to the load.

The dynamic stress pattern of the running crack can be thought of as the superposition of a large number of stress waves, each associated with a small increment of crack extension. The high frequency "noise" due to the fine scale irregularities of the fracturing process will be mainly lost by damping close to the crack tip. The corresponding energy loss, relatively small, can be properly considered as a portion of the energy loss rate, $\mathcal{G}$. However, losses of energy from the more uniform stress wave pattern may occur during reflection at corners, edges, and surfaces of the specimen as well as in the body of the material. Energy losses of this kind cannot be represented as a portion of $\mathcal{G}$ and must be accounted for in Eq 15, possibly by modification of the third term. In addition the analysis complexities of the dynamic problem provide strong motivation toward use of an oversimplified model of the specimen which has fewer degrees of freedom of motion. This adds to the difficulty of making a proper formulation of the term dT/dt in Eq 15. In general it is necessary to bear in mind that the parameters K and $\mathcal{G}$ for a running crack are defined properly only by the stresses and displacements close to the crack tip. In practical terms this means that K should be determined from the moving linear-elastic crack model which provides a best fit to the stress field close to the crack tip and outside of the crack-tip plastic zone.

When interpretation allowances are made for the points just noted, dynamic analysis determinations of K during crack propagation, including those based directly on Eq 15, are of considerable interest. In ideal concept, a complete prediction of run-arrest behavior during crack propagation requires knowledge of K at the start of rapid fracturing, the propagation behavior curve in terms of crack speed versus K, and analysis methods appropriate for dynamic aspects of the given problem. Because of the inherent analysis complexities, such oversimplifications as may be necessary to obtain approximate results are allowable and provide useful experience toward further development of dynamic analysis techniques. For example, the dynamic analysis computations and experiments reported in Ref *6*, which deal mainly with crack propagation in DCB specimens, show a substantial degree of agreement between computed predictions and experimental results. Extension of dynamic analysis capabilities to two-dimensional problems is desirable in order to study crack propagation problems which resemble cracks in service components.

Running Crack Behaviors

Figure 1 is taken from current dynamic photoelastic research at the University of Maryland. The figure shows measurements of crack speed as a function of K for running cracks in 9.5 and 12.7-mm (thickness) plates of Homalite 100, a transparent material. Velocities were inferred from observed crack-tip positions using a 16 frame multiflash camera of the Cranz-Schardin type. The experiments were conducted at room temperature. K values were obtained from measurements of the isochromatic fringes close to the crack tip.

The available information on crack speed as a function of K for brittle fracturing of structural steel [*2,3*] shows features which are generally similar to those shown in Fig. 1. In the low-velocity range, K is not sensitive to crack speed. In the high-velocity range, crack speed is not sensitive to the K value. It can be noted that several measurement points are plotted at zero crack speed. These points were derived from flash photographs which showed the crack-tip isochromatic fringe pattern at a position of temporary arrest. Within the accuracy of these studies there was no evi-

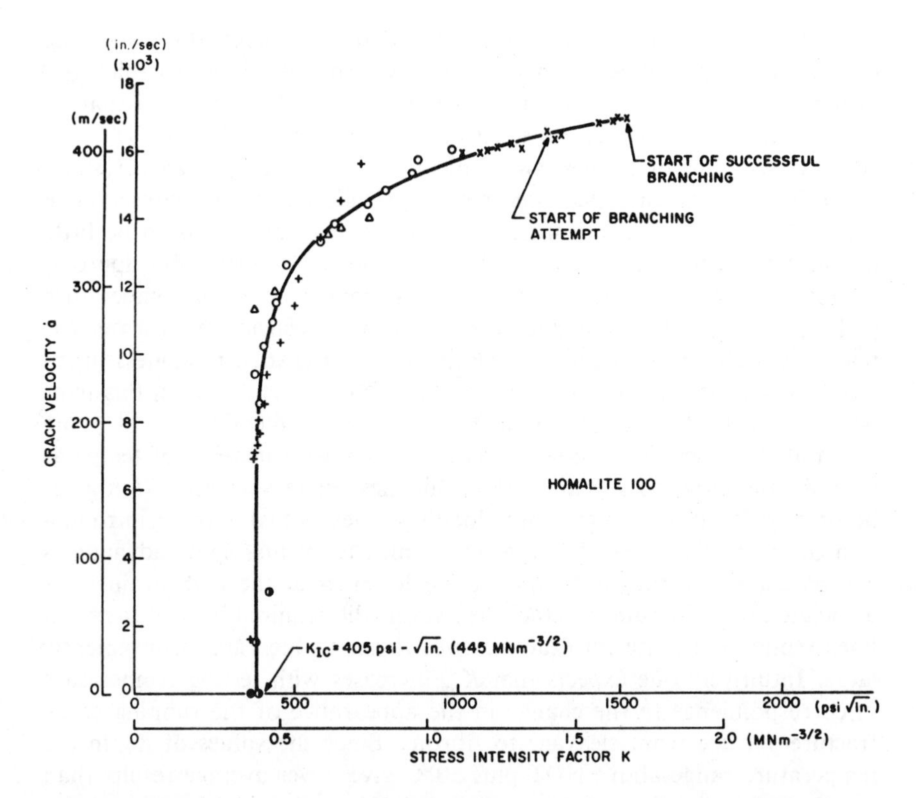

FIG. 1—*Measurements of crack speed as a function of the stress intensity factor,* K, *for Homalite 100.*

dence for a difference in the K value for a low-velocity crack approaching arrest, in a temporary arrest condition, and just after reinitiation. The upper limiting crack speed was $0.31c_2$. As would be suggested by Table 1, the velocities encountered in these experiments were not large enough to reveal a significant dynamic alteration of the crack-tip stress pattern.

Reference *7* shows graphs of crack speed as a function of $\mathcal{G}$ for three glasses of different composition. The limiting crack speeds were quite different: 1163, 1512, and 1958 m/s. All three graphs are in general agreement with the relationship shown in Fig. 1.

Minimum Resistance to a Running Crack

In Fig. 1, the graph of crack speed versus K is nearly vertical at minimum K value which will be termed, K_{Im}. Any reduction of K below K_{Im} will result in crack arrest. Thus measurements directed toward evaluation of

K_{Im} represent a natural choice for a simplified experiment which attempts to measure only a single toughness property associated with dynamic fracturing. Measurements of the kinds termed K_{Id} and K_{Ia} are of this nature [8,9]. In the case of structural steels and at temperatures below NDT plus 30°C, measurements of these two kinds appear to give equilvalent results. There is some evidence that such results provide moderately conservative estimates of K_{Im} at low temperatures. However, there seems to be little doubt that results from either of these methods provide useful approximations to the value of K_{Im} across a wide range of testing temperature [10]. In the case of A533B steel, a material of special interest for nuclear reactor vessels, there is considerable interest in dynamic toughness properties of the material at temperature above NDT plus 30°C. In this temperature range the specimen thickness necessary for conditions of plane strain at the crack front moves rapidly upward with increase of temperature. As the required specimen plate thickness increases above 75 mm, it becomes difficult to achieve short loading times (1 ms) without introduction of stress waves. In the case of K_{Ia} measurements, some advantages can be claimed through elevation of yield stress at the high-strain rates associated with the running crack. However, the required bulk of the specimen tends to increase for other reasons to sizes which are inconveniently large. Intuitively one expects that K_{Im} increases with testing temperature in correspondence to the change in the appearance of the running crack fracture surface from cleavage to fibrous. Since the values of K_{Ia} in the temperature range above NDT plus 50°C give lower average results than current values of K_{Id}, acceptance of the K_{Ia} results in this temperature range as indicative of a lower bound for K_{Im} would appear to represent sensible engineering practice. The K_{Ia} test results need to be extended somehow to higher values of temperature and toughness and uncertainty factors remain which need additional study.

The uncertainty factors are mainly of two kinds: implications from dynamic stress field analysis and influences due to use of face grooves. K_{Id} measurements escape these uncertainties. However, as just noted, at temperatures above NDT plus 50°C, a conservative estimate of K_{Im} may require observation of crack arrest after some segment of rapid propagation. Dynamic stress field analysis [6] has shown that values of K_{Ia}, which are computed using the static stress field just after crack arrest, will tend to decrease with increase in length of the run-arrest segment in a DCB specimen. This prediction depends upon use of Eq 15, may overestimate dynamic influences, and has not been clearly demonstrated using results with structural steel specimens. However, the uncertainty on this score is reduced to minor proportions by restricting the length of the run-arrest segment used in a K_{Ia} measurement. A restriction of this nature was introduced early in the development of K_{Ia} testing for other reasons.

Complexities Due to Use of Face Grooves

Even in the absence of face grooves, the stress field near the leading edge of a brittle crack traversing a plate has unavoidable complexities. In the ideal case of a crack-tip plastic zone of negligible size, the stress state close enough to the crack front approaches one of plane strain except at the points of intersection of the crack front with the specimen faces where the stress is three-dimensional. At distances on the order of one-half plate thickness from the crack front, the stress field is nearly one of two-dimensional plane stress. A J-integral determination of $\mathcal{G}$ in this region will provide the average value of $\mathcal{G}$ across the leading edge of the crack. The degree of uniformity of the actual plane-strain K along the crack front will depend upon crack front curvature. The influence upon K of the three-dimensional stress fields at each extremity of the leading edge is uncertain. If now we allow the natural development of crack-tip plastic zones across the leading edge and consider propagation of this disturbance as a running crack, it is clear that the natural crack speed near the specimen faces is unlikely to match the natural speed of the two-dimensional strain field in central portions of the crack front because the plastic zones are of different character. This expectation is verified adequately from study of fracture surfaces of running cracks. In the case of a structural steel plate, the natural crack speed adjacent to the specimen faces tends to be too slow, and the side boundary separation process can only keep up with the central region by intermittent segmental separations. In order to maintain a crack front of minimum curvature, face grooves were introduced. The procedure preferred by Crosley and Ripling [*9*] employs face grooves to a depth of one-eight plate thickness from each specimen face. The notch shape and root radius are similar to those used in the notching of V-notch Charpy specimens. As with the specimen which has no face grooves, the value of $\mathcal{G}$ from general analysis of the region containing the crack front is equal to the average value of $\mathcal{G}$ across the leading edge in the reduced sections. It seems doubtful that face grooves of relatively small depth increase the side boundary three-dimensional effects to a harmful degree. The face grooves substantially reduce the tendency of the crack front to lag near the side boundaries of the leading edge. Furthermore some guidance of the crack is necessary to permit use of DCB and contoured DCB specimens.

Judging from results so far obtained with specimens of A533B steel, as the testing temperature increases above the NDT temperature, the effectiveness of the moderate depth face grooves in preventing side boundary lag of the crack front decreases. For a given size specimen one would expect that out-of-plane forward separations, leading to loss of crack direction control, would occur when the toughness and testing temperature become large enough, and this has been observed. There are two obvious remedies. One is to substantially increase the specimen dimensions including thickness. This remedy is expensive and a factor of two increase of specimen size may permit only a 40 percent increase in the measurable crack arrest toughness. The second remedy is to increase the depth of the face grooves. If deep face grooves are used, even rather long paths of the running crack can be held to the midline of a DCB specimen. However, it is necessary to consider whether the behavior of the running crack will then model the behavior of a two-dimensional plane-strain crack propagating in a thick walled pressure vessel. Since the three-dimensional zones, always present near the face grooves, do not diminish in size with face groove depth, any increase of the fractional depth of the face grooves subtracts from the size and influence of the nearly two-dimensional central region. This handicaps and may prevent domination of crack extension behavior by the region of the crack front which can be regarded as nearly in a condition of two-dimensional plane strain as would be necessary for the intended application of the experimental work.

References

[1] Broberg, K. B., *Journal of Applied Mechanics,* Vol. 31, 1964, p. 546.
[2] Irwin, G. R., *Journal of Basic Engineering,* Sept. 1969, p. 519.
[3] Clark, A. B. J. and Irwin, G. R., *Experimental Mechanics,* June 1966.
[4] Yoffe, E. H., *Philosopical Magazine,* Vol. 42, 1951, p. 739.
[5] Rice, J. R. in *Fracture,* Chapter 3, Vol. II, Academic Press, New York, 1968, p. 210.
[6] Hahn, G. T., Hoagland, R. G., Kanninen, M. F., Popelar, C., Rosenfield, A. R., and deCampos, V. S., "Critical Experiments, Measurements, and Analyses to Establish a Crack Arrest Methodology for Nuclear Pressure Vessel Steels," Report No. BMI-1937, Battelle Columbus Laboratories, Columbus, Ohio, 1975.
[7] Döll, W., *International Journal of Fracture,* Vol. II, 1975, pp. 184–186.
[8] Irwin, G. R., Krafft, J. M., Paris, P. C., and Wells, A. A., "Basic Aspects of Crack Growth and Fracture," Report 6598, Naval Research Laboratory, Nov. 1967.
[9] Crosley, P. B. and Ripling, E. J., *Nuclear Engineering and Design,* Vol. 17, 1971, pp. 32–45.
[10] Irwin, G. R., "Comments on Dynamic Fracture Testing," *Proceedings of the International Conference on Dynamic Fracture Toughness,* The Welding Institute, Abington, Cambridge, England, 1976, Paper No. 1.

M. F. Kanninen, [1] *C. Popelar,* [2] *and P. C. Gehlen* [1]

Dynamic Analysis of Crack Propagation and Arrest in the Double-Cantilever-Beam Specimen

REFERENCE: Kanninen, M. F., Popelar, C., and Gehlen, P. C., "**Dynamic Analysis of Crack Propagation and Arrest in the Double-Cantilever-Beam Specimen,**" *Fast Fracture and Crack Arrest, ASTM STP 627,* G. T. Hahn and M. F. Kanninen, Eds., American Society for Testing and Materials, 1977, pp. 19–38.

ABSTRACT: A simple one-dimensional analysis model was developed previously for rapid unstable crack propagation and arrest in wedge-loaded rectangular double-cantilever-beam (DCB) specimens. In this paper, the model is generalized to treat contoured specimens and machine-loading conditions. The development starts from the basic equations of the two-dimensional theory of elasticity with inertia forces included. Exploiting the beam-like geometry of the DCB specimen results in governing equations that are analogous to a variable-height Timoshenko beam partly supported by a generalized elastic foundation. These are solved by a finite-difference method. Crack propagation arrest results illustrating the effect of specimen geometry and loading conditions are described in the paper.

KEY WORDS: fracture properties, crack propagation, crack arrest, beam on elastic foundations, models, dynamic toughness, double cantilever beam specimen

Hahn et al [*1,2*] [3] have shown that, in addition to the usual ingredients of fracture mechanics, three further considerations must be included in the analysis of rapid, unstable crack propagation and crack arrest in a structure. First, it may be necessary to include inertia forces even though the crack speeds are not necessarily comparable to the elastic wave speeds. Second, in addition to recovered strain energy, crack growth may be supported by a kinetic energy contribution. Third, the energy required by the fracture process is a material property that can depend upon the crack speed. A methodology which generalizes ordinary (static) linear elastic fracture mechanics to account for these three effects has now been fairly

[1]Senior research scientist and principal researcher, respectively, Applied Solid Mechanics Section, Battelle Columbus Laboratories, Columbus, Ohio 43201.

[2]Professor, Engineering Mechanics Department, Ohio State University, Columbus, Ohio 43210.

[3]The italic numbers in brackets refer to the list of references appended to this paper.

well developed. For definiteness, it has been termed "dynamic-fracture mechanics."

The basis of dynamic-fracture mechanics is as follows. Consider a system in which the inelastic processes associated with crack growth are confined to an infinitesimally small neighborhood of the crack tip. The dynamic crack-driving force (generalized energy-release rate) $\mathcal{G}$ for a through-wall crack can then be written as

$$\mathcal{G} = \frac{1}{b}\left\{\frac{dW}{d\mathcal{a}} - \frac{dU}{d\mathcal{a}} - \frac{dT}{d\mathcal{a}}\right\} \tag{1}$$

where

W = work done by the external loads acting on the system,
U = elastic-strain energy of the system,
T = kinetic energy,
$\mathcal{a}$ = crack length, and
b = wall thickness.[4]

Physically, $\mathcal{G}$ is the energy per unit area of crack extension that is available to support crack growth. If $\mathcal{R}$ denotes the energy dissipation rate per unit area of crack advance, crack propagation will occur when, and only when

$$\mathcal{G}(t, V) = \mathcal{R}(V) \tag{2}$$

where

t = time and
V = crack speed.

If $\mathcal{G} < \mathcal{R}$, there can be no extension of the crack. This is the condition which exists both prior to crack-growth initiation and at the point of arrest of unstable crack propagation. Thus, in dynamic-fracture mechanics, crack arrest occurs simply as a limiting case of a general crack propagation theory and not as a unique event.

A simple dynamic-fracture mechanics-analysis model for the double cantilever beam (DCB) specimen was developed in previous works [*3–5*]. This model, which was analogous to a Timoshenko beam on a generalized elastic foundation, was confined to rectangular specimens with crack propagation occurring under fixed wedge-loading conditions. In this paper, the derivation of the governing equations required to treat a wider range of DCB specimen geometries and loading conditions is given. Specifically, the model has been generalized to treat the kind of arbitrarily contoured DCB specimens shown in Fig. 1 together with elastic interac-

[4]Modification of Eq 1 to treat a crack propagating in a wall of variable thickness can be made in an obvious way.

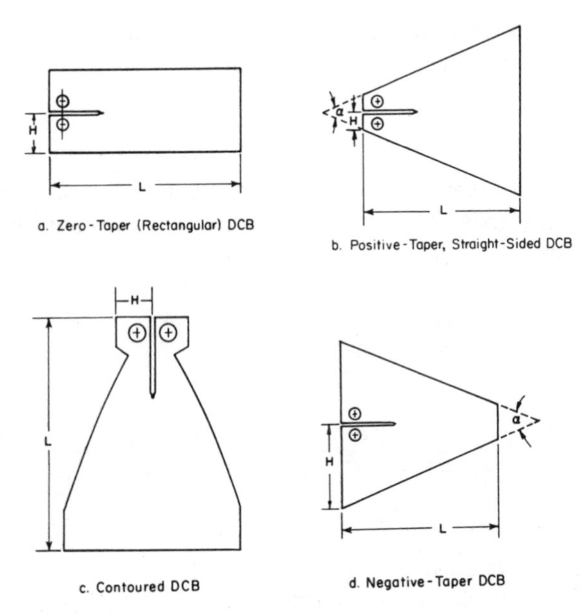

FIG. 1—*Typical DCB specimen shapes that can be treated with the one-dimensional model for both wedge and machine-loading conditions.*

tions between the machine loading and the specimen. Computational results are given in the paper which explore the effect of these variables on the use of the DCB specimen as a vehicle for studying the fundamentals of dynamic-crack propagation and crack arrest.

Development of the Theoretical Model

The equations of motion for the "beam-on-elastic foundation" model of the DCB specimen have their origins in the theory of elasticity. They are obtained by exploiting simplifications suggested by the beam-like character of the DCB specimen which result in equations similar to those of the Timoshenko beam [*6*]. Added to these simplifications are two further assumptions on the deformation in the uncracked section of the specimen.[5] These are that (1) a vertical force exists at each point along the specimen that is directly proportional to the average displacement of the cross section at that point, and (2) a couple exists at each point along the specimen that is proportional to the average rotation of the cross section at that point. These two assumptions provide a foundation for the beam which includes the effect of rotation, that is, as in a generalized or Pasternak Foundation [*7*]. Consequently, when it is convenient to do so,

[5]For symmetrical (Mode I) loading, the crack plane of the DCB specimen is a plane of symmetry. Therefore, only the upper half of the specimen need be considered.

the model derived from here can be viewed as a Timoshenko beam partly supported by a generalized elastic foundation.

Basic Equations of the Model

The x-y plane is taken parallel to the crack plane with the x-axis directed along the neutral axis. The z-axis is directed vertically upward. The pertinent equations of motion of elasticity theory can then be written as

$$\frac{\partial \sigma_x}{\partial x} + \frac{\partial \tau_{yx}}{\partial y} + \frac{\partial \tau_{zx}}{\partial z} = \rho \frac{\partial^2 u_x}{\partial t^2} \quad (3)$$

$$\frac{\partial \tau_{xz}}{\partial x} + \frac{\partial \tau_{yz}}{\partial y} + \frac{\partial \sigma_z}{\partial z} = \rho \frac{\partial^2 u_z}{\partial t^2} \quad (4)$$

where

$\sigma_x, \tau_{yx}, \ldots$ = stresses,
u_x and u_z = displacement components,
ρ = mass density, and
t = time.

An integration of Eq 4 over the cross-sectional area $A = A(x)$ at some generic position x along the length of the specimen gives

$$\frac{\partial}{\partial x} \iint_A \tau_{xz}\, dy\, dz + \iint_A \left[\frac{\partial \tau_{yx}}{\partial y} + \frac{\partial \sigma_z}{\partial z} \right] dy\, dz = \rho \frac{\partial^2}{\partial t^2} \iint_A u_z\, dy\, dz \quad (5)$$

Assuming that the integrals exist, it is convenient to define the transverse shearing force as

$$S = \iint_A \tau_{xz}\, dy\, dz \quad (6)$$

The average deflection w can similarly be defined by

$$w = \frac{1}{A} \iint_A u_z dy\, dz \quad (7)$$

By application of the divergence theoreum, Cowper [6] has shown that the second integral of Eq 5 is the transverse load p per unit of length. In accord with the first assumption just stated, this can be written as

$$p = -k_e w \tag{8}$$

where k_e is an extensional stiffness arising from the constraint existing when the specimen is not cracked. Using Eqs 6–8, Eq 5 then becomes

$$\frac{\partial S}{\partial x} - k_e w = \rho A \frac{\partial^2 w}{\partial t^2} \tag{9}$$

This is the first of four basic relations for the model.

It is next convenient to define the bending moment M and the mean rotation ψ of the cross section at the position x in a similar way to Eqs 6 and 7. These are

$$M = \iint_A z\sigma_x dy\, dz \tag{10}$$

and

$$\psi = -\frac{1}{I}\iint_A z u_x dy\, dz \tag{11}$$

where I is the moment of inertia of the cross section about the y-axis. If Eq 3 is multiplied through by z and integrated over the cross-sectional area, it follows that

$$\frac{\partial M}{\partial x} + \iint_A z\left[\frac{\partial \tau_{yx}}{\partial y} + \frac{\partial \tau_{zx}}{\partial z}\right] dy\, dz = -\rho I \frac{\partial^2 \psi}{\partial t^2} \tag{12}$$

The integral of Eq 12 may be written as

$$\iint_A z\left[\frac{\partial \tau_{yx}}{\partial y} + \frac{\partial \tau_{zx}}{\partial z}\right] dy\, dz = \iint_A \left[\frac{\partial}{\partial y}(z\tau_{yx}) + \frac{\partial}{\partial z}(z\tau_{zx})\right] dy\, dz - \iint_A \tau_{zx} dy\, dz \tag{13}$$

The first integral on the right-hand side of Eq 13 is the couple q per unit of length. In accord with the second assumption just stated, q is just proportional to the mean rotation. Hence, it can be expressed as

$$q = k_r\psi \tag{14}$$

where k_r is the rotational stiffness of the "foundation." The second integral on the right of Eq 13 is simply S. Therefore, Eq 12 can be written as

$$\frac{\partial M}{\partial x} + k_r\psi - S = -\rho I \frac{\partial^2\psi}{\partial t^2} \tag{15}$$

which is the second basic equation of the model.

The stresses σ_y and σ_z are assumed to be negligible compared to σ_x. Thus, Hooke's law for the strain along the length of the specimen reduces to

$$E\frac{\partial u_x}{\partial x} = \sigma_x \tag{16}$$

Upon multiplying Eq 16 through by z, integrating over the cross section, and making use of Eqs 10 and 11, then

$$M = -EI\frac{\partial\psi}{\partial x} \tag{17}$$

which gives the third of the four basic relations.

Finally, Hooke's law for the shearing stress provides that

$$G\left[\frac{\partial u_x}{\partial z} + \frac{\partial u_z}{\partial x}\right] = \tau_{xz} \tag{18}$$

An integration of Eq 18 over the cross section yields

$$\iint_A \frac{\partial u_x}{\partial z}\,dy\,dz + \frac{\partial}{\partial x}\iint_A u_z dy\,dz = \frac{1}{G}\iint_A \tau_{xz}dy\,dz \tag{19}$$

Following Cowper [7], u_x can be written as

$$u_x = \frac{1}{A}\iint_A u_x dy\,dz - z\psi + u_x' \tag{20}$$

If the cross-sectional area does not vary too rapidly with x, then the introduction of Eqs 7 and 20 into Eq 19 yields the fourth and last of the basic equations for the model. This is

$$\frac{\partial w}{\partial x} - \psi = \frac{S}{\kappa GS} \tag{21}$$

where, Cowper's "shear coefficient" κ is defined such that

$$\kappa \iint_A \left[\tau_{xz} - G \frac{\partial u_x'}{\partial z} \right] dy\, dz = S \tag{22}$$

Cowper has determined values of κ for a variety of cross sections and, in particular, found $\kappa = 10(1 + \nu)/(12 + 11\nu)$ for the rectangular section. Anticipating that the results will not be too sensitive to Poisson's ratio, ν, it has been assumed that $\nu = 3/11 = 0.273$ to simplify κ. Note that this is nearly the value for steel.

Equations of Motion for the DCB Specimen

The four basic equations for the model derived in Eqs 9, 15, 17, and 21, contain four dependent variables. These equations can be simplified by eliminating M and S. Two further steps are required to adapt the result for the DCB specimen. The first is to note that the terms in which k_e and k_r appear do not exist in the cracked region. The second is to introduce a term to represent a specified external force P exerted on the load pins. This gives the most general form of the equations of motion for the one-dimensional "beam-on-elastic foundation" model of the DCB specimen. These are the two coupled equations given by

$$\frac{\partial}{\partial x}\left\{ \kappa GA \left[\frac{\partial w}{\partial x} - \psi \right] \right\} - k_e w H(x - a) = \rho A \frac{\partial^2 w}{\partial t^2} - \frac{P}{b}\,\delta(x - x_o) \tag{23}$$

$$\frac{\partial}{\partial x}\left[EI \frac{\partial \psi}{\partial x} \right] + \kappa GA \left[\frac{\partial w}{\partial x} - \psi \right] - k_r \psi H(x - a) = \rho I \frac{\partial^2 \psi}{\partial t^2} \tag{24}$$

where H is the Heaviside step function and δ is the Dirac delta function.

In Eq 23, the term $P/b\ \delta(x - x_o)$ represents a force exerted at the point $x = x_o$, that is, the position of the load pins, positive in the direction of positive w. For fixed wedge loadings, P is unknown, and, instead, a displacement constraint is imposed at the contact point such that the pin displacement cannot ever be less (it can be greater) than its initial value. For machine loading, an auxiliary computation must be performed to calculate the value of P arising from the machine-specimen interaction. This has been done by considering that elastic rods are attached to the specimen with a large rigid mass included to account for the grips. A concurrent finite difference calculation for the load rods is then performed. The boundary conditions in this computation are that the axial displacement of the rod is fixed at the "machine" end while the displacement at the end attached to the specimen matches the specimen's pin displacement.

Equations 23 and 24 apply for any specimen cross-sectional shape. Specializing to a rectangular cross section and taking $\nu = 0.273$ allows the following relations to be introduced

$$A = bh$$

$$I = \frac{1}{12} bh^3$$

$$\kappa GA = \frac{1}{3} Ebh$$

$$k_e = \frac{2Eb}{h}$$

$$k_r = \frac{1}{6} Ebh$$

where $h = h(x)$ is the half-height of the specimen, $b = b(x)$ is the specimen thickness, and $E = E(x)$ is the elastic modulus. Note that b is not necessarily equal to the thickness of the specimen on the crack plane in a side-grooved specimen. To the degree of approximation used here, the latter quantity, designated here as B, will affect the energy absorption rate during crack extension (see next), but not the mechanical response of the specimen.

The situation of most interest here is that in which E and b are constant, and only the specimen height h varies, as in a contoured DCB specimen. Using these relations for a rectangular cross section, the equations of motion can be written for this situation as

$$\frac{\partial^2 w}{\partial x^2} - \frac{\partial \Psi}{\partial x} + \frac{1}{h}\frac{\partial h}{\partial x}\left[\frac{\partial w}{\partial x} - \Psi\right] - \frac{6}{h^2} H(x - a)w = \frac{3}{C_o^2}\frac{\partial^2 w}{\partial t^2} - \frac{3P\delta(x - x_o)}{Eb^2 h} \tag{25}$$

and

$$\frac{\partial^2 \Psi}{\partial x^2} + \frac{3}{h}\frac{\partial h}{\partial x}\frac{\partial \Psi}{\partial x} + \frac{4}{h^2}\left[\frac{\partial w}{\partial x} - \Psi\right] - \frac{2}{h^2} H(x - a)\Psi = \frac{1}{C_o^2}\frac{\partial^2 \Psi}{\partial t^2} \quad (26)$$

where $C_o^2 = E/\rho$. These are the governing equations of motion to be used in the following. Note that the characteristic wave speeds in this system are C_o and $C_o/\sqrt{3}$, just as in the constant h case.

Dynamic Crack-Driving Force for the DCB Specimen

Equations 25 and 26 for the contoured DCB specimen have the same form as a variable-height Timoshenko beam-on-a-generalized elastic foundation. The kinetic energy T and the strain energy U for the DCB specimen are as usual for the Timoshenko beam except that now the strain energy for the specimen must include the contribution of the foundation. The total strain and kinetic energies for both halves of the specimen therefore are

$$U = \int_o^L \left\{ EI\left(\frac{\partial \psi}{\partial x}\right)^2 + \kappa GA\left(\frac{\partial w}{\partial x} - \psi\right)^2 + H(x - a)[k_e w^2 + k_r \psi^2]\right\} dx \quad (27)$$

and

$$T = \int_o^L \left\{ \rho A\left(\frac{\partial w}{\partial t}\right)^2 + \rho I\left(\frac{\partial \psi}{\partial t}\right)^2 \right\} dx \quad (28)$$

where L denotes the overall length of the specimen.

By substituting Eqs 27 and 28 into Eq 1, interchanging differentiation and integration where necessary, after some manipulation the dynamic energy-release rate is found to be

$$\mathcal{G} = \frac{1}{B}[k_e w^2 + k_r \psi^2]_{x = a(t)} \quad (29)$$

where B is the width of the crack plane. Specializing to a rectangular cross section then gives

$$\mathcal{G} = \frac{Eb}{6B}\left\{ \frac{12}{h} w^2 + h\Psi^2 \right\}_{x = \mathcal{a}(t)} \tag{30}$$

where $\mathcal{G} = \mathcal{G}(\mathcal{a},t)$ denotes the dynamic energy-release rate for the DCB analysis. Note that $\mathcal{G}$, as calculated from Eq 30, is a local property of the crack tip (at least to the degree of approximation involved in the model) despite the fact that it was derived from apparently global concepts via Eq 1.

Computational Procedure

To perform a computation for a given DCB specimen geometry and loading condition, Eqs 25 and 26 are put into finite difference form. Crack growth as a function of time is then determined from the finite difference method using Eq 30. Note that, as can be seen from Eq 2, this requires the function $\mathcal{R} = \mathcal{R}(V)$ to be specified in advance. Because of the connection that exists between the stress intensity factor and the crack driving force [*8,9*], this quantity can be equivalently specified in terms of a function $K_D = K_D(V)$. The latter terminology is convenient for experimental and application purposes and, therefore, will be used in the following.

Crack propagation experiments conducted by Hahn et al [*1,2*] employ an initially blunted crack tip. This permits a large amount of energy to be stored in the specimen at the onset of crack growth, causing the crack to propagate at a high speed. The speed can be controlled by the radius of curvature of the blunted crack tip. The starting configuration is characterized conveniently by the parameter K_q which is the ostensible linear elastic stress intensity factor existing at the start of crack growth. Thus, the blunter the notch, the higher the value of K_q and the higher the crack speed to be expected in the test.

There are two points of view that could be taken in incorporating this effect into the model. One is to consider that the blunt crack tip alters the intrinsic energy absorption rate of the material in the vicinity of the initial crack tip so that crack advance absorbs an amount of energy corresponding to K_q initially. This is probably the more correct approach. However, as shown in Ref *10*, it cannot be applied in the one-dimensional model without extremely perturbing computational results. For this reason, an alternative approach was adopted. This is to view the effect of the blunting as reducing the crack driving force without changing its energy absorption requirement. To implement this, an artificial constraint is imposed on the crack-tip region via a point force and couple. This forces the first increment of crack advance to correspond to the value $K_D(O)$.

One difficulty is connected with the imposition of the point force and couple. This is that the initial energy content in the specimen is greater than the level associated with the specified K_q level. Because the computation is invariant with respect to the ratio of $K_q/K_D(O)$, this does not necessarily introduce an error into the computation. However, care must be taken to correctly interpret the K_q value when K_D values are to be extracted from the experiments with the help of the analysis.

Figure 2 illustrates how the dynamic crack-propagation criterion is implemented. In the upper figure, the hypothetical crack speed is calculated on the basis that, if an increment of crack growth were to occur at some time following the last previous growth increment, the actual speed would be in inverse proportion to the time. For a specified energy dissipation rate $\mathcal{R}$ that is a function of crack speed, the crack tip's energy requirement is known once the hypothetical speed is determined. This is shown as the decreasing curve in the lower portion of Fig. 2. A typical computational result for the crack-driving force, as obtained from Eq 30, is also shown. Where these two curves intersect (that is, where $\mathcal{G} = \mathcal{R}$), crack growth occurs.

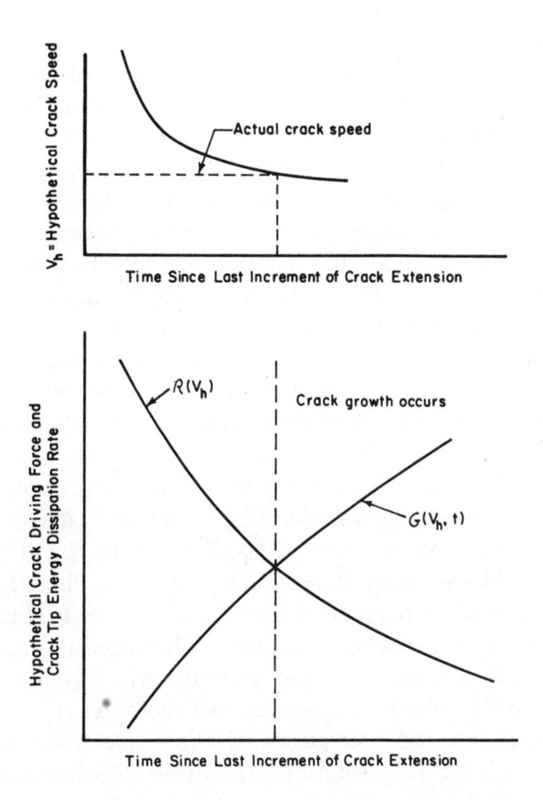

FIG. 2—*Graphical illustration of dynamic crack propagation criterion for speed-dependent materials.*

Verification of the Analysis Model

In the mathematical approach taken in this work, as in all models based on linear elasticity, the irreversible energy dissipation associated with crack propagation in a real material cannot be dealt with directly. Instead, such effects are taken into account by considering that all energy dissipation occurs in the near vicinity of the crack tip and, hence, that it can be represented by the material property $\mathcal{R}$. Therefore, $\mathcal{R}$ may depend upon the crack speed, but not upon the crack length or other dimensions of the body containing the propagating crack.

The model may be vulnerable to criticism on this point. It has been suggested that significant energy losses can occur from stress-wave reflections at corners, edges, and surfaces of the body [*11*]. In view of this, it may appear that a proper analysis cannot be obtained from a simplified model having few degrees of freedom of motion, particularly in view of the notion that the parameters K and $\mathcal{G}$ can be defined only by the stresses and displacements close to the crack tip. To the extent that these are valid, they are serious objections. However, as the following will attempt to show, they are not.

First of all, from the derivation of the equations of motion given previously, the model clearly has its origins in the dynamic theory of elasticity for a plane medium. Hence, any effects occurring in a two-dimensional initial value-boundary value-problem of linear elasticity, to a good approximation, will appear in this model as well. This, of course, includes the fundamental energy conservation principle. Because of the general acceptance of linear elasticity to characterize unstable crack propagation, energy losses stemming from viscous-type internal damping far from the crack tip are not at issue here. This is logical because of the extremely short duration of a crack propagation/arrest event; typically 100 μs. In time intervals this small, viscous damping does not become significant. Tangible evidence for the negligible effect of viscous damping during rapid crack propagation might be found in the work of Kanninen et al [*12*]. They showed that experimental results for both steel and a viscoelastic material, polymethylmethacrylate (PMMA), compared very well for the same dimensionless ratio of crack speed to the elastic bar-wave speed. Since PMMA is much more viscous than steel, the effect of viscous damping during crack propagation, therefore, must be negligible.

In view of the approximations that were introduced in the derivation of the model given in this paper, it may be appropriate to raise the question of how accurate the one-dimensional model really is. If so, it can be answered by comparing the predictions of the model with those of more rigorous theory of elasticity-solution procedures. Comparisons with static boundary point collocation schemes given in Refs *3,4* have already shown that the model is quite realistic in the static case. In the dynamic case, comparisons with two-dimensional finite-difference calculations show excellent agreement with the model. The results given by Shmuely and Peretz [*13*] can be cited here. In addition, calculations have been made with a finite-difference method developed at Battelle's Columbus Laboratories, and these also show good agreement, as follows.

Typical crack propagation histories calculated with a preliminary version of our two-dimensional finite-difference method and with the one-dimensional model described in this paper are shown in Fig. 3. The results are for a rectangular DCB specimen with a crack speed independent fracture toughness $K_D = K_c$ and a starting condition corresponding to $K_q = 2K_c$. It can be readily seen that the improvement obtained by the more precise treatment is quite modest. In particular, the crack speeds predicted by the two different models differ by only 6 percent, from 1140 m/s in the one-dimensional model to 1080 m/s in the two-dimensional model. The predicted arrest length of the two-dimensional model is approximately 15 percent smaller than that of the one-dimensional model. Certain minor improvements yet to be incorporated in the two-dimensional computation plus the fact that the one-dimensional model, as discussed previously, overestimates the energy stored in the specimen at the onset of crack propagation for a given specified K_q, when corrected, could be expected to diminish even these small differences.

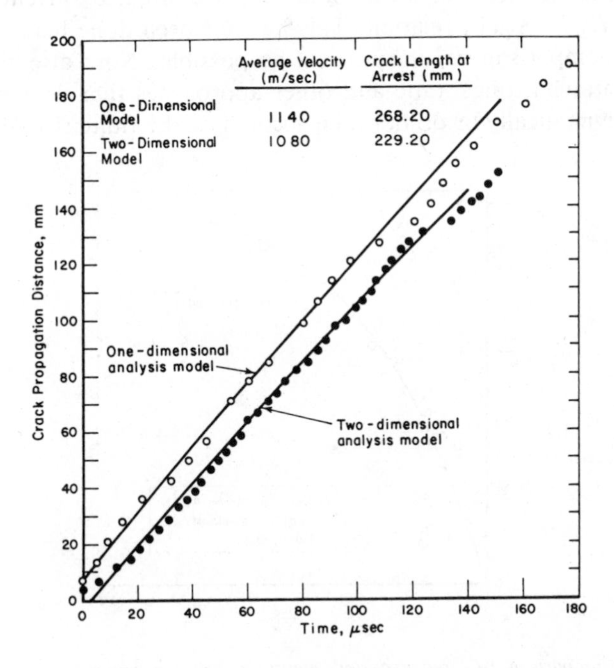

FIG. 3—*Calculated crack propagation and arrest for specimen* $K_q = 2K_c$.

Comparisons of the predictions of the one-dimensional model with experiments, as described by Hahn et al [*1,2*] give further confidence in this approach. There are two decisive pieces of evidence. First, qualitatively, the model duplicates the linear crack length-time result usually observed in DCB experiments for any of a variety of postulated $K_D = K_D(V)$ behaviors. This is not a trivial result. In fact, it is this test that disqualified quasistatic and even infinite medium dynamic analyses of the DCB specimen. These approaches invariably predict nonlinear crack growth, often with peak crack speeds far in excess of any measured values.

A second experimentally based piece of evidence for the validity of the model given in this paper is the comparison that can be made with the two least ambiguous experimentally determined quantities in a DCB test: the average crack speed and the crack length at arrest. Such a comparison is shown in Fig. 4. It is important to understand that the model can be always forced to match (by trial and error) either a specified crack speed or an arrest point by simply adjusting the ratio of K_q/K_c. However, the calculation cannot be forced to match them both. The fact, evident from Fig. 4, that it does so to a very good approximation, therefore, can be taken as a basic verification of the validity of the model.

Note that crack-speed independent behavior, that is, $K_D = K_c$, was used for the calculations presented in Fig. 4. Further improvement in the comparison, therefore, could be obtained, if desired, by inventing an appropriate $K_D = K_D(V)$ relation. This has not been done here in order to keep the comparison as unequivocal as possible. Note also that, as already mentioned, quasistatic and other approaches that do not treat the problem dynamically or do not take account of the finite size of the speci-

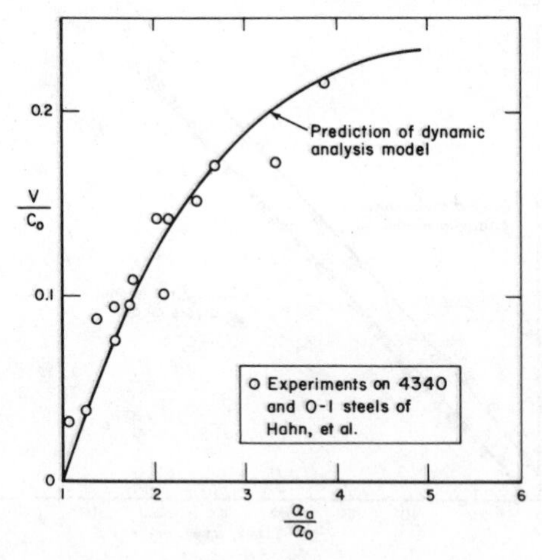

FIG. 4—*Comparison of predicted and measured relation between steady-state crack speed in a DCB specimen and crack length at arrest.*

men or both, cannot be admitted to comparison like that of Fig. 4 because they do not predict a virtually constant crack speed.

To summarize, there is good reason to believe that a material behaves in a linear elastic fashion during rapid crack propagation. Consequently, aside from the near vicinity of the crack tip, energy is conserved in the body. Further, it will distribute itself during crack propagation according to the equations of dynamic elasticity. The one-dimensional analysis model for the DCB specimen is based in the linear theory of elasticity for plane media and the assumptions introduced to simplify the numerical computations do not significantly alter this fact. Hence, the crack-driving force $\mathcal{G}$ derived from an energy-balance point of view must be fundamentally correct for the boundary conditions and initial conditions under consideration. As shown previously, $\mathcal{G}$ can (and is) given a local crack-tip interpretation. By using the relation obtained by Freund [*8*] and generalized by Nilsson [*9*] which connects $\mathcal{G}$ and K for the dynamic problem, the model can be equivalently used to predict dynamic stress intensity factors. While not rigorously exact, there is an abundance of both experimental and theoretical evidence which shows that such predictions are realistic.

Discussion of Computational Results

The analysis procedure just described has been used to examine the influence of DCB specimen geometry, the loading system, and other testing variables on crack propagation and crack arrest. Complete details of these calculations are given in Ref *1*. Some of the highlights are as follows.

The kinds of specimen shapes for which calculations can be performed with the model are shown in Fig. 1. For each specimen shape, both a wedge-loaded and machine-loaded calculation have been generally performed. Typical example results are shown in Fig. 5. A further variable that enters the calculations is the choice of the function $K_D = K_D(V)$ which represents the material's fracture energy requirement. The effect of this property will not be investigated here, however. The following discussions are based on calculations using $K_D = K_c$. For clarity in the following, the discussion will refer to K_c when referring to the onset of growth and to K_D when describing crack propagation or crack arrest. Note that the parameter K_a here refers to the statically calculated stress intensity factor following arrest.

The most important result of the calculations is that the crack propagation and arrest events in both the contoured DCB and in the positive and negative taper DCB specimens turn out to be quite similar to those described in Refs *4,5* for the rectangular DCB specimen. In all of these configurations, the crack begins to propagate at full speed (no acceleration period is evident) and continues at essentially constant velocity over most

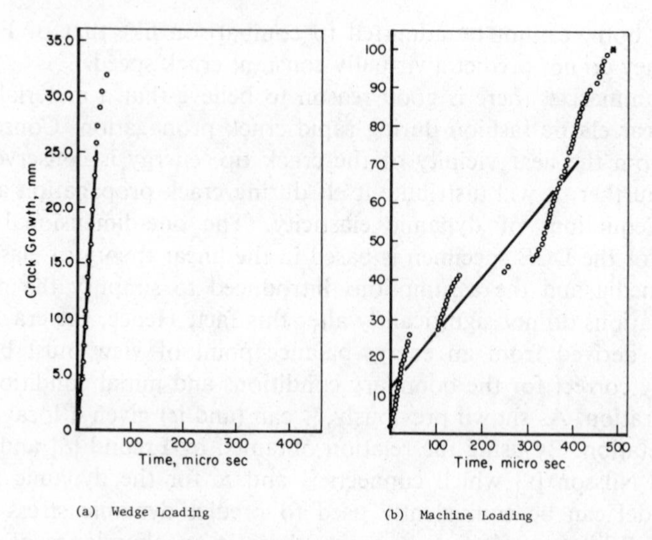

FIG. 5—*Calculated crack propagation and arrest in a contoured DCB specimen.*

of the event. Crack arrest is fairly abrupt. For rigid wedge loading, re-initiation of growth does not typically occur, for example, see Figs. 3 and 5*a*. For machine loading systems, on the other hand, the crack usually restarts after a short period of time, for example, 50 μs, propagates, and arrests, repeating this sequence several times before the final arrest [see Fig. 5*b*].

Figure 6 shows a further result of load-specimen interaction. Thus, the loading system has a significant effect upon the crack history. In comparison, the specimen geometry has a lesser effect. This can be seen also from Fig. 7.

The most important quantitative result of Fig. 7 is that all of the configurations show a systematic decrease in K_a as K_q is increased. Some minor variances among the different configurations also occur. For example, the difference between K_a and K_D is greater for rectangular DCB specimens than for contoured specimens. For modest K_q values, for example, $K_q/K_c = 1.2$, K_a values derived from the contoured specimens are reasonably good approximations of K_D. Nevertheless, the variation of K_a with K_q shows that K_a is not a basically correct crack arrest criterion. Computational results show that the discrepancy increases systematically in going from the positive to the negative taper specimen at small K_q values, while the reverse is true for large K_q values.

For the same type of loading and initial crack length $\mathcal{a}_o$, crack speeds and crack jump distances are largest in the negative taper DCB, smallest in the positive taper and contoured DCB. However, these variations are generally quite modest. There would seem to be little incentive for metic-

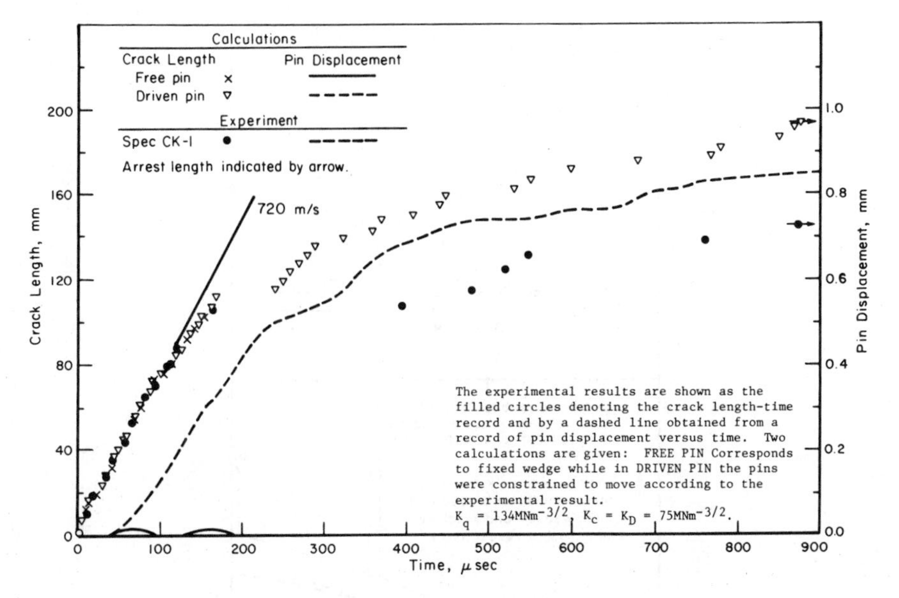

FIG. 6—*Comparison of the predictions of the model with experiment.*

ulously designing a nonuniform DCB specimen for investigating dynamic events, therefore.

The computational results indicate that the loading system can have a large effect on the character of propagation and arrest in DCB specimens. Complaint loading systems transfer additional energy to the specimen while the crack is propagating. As already pointed up, this often leads to reinitiation of growth. Note that, since a certain amount of time is required to transfer energy from the loading system to the crack tip, the initial period of propagation and the initial velocity is unaffected by the loading system. Crack velocity measurements, therefore, can provide a relatively unambiguous measure of K_D even though the extent of propagation and the number of halts and restarts can be changed radically by changing the loading system.

The extent of propagation appears to be relatively insensitive to the mass of the loading system at constant compliance. Thus, the K_a values calculated are relatively insensitive to the loading system. But, this result should be accepted with caution in view of the uncertainty in determining the final arrest point. The relatively long duration of propagation events involving many halts and restarts also means that the neglect of energy dissipation at points other than the crack tip becomes less realistic. This further complicates the interpretation of K_a. Wedge loading, with its more restricted and possibly better defined crack propagation and arrest event, may thus offer significant advantages over the more compliant tensile loading.

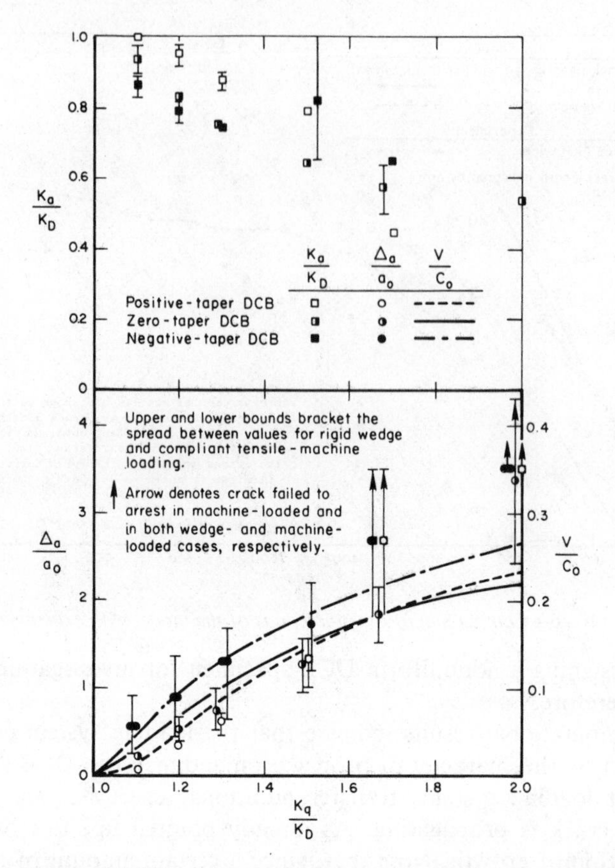

FIG. 7—*Influence of DCB specimen geometry on calculated crack propagation and arrest parameters for* $K_D = K_c$.

Finally, the model can be used to investigate the conditions following crack arrest. Kalthoff [*14*] has shown experimentally that the conditions following arrest remain dynamic for a substantial period of time. Specifically, he has found that the dynamic stress intensity factor oscillates about the static value. As shown in Fig. 8, the analysis qualitatively predicts the same behavior.

Conclusions

It has been shown in this paper that the one-dimensional analysis model developed to treat rapid unstable crack propagation and crack arrest in nonuniform DCB specimens for various loading conditions offers an adequate representation of these events. Moreover, it does so in a very economical fashion. This permits a great number of variations and assump-

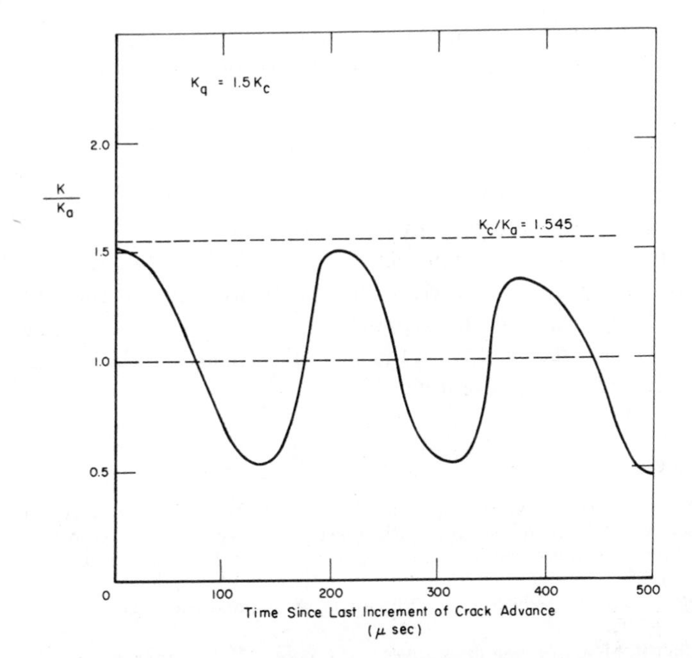

FIG. 8—*Ratio of the dynamic stress intensity factor following crack arrest to the static stress intensity factor corresponding to the crack length at arrest as a function of time.*

tions to be explored. Consequently, even though highly precise two-dimensional computational models are now available, the simple one-dimensional model will remain useful to help refine and interpret laboratory experimental results.

The model described in this paper demonstrates the importance of including both inertia effects and finite specimen boundaries. It is frequently argued that a dynamic analysis is unimportant if the crack speed is small compared to the Rayleigh speed. This is true for the rather academic problem in which the specimen is unbounded. But, to demonstrate that this generalization is not universally valid, one only needs to consider a finite body where reinitiation of crack growth has been observed. It is impossible to explain the reinitiation of crack growth after the crack has momentarily come to a halt, that is, zero crack speed, without a fully dynamic analysis that allows the return of energy to the crack tip. Consequently, intuition based on static concepts can be highly misleading in fully dynamic situations such as the arrest of a rapidly propagating crack.

The use of an analysis model based on the dynamic fracture-mechanics approach can offer vital information with regard to a crack-arrest design methodology. The static approximation will overestimate the capability of a structure to arrest a running crack. This may be true even if the minimum value of K_D is used in the analysis. Consequently, to assure the integrity of the structure, should unstable crack propagation occur, a dynamic analysis and the complete $K_D = K_D(V)$ relation must be used.

Acknowledgments

This paper is based upon research work supported by the U.S. Nuclear Regulatory Commission, contract number W-7405-eng-92, and the Naval Ship Systems Command, contract number N00024-72-C-5142. The opinions and conclusions presented in this paper are those of the authors and not necessarily those of the supporting agencies. Helpful comments and suggestions were received from the authors' colleagues G. T. Hahn, R. G. Hoagland, and A. R. Rosenfield.

References

[*1*] Hahn, G. T. et al, "Critical Experiments, Measurements and Analyses to Establish a Crack-Arrest Methodology for Nuclear Pressure Vessel Steels," Reports to the U.S. Nuclear Regulatory Commission, Battelle Columbus Laboratories, Columbus, Ohio, 1974-1975.

[*2*] Hoagland, R. G., Gehlen, P. C., Rosenfield, A. R., and Hahn, G. T., this publication, pp. 177-202.

[*3*] Kanninen, M. F., *International Journal of Fracture,* Vol. 9, 1973, p. 83.

[*4*] Kanninen, M. F., *International Journal of Fracture,* Vol. 10, 1974, p. 415.

[*5*] Kanninen, M. F., *Prospects of Fracture Mechanics,* G. C. Sih et al., Eds., 1974, p. 251.

[*6*] Cowper, G. R., *Journal of Applied Mechanics,* Vol. 33, 1966, p. 335.

[*7*] Kerr, A. D., *Journal of Applied Mechanics,* Vol. 31, 1964, p. 491.

[*8*] Freund, L. B., *Journal of Mechanics and Physics of Solids,* Vol. 20, 1972, p. 141, Vol. 21, 1973, p. 47.

[*9*] Nilsson, F., *Journal of Elasticity,* Vol. 4, 1974, p. 73.

[*10*] Hahn, G. T., Hoagland, R. G., Kanninen, M. F., and Rosenfield, A. R. in *Dynamic Crack Propagation,* G. C. Sih, Ed., Noordhoff International Publishing, Leyden, The Netherlands, 1973, p. 649.

[*11*] Irwin, G. R., this publication, pp. 7-18.

[*12*] Kanninen, M. F., Rosenfield, A. R., and Hoagland, R. G. in *Deformation and Fracture of High Polymers,* H. H. Kausch, Ed., Plenum Press, New York, 1973, p. 471.

[*13*] Shumely, M. and Peretz, D., *International Journal of Solids and Structures,* Vol. 12, 1976, p. 67.

[*14*] Kalthoff, J. F., Beinert, J., and Winkler, S., this publication, pp. 161-176.

Takeshi Kanazawa,[1] *Susumu Machida,*[1] *and Tokuo Teramoto*[1]

Preliminary Approaches to Experimental and Numerical Study on Fast Crack Propagation and Crack Arrest

REFERENCE: Kanazawa, Takeshi, Machida, Susumu, and Teramoto, Tokuo, "**Preliminary Approaches to Experimental and Numerical Study on Fast Crack Propagation and Crack Arrest,**" *Fast Fracture and Crack Arrest, ASTM STP 627,* G. T. Hahn and M. F. Kanninen, Eds., American Society for Testing and Materials, 1977, pp. 39–58.

ABSTRACT: Within the limit of relatively short arrested crack, static approximation by applying linear fracture mechanics has yielded useful results for theoretical interpretation and practical application of currently used brittle fracture propagation arrest test (the concept of arrest toughness). But later experimental investigations using very wide specimens (1300 to 2500-mm-wide plates) have revealed that this simple interpretation fails to have a consistency with the case of a long arrested crack. For the inadequacy of static approximation based on arrest toughness concept, the concept of an effective stress intensity factor has been introduced from a practical point of view without a clear quantitative explanation for it. In search of a more relevant theory for fast crack propagation and to see how the neglect of dynamic aspects affects the interpretation of unstable crack propagation arrest test and philosophy of crack arrest design, a dynamic fracture mechanics analysis was made with the use of the finite-difference method to solve the equation of motion for the two-dimensional elastic problem.

Results of a numerical experiment are presented, and experimental results for polymethylmethacrylate specimen and structural steels are discussed in terms of dynamic fracture mechanics analysis with a focus on energetic aspect of the crack propagation processes.

KEY WORDS: fracture properties, cracks, crack propagation, crack arrest, dynamic fracture mechanics, arrest toughness

Since the shipbuilding industries experienced a number of casualties due to brittle fracture, most naval architects have been forced to be interested in the brittle behavior of low- and medium-strength structural steels. While

[1]Professor, associate professor, and graduate student, respectively, Faculty of Engineering, University of Tokyo, Bunkyo-ku, Tokyo, Japan.

the linear fracture mechanics was originated and applied to ultrahigh strength steels and other special alloys in space engineering in the United States, Japanese research groups were trying to use fracture mechanics to interprete the results of brittle fracture propagation arrest tests using wide plate specimens.

Within the limit of relatively short arrested cracks, static approximation using the linear fracture mechanics concept or the arrest toughness concept has yielded useful results for theoretical interpretation and design application of currently used brittle fracture propagation arrest tests. But later experimental investigations using very wide specimens (1300 and 2500-mm-wide plates) have revealed that this simple interpretation fail to be consistent with a long arrested crack. The first part of this paper gives a brief review of this story and describes how this inconsistency has been settled on a practical basis such as design and evaluation.

Recently, unstable ductile fracture observed in pressurized structures such as pipings, pressure vessels, etc. has emerged as a recent topic of engineering interest. A comprehensive study on this problem going on at Battelle's Columbus Laboratories [*1*][2] is very interesting to the authors who have much experience with experimental study on unstable brittle fracture and crack arrest, particularly for their persistence to the invalidation of the arrest toughness concept.

In search of a most reasonable theory of fast fracture and crack arrest and to study how the neglect of dynamic aspects affects the interpretation of the results of unstable fast crack propagation arrest test and the philosophy of crack design, the authors began with dynamic fracture mechanics analysis of crack propagation and arrest using a finite-difference method. The results of the analysis were compared with experiments using polymethylmethacrylate (PMMA) specimens, and the previous data on structural steels are discussed in terms of dynamic fracture mechanics analysis. The second part of this paper describes a preliminary result.

Brittle Crack Propagation Arrest Test Using Very Wide Plate Specimens

A simple fracture mechanics concept has been successfully applied to the analysis of the experimental results of several kinds of brittle crack arresters using medium size specimen (500 mm wide) [*2–7*]. This analysis is based on the arrest toughness concept and the consideration that the dynamic aspect of the stress intensity factor or strain energy release rate can be neglected because the crack length is relatively small and a crack just before arresting or a crack running at a speed near to the lower critical velocity of brittle crack is considered.

In the case of large welded steel constructions such as ships, however,

[2]The italic numbers in brackets refer to the list of references appended to this paper.

the occurrence of a very large brittle crack is presumed. When a brittle crack extends to very large-scale crack, however, it is questionable whether this simple consideration is valid or not. Relative to this problem, two extensive experimental research projects have been conducted in Japan by the Ship Research Institute of the Ministry of Transportation [8] and the University of Tokyo [9], using 1300 and 2400-mm-wide plate specimens, respectively.

Examples of the test results in terms of log K_c versus $1/T$, where K_c is the nominal arrest toughness or K value at arrest point and T is temperature, are shown in Fig. 1. Particulars of four kinds of test shown in Fig. 1 are given in Table 1. The solid circles denoted as *DG* are data ob-

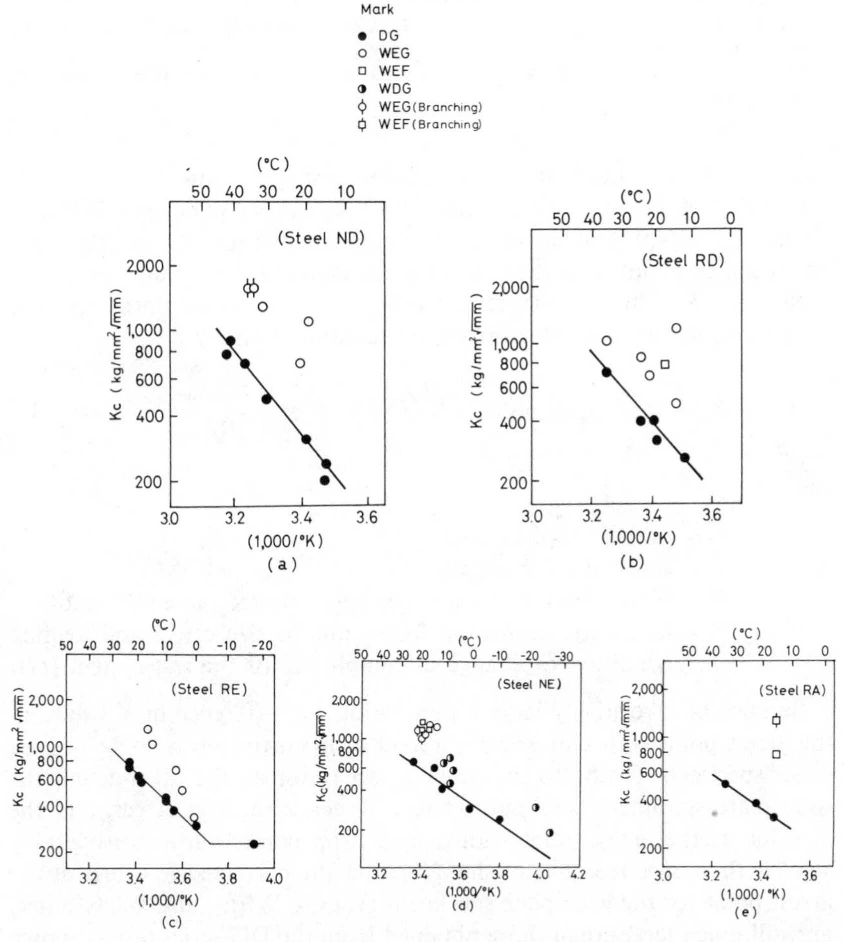

FIG. 1—*Relation between* K_c *value and temperature at crack arrested points* ((a) *for normalized D-class steel,* (b) *for as-rolled D-class steel,* (c) *for as-rolled E-class steel* (d) *for normalized E-class steel and* (e) *for as-rolled A-class steel*).

TABLE 1—*Particulars of four kinds of crack propagation arrest test.*

Name of Test Series	Temperature Distribution	Plate Width B, mm	Aspect Ratio, λ	Grade of Steel (NK code) [a]
Double tension test of standard size (DG)	gradient	500	3	A, D, and E
Esso test with gradient temperature of wide plate (WEG)	gradient	2400	0.9	D and E
Esso test with flat temperature of wide hybrid plate (WEF)	flat	2400	0.9	A + D or E [b]
Double tension test of wide plate (WDG)	gradient	1000	2	E

[a] A, D, and E designate Grade A, D, and E Steel of the Unified Specification of Ship Classification Societies.

[b] A-class steel is used as crack starter plate and D- or E-class steel is used as crack arrester plate.

tained from the standard double tension test (500-mm-wide specimen, temperature gradient type crack arrest test), and they can be approximately considered to represent the material toughness against crack propagation, which can be handled on the basis of a linear fracture mechanics criterion.

Nominal K value at crack arrest point based on static linear fracture mechanics, K_c, was computed from the equation given by

$$K_c = K \text{ at arrest point } = \sigma \sqrt{\pi c} \times F \times \left(\frac{P_i(c)}{P_i^0} \right) \tag{1}$$

where

σ = initially applied stress,
c = arrested crack length,
F = correction factor for single edge cracked plate [*10*], and
$P_i(c)/P_i^0$ = load drop correction factor due to size effect and loading condition or change in compliance of the test system [*11*].

Because of a relatively large aspect ratio, the difference in K values at the arrest point with and without a load drop correction is slight in DG-series specimen. Owing to the small aspect ratio, on the other hand, the wide plate specimens were subject to a larger load drop effect, and the K value at the arrest point with a load drop correction is considerably smaller than an uncorrected value [*11*]. But the corrected K values at the arrest point for the wide plate specimens (WEG-, WEF-, and WDG-series) are still much larger than those obtained from the DG-series test as shown in Fig. 1 *a* to *e*.

Figure 2 shows examples of crack speed measured in each test series

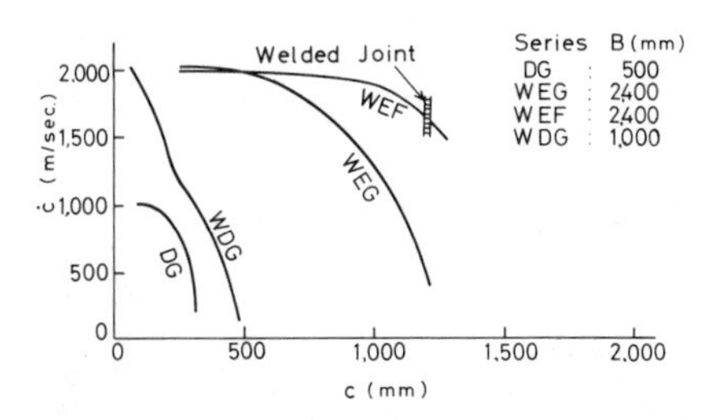

FIG. 2—*Comparison of crack speeds.*

given in Table 1. Note that crack speed in the wide plate specimen is much higher than in the DG specimen for the most part of propagation.

The considerable discrepancy between K_c values obtained from wide specimens and those from the standard specimens (DG specimens) as seen in Fig. 1 suggests that the estimation of K value (parameter characterizing crack driving force) based on simple static approximation is apparently invalidated possibly by intrinsically dynamic features involved in an extensive propagation of brittle crack such as observed in the wide specimens.

Effective Crack Length and Effective Stress Intensity Factor

For the foregoing discrepancy, Kihara et al [8] proposed to use the concept of "effective crack length, c_{eff}." They inferred that a brittle crack, propagated extensively, no longer had a crack length effect on K value such as expressed by the form derived from static calculation (Eq 1), but apparently the crack extension force for a propagating crack longer than about 200 mm seems to have a value smaller than the computed value based on static linear fracture mechanics, in other words, a very long crack behaves as if it has a length shorter than actual length. They defined c_{eff} as a virtual crack length so that the arrest temperature estimated from the standard crack arrest test is compatible with the experimental results for long arrested crack using c_{eff} instead of actual crack length c, and they obtained an empirical relation between c_{eff} and c.

The foregoing wide plate test results are presented in terms of the effective crack length concept in Fig. 3 for gradient temperature type arrest tests (WEG and WDG) and in Fig. 4 for flat temperature type hybrid arrest test (WEF), respectively. Mark with downward arrow in Fig. 4 corresponding to "no-go" data means that c_{eff} value is smaller than the plotted value and vice versa for mark with upward arrow corresponding to "go-through" data. Because of considerable data scatter as seen in these results, c_{eff} concept does not work well and c_{eff} fails to be a useful quantity defined as a function of c.

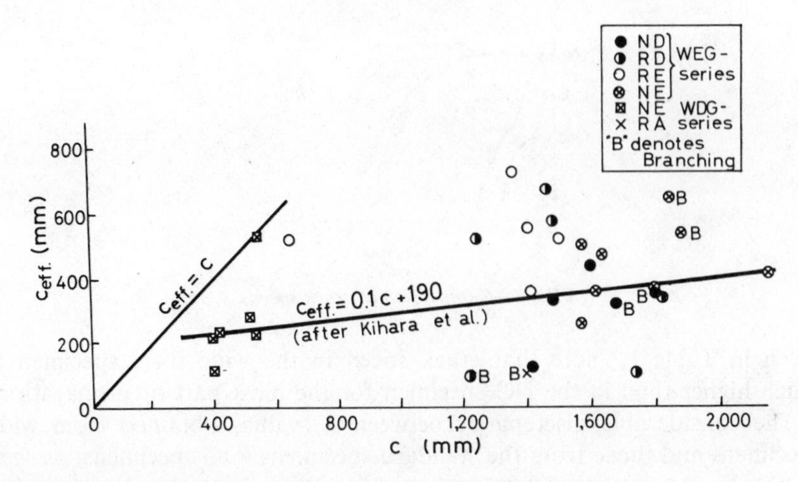

FIG. 3—*Relation between* c *and* c_{eff} *for WEG- and WDG-series* (N *or* R *means normalized or as-rolled steel, respectively*).

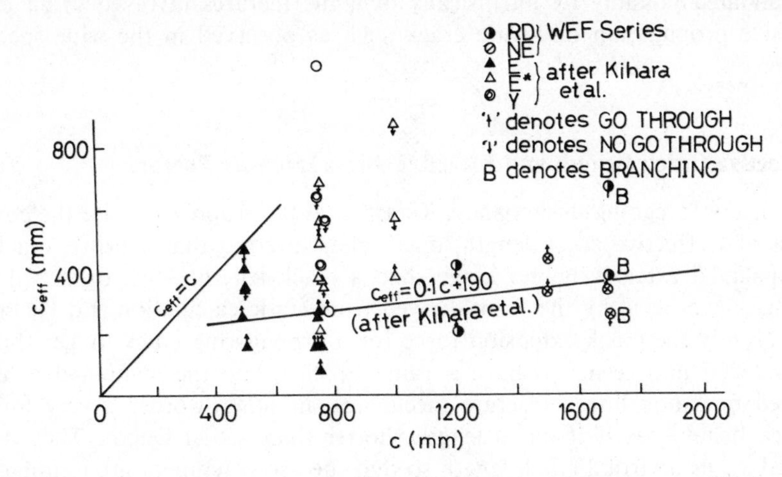

FIG. 4—*Relation between* c *and* c_{eff} *for WEF-series* (N *or* R *means normalized or as-rolled steel, respectively*).

It is obvious from physical consideration that any parameter dominating brittle crack propagation must be of a quantity characterizing stress and strain distributions around the crack tip. Thus, it is more reasonable to introduce the concept of "effectiveness" into K value, denoted as K_{eff}, which is one of the useful parameters characterizing a mechanical situation around the crack tip, rather than introducing the effectiveness concept into crack length only.

Figures 5 and 6 show K_{eff} versus nominal $K(K_{nom})$ obtained in a similar way of reasoning as with c_{eff} for the results of gradient temperature type

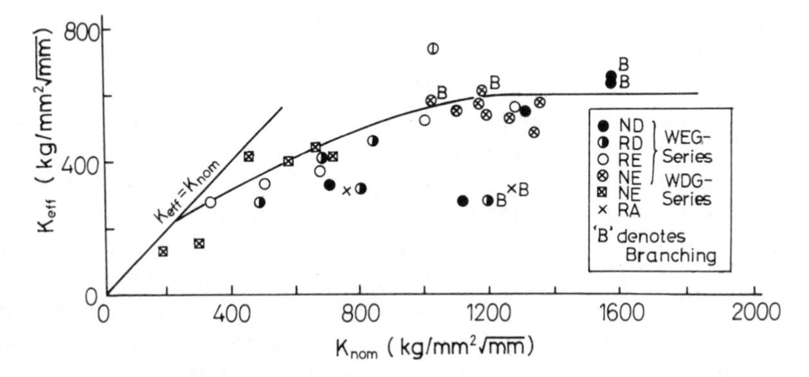

FIG. 5—*Relation between nominal* K *and* K_{eff} *for WEG- and WDG-series* (N *or* R *means normalized or as-rolled steel, respectively*).

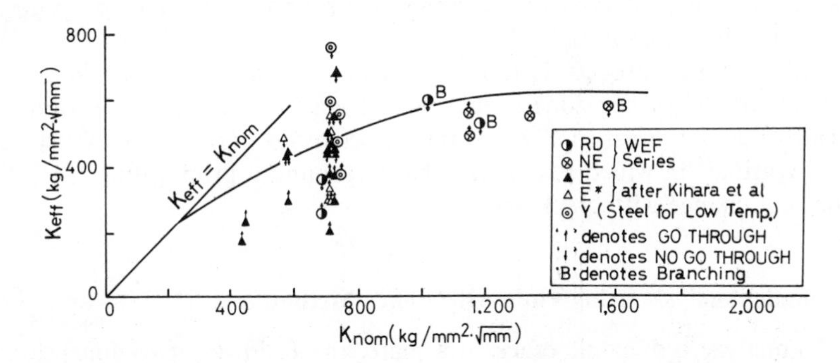

FIG. 6—*Relation between nominal* K *and* K_{eff} *for WEF-series* (N *or* R *means normalized or as-rolled steel, respectively*).

crack arrest tests and flat temperature type hybrid plate crack arrest test, respectively. In this case, K_{nom} is the stress intensity factor at the arrest point or the arrest toughness computed on a statical basis using actual arrested crack length, and K_{eff} is the arrest toughness at a corresponding temperature obtained from the standard arrest test (DG-series). The downward and upward arrows in Fig. 6 correspond to "go-through" and "no-go" data, respectively.

Arrest of an extremely long crack may be better handled on a statical basis in terms of "effective K value, K_{eff}" than "effective crack length, c_{eff}" because smaller data scatter in Figs. 5 and 6 than in Figs. 3 and 4. Moreover the concept of K_{eff} is applicable to a crack propagating through arbitrary distributed stress field due to a mechanical crack arrester, residual stress, etc. for which the application of concept of c_{eff} is irrelevant [*12*].

It is noted that the K_{eff} concept is not a physical explanation for the experimental observations, but rather an arbitrary defined fictitious quantity for the very wide plate test results yielding the same material parameter as the standard arrest test results on the basis of the formality of static linear fracture mechanics and arrest toughness concept.

By measuring the strain field [13,14] around a propagating crack tip under uniform tension using a 6-ft-wide test specimen, however, it was found that since the propagating crack was relatively small the crack-tip strain distribution was almost equal to that calculated for a stationary crack, but it did seem to attain a sort of steady state after the crack propagated to a certain extent. No doubt the features of stress and strain distributions near the crack tip play a decisive role, because they characterize the energy flow to drive the crack. In ordinary structural steels, most of energy dissipation is caused by plastic deformation around the running-crack tip; thus, the plastic wave propagation plays an important part of the plastic deformation around the tip of a crack which propagates at a very high velocity [15,16].

Although this process is too complicated for an exact calculation of the size of the plastic zone ahead of a propagating crack, the saturating trend of K_{eff} as seen in Figs. 5 and 6, seems to correspond to "steady propagation" in which strain distribution around a propagating crack tip does not change with crack extension.

Dynamic Analysis Using Finite-Difference Method

To analyze a dynamic crack in a plate, the following two-dimensional equations of motion in an elastic medium were used

$$\frac{\partial^2 u}{\partial t^2} = C_1^2 \frac{\partial^2 u}{\partial x^2} + (C_1^2 - C_2^2)\frac{\partial^2 v}{\partial x \partial y} + C_2^2 \frac{\partial^2 u}{\partial y^2}$$

$$\frac{\partial^2 v}{\partial t^2} = C_2^2 \frac{\partial^2 v}{\partial x^2} + (C_1^2 - C_2^2)\frac{\partial^2 u}{\partial x \partial y} + C_1^2 \frac{\partial^2 v}{\partial y^2} \qquad (2)$$

where C_1 and C_2 are the dilatational and shear wave speed, respectively. u and v are the displacements in the x- and y-directions, respectively. Taking the x-axis as the crack line, dynamic analysis of a crack in a plate with finite boundary was made by solving Eq 2 with relevant boundary and initial conditions using the finite-difference method.

The time increment Δt was chosen to satisfy the following inequality on the basis of general theory for stability of the numerical solution

$$0 < \frac{C_1 \Delta t}{h} < 1 \qquad (3)$$

where h is mesh spacing. Shmuely et al [17] reported that $C_1\Delta t/h$ would be less than 0.86 for stability of the numerical solution in the case of Poisson's ratio $\nu = 0.25$, but the figure of the upper bound of $C_1\Delta t/h$ might be increased with higher value of ν. In this paper, $C_1\Delta t/h = 0.5$, $\nu = 0.3$ for structural steel, and $\nu = 0.36$ for PMMA were adopted, respectively.

As a preliminary to examine the validity of the present method of analysis, several illustrative problems were solved. The network of a quarter plane containing a crack is as shown in Fig. 7 in which c is half crack length, and breadth B and height H are of 50 to $100h$, length, respectively. The location of the crack tip is assumed at the middle point of the square mesh.

Figure 8 shows time variation of dimensionless normal stress in the y-direction at three fixed points A, B, and C ahead of a crack (as shown in the inset of the figure) when a crack of length $2c = 11h$ opens up suddenly in a plate ($B = 50h$, $H = 50h$) subjected uniform vertical tensile stress T.

The solution of this problem is obtained by the superposition of the following two cases: (*a*) a crack in the externally free stressed plate is subjected suddenly by crack open-up pressure T, and (*b*) the plate containing no crack is under uniform vertical tensile stress T. This figure shows that after stress wave passes through the points A, B, and C, stress at these points seem to attain the steady value until the arrival of reflected waves from free boundary of the plate. The steady values of stresses at various points attained at $C_1T/h = 150$ are compared with those for corresponding static problem obtained by Sneddon [18] as shown in Fig. 9 in terms of stress distribution in the vicinity of crack tip along the lines I ($y = 0$), II ($y = h/2$), and III ($y = 3h/2$).

Another illustrative problem solved in a crack extending in a plate (B

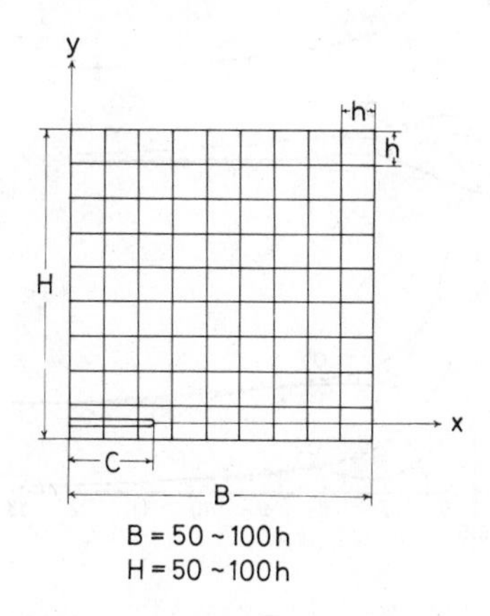

FIG. 7—*Network used in calculation.*

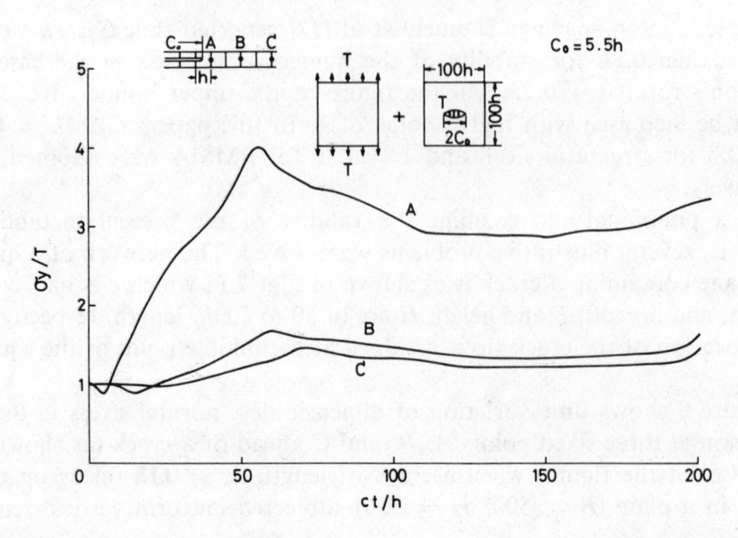

FIG. 8—*Time variation of dimensionless stress at three fixed points ahead of a crack.*

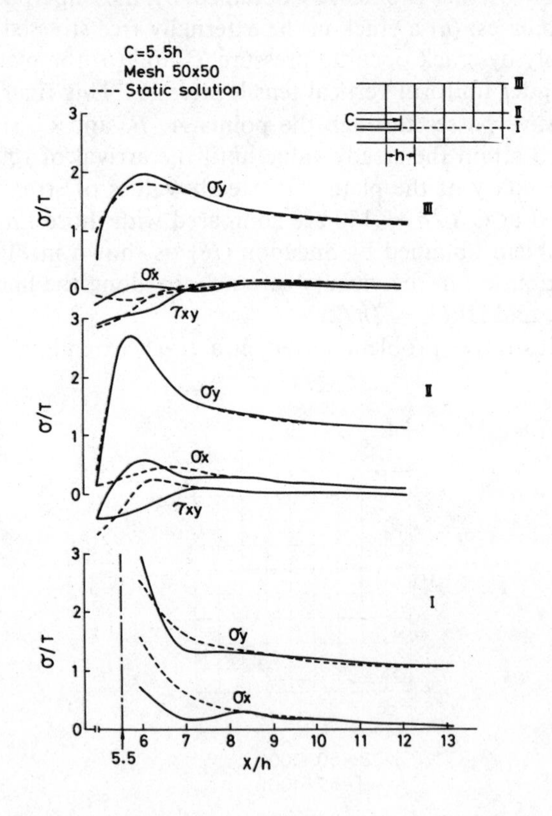

FIG. 9—*Stress distribution around a crack tip in steady state.*

$= 70h$, $H = 70h$) at constant speed from an initial crack length of $2c = 2 \times 5.5h$. The stress distribution along the crack line and the configuration of the crack opening displacement are shown in Figs. 10 and 11, respectively, compared with the analytical solution as indicated with dotted line (infinite plate) obtained by Broberg [19]. The wavy configurations seen in Fig. 11 for relatively slow crack may be due to the incremental crack growth naturally associated with the finite-difference method, which does not satisfactorily simulate the "continuous" crack extension for such slower crack speeds, but rather "intermittent" crack extension. After all, the finite-difference solution of Eq 2 seems to provide a useful method for analysis of dynamic crack propagation especially for higher crack speed which necessitates proper account for dynamic effect.

For the energy flow at the running crack tip, the energy rate, J_d, available to extend the crack is expressed by the following form which is a dynamic version of path-independent J-integral [20]

$$J_d = \int_\Gamma [(W + \frac{1}{2} \rho V^2 \frac{\partial u_i}{\partial x} \times \frac{\partial u_i}{\partial x}) \, dy - T_i \frac{\partial u_i}{\partial x} \, ds] \tag{4}$$

where

W = strain energy density,
ρ = density,
V = crack speed,
T_i = boundary traction along Γ, and
ds = element of arc length counterclockwise along Γ which encloses the crack tip region.

This equation is strictly valid for a constant crack speed. But even in a nonsteady state, when the effect of acceleration is relatively small, that is, velocity of a crack increases or decreases gradually, Eq 4 seems to be nearly correct in some divided region. Since it might be better for the J_d contour integral path to be small because it is affected intensively by crack tip behavior, contour path of $6h$ wide and $6h$ high around the moving crack tip is adopted successfully.

In Fig. 12, $K_{Jd} (= \sqrt{EJ_d})$ values calculated through Eq 4 are compared with crack closure energy rate K_d, calculated by the following formula [18] using Broberg's solution [19]

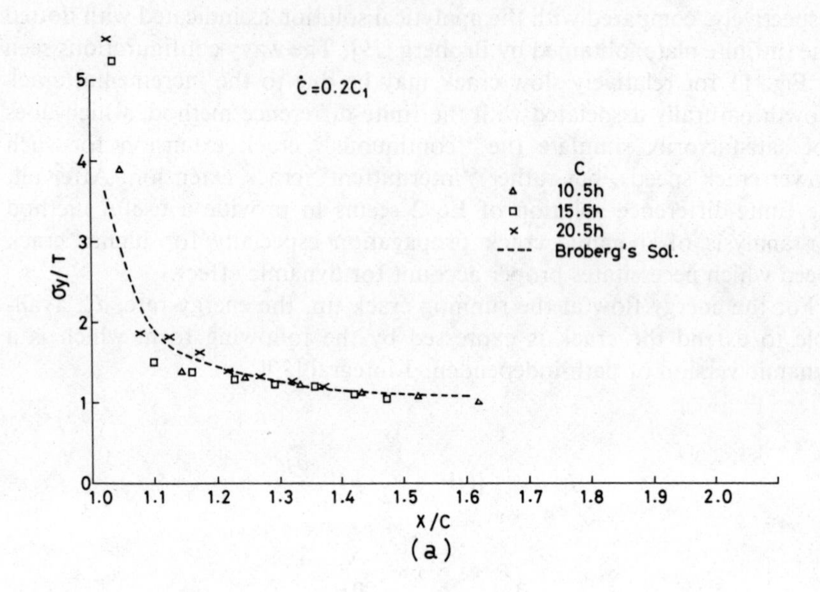

Ċ=0.2C1
C
10.5h
15.5h
20.5h
Broberg's Sol.
σy/T
X/C

(a)

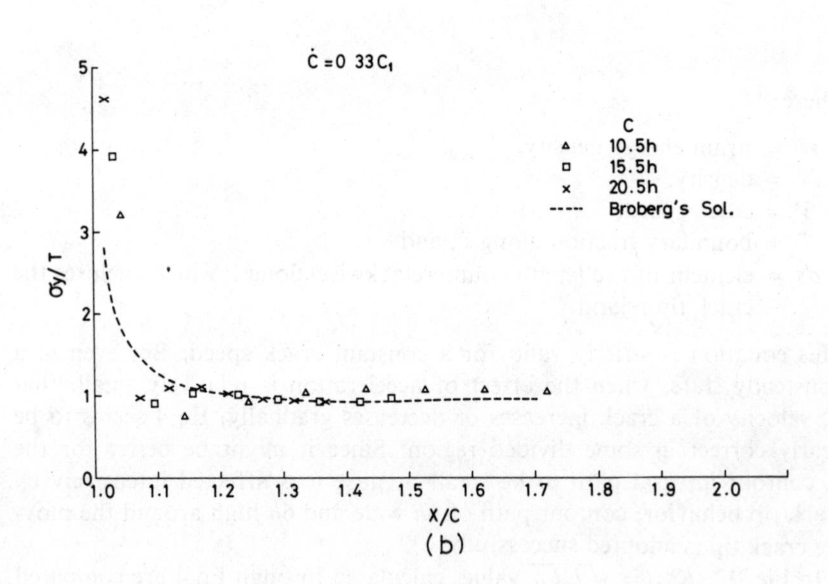

Ċ=0 33C1
C
10.5h
15.5h
20.5h
Broberg's Sol.
σy/T
X/C

(b)

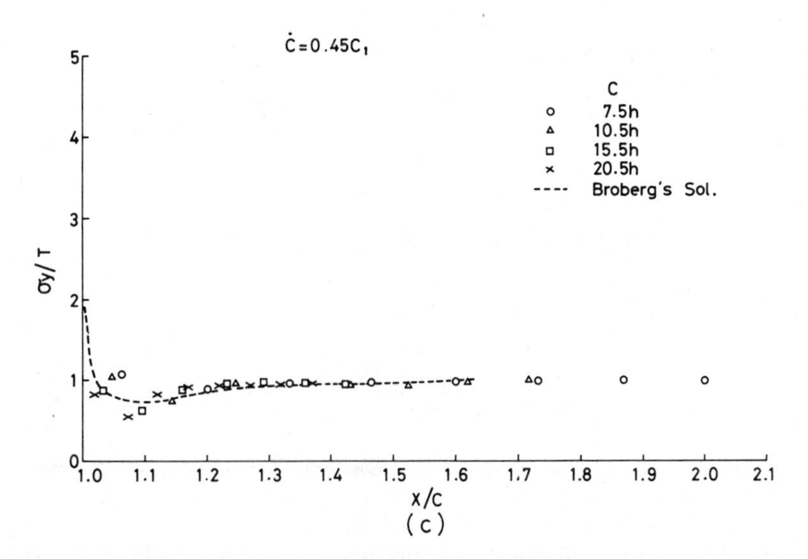

FIG. 10—*Stress distribution along crack line of a crack extending at constant speed.*

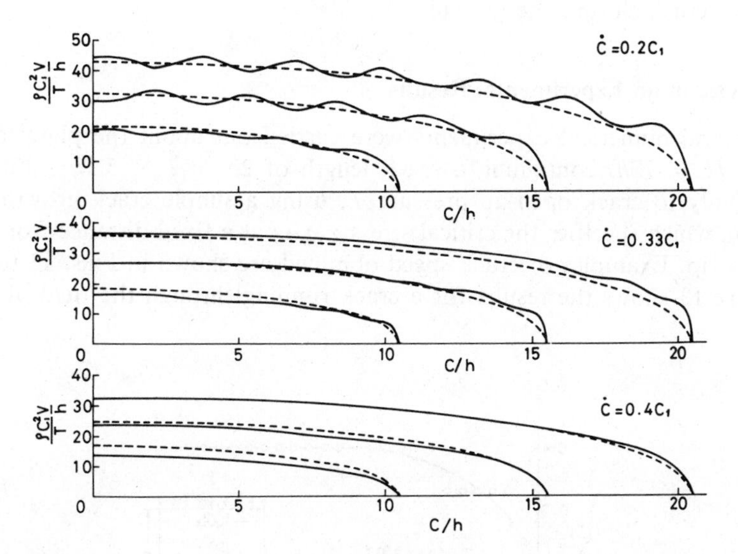

FIG. 11—*Configuration of crack opening displacement of a crack extending at constant speed.*

$$K_d = (E \lim_{\Delta c \to 0} \frac{1}{\Delta c} \int_c^{c+\Delta c} \sigma_y \times V dx)^{1/2} \tag{5}$$

where

σ_y = dynamic stress in the *y*-direction along a crack line and
V = dynamic crack opening displacement.

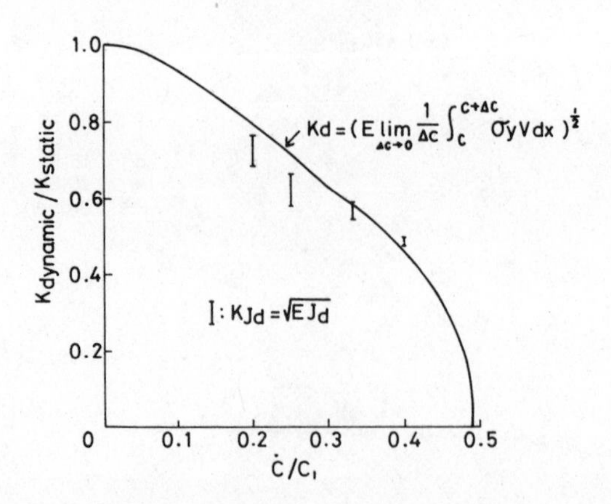

FIG. 12—*Dimensionless dynamic* K *calculated from* J_d *value versus crack speed.*

Symbol bar I in this figure shows the range in which calculated K_{Jd} value exists. In the sequel, it is found that J_d value seems to be physically equivalent to crack closure energy rate.

Discussion on Experimental Results

Several numerical experiments were carried out about the plate ($B = 70h$, $H = 70h$) containing a crack length of $2c = 2 \times 5.5h$ subjected suddenly to crack open-up pressure T, using a simple crack growth criterion which specifies the critical stress $\sigma_{Yc}(A)$ at a fixed distance from the crack tip. Examples of crack speed obtained are shown in Figs. 13 to 15. Figure 13 shows the results for a crack running through the field of uni-

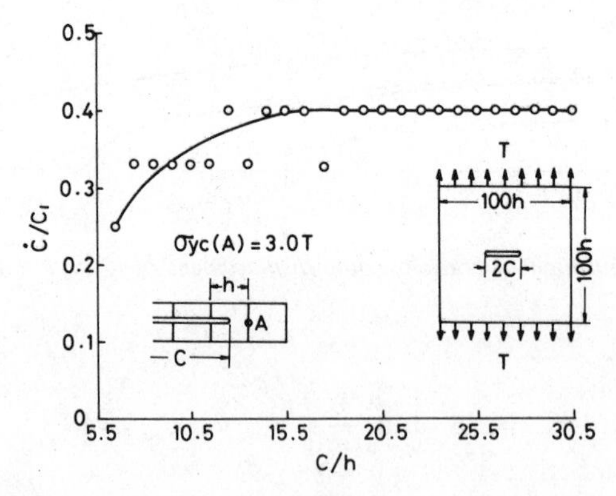

FIG. 13—*Crack length variation of crack speed for a crack traversing uniform stress and uniform material resistance field.*

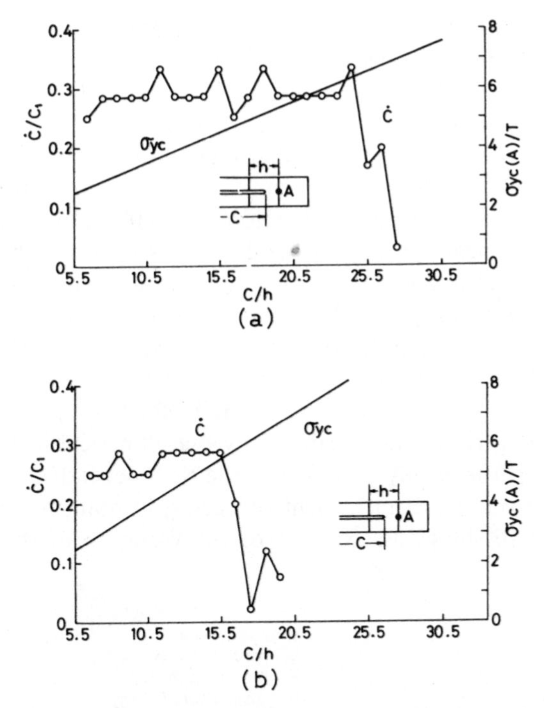

FIG. 14—*Crack length variation of crack speed for a crack running into linearly increasing material resistance field.*

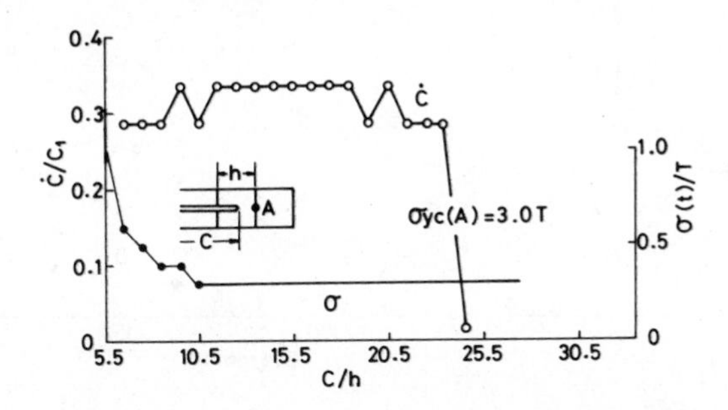

FIG. 15—*Crack length variation of crack speed subjected to load drop effect.*

form material resistance or constant critical stress for crack growth $\sigma_{Yc}(A) = 3.0T$. The crack is accelerated to a terminal speed, and this general trend agrees with many reported experimental observations. When a crack runs into a linearly increasing material resistance field, such as temperature gradient type crack arrest test, the crack will be decelerated and finally arrested. Figure 14 shows the results for a crack traversing the field of linearly increasing material resistance, and this qualitatively compares well with the experimental observations shown in Fig. 2. Figure 15 shows the decreasing open-up pressure $\sigma(t)$ with time, which somehow simulates a crack subjected to load drop effect or a crack running into a decreasing stress field such as a crack arrest test using a bending or a wedge opening specimen under fixed grip condition or both.

Series of crack arrest tests were conducted using 10-mm-thick PMMA. The specimens used are single-edge-notched 300-mm-wide and 280-mm-long plates. The mean velocity of the crack was measured by crack detector gages mounted along a crack propagating line, and a load drop was recorded by strain gages plated on the rod of the setting apparatus. This material fractured in a relatively brittle manner. The measured crack speeds range from 120 to 540 m/s, that is, relative speeds with respect to dilatational wave (2.15×10^3 m/s for the PMMA used) are 0.06 to 0.25. The experimental results are analyzed by the numerical method using the crack speed experimentally obtained as the time-dependent boundary condition and the statical displacement of each grid point as the initial condition. Figure 16 shows an example of the variation of the energy components with crack length, that is, external load work done W, kinetic energy K, strain energy U, and dissipated energy D. Figure 17 shows an example of variation of dynamic fracture toughness K_{Jd} with crack extension, which is defined by

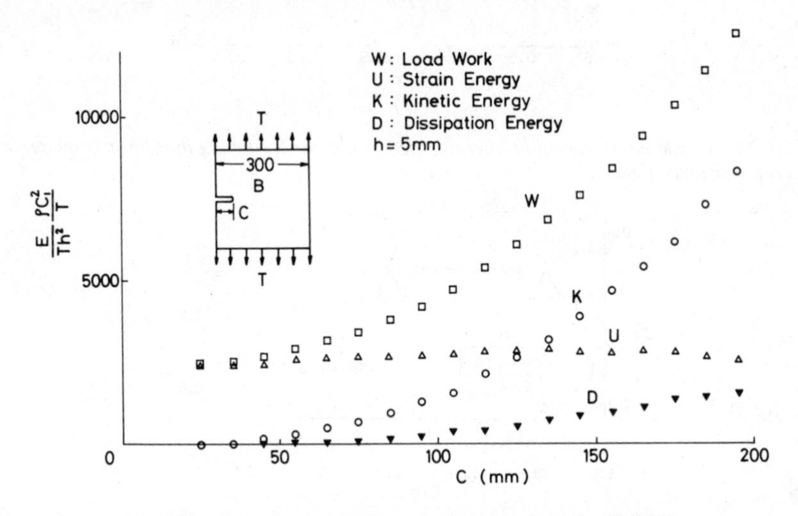

FIG. 16—*Energy changes due to extension of crack* (*PMMA*).

$$K_{Jd} = \sqrt{E \frac{dD}{dC}} \tag{6}$$

where E denotes Young's modulus.

Variation of crack speed is also shown in the same figure deplicting crack speed dependence of material toughness. Taking K_{Jd} values at maximum crack speed for each of the specimens, its crack speed dependence can be summarized as shown in Fig. 18. The dotted line, shown in the figure, is the variation of K_d value with crack speed obtained by Green et al [22] using high-speed photography of PMMA. The increasing trend in toughness with crack speed as obtained by Green et al [22] seems to support the experimental observations that the roughness of fractured surface increases with crack speeds.

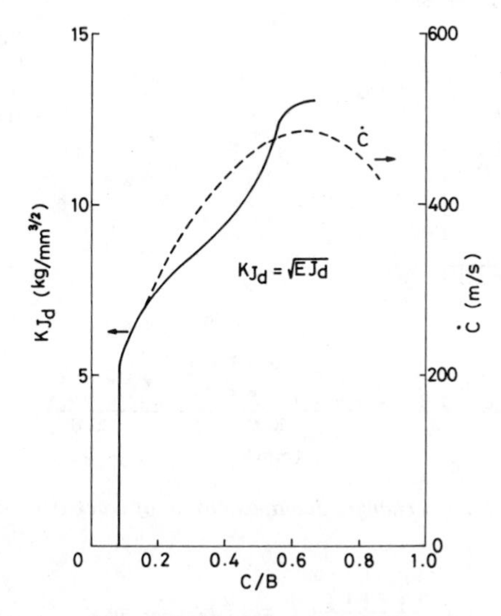

FIG. 17—*Variation of dynamic fracture toughness* K_{Jd} *with crack extension.*

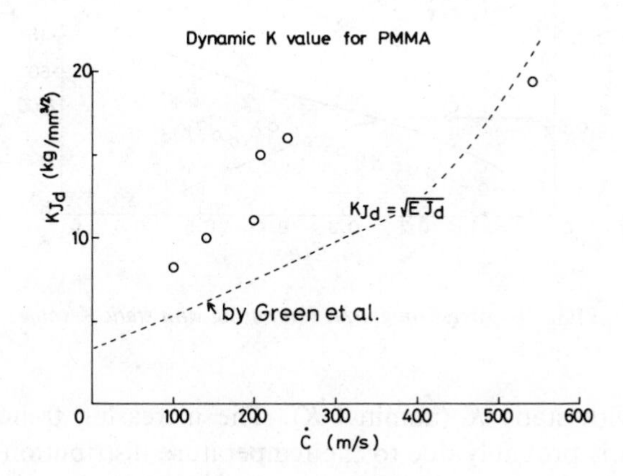

FIG. 18—*Crack speed dependence of* K_{Jd}.

A similar analysis was made on the previously mentioned experimental result using a 2400-mm-wide steel plate specimen. An example of energetics calculated using experimental crack speed data is shown in Fig. 19. The test is a gradient temperature type ESSO crack arrest test with about a 1450-mm-long arrested crack. The experimental observation showed that the fixed grip condition was realized approximately in this case. The saturating feature seen in dissipation energy implies that the crack should come to be arrested. Figure 20 shows crack length variation of K_{Jd} value

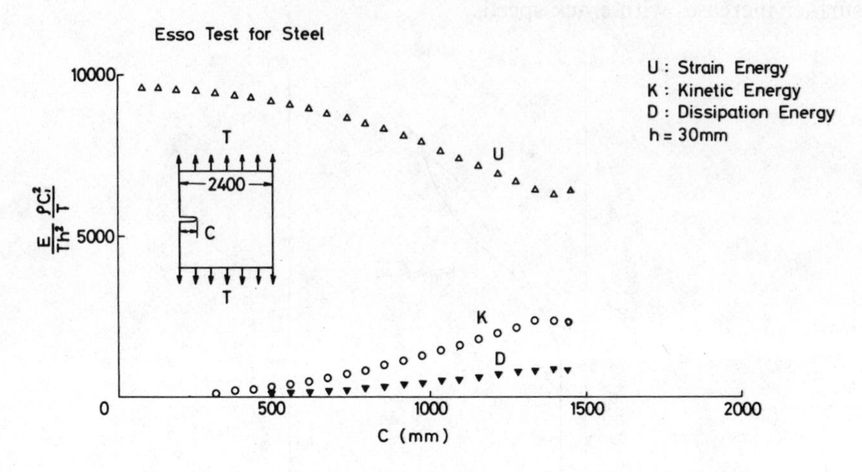

FIG. 19—*Energy changes due to extension of crack (structural steel).*

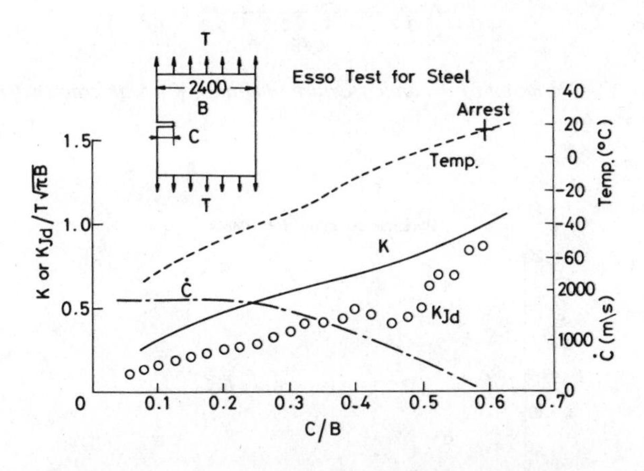

FIG. 20—*Arrest toughness comparing with static* K *value.*

compared with static K (nominal K). The increasing trend in K_{Jd} with crack length is probably due to the temperature distribution of the specimen, which is also shown in the same figure. Note that the K_{Jd} value is smaller than nominal K value at the arrest point. But this difference is not enough to explain such descrepancy fully, as shown in Fig. 1.

Conclusions

It is shown that the dynamic analysis using the finite-difference method applied to the equation of motion in elastic medium will provide a useful tool to investigate the dynamic aspect involved in fast fracture and crack arrest. But the preliminary study reported in this paper has revealed that considerable refinement is needed in the current theories of crack propagation and arrest.

As to how far this preliminary work can go, no definite judgment could be made regarding the controversy on two major concepts; the arrest toughness concept and the total energy or recoverable kinetic energy concept.

References

[1] Hahn, G. T., Hoagland, R. G., Kanninen, M. F., Rosenfield, A. R., and Sejnoha, R., "Fast Fracture Resistance and Crack Arrest in Structural Steels," SSC-42, Ship Structure Committee, 1973.

[2] Kanazawa, T., Machida, S., and Matoba, M., *Journal of the Society of Naval Architects of Japan,* No. 115, 1964, p. 78.

[3] Kanazawa, T., Machida, S., and Matoba, M., *Journal of the Society of Naval Architects of Japan,* No. 116, 1964, p. 124.

[4] Yoshiki, M., Kanazawa, T., and Machida, S., *Journal of the Society of Naval Architects of Japan,* No. 118, 1965, p. 192.

[5] Kanazawa, T., Machida, S., and Ohyagi, M., *Journal of the Society of Naval Architects of Japan,* No. 121, 1967, p. 225.

[6] Kanazawa, T., Machida, S., and Ohyagi, M., *Journal of the Society of Naval Architects of Japan,* No. 122, 1967, p. 200.

[7] Kanazawa, T., Machida, S., and Doi, H., *Journal of the Society of Naval Architects of Japan,* No. 124, 1968, p. 321.

[8] Kihara, H., Kanazawa, T., Ikeda, K., Okabe, T., and Yajima, H., *Journal of the Society of Naval Architects of Japan,* No. 122, 1967, p. 191, and No. 124, 1968, p. 331.

[9] "Investigation on Brittle Fracture Control in Large Ships," Report No. 108, Technical Report of Japan Ship Research Association, 1970.

[10] Ishida, M., "Application and Extension of Fracture Mechanics," 3rd Symposium of the Japanese Society of Mechanical Engineers, 10–11 June 1971, Yumoto, Hakone, Japan.

[11] Kanazawa, T., Machida, S., Yajima, H., and Aoki, M., *Journal of the Society of the Naval Architects of Japan,* No. 130, 1971, p. 343 and IIW Document X-667-72, 1972.

[12] Machida, S. and Aoki, M., *Journal of the Society of Naval Architects of Japan,* No. 131, 1972, p. 367.

[13] Rolfe, S. T. and Hall, W. J., *Experimental Mechanics,* No. 9, Sept. 1961, p. 113.

[14] Pratt, P. L. and Stock, T. A. C., *Proceedings of the Royal Society,* Series A, Vol. 285, 1965, p. 73.

[15] Ishibashi, T., *Journal of the Society of Mechanical Engineers,* Vol. 63, No. 496, 1960, p. 11.

[16] Hall, E. O., *Journal of the Mechanics and Physics of Solids,* Vol. 1, 1953, p. 227.

[17] Shumely, M. and Peretz, D., *International Journal of Solids and Structure,* Vol. 12, 1976, p. 67.

[18] Sneddon, I. N., *Fourier Transforms,* McGraw-Hill, New York, 1951, p. 427.
[19] Broberg, K. B., *Arkiv för Fysik,* 1960, pp. 35–38.
[20] Sih, G. C. in *Inelastic Behavior of Solids,* Kanninen, M. F. et al, Eds., McGraw-Hill, New York, 1969, Part 5, pp. 607–639.
[21] Erdogan, F. in *Fracture,* Vol. II, Liebowitz, H., Ed., Academic Press, New York and London, 1968, Chapter 5, pp. 497–590.
[22] Green, A. K. and Pratt, P. L., *Engineering Fracture Mechanics,* Vol. 6, 1974, p. 71.

J. D. Achenbach[1] *and P. K. Tolikas*[1]

Elastodynamic Effects on Crack Arrest

REFERENCE: Achenbach, J. D. and Tolikas, P. K., "**Elastodynamic Effects on Crack Arrest,**" *Fast Fracture and Crack Arrest, ASTM STP 627,* G. T. Hahn and M. F. Kanninen, Eds., American Society for Testing and Materials, 1977, pp. 59–76.

ABSTRACT: The first part of the paper is concerned with the elastodynamic stress field in the vicinity of a rapidly propagating crack tip. Elastodynamic stress intensity factors and their role in the fracture criterion of the balance of rates of energies are discussed. The remainder of the paper deals with the near-tip stress field for a sudden discontinuous change of the speed of a rapidly propagating crack tip, including the case that the crack tip is suddenly arrested. Analytical expressions are derived for the elastodynamic stress intensity factor, for the case that the crack-tip speed instantaneously changes from c_1 to c_2, where $c_2 < c_1$. Arrest, or continued propagation of a crack tip at a reduced speed are investigated on the basis of the fracture criterion of the balance of rates of energies.

KEY WORDS: crack propagation, elastodynamic stresses, stress intensity, crack arrest, fracture properties

Much analytical information is available on elastodynamic stress fields in the vicinity of a propagating crack tip. Elastodynamic effects generated by rapid crack propagation, as well as by the diffraction of incident stress waves, have been investigated in detail. In these investigations elastodynamic stress intensity factors are computed and subsequently entered in the fracture criterion of the balance of rates of energies, to analyze conditions for crack propagation and to determine crack tip speeds. In a recent review article [*1*],[2] a number of observations on elastodynamic effects are discussed on the basis of solutions of example problems. Another review article by Freund [*2*] also discusses in detail elastodynamic crack-tip stress fields.

In this paper we are interested in sudden discontinuous changes of the speed of the crack tip, including the case that the crack tip is suddenly

[1] Professor of civil engineering and graduate student, respectively, Department of Civil Engineering, Northwestern University, Evanston, Ill. 60201.

[2] The italic numbers in brackets refer to the list of references appended to this paper.

arrested. After a statement of some known results for near-tip elastodynamic stress fields, we derive an analytical expression for the elastodynamic stress intensity factor, for the case that the crack-tip speed instantaneously changes from c_1 to c_2, where $c_2 < c_1$. Some implications of the results for crack arrest are discussed within the context of the balance of rates of energies.

Next we consider some specific applications of the results to the case of a crack which extends at a constant velocity from a central point in a uniform tensile field. For this case constant speed of crack propagation is not consistent with the fracture criterion of the balance of rates of energies, at least not for constant specific crack extension energy. A constant velocity central crack may possibly be thought of as a crack propagating along a preexisting weak plane, at a high speed, and this speed is considered an average over a small time interval. The question of interest now is whether a crack which initially extends over a preexisting flaw with weak cohesive forces will or will not penetrate the full material. Arrest or continued propagation of cracks at reduced speeds are investigated on the basis of the balance of rates of energies fracture criterion. Analogous investigations for the case of antiplane strain were carried out in Ref *3*.

Some Results for the Near-Tip Fields

The general nature of elastodynamic near-tip fields for the case that the tip of a crack propagates rapidly along a rather arbitrary but smooth trajectory in a two-dimensional geometry, was discussed by several authors [*1,2*]. Here we consider the special case of a crack propagating in its own plane. The two-dimensional geometry is shown in Fig. 1. The speed of the crack tip is $c(t)$, where $c(t)$ is positive. A system of moving polar coordinates is centered at the moving crack tip, as shown in Fig. 1.

For the case of symmetric opening up of the crack (Mode I), we have in the vicinity of the crack tip

$$\tau_\theta \sim \frac{1}{(2\pi)^{1/2}} \frac{1}{r^{1/2}} k_I(t,c)\, T_\theta^I(\theta,c) \tag{1}$$

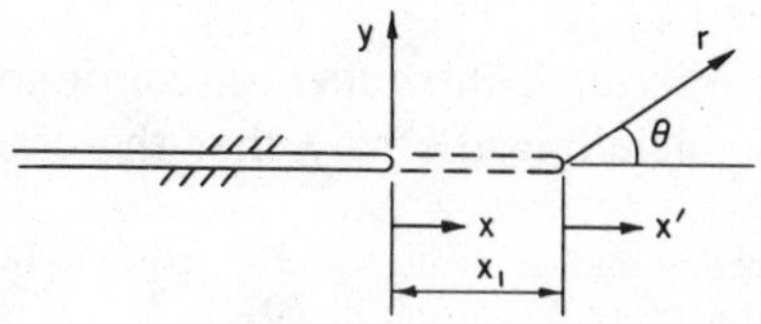

FIG. 1—*Two-dimensional geometry of a propagating crack.*

In Eq 1, $T_\theta^{\mathrm{I}}(0,c) = 1$, and $k_{\mathrm{I}}(t,c)$ is the elastodynamic stress intensity factor. The function $T_\theta^{\mathrm{I}}(\theta,c)$, which is of a rather complicated form, is explicitly stated in Ref *4*. It is of note that the maximum value of $T_\theta^{\mathrm{I}}(\theta,c)$ moves out of the plane $\theta = 0$ (the plane of crack propagation) as $c(t)$ increases beyond a certain value.

For a semi-infinite crack and quasi-static external loads, the elastodynamic stress intensity factor can be expressed in the form [5]

$$k_{\mathrm{I}}(t,c) = \left[S_{+}\left(\frac{1}{c}, \frac{1}{c}\right)\right]^{-1} \frac{c_R - c}{c_R} \left(\frac{c_L}{c_L - c}\right)^{1/2} K_{\mathrm{I}}(t) \tag{2}$$

where $K_{\mathrm{I}}(t)$ is the stress intensity factor for the corresponding quasi-static problem, that is, as $\rho \rightarrow 0$. The function $S_{+}(\zeta,s)$ is defined by Eq 49, and c_R is the velocity of Rayleigh surface waves. Equation 2 is also valid for a crack of finite length but only for small times compared to travel times of disturbances from the boundaries or from the other crack tip.

On the crack surfaces just behind the moving crack tip, the crack opening displacement is

$$v \sim V(t)\, r^{1/2} \tag{3}$$

where

$$V(t) = -\left(\frac{2}{\pi}\right)^{1/2} \frac{\beta^2}{\mu} \frac{(1 - \alpha^2)^{1/2}}{D(\alpha,\beta)} k_{\mathrm{I}}(t,c) \tag{4}$$

In Eq 4

$$\alpha = \frac{c(t)}{c_L}, \qquad c_L = \left(\frac{\lambda + 2\mu}{\rho}\right)^{1/2} \tag{5}$$

$$\beta = \frac{c(t)}{c_T}, \qquad c_T = \left(\frac{\mu}{\rho}\right)^{1/2} \tag{6}$$

and $D(\alpha,\beta)$ is defined as

$$D(\alpha,\beta) = (\beta^2 - 2)^2 - 4(1 - \alpha^2)^{1/2}(1 - \beta^2)^{1/2} \tag{7}$$

It follows from Eqs 4 and 1 that the near-tip stress field may be expressed in terms of $V(t)$ by

$$\tau_\theta \sim -\frac{\mu}{r^{1/2}} \frac{D(\alpha,\beta)}{2(1-\alpha^2)^{1/2}} \frac{1}{\beta^2} V(t) T_\theta^{\mathrm{I}}(\theta,c) \tag{8}$$

A propagating crack tip acts as an energy sink. It is quite simple to compute the flux of energy into the crack tip. A detailed discussion can be found in Ref *1*, as well as in the papers by Atkinson and Eshelby [*6*], Kostrov and Nikitin [*7*], and by Freund [*8*]. The result is

$$F = -\frac{c^3(1-\alpha^2)^{1/2}\,[k_{\mathrm{I}}(t,c)]^2}{2\mu c_T{}^2 D(\alpha,\beta)} \tag{9}$$

The balance of rates of energies then provides the following necessary condition for fracture

$$F = 2c\,\Gamma(c) \tag{10}$$

Here $2\Gamma(c)$ is the specific energy of crack extension, that is, the energy required to produce one unit of new crack length. For purely brittle fracture $\Gamma(c)$ becomes the specific surface energy. In general Γ may depend on the speed of crack propagation, that is, $\Gamma = \Gamma(c)$.

For slow propagation of the crack tip (that is, the limit $c \rightarrow 0$), Eq 9 reduces to

$$F = \frac{c_L{}^2[K_{\mathrm{I}}(t)]^2 c}{4\mu(c_L{}^2 - c_T{}^2)} = \frac{1-\nu^2}{E}[K_{\mathrm{I}}(t)]^2 c \tag{11}$$

By combining this result with Eq 10, it follows that K_{I} equals the toughness for fracture initiation, K_{Ic}, that is

$$K_{\mathrm{I}} = K_{\mathrm{Ic}} = \left[\frac{2\Gamma(0)E}{1-\nu^2}\right]^{1/2} \tag{12}$$

Thus, for a slowly propagating crack the usual fracture toughness enters as a material property, and the stress intensity factor equals the fracture toughness K_{Ic} while the crack propagates. The latter provides a condition for the computation of the corresponding external loads. In this computation the precise magnitude of c is immaterial, but c should be small so that elastodynamic effects can be ignored.

At higher speeds of crack propagation Eq 10 is an equation for the computation of c, provided that the stress analysis problem of expressing

$k_I(t,c)$ in terms of the external loads, the geometry, and with c as an arbitrary parameter, can be solved. Once the actual speed of crack propagation has been obtained, Eq 10 can be used to express $k_I(t,c)$ explicitly in terms of $\Gamma(c)$ as

$$k_I(t,c) = \left[\frac{-4\Gamma(c)\mu c_T^2 D(\alpha,\beta)}{c^2(1-\alpha^2)^{1/2}}\right]^{1/2} \tag{13}$$

Thus $k_I(t,c)$ strongly depends on the speed of crack propagation. It is evident that the elastodynamic stress intensity factor is not equal to K_{Ic} while the crack propagates, but rather the expression

$$-2\alpha^2(1-\alpha^2)^{1/2}(c_L^2 - c_T^2)[k_I(t,c)]^2\,\Gamma(0)/c_T^2\Gamma(c)D(\alpha,\beta)$$

maintains a value equal to $(K_{Ic})^2$. Alternatively one can define a dynamic fracture toughness as

$$K_{ID} = \left[-\frac{1}{2}\frac{c_T^2}{c_L^2 - c_T^2}\;\frac{D(\alpha,\beta)}{\alpha^2(1-\alpha^2)^{1/2}}\;\frac{\Gamma(c)}{\Gamma(0)}\right]^{1/2} K_{Ic} \tag{14}$$

Then it can be stated that $k_I(t,c) = K_{ID}$ during fast crack propagation.

Computational work in elastodynamic fracture mechanics would simplify considerably if Γ could be assumed constant. Unfortunately there is considerable experimental evidence which suggests that Γ does depend on the speed of crack propagation. It is possible to determine Γ if for a rapidly propagating crack both $k_I(t,c)$ and c are measured. Figure 6 of the paper by Kalthoff et al [9] contains the required information for Araldite B. The figure shows that in the initial stages of crack propagation both $k_I(t,c)$ and c are constants. Their values have been tabulated in Table 1.

TABLE 1—*Specific fracture energy of Araldite B computed from results presented in Ref 9; c_L = 2400 m/s, Poisson's ratio = 0.392.*

Specimen No.	K_{ID}, MN/m$^{3/2}$	c_{max}, m/s	$2\mu\Gamma$, MN^2/m^3
35,4,21	1.09	295	0.388
8	0.972	272	0.306
17	0.875	207	0.242
24	0.764	108	0.18
62	0.694	15	0.148

These values can then be substituted in

$$\Gamma = -\frac{1}{4\mu}\left(\frac{c}{c_T}\right)^2 \frac{(1 - \alpha^2)^{1/2}}{D(\alpha, \beta)} [k_I(t, c)]^2 \tag{15}$$

which is again obtained from Eq 10. The results are listed in Table 1, and it is evident that $\Gamma(c)$ is an increasing function of c.

It has become customary to compare the elastodynamic stress intensity factor $k_I(t, c)$ with the elastostatic stress intensity factor $K_I(t)$. The comparison is usually for the same applied external loads, so that the difference between $k_I(t,c)$ and $K_I(t)$ then reflects the difference between elastostatic and elastodynamic stress analysis. For the case of a semiinfinite crack the ratio $k_I(t,c)/K_I(t)$ immediately follows from Eq 2. In the range $0 < c < c_R$ this ratio is less than unity. For problems of finite geometry, elastodynamic stress analysis is much more complicated, and a simple general result is not available.

It is, however, also useful to think of the two stress intensity factors in terms of the ones which the material actually experiences during the process of crack propagation, that is, the stress intensity factors which would be measured in experiments. Here the stress intensity factor would be elastostatic when $c/c_R \ll 1$, and the specific magnitude of c/c_R would not matter. The ratio $k_I(t,c)/K_I(t)$ immediately follows from Eq 14, and is given by the bracketed term. The factor $D(\alpha,\beta)/\alpha^2 (1 - \alpha^2)^{1/2}$ decreases with increasing crack speed. On the other hand $\Gamma(c)$ generally increases as c increases. Thus, it is possible that the stress intensity factor at high speeds of crack propagation is greater than the one at low speeds.

Discontinuous Change of Crack-Tip Speed

The objective of this section is to investigate the conditions which may cause a drastic change in the tip speed of a propagating crack. Let us consider a fixed coordinate system x, y, with time being denoted t and suppose that at time $t = t_1$ a moving crack tip is located at a position defined by $x = x_1$, see Fig. 1. The instantaneous velocity of the crack tip is $c_1 = c(t_1)$. Now we assume that at this moment the crack-tip speed changes, and the crack continues to propagate with a new velocity c_2 ($c_2 < c_1$). If the crack would propagate a little bit beyond position $x = x_1$ with velocity $c_1 = c(t_1)$, the crack opening displacement in the coordinates x' and t', where

$$t' = t - t_1, \quad x' = x - x_1$$

would follow from Eq 3 as

$$v \sim V_1 (c_1 t' - x')^{1/2}, \quad V_1 = V(t_1) \tag{16}$$

Here it is implied that $t' \ll t$ and $x' \ll x$. However, the crack does not propagate with velocity c_1, but rather with velocity c_2, and thus, the crack opening given by Eq 16 must be closed for $x' > c_2 t'$.

To analyze the fields near the crack tip propagating with velocity c_2, it is convenient to introduce the new variable q as

$$q = x' - c_2 t' \tag{17}$$

Relative to q and t', the crack opening displacement is

$$v \sim f(q, t') = V_1[(c_1 - c_2)t' - q]^{1/2} \tag{18}$$

On the field corresponding to the crack tip which continues to propagate with velocity c_1, we now superimpose the solution to the boundary-initial-value problem for $y \geqslant 0$ with quiescent initial conditions, and with the following boundary conditions at $y = 0$

$$q < 0, \quad \tau_y = 0 \tag{19}$$

$$-\infty < q < \infty, \quad \tau_{yx} = 0 \tag{20}$$

$$q > (c_1 - c_2)t', \quad v = 0 \tag{21}$$

$$0 < q < (c_1 - c_2)t', \quad v = -f(q, t') \tag{22}$$

The superposition of the solution satisfying Eqs 19 to 22 on the initial problem (of a crack propagating with instantaneous velocity c_1), produces the case that the crack continues its symmetrical (Mode I) propagation with the new velocity c_2. This solution is valid for $t' \ll t$. In physical terms the solution satisfying Eqs 19 to 22 gives the necessary traction for closing with velocity $c_1 - c_2$ a slit extending with velocity c_1.

The near-tip stress τ_y for the boundary conditions (Eqs 19 to 22) is given in the Appendix, Eq 48. This expression for τ_y should show two singularities, namely, one at $q = (c_1 - c_2)t'$ and one at $q = 0$. The singularity at $q = (c_1 - c_2)t'$, that is, $x' = c_1 t'$, must cancel the singularity at $x' = c_1 t'$ for the original crack, while the singularity at $q = 0$ $(x' = c_2 t')$ is the singularity at the crack tip propagating with the new velocity c_2. The actual computation of the stress near $q = (c_1 - c_2)t'$ is rather lengthy, since it involves the evaluation of several complicated integrals. The result is indeed equal and opposite to Eq 8 evaluated at $t = t_1$ and for $c = c_1$. The stress near $q = 0$ is easier to evaluate. It follows from Eq 48 as

$$\tau_y = -\frac{\mu}{r^{1/2}}\frac{D(\alpha_1, \beta_1)}{2(1-\alpha_1^2)^{1/2}\beta_1^2}\,h(c_1, c_2)\,V_1\,T_\theta^{\mathrm{I}}(\theta, c_2) \tag{23}$$

where

$$\alpha_1 = c_1/c_L, \quad \beta_1 = c_1/c_T \tag{24a, b}$$

and

$$h(c_1, c_2) = \frac{c_R - c_2}{c_R - c_1}\left(\frac{c_L - c_1}{c_L - c_2}\right)^{1/2}\frac{1}{S_+(-s_{12}, 1/c_2)} \tag{25}$$

The function $S_+(-s_{12}, 1/c_2)$ follows from Eq 49.

Eliminating V_1 by the use of Eq 4, the stress intensity factor at the new speed c_2 is obtained as

$$k_{\mathrm{I}}(t_1, c_2) = h(c_1, c_2)\,k_{\mathrm{I}}(t_1, c_1) \tag{26}$$

For $c_2 = c_1$, we find $h(c_1, c_2) = 1$. For various values of c_2/c_1, the function $h(c_1, c_2)$ is plotted versus c_1/c_R in Fig. 2. It is noted that the elastodynamic stress intensity factor always increases when the crack speed decreases. The relative increase becomes larger for larger c_1. As c_1 approaches the velocity of Rayleigh waves, the function $h(c_1, c_2)$ increases beyond bounds, because the elastodynamic stress intensity factor for the original crack speed c_1 approaches zero.

If $k_{\mathrm{I}}(t, c)$ is of the form given by Eq 2, we find for $c_2 = 0$

$$k_{\mathrm{I}}(t_1, 0) = K_{\mathrm{I}}(t_1) \tag{27}$$

It can be shown that for a discontinuous change of the speed of crack propagation of the tip of a semi-infinite crack, the new near-tip stress field is obtained by simply substituting c_2 for c_1 in Eq 2. This is not true if $k_{\mathrm{I}}(t, c)$ is not of the form given by Eq 2.

The ratio of the specific crack extension energies required for an instantaneous change of speed from $c = c_1$ to $c = c_2$, where $c_2 < c_1$, follows immediately from Eqs 10, 9, 8, and 23 as

$$\frac{\Gamma_2}{\Gamma_1} = \frac{c_2^2[1-\alpha_2^2]^{1/2}}{c_1^2[1-\alpha_1^2]^{1/2}}\,\frac{D(\alpha_1, \beta_1)}{D(\alpha_2, \beta_2)}\,[h(c_1, c_2)]^2 \tag{28}$$

Here α_2 and β_2 are defined analogously to Eqs 24a,b. In the limit $c_2 \to 0$, Eq 28 reduces to

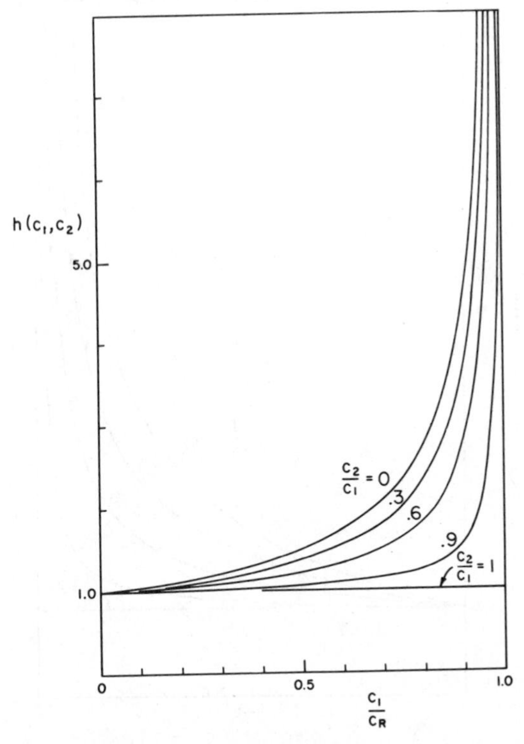

FIG. 2—*Ratio of elastodynamic stress intensity factors for a sudden change of crack-tip speed from* c_1 *to* c_2 *(plane strain, Poisson's ratio* $\nu = 0.33$*).*

$$\frac{\Gamma_o}{\Gamma_1} = -\frac{1}{2}\,\frac{D(\alpha_1,\beta_1)}{c_1^2[1-\alpha_1^2]^{1/2}}\,\frac{c_L^2c_T^2}{c_L^2-c_T^2}\,[h(c_1,0)]^2 \tag{29}$$

The ratio Γ_2/Γ_1 is plotted versus c_1/c_R in Fig. 3. If a crack is to be suddenly arrested, the higher the initial crack tip speed c_1, the larger ratio of specific crack extension energies is required across the plane at which the crack is arrested.

Central Crack

Elastodynamic fields for a crack extending symmetrically with a constant velocity from a single point in a uniform stress field of magnitude σ_0 can be treated rigorously. The solution for the plane case, which is illustrated by Fig. 4 was given by Broberg [*10*]. Stress distributions in the plane of the crack for Broberg's problem were presented by Kamei and Yokobori [*11*].

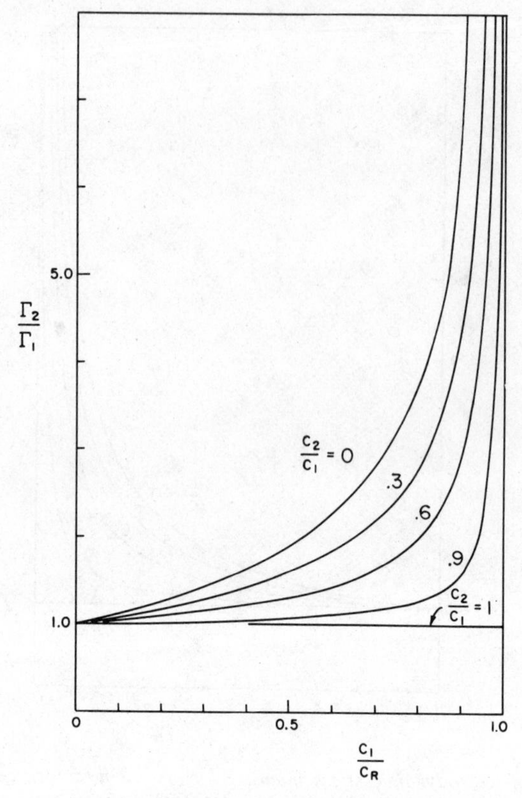

FIG. 3—*Ratio of specific crack extension energies required for a sudden change of crack-tip speed from* c_1 *to* c_2 *(plane strain, Poisson's ratio* $\nu = 0.33$*).*

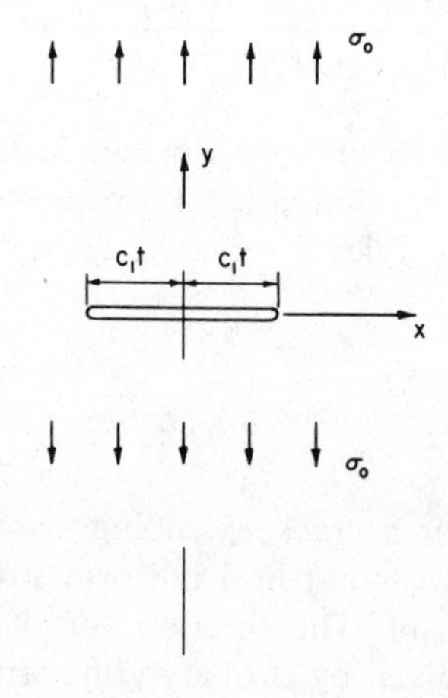

FIG. 4—*Central crack in a uniform tensile field.*

The crack opening displacement for Broberg's problem is of the following form, see Eq 35 of Ref *10*.

$$v = \frac{\sigma_o}{\rho c_L^2} \frac{1 - \alpha_1^2}{g(\alpha_1)} (c_1^2 t^2 - x^2)^{1/2} \tag{30}$$

where α_1 is defined by Eq 24. Here c_1 is the speed of the crack tip, and $g(\alpha_1)$ is a rather complicated function which is given by Eq 25 of Ref *10*. In the vicinity of the crack tip at x positive, the crack opening displacement is of course of the form given by Eq 3, with $V(t)$ defined by

$$V(t) = \frac{\sigma_o}{\rho c_L^2} \frac{1 - \alpha_1^2}{g(\alpha_1)} (2c_1 t)^{1/2} \tag{31}$$

The corresponding stress intensity factor follows immediately from Eq 8 as

$$k_1(t, c_1) = -(\pi c_1 t)^{1/2} \frac{D(\alpha_1, \beta_1)}{g(\alpha_1)} (1 - \alpha_1^2)^{1/2} \frac{\alpha_1^2}{\beta_1^4} \sigma_o \tag{32}$$

Substituting this expression in Eq 9, it is noted that F linearly increases with time for a central crack extending with a constant speed. Since Γ generally is not linear in time, Eq 10 can not be satisfied by a central crack expanding with a constant velocity.

Nevertheless, we will examine the arrest of a constant velocity central crack, since such a crack models some physically interesting situations. For example, a constant velocity central crack may be thought of as being induced by a rapid external cutting process in a thin plate. If the cutting process continues over a certain length, and is then terminated, the possible subsequent further extension of the crack on its own follows from the results given here. Another interpretation of the constant velocity central crack is that it models a crack propagating along a preexisting weak plane, at a high velocity close to the Rayleigh wave velocity. The question of interest is whether a crack which initially extends over a preexisting flaw with weak cohesive forces will or will not penetrate the full material.

Suppose the crack extends with velocity c_1 until time t_1. The total width of the crack then is $2a = 2c_1 t_1$. At time t_1 the speeds of the crack tips change from c_1 to c_2, where $c_2 < c_1$. The instantaneous stress intensity factor immediately follows from Eqs 26 and 32 as

$$k_1(t_1, c_2) = -h(c_1, c_2)(\pi a)^{1/2} \frac{D(\alpha_1, \beta_1)}{g(\alpha_1)} (1 - \alpha_1^2)^{1/2} \frac{\alpha_1^2}{\beta_1^4} \sigma_o \tag{33}$$

The corresponding quasi-static stress intensity factor is $K_1 = \sigma_o (\pi a)^{1/2}$.

In Fig. 5 the ratio of the elastodynamic and the quasi-static stress intensity factors has been plotted for a crack which extends to a length $2a$ with velocity c_1, and then continues its extension with velocity c_2. The computations are for the case of plane stress, where

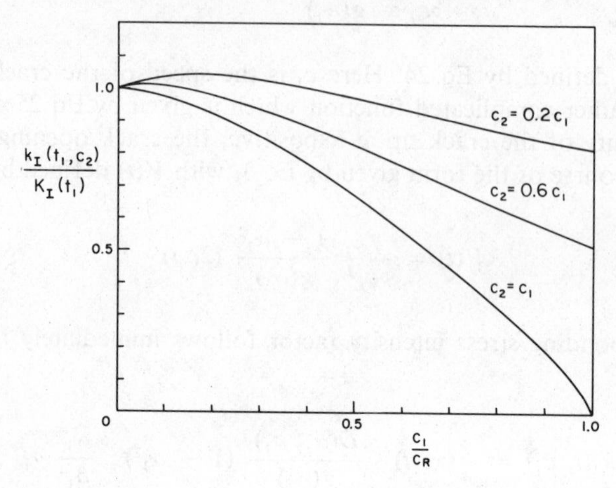

FIG. 5—*Ratio of elastodynamic and elastostatic stress intensity factors (plane stress, ν = 0.33) for a central crack whose crack-tip speed suddenly changes.*

$$c_L = \left[\frac{4\mu(\lambda + \mu)}{\rho(\lambda + 2\mu)}\right]^{1/2}; \quad \frac{c_L}{c_T} = \left(\frac{2}{1 - \nu}\right)^{1/2} \qquad (34a, b)$$

Here ν is Poisson's ratio. In Fig. 6, $k_1(t_1, 0)/K_1$ is plotted for a crack which extends to a length $2a$ with velocity c_1 and is then arrested.

The flux of energy into the crack tip upon a change of velocity follows by substitution of Eq 33 into Eq 9. The combination of this result with the balance of rates of energies, Eq 10, yields an equation from which a number of interesting conclusions can be drawn. Let us first consider the case that the original crack is created by cutting with velocity c_1. The critical stress which will cause the crack to propagate immediately after the cutting process is stopped, can then be obtained from Eqs 33, 9, and 10 by setting $c_2 = 0$. We find

$$\frac{(\sigma_o)_{cr}}{(\sigma_o)_{cr\,qs}} = \frac{\beta_1^4}{\alpha_1^2} \frac{g(\alpha_1)}{D(\alpha_1, \beta_1)} \frac{1}{(1 - \alpha_1^2)^{1/2}}$$

$$\frac{1}{(1 - \alpha_1)^{1/2}} \left(1 - \frac{c_1}{c_R}\right) S_+ \left(-\frac{1}{c_1}, \infty\right) \qquad (35)$$

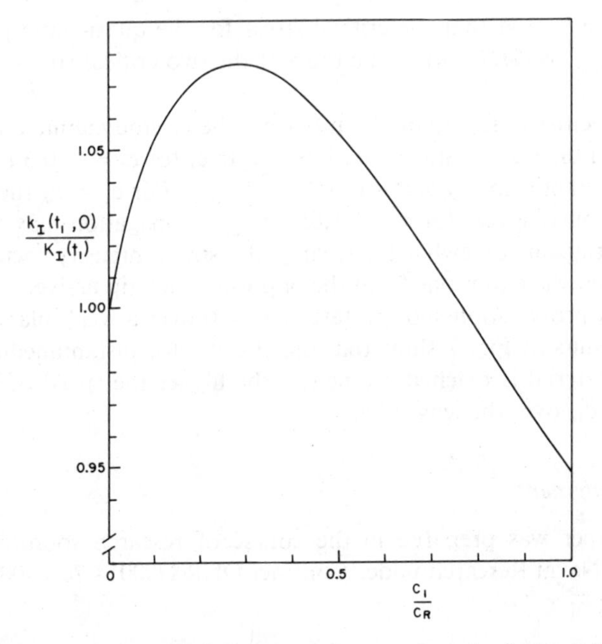

FIG. 6—*Ratio of elastodynamic and elastostatic stress intensity factors (plane stress, ν = 0.33) for sudden arrest of a central crack.*

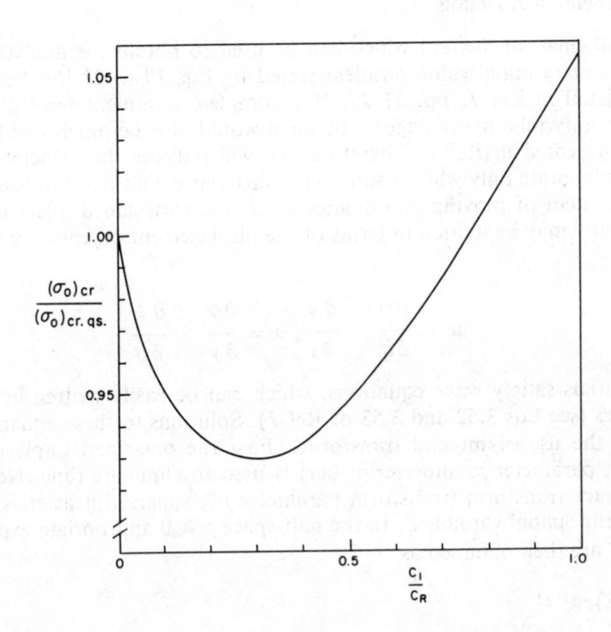

FIG. 7—*Ratio of elastodynamic and elastostatic critical stresses (plane stress, ν = 0.33) for a central crack.*

Here we have used that the critical stress for the quasi-static plane stress case, $(\sigma_o)_{cr\ qs}$, is $(2E\Gamma/\pi a)^{1/2}$. The ratio of the two critical stresses is plotted versus c_1/c_R in Fig. 7.

For velocities c_1 less than about 0.7 c_R, the elastodynamic critical stress is less than the elastostatic value. For example, for $c_1 = \backsim 0.3\ c_R$ the crack will not instantaneously arrest if $\sigma_o > 0.93\ \sigma_{cr\ qs}$. For $c_1 = c_R$ the crack will instantaneously arrest for $\sigma < \backsim 1.057\ \sigma_{cr\ qs}$. Propagation may then, however, start again somewhat later, since the stress intensity factor may increase when wave motions from the opposite crack tip arrive.

If crack propagation should start at $x = 0$ over a weak plane of length $2a$, the results of Fig. 7 show that the chances for instantaneous arrest as the full material is reached are better, the higher the speed of crack propagation, c_1, over the length $2a$.

Acknowledgment

This paper was prepared in the course of research sponsored by the Office of Naval Research under Contract ONR N00014-76-C-0063.

APPENDIX

Some Mathematical Details

The mathematical method which can be used to obtain the analytical solution of the boundary-initial-value problem stated by Eqs 19 to 22 has been discussed in great detail in Ref *1*, pp. 21-27. If a complete treatment were given here, it would not only take many pages, but there would also be much overlap with the material presented in Ref *1*. Therefore, we will indicate the principal manipulations and elaborate only when a substantial difference with Ref *1* appears.

In the system of moving coordinates q, y, t, the cartesian displacement components u and v may be written in terms of the displacement potentials ϕ and ψ as

$$u = \frac{\partial \phi}{\partial q} + \frac{\partial \psi}{\partial y}, \quad v = \frac{\partial \phi}{\partial y} - \frac{\partial \psi}{\partial q}$$

The potentials satisfy wave equations, which can be easily written in the moving coordinates (see Eqs 3.52 and 3.53 of Ref *1*). Solutions to these equations are obtained by the use of integral transforms. First the one-sided Laplace transform (transform parameter p, superscript bar) is used to eliminate time. Next the two-sided Laplace transform (transform parameter $p\zeta$, superscript asterisk) is used to eliminate the spatial variable q. In the half-space $y \geqslant 0$ appropriate expressions for $\bar{\phi}^*$ and $\bar{\psi}^*$ are then obtained as

$$\bar{\Phi} = \Phi\,(p,\zeta)e^{-p\gamma_L y}$$

$$\bar{\psi}^* = \Psi(p,\zeta)e^{-p\gamma_T y}$$

$\gamma_L^2 = s_L^2(1 - c_2\zeta)^2 - \zeta^2;\ s_L = 1/c_L$

$\gamma_T^2 = s_T^2(1 - c_2\zeta)^2 - \zeta^2;\ s_T = 1/c_T$

It should be noted that subscript 2 replaces subscript F used in Ref *1*.

Application of the Laplace transforms to the boundary conditions Eqs 19 to 22 results in

$$\bar{\tau}_y^* = \bar{\tau}_{y+}^* \tag{36}$$

$$\bar{\tau}_{xy}^* = 0 \tag{37}$$

$$\bar{v}^* = \bar{f}^* + \bar{v}_-^* \tag{38}$$

Here $\bar{f}^*$ is the transform of the known part of the displacement in the range $0 < q < (c_1 - c_2)t$, and $\bar{v}_-^*$ is the transform of the unknown part of the displacement for $q < 0$. Taking the one-sided Laplace transform with respect to time first, we easily find from Eq 18

$$\bar{f}^*(p,\zeta) = -\frac{\sqrt{\pi}}{2}\frac{V_1}{p^{5/2}}\frac{(c_1 - c_2)^{1/2}}{\zeta + s_{12}} \tag{39}$$

where

$$s_{12} = \frac{1}{c_1 - c_2}$$

The transforms $\bar{\tau}_{y+}^*$ and $\bar{v}_-^*$, which are as yet unknown functions of p and ζ, are analytic functions of ζ in half planes determined by the asymptotic behavior of the functions $\bar{\tau}_{y+}$ and $\bar{v}$ as $|q| \rightarrow 0$. The common strip of analyticity is

$$-\frac{1}{c_L - c_2} < Re(\zeta) < \frac{1}{c_L + c_2} \tag{40}$$

Writing the stresses and the displacement v in terms of the potentials ϕ and ψ, and employing the transforms of these expressions in the transformed boundary conditions Eqs 36 to 38, and subsequently eliminating $\Phi(p,\zeta)$ and $\Psi(p,\zeta)$, we are left with the following Wiener-Hopf type equation

$$-\frac{p}{\gamma_L}\frac{s_2^2}{s_T^2}\frac{K(\zeta)}{(\zeta - s_2)^2}$$

$$\left[\bar{f}^* + \bar{v}_-^*\right] = \frac{1}{\mu}\bar{\tau}_{y+}^* \tag{41}$$

where $s_2 = 1/c_2$, and

$$K(\zeta) = 4\zeta^2 \gamma_L \gamma_T + (\gamma_T^2 - \zeta^2)^2$$

Following the steps indicated by Eqs 3.82–3.93 of Ref *1*, Eq 41 can be rewritten as

$$pC\frac{s_F^2}{s_T^2}(\zeta - \zeta_1)\frac{S_-(\zeta)}{\gamma_{L-}(\zeta)}\bar{v}_-^* = P + \frac{1}{\mu}\frac{1}{\zeta + \zeta_2}\frac{\gamma_{L+}(\zeta)}{S_+(\zeta)}\bar{\tau}_{y+}^* \tag{42}$$

where

$$P = \frac{B}{p^{3/2}}\frac{\zeta - \zeta_1}{\zeta + s_{12}}\frac{S_-(\zeta)}{\gamma_{L-}(\zeta)}$$

$$B = \frac{\sqrt{\pi}}{2}\frac{s_2^2}{s_T^2}(c_1 - c_2)^{1/2}V_1C$$

Here some deviations occur from the treatment of pp. 21–27 of Ref *1*, in that P is a different expression.

What remains to be done is to split P into the sum of two functions

$$P = P_+ + P_- \tag{43}$$

where P_+ and P are analytic, respectively, in the two half planes whose strip of overlap is defined by Eq 40. It is apparent that P is analytic in the half plane $Re(\zeta) < s_{12}$ with the exception of a simple pole appearing at

$$\zeta = -s_{12}$$

Adding and subtracting the contribution due to the pole we can write

$$P_+ = \frac{B}{p^{3/2}}\frac{1}{\zeta + s_{12}}F(-s_{12}) \tag{44}$$

$$P_- = \frac{B}{p^{3/2}}\frac{1}{\zeta + s_{12}}\left[F(\zeta) - F(-s_{12})\right] \tag{45}$$

where

$$F(\zeta) = (\zeta - \zeta_1)\frac{S_-(\zeta)}{\gamma_{L-}(\zeta)}$$

Substituting Eqs 44 and 45 into Eq 43, and subsequently substituting the result in Eq 42, we arrive at a Wiener-Hopf type equation, which is of exactly the same form as Eq 3.97 of Ref *1*. By the usual arguments, which are stated on p. 27 of Ref *1*, we obtain

$$\bar{\tau}_{y+}{}^* = -\frac{1}{p^{1/2}}\mu BF(-s_{12})\,\bar{\sigma}^* \tag{46}$$

where

$$\bar{\sigma}^* = \frac{1}{p}\frac{G(\zeta)}{\zeta + s_{12}}$$

$$G(\zeta) = \frac{(\zeta + \zeta_2)S_+(\zeta)}{\gamma_{L+}(\zeta)}$$

It remains to invert the integral transforms. An inversion completely equivalent to the inversion of $\bar{\sigma}^*$ is given by Eqs 3.105 and following of Ref *1*. The result is

$$\sigma = \frac{1}{\pi}\frac{1}{q}\frac{Im[\mathrm{G}(-t/q)]}{-s_{12}+t/q}$$

This expression can be rewritten as

$$\sigma = \frac{1}{\pi}\frac{1}{q^{1/2}}\left(\frac{c_L}{c_L - c_2}\right)^{1/2}\frac{t - qs_{R2}}{t - qs_{12}}\frac{S_+(-t/q)}{(t - qs_{L2})^{1/2}} \tag{47}$$

where $t > qs_{L2}$, and

$$s_{R2} = \zeta_2 = \frac{1}{c_R - c_2};\; s_{L2} = \frac{1}{c_L - c_2}$$

The inverse of $1/p^{1/2}$ is $1/(\pi t')^{1/2}$. By using the convolution integral for the one-sided Laplace transform, the inverse of $\bar{\tau}_{y+}{}^*$ then follows from Eqs 46 and 47 as

$$\tau_y = -\frac{\mu BF(-s_{12})}{\pi^{3/2}q^{1/2}}\left(\frac{c_L}{c_L - c_2}\right)^{1/2}\int_{qs_{L2}}^{t'}\frac{(\eta - qs_{R2})S_+(-\eta/q)\,d\eta}{(t - \eta)^{1/2}(\eta - qs_{L2})^{1/2}(\eta - qs_{12})} \tag{48}$$

In the limit $q \rightarrow 0$, Eq 48 can be evaluated. Since $S_+(-\infty) = 1$, and using the definitions of B and $F(\zeta)$ given earlier, we find Eq 23.

The function $S_+(\zeta)$ is stated by Eq 3.90 of Ref *1*. In this expression the velocity c_2 appears as a parameter. For reference purposes we restate $S_\pm(\zeta)$ as $S_\pm(\zeta,s)$, where

$$S_\pm(\zeta,s) = \exp\left\{-\frac{1}{\pi}\int_{a_\pm}^{b_\pm}\tan^{-1}[f(\eta,s)]\frac{d\eta}{\eta \pm \zeta}\right\} \tag{49}$$

where

$$f(\eta,s) = \frac{4\eta^2|\gamma_L|\,|\gamma_T|}{(2\eta^2 - s_T^2 - s_T^2\eta^2/s^2 \mp 2s_T^2\eta/s)^2}$$

$$a_+ = \frac{1}{c_L - 1/s} \qquad b_+ = \frac{1}{c_T - 1/s}$$

$$a_- = \frac{1}{c_L + 1/s} \qquad b_- = \frac{1}{c_T + 1/s}$$

Thus $S_+(\zeta)$ appearing in this Appendix follows from Eq 49 by setting $s = 1/c_2$.

References

[1] Achenbach, J. D., *Mechanics Today,* Vol. I, S. Nemat-Nasser, Ed., Pergamon, New York, 1972, p. 1.
[2] Freund, L. B., *Mechanics Today,* Vol. III, S. Nemat-Nasser, Ed., Pergamon, New York, in press.
[3] Kennedy, T. C. and Achenbach, J. D., *Journal of Elasticity,* Vol. 3, No. 4, 1973, pp. 277–288.
[4] Achenbach, J. D., *Proceedings of the 14th International Congress Theoretical and Applied Mechanics,* W. T. Koiter, Ed., North-Holland, Amsterdam, 1976, pp. 71–87.
[5] Freund, L. B., *Journal of the Mechanics and Physics of Solids,* Vol. 20, 1972, pp. 129–140.
[6] Atkinson, C. and Eshelby, J. D., *International Journal of Fracture Mechanics,* Vol. 4, 1968, p. 3.
[7] Kostrov, B. V. and Nikitin, L. V., *Archiwum Mechaniki Stosowanej,* Vol. 22, 1970, p. 749.
[8] Freund, L. B., *Journal of Elasticity*, Vol. 2, 1972, p. 341.
[9] Kalthoff, J. F., Beinert, J., and Winkler, S., this publication, pp. 161–176.
[10] Broberg, K. B., *Arkiv för Fysik,* Vol. 18, 1960, p. 159.
[11] Kamei, A. and Yokobori, T., *Strength and Fracture of Materials,* Vol. 3, 1967, p. 103.
[12] Freund, L. B., *Journal of the Mechanics and Physics of Solids,* Vol. 21, 1973, pp. 47–61.

Fred Nilsson[1]

A Suddenly Stopping Crack in an Infinite Strip Under Tearing Action

REFERENCE: Nilsson, Fred, "**A Suddenly Stopping Crack in an Infinite Strip Under Tearing Action,**" *Fast Fracture and Crack Arrest, ASTM STP 627,* G. T. Hahn and M. F. Kanninen, Eds., American Society for Testing and Materials, 1977, pp. 77–91.

ABSTRACT: A problem for a clamped infinite strip, with a semi-infinite running crack under antiplane strain is considered. It is assumed that the crack initially moves steadily and then suddenly stops. By appropriate superpositioning of certain elementary problems, the stress intensity factor after the arrest is determined. This is achieved by application of the Wiener-Hopf method, and the result is given in Laplace transformed form. The inversion is done by numerical methods. For the short-time behavior explicit relations are derived. These are also applicable to other problems. The nature of the solution is discussed, and a criterion for momentaneous arrest is given.

KEY WORDS: crack propagation, crack arrest, dynamic stress intensity, infinite strip, fracture properties

We know today in principle quite well how a correct treatment of the problem of crack arrest in elastic bodies should be performed. Suppose that for a given geometry under given boundary conditions, the stress intensity factor (K) (or equivalently the crack extension force (G)) can be calculated for an arbitrary crack-growth history, dynamic effects taken into account. If furthermore the critical stress intensity factor (K_c) is known as a function of crack speed, the correct crack-growth trajectory is then the one which makes these two quantities equal during the period when the crack is moving.

A possible arrest point is a point where the growth equation has the solution zero velocity. To see if this actually is an arrest point, it must be checked that K does not reach a level where a restart is possible. If this level is reached the following crack-growth history must again be calcu-

[1]Doctor of technology, Department of Strength of Materials and Solid Mechanics, Royal Institute of Technology, Stockholm, Sweden.

lated. This process has to be continued until all requirements for a complete arrest are fulfilled.

The outined scheme is difficult to perform and can only be realized by numerical methods. The development of computer programs able to handle this kind of problems is under way, but still results are lacking with exception for the double-cantilever-beam (DCB) geometry [*1, 2*].[2]

It is, therefore, of interest to consider idealized problems which lend themselves to analytical treatment. Although we can not in this way hope to describe crack arrest properly, useful qualitative information can be extracted from this type of solutions.

In a recent paper [*3*] one class of such problems is considered. It is assumed that a crack propagates steadily under plane conditions. The crack suddenly stops, and K after the stopping is sought. A method for calculating K for this case was given in Ref *3*. One particular example, the clamped infinite strip, was considered in more detail. It was possible to obtain an approximate solution up to the time when diffraction effects set in. Mathematical difficulties prohibited a solution beyond that time.

The Mode III version of this problem is much simpler, and we will here attempt a long time solution.

Strip Problem and Method of Solution

Consider a strip of an elastic material (Fig. 1) situated between $y = \pm h$ in fixed x,y-system. The state is one of antiplane strain, and the only nonvanishing displacement component is denoted w. The strip is bisected by a semi-infinite crack, initially moving steadily with velocity V. The crack surfaces are stress-free and the remaining boundary conditions are given by [*1*]

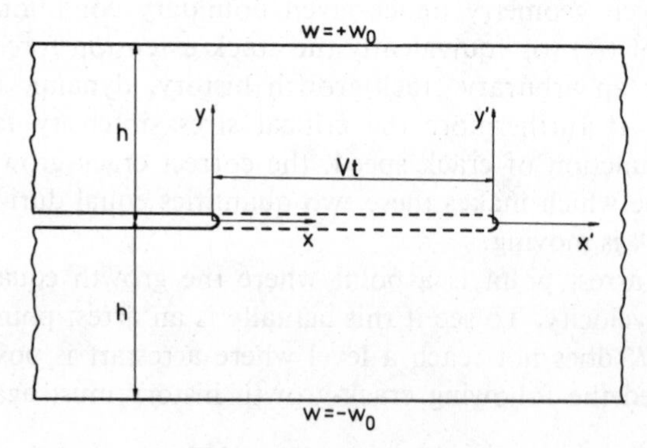

FIG. 1—*The strip problem.*

[2]The italic numbers in brackets refer to the list of references appended to this paper.

$$y = \pm h: \qquad w = \pm w_o \tag{1}$$

This problem has been solved by Field and Baker [4] and later by Sih and Chen [5].

Introduce a moving coordinate system attached to the tip, that is

$$x' = x - Vt \tag{2}$$

$$y' = y \tag{3}$$

Denote the displacement of the upper crack surface $w_s(x')$. The conditions along $y = 0$ can then be written with respect to the fixed system.

$$y = 0: \qquad \tau_{yz} = \mu w,_y = 0 \qquad -\infty < x < Vt \tag{4}$$

$$w = w_s(x - Vt) \qquad -\infty < x < Vt \tag{5}$$

$$w = 0 \qquad 0 < x < \infty \tag{6}$$

μ here denotes the shear modulus of the material.

The problem we want to solve is the following. Suppose that the crack suddenly stops at $t = 0$. We want to obtain the stress intensity factor after the stopping. In order to do this, we consider an auxiliary problem defined by the following set of boundary conditions.

$$y = h: \qquad w = 0 \tag{7}$$

$$y = 0: \qquad \tau_{yz} = \mu w,_y = 0 \qquad -\infty < x < 0 \tag{8}$$

$$w = H(Vt - x) \qquad 0 < x < \infty \tag{9}$$

where H denotes the unit step function. These conditions can be interpreted as a screw dislocation of strength 2, which suddenly appears and moves along the positive x-axis. Let $q^*(x,y,t;\ V)$ denote the solution for a field quantity. Consider now a family of such dislocations starting at different times ξ and each with strength $2\Delta(\xi)$. The corresponding field quantity due to all these dislocations is then given by the convolution integral

$$q(x,y,t;\ V) = \int_{\xi=0}^{t} q^*(x,y,t - \xi;\ V)\,\Delta(\xi)\,d\xi \tag{10}$$

Specifically we choose

$$\Delta(\xi) = -\frac{\partial w_s^*(\xi)}{\partial \xi}\,d\xi \tag{11}$$

where

$$w_s^*(\xi) = w_s(-V\xi) \tag{12}$$

The displacement of the crack surface due to these dislocations is according to Eqs 7–12.

$$w_{\text{disl}} = \int_{\xi=0}^{t} - H(V(t-\xi) - x) \frac{\partial w_s^*(\xi)}{\partial \xi} d\xi, \; y = 0, x > 0 \tag{13}$$

After integration this reduces to

$$w_{\text{disl}} = -w_s(x - Vt) \times H(Vt - x) \qquad y = 0, x > 0 \tag{14}$$

Superposing this problem onto the moving crack problem, we immediately find that all boundary conditions for the problem of the stopping crack are fulfilled.

As will be shown later, the stresses at $x = +0$ are given for the dislocation problem by

$$\tau_{yz} \underset{x \to +0}{\to} \frac{K_{\text{disl}}(t; V)}{(2\pi x)^{1/2}} \qquad y = 0 \tag{15}$$

By using Eq 10, the stress intensity factor for the stopped crack is then

$$K(t) = -\int_{\xi=0}^{t} K_{\text{disl}}(t - \xi; V) \frac{\partial w_s^*(\xi)}{\partial \xi} d\xi \tag{16}$$

It may be noted that this method is similar to the one used by Freund [6–7] for solution of related problems.

From Ref 5 the derivative of $w_s(\xi)$ is found to be

$$\frac{\partial w^*(\xi)}{\partial \xi} = -\frac{w_o V}{h\beta} (e^{\pi V\xi/\beta h} - 1)^{-1/2} \tag{17}$$

with

$$\beta = (1 - V^2/C^2)^{1/2} \tag{18}$$

and

$$C^2 = \frac{\mu}{\rho} \tag{19}$$

ρ is the density of the material. In the course of the analysis it is convenient to have the Laplace transform of Eq 17. From Ref *8* this is given by

$$\mathcal{L}\left(\frac{\partial w_s^*(\xi)}{\partial \xi}\right) = -\frac{w_o}{\sqrt{\pi}} \frac{\Gamma\left(\frac{p\beta h}{\pi V} + \frac{1}{2}\right)}{\Gamma\left(\frac{p\beta h}{\pi V} + 1\right)} \tag{20}$$

where p is the transform variable and Γ is the gamma function.

Solution of the Dislocation Problem

In this section the problem set by Eqs 7–9 will be solved by the Wiener-Hopf method. The solution has to satisfy the wave equation

$$w,_{xx} + w,_{yy} = \frac{1}{C^2} w \tag{21}$$

Along the x-axis the shear-stress τ_{yz} for $x > 0$ and the displacement w for $x < 0$ are unknown. We transform the quantities in the following way.

$$\bar{\bar{w}}(s,p,y) = \int_{x=-\infty}^{\infty} \int_{t=0}^{\infty} w(x,y,t)\, e^{isx - pt}\, dtdx \tag{22}$$

The solution of the transformed wave equation is

$$\bar{\bar{w}}(s,p,y) = A(s,p)\, e^{\gamma y} + B(s,p) e^{-\gamma y} \tag{23}$$

$$\gamma = (s^2 + p^2/C^2)^{1/2} \tag{24}$$

where the branch of the square-root function which approaches positive real numbers when $s \rightarrow +\infty$ is chosen.

Transformation of the boundary conditions gives

$$y = h\colon \bar{\bar{w}} = 0 \tag{25}$$

$$y = 0\colon \bar{\bar{w}},_y = \frac{1}{\mu} H_+(s,p) \tag{26}$$

$$\bar{\bar{w}} = -\frac{1}{p(is - p/V)} + J_-(s,p) \tag{27}$$

where $H_+(s,p)$ and $J_-(s,p)$ are the transforms of $\tau_{yz}(x > 0)$ and $w(x < 0)$, respectively. If $Re(p) > 0$, the regions of analyticity can be summarized as

$$H_+(s,p) \quad \text{regular in } Im(s) > -Re(p/C)$$

$$J_-(s,p) \quad \text{regular in } Im(s) < +Re(p/C)$$

$$-\frac{1}{p} \times \frac{1}{is - p/V} \quad \text{regular in } Im(s) > -Re(p/V)$$

There is, consequently, a strip of common analyticity. Determination of $A(s,p)$ and $B(s,p)$ results in the following Wiener-Hopf equation valid in the strip.

$$K(s,p)\left(J_-(s,p) - \frac{1}{p(is - p/V)}\right) = \frac{1}{\mu} H_+(s,p) \tag{28}$$

$$K(s,p) = \gamma \coth \gamma h = K_-(s,p)\, K_+(s,p) \tag{29}$$

The factorization of $K(s,p)$ was given in Ref *9* for the more general case when the coordinate system (x,y) is moving. Specializing to a stationary system we obtain for the present case

$$K_+(s,p) = \frac{1}{\sqrt{h}} \prod_{n=1}^{\infty} \frac{(s + i\eta_{n-\frac{1}{2}}{}^{\pm})\, n}{(s + i\eta_n{}^{\pm})\,(n - \frac{1}{2})} \tag{30}$$

with

$$\eta_n{}^{\pm} = \pm\left(\frac{p^2}{C^2} + \frac{n^2\pi^2}{h^2}\right)^{\frac{1}{2}} \tag{31}$$

It can be verified that these products converge. It is furthermore concluded that

$$K_+(s,p) \text{ regular and nonzero in } Im(s) > -Re(p/C)$$

$$K_-(s,p) \text{ regular and nonzero in } Im(s) < +Re(p/C)$$

Equation 28 can be rearranged as follows

$$\begin{aligned} K_-(s,p)\, J_-(s,p) - \frac{K_-(s,p) - K_-(p/iV,p)}{p(is - p/V)} &= \\ \frac{1}{\mu}\frac{H_+(s,p)}{K_+(s,p)} + \frac{K_-(p/iV,p)}{p(is - p/V)} &= E(s) \end{aligned} \tag{32}$$

The left member is analytic in $Im(s) < Re(p/C)$ and the right member in $Im(s) > -Re(p/C)$. By analytic continuation $E(s)$ is analytic and nonsingular over the entire s-plane. By knowledge of the character of the solution as $s \rightarrow +\infty$ $(x \rightarrow +0)$, it can be shown with aid of Liouville's theorem that $E(s)$ must be identically zero. We can then solve Eq 32

$$H_+(s,p) = -\frac{\mu K_+(s,p)\, K_-(p/iV,p)}{p(is - p/V)} \tag{33}$$

For large values of s, $K_+(s,p)$ can be written [9].

$$K_+(s,p) \rightarrow h \left(\frac{s}{i}\right)^{1/2} \qquad Re(s) \rightarrow +\infty \tag{34}$$

Furthermore we have from Eqs 30 and 31

$$K_-(p/iV,p) = \frac{1}{\sqrt{h}} \prod_{n=1}^{\infty} \frac{\left\{1 + \alpha\left[1 + \left(\dfrac{\pi(n - \frac{1}{2})}{p^*}\right)^2\right]^{1/2}\right\} n}{\left\{1 + \alpha\left[1 + \left(\dfrac{\pi n}{p^*}\right)^2\right]^{1/2}\right\} (n - \frac{1}{2})} = \frac{\bar{f}(p^*)}{\sqrt{h}} \tag{35}$$

with

$$p^* = \frac{ph}{C}$$

$$\alpha = \frac{V}{C}$$

For large values of s, $H_+(s,p)$ can be written

$$H_+(s,p) \rightarrow \mu \frac{\bar{f}(p^*)}{p} (-hs)^{-1/2} \qquad Re(s) \rightarrow +\infty \tag{36}$$

Application of the asymptotic properties of the Fourier transform then leads to the following result.

$$\bar{\tau}_{yz} \underset{x \to +0}{\to} \mu \left(\frac{2}{h}\right)^{1/2} (2\pi x)^{-1/2} \frac{\bar{f}(p^*)}{p} \tag{37}$$

The Laplace transform of the stress intensity factor is thus

$$\bar{K}_{\text{disl}}(p) = \mu \left(\frac{2}{h}\right)^{1/2} \frac{\bar{f}(p^*)}{p} \tag{38}$$

The convolution property of the Laplace transform can be applied to the integral in Eq 16. Equations 20 and 38 yield the following expression for the Laplace transform of the stress intensity factor after the stopping.

$$\bar{K}(p) = \mu\, w_o \left(\frac{2}{h}\right)^{1/2} \times \frac{h}{C} \left[\frac{\bar{f}(p^*)\,\Gamma\left(p^* \dfrac{\beta}{\pi\alpha} + 1/2\right)}{\sqrt{\pi}\, p^*\, \Gamma\left(p^* \dfrac{\beta}{\pi\alpha} + 1\right)} \right] \tag{39}$$

The quantity $\mu w_o (2/h)^{1/2}$ is recognized as the static stress intensity factor. Thus, we can write

$$K(t) = K_{\text{stat}}\, g\left(\frac{tC}{h}, V\right) \tag{40}$$

where $g(t)$ is the inverse of the quantity within the brackets of Eq 39.

In order to obtain this inverse, numerical methods have to be applied as described next. We will, however, first discuss some asymptotic properties of the solution.

Short-Time Solution

By using asymptotic expansions and Stirling's formula, it can be shown for large values of p, Eq 38 can be written

$$\bar{K}_{\text{disl}}(p) \underset{Re(p) \to +\infty}{\to} \mu \left(\frac{2}{C}\right)^{1/2} \frac{\left(1 + \dfrac{1}{\alpha}\right)^{1/2}}{p^{1/2}} \tag{41}$$

This expression can be directly inverted, and the result is exactly valid up to $tC/h = 2$, that is, as long as the strip acts as a half plane

$$K_{\text{disl}}(t) = \mu \left(\frac{2}{\pi C}\right)^{1/2} \left(1 + \frac{1}{\alpha}\right)^{1/2} t^{-1/2} \qquad 0 < t < \frac{2h}{c} \tag{42}$$

This result is obviously not limited only to the strip problem. Using Eq 16 we obtain the following relation valid in the short-time range for any problem of this kind.

$$K(t) = -\mu \left(\frac{2}{\pi C}\right)^{1/2} \left(1 + \frac{1}{\alpha}\right)^{1/2} \int_{\xi=0}^{t} \frac{1}{(t - \xi)^{1/2}} \frac{\partial w_s^*(\xi)}{\partial \xi} d\xi \quad (43)$$

In the special case of the strip problem we obtain from Eq 17 after some algebra

$$\frac{K(t)}{K_{stat}} = \left(\frac{\alpha}{\pi(1 - \alpha)}\right)^{1/2} \int_{\xi=0}^{tC/h} (e^{\pi\alpha\xi/\beta} - 1)^{-1/2} \left(\frac{tC}{h} - \xi\right)^{-1/2} d\xi, \ t < \frac{2h}{C} \quad (44)$$

This integral was evaluated by an adaptive three-point Gaussian quadrature subroutine from the (HSL) Harwell Subroutine Library [*10*]. This routine has the advantage of being able to handle singularities of the kind occurring in the integrand of Eq 44 for $\xi = 0$ and $\xi = tC/h$. The resulting values are shown in Figs. 2–5 and can be regarded as exact.

A simple relation can be derived for $K(+0)$ that is, the stress intensity factor immediately after the arrest. Only the singular part of w_s contributes as time approaches zero. The singular part of the surface displacement is

$$w_s(x') \rightarrow \frac{K_D}{\mu\beta} \times \left(\frac{-2x'}{\pi}\right)^{1/2} \text{ as } x' \rightarrow -0 \quad (45)$$

where K_D is the stress intensity factor for the steadily moving crack. Insertion at Eq 45 into Eq 43 and integration gives the following result for $K(+0)$

$$K(+0) = (1 - \alpha)^{-1/2} K_D \quad (46)$$

The factor $(1 - \alpha)^{-1/2}$ increases monotonically from unity at zero velocity to infinity when the crack velocity equals C. It is interesting to notice that Eq 46 is the same as the result obtained for the stopping semi-infinite crack in an unbounded medium [*11*], even if this crack moves nonuniformly. Equation 46 thus has a rather wide range of application, although we can not presently claim its general validity.

Employing the relation between K and the crack extension force G, we obtain an equation for $G(+0)$ analogous to Eq 46.

$$G(+0) = \left(\frac{1 + \alpha}{1 - \alpha}\right)^{1/2} G_D \quad (47)$$

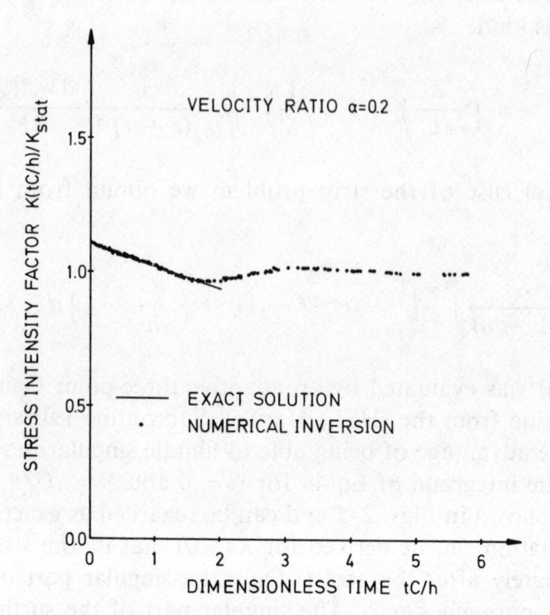

FIG. 2—*Nondimensional stress intensity factor,* V/C = *0.2.*

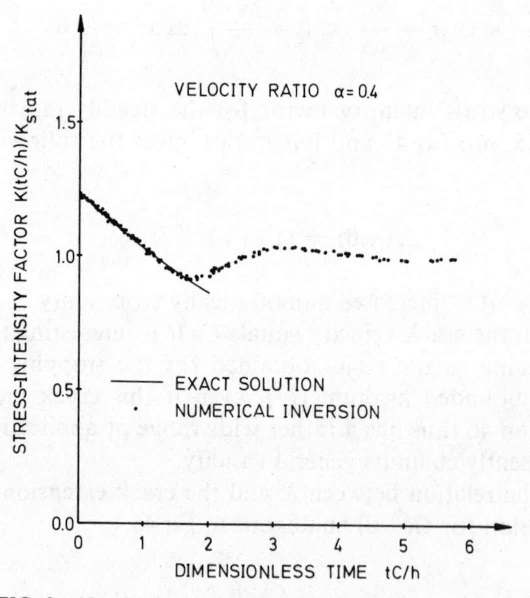

FIG. 3—*Nondimensional stress intensity factor,* V/C = *0.4.*

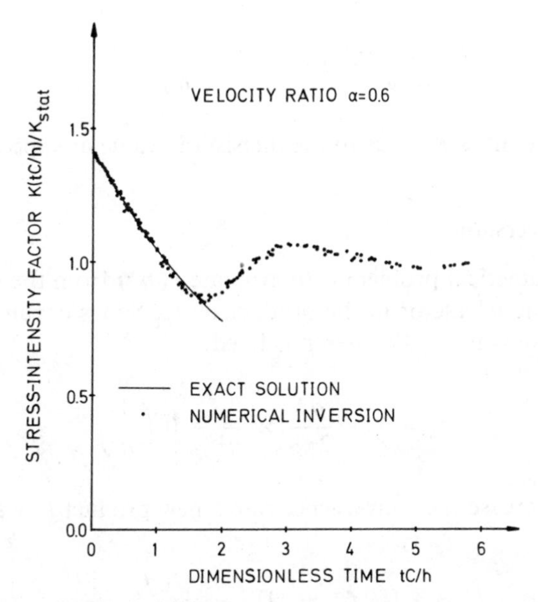

FIG. 4—*Nondimensional stress intensity factor,* V/C = *0.6.*

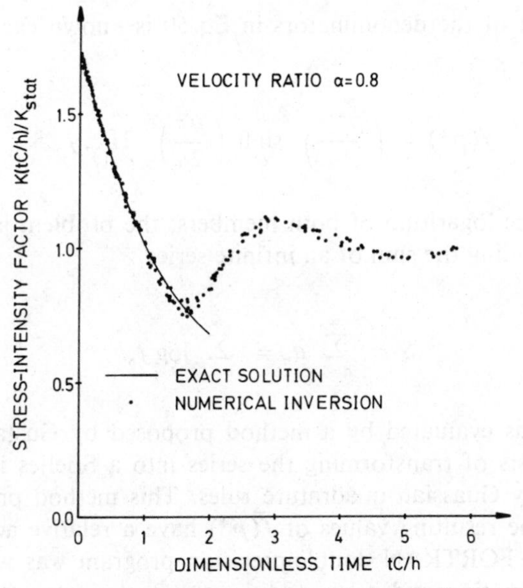

FIG. 5—*Nondimensional stress intensity factor,* V/C = *0.8.*

Here G_D is the crack extension force for the steadily moving crack.
From Eq 39 we also have

$$\lim_{p \to +0} p\, K(p) = \mu\, w_o \left(\frac{2}{h}\right)^{1/2} \tag{48}$$

Thus for large times K tends to the quasistatic value as expected.

Numerical Inversion

The first numerical problem is to evaluate $\bar{f}(p^*)$ from the infinite product. Denote the nth factor in the product by f_n. Series expansion of a certain factor results in Eq 49 when p is fixed.

$$f_n = 1 + \frac{p^*}{2\pi\alpha} \times \frac{1}{n^2} + 0\left(\frac{1}{n^3}\right) \tag{49}$$

In order to increase the convergence rate a new product f' was defined.

$$f' = \prod_{n=1}^{\infty} f_n' = \prod_{n=1}^{\infty} \frac{f_n}{1 + \dfrac{p^*}{2\pi\alpha} \times \dfrac{1}{n^2}} \tag{50}$$

The product of the denominators in Eq 50 is known exactly. We thus obtain

$$f(p^*) = \left(\frac{p^*\pi}{2\alpha}\right)^{-1/2} \sinh\left(\frac{p\pi}{2\alpha}\right)^{1/2} \prod_{n=1}^{\infty} f_n' \tag{51}$$

By taking the logarithm of both members, the problem is transformed into that of finding the sum of an infinite series.

$$S = \sum_{n=1}^{\infty} a_n = \sum_{n=1}^{\infty} \log f_n' \tag{52}$$

The sum was evaluated by a method proposed by Gustafson [12]. In brief, it consists of transforming the series into a Stieljes integral which is evaluated by Guassian quadrature rules. This method proved very efficient, and the resulting values of $\bar{f}(p^*)$ have a relative accuracy better than 10^{-10}. A FORTRAN double-precision program was written to perform the summation and other additional calculations needed to obtain $\bar{K}(p^*)$ values.

The method used for the numerical inversion is described by Bellman et al [13]. If $g(t)$ is the time function and $\bar{g}(p)$ its transform, one has

$$g(a\, t_i^{(N)}) = k_{ij}^{(N)} \frac{\bar{g}(p = j/a)}{a} \qquad i, j = 1, 2 \ldots N \tag{53}$$

Here a is a positive scaling parameter. The time points $t_i^{(N)}$ and the matrix $k_{ij}^{(N)}$ are fixed for each N and can be found in Ref *13* for N up to 15. The matrix is ill conditioned with large elements of changing sign, and this ill conditioning worsens with N. This was reflected in the present calculations, since for $N > 12$ tendencies for numerical instability occurred. This is due to the fact that the matrix elements are so large that the error of $\bar{f}(p^*)$ significantly affects the result. In Figs. 2–5 results from calculations with $N = 7 - 12$ and $a = 1,2,3,4,5$ are shown together with the exact solution for $t \leqslant 2h/c$.

All figures reveal the same behavior. The numerical points follow the exact solution well up to $tC/h \approx 1.4$. Then a certain scatter occurs, and a considerable discrepancy as compared to the exact solution is seen. The agreement with the exact solution is fairly good for low α values. For large α values (for example, $\alpha = 0.8$), both the disagreement and the scatter is larger. The reason for this is probably that the true solution has discontinuities in the derivative, that is, at $tC/h = 2$. This behavior is not possible to reproduce with the numerical method, unless very large values of N are used, which cannot be done for the just mentioned reasons. Several other real inversion formulae were tried, but these yielded even worse results. A possibly better way of handling this type of problems is perhaps to use numerical integration on the complex inversion formula [14]. One problem is, however, that it then is necessary to evaluate the infinite product for complex p values. Some results indicate that the convergence in this case is much slower than for real p values.

Discussion

Although one can not obtain any precise quantitative information of the large-time behavior, several interesting qualitative conclusions can be drawn. Thus, it is observed that K immediately after the stopping reaches a high value, then decreases and oscillates around the quasi-static value. The amplitude of these oscillations is clearly decreasing with time. It is also seen that an increase of V gives larger oscillations. These observations are in qualitative agreement with experimental findings by Kalthoff [15].

The present method can be easily extended to the somewhat more general problem where the crack velocity after the jump is not zero but has a finite value lower than V. No major changes in the described analysis need to be done. We can expect that the results will be similar to the ones given here.

It is of interest to discuss under what conditions a sudden arrest of the assumed kind is possible. Suppose that a crack hits the interface of two materials with identical elastic properties but with different fracture properties but with different fracture properties. The first material has a certain relation between velocity and critical crack extension force, say $G_c^{\text{I}}(V)$ (Fig. 6). The other material has another relation $G_c^{\text{II}}(V)$, where

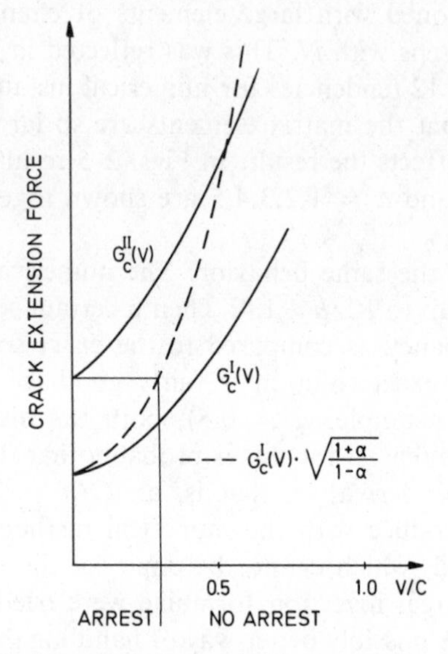

FIG. 6—*Hypothetical example of momentaneous arrest.*

$G^{\text{II}} > G^{\text{I}}$ and both are ever increasing. It can then be concluded that a necessary condition for a momentaneous arrest is

$$G_c^{\text{I}}(V) \times \left(\frac{1+\alpha}{1-\alpha}\right)^{1/2} \leq G_c^{\text{II}}(V = 0) \tag{54}$$

If the crack is momentaneously arrested, growth can not be reinitiated since G never reaches the level $G_c^{\text{II}}(0)$ again (see Figs. 2–5). On the other hand if the crack is not arrested completely but continues to move at a low velocity, the behavior of K after the velocity jump will presumably be approximately the same as shown in the figures. The crack can then come to a halt during the decreasing of K, but crack growth may well start again when K becomes larger. Dynamical effects thus play an important role in the crack arrest process.

The results derived in this paper can be of interest for experimental work. Relation (Eq 54) or an extended version for the case when a complete arrest does not occur, for example, can be of value in evaluation of material behavior. A corresponding relation for Mode I problems is given in Ref *3*. It is also valuable to have exact relations of this kind, when testing numerical methods such as finite-element method (FEM).

We finally note that although the behavior of K immediately after the stopping is identical to Eshelby's solution, the long time behavior is completely different. Therefore, one cannot construct the solution for nonuniform motion in a corresponding way.

Acknowledgment

The author wants to express his gratitude to Dr. S. Å. Gustafsson for giving valuable advice regarding the numerical work. I also want to thank Professor J. Carlsson for checking the manuscript.

References

[*1*] Kanninen, M. F. in *Prospects of Fracture Mechanics,* G. C. Sih et al, Eds., Noordhoff International Publishing, Leyden, The Netherlands, 1974, pp. 251–266.

[*2*] Shumely, M. and Peretz, D., *International Journal of Solids Structures,* Vol. 12, No. 1, Jan. 1976, pp. 67–79.

[*3*] Nilsson, F., "Sudden Arrest of Steadily Moving Cracks," presented at Conference of Dynamic Fracture Toughness, London, July 1976.

[*4*] Field, F. A. and Baker, B. R., *Journal of Applied Mechanics, Transactions,* American Society of Mechanical Engineers, Series E, Vol. 29, No. 2, June 1962, pp. 436–437.

[*5*] Sih, G. C. and Chen, E. P., *Journal of Franklin Institute,* Vol. 290, No. 1, July 1970, pp. 25–35.

[*6*] Freund, L. B., *International Journal of Engineering Science,* Vol. 12, No. 2, Feb. 1974, pp. 179–189.

[*7*] Freund, L. B. in *Mechanics Today,* Vol. 3, S. Nemat-Nasser, Ed., Pergamon, New York and London, 1976, pp. 55–91.

[*8*] Erdélyi, A., Magnus, W., Oberhettinger, F., Tricomi, F. G., *Tables of Integral Transforms,* McGraw-Hill, New York, 1954.

[*9*] Nilsson, F. in *Dynamic Crack Propagation,* G. C. Sih, Ed., Noordhoff International Publishing, Leyden, The Netherlands, 1973, pp. 543–551.

[*10*] Hopper, M. J., *Harwell Subroutine Library,* Theoretical Physics Division, Atomic Energy Research Establishment, Harwell, England, 1973, p. 55.

[*11*] Eshelby, J. D., *Journal of the Mechanics and Physics of Solids,* Vol. 17, No. 3, June 1969, pp. 77–200.

[*12*] Gustafsson, S. Å., *SIAM Journal of Numerical Analysis,* Vol. 10, No. 6, Dec. 1973, pp. 1080–1090.

[*13*] Bellman, R., Kalaba, R., and Locket, J., *Numerical Inversion the Laplace Transform,* Elsevier, Amsterdam, 1966.

[*14*] Gustafsson, S. Å. and Dahlquist, G., *Methoden und Verfahren der Mathematischen Physik,* Band 6, Feb. 1972, pp. 93–112.

[*15*] Kalthoff, J. F., Winkler, S., and Beinert, J., "Dynamic Stress-Intensity Factors for Arresting Cracks in DCB Specimens," to appear in *International Journal of Fracture,* 1976.

Numerical Analysis Methods for Fast Fracture and Crack Arrest

A. S. Kobayashi, [1] *A. F. Emery,* [1] *and S. Mall* [1]

Dynamic Finite Element and Dynamic Photoelastic Analyses of Crack Arrest in Homalite-100 Plates

REFERENCE: Kobayashi, A. S., Emery, A. F., and Mall, S., "**Dynamic Finite Element and Dynamic Photoelastic Analyses of Crack Arrest in Homalite-100 Plates,**" *Fast Fracture and Crack Arrest, ASTM STP 627,* G. T. Hahn and M. F. Kanninen, Eds., American Society for Testing and Materials, 1977, pp. 95–108.

ABSTRACT: A dynamic finite element code, HONDO, was used to analyze four dynamic photoelastic experiments in which the propagating crack arrested. The time-averaged crack-tip velocity in the finite element model was matched with the measured crack-tip velocity in the dynamic photoelastic experiments. Dynamic energy release rates were computed by a procedure similar to that used in computing strain energy release rate in static finite element analysis. These directly computed dynamic energy release rates at crack arrest agreed reasonably well with those computed from the dynamic stress intensity factors determined photoelastically. The energy release rates at crack arrest in the four Homalite-100 plates were approximately 50 percent of the critical strain energy release rate, $\mathcal{G}_C$, and were approximately 80 percent of the corresponding static strain energy release rates.

KEY WORDS: fracture dynamics, crack propagation, crack arrest, dynamic photoelasticity, dynamic finite element, fracture properties

In a previous paper [*1*],[2] the authors demonstrated the use of a dynamic finite element code, HONDO [*2*] in modeling the dynamic fracture responses of Homalite-100 single-edged notch tension plates used in dynamic photoelastic experiments. The motivation of such dynamic finite element analysis was to verify previously obtained results on dynamic fracture [*3–5*] by an independent procedure in order to clarify some of the discrepancies between the dynamic photoelastic results obtained at the University of Maryland [*6*] and those just mentioned. A brief account of these differences is given in the following.

[1]Professors and graduate student, respectively, University of Washington, Department of Mechanical Engineering, Seattle, Wash. 98195.

[2]The italic numbers in brackets refer to the list of references appended to this paper.

The dynamic photoelasticity results obtained at the University of Washington in essence showed that the dynamic stress intensity factors at crack arrest varied from a high value of approximately 90 percent of the fracture toughness in an impacted, stringer reinforced pretensioned panel to a low value of approximately 50 percent of the fracture toughness in a wedge-loaded double-cantilever-beam (DCB) specimen with a blunt starter crack [*7*]. The specimens were all machined from 3/8-in.-thick Homalite-100 plates from the same batch. This problem dependence of crack arrest stress intensity factor is not new and has been advanced by investigators at Battelle-Columbus Laboratories [*8,9*] in contrast to the notion that the crack arrest stress intensity factor is a material property [*10,11*]. In particular, Ref *9* discusses the quantitative agreement between the dynamic photoelasticity results of the DCB experiments and the analytical results obtained by Kanninen's dynamic fracture model of a DCB specimen.

Similar dynamic photoelastic investigations by the University of Maryland investigators using single-edged notch specimen three to four times larger in size and machined from 3/4-in.-thick Homalite-100 plates showed that the arrest stress intensity factor was approximately equal to its static fracture toughness [*6*]. Moreover, the observed rapid fluctuations in dynamic stress intensity factors during crack propagation were completely absent in the Maryland series of dynamic photoelasticity experiments. Since the increased optical sensitivity obtained through the use of thicker photoelastic specimens and the three parameter characterizations of isochromatic lobes used by the Maryland investigators implied increased accuracy in their photoelastic experiments, a review of the accuracy of our series of dynamic photoelastic experiments became necessary. The method used for this independent check was a dynamic finite element analysis of previously conducted dynamic photoelastic experiments. In particular, this paper reports a comparative study on four similar single-edged notch specimens where the dynamic crack arrested after propagating 70 to 98 percent of the specimen width.

Dynamic Finite Element Analysis

The dynamic finite element code, HONDO [*2*], used in this investigation is based on an explicit time integration scheme and constant strain quadrilateral elements. The code is capable of handling geometric nonlinearity as well as nonlinear material properties involving viscoplastic material and time dependent boundary conditions. Crack-tip motion in this paper was modeled by discontinuous jumps where the crack tip moved from one finite element node to another at discrete time intervals. The time-averaged crack velocities were then equated to the measured crack velocities in the fracturing Homalite-100 plates.

The discrete propagations of crack tip in the dynamic finite element analysis generated significant oscillations in the states of stress and displacements surrounding the crack tip. Time-averaged normal stresses in front of the advancing crack tip and the corresponding time-averaged crack opening displacements (COD) after crack advance were used to compute directly the dynamic energy released due to one nodal distance of crack advance in an incremental time. Details of the numerical procedure as well as an accuracy check of the procedure are described in Ref *1*.

The averaged dynamic material properties of Homalite-100 plate necessary for dynamic finite element analysis were those determined by Bradley [*3*]. The dynamic modulus of elasticity, dynamic Poisson's ratio, and static fracture toughness are 675 ksi (4.65 GPa), 0.345, and 579 psi $\sqrt{\text{in.}}$ (636 Pa$\sqrt{\text{m}}$), respectively. The dynamic stress-optic coefficient necessary for interpreting the dynamic photoelastic patterns is 155 psi·in./fringe (27.1 Pa·m/fringe).

Dynamic Photoelastic Analysis

Two previously reported dynamic photoelastic experiments [*3*] as well as two additional experiments, all involving 3/8-in.-thick Homalite-100 plates with linearly decreasing edge displacements, were analyzed by the dynamic finite element method. The starter cracks in all four specimens were sawed and chiseled with an approximate initial crack length of 1/2 in. (12.5 mm). The linearly varying edge displacements were increased gradually until the crack-tip condition reached criticality at which point the crack propagated and arrested at 70 to 98 percent of the plate width, all within 1 ms. Figure 1 shows typical dynamic photoelastic patterns in a single-edged notch plate where the crack arrested at approximately 90 percent of the plate width. Details of the procedure for determining dynamic stress intensity factors from the dynamic isochromatic fringes and the dynamic energy release rates are described in Refs *3* and *1*, respectively. In addition, the increased accuracy in dynamic stress intensity factor determination by using a more sophisticated four-term William's stress function [*12*] instead of the two-term approximation used in most of the author's previous investigations is discussed in Ref *7*. Dynamic energy release rate, $\mathcal{G}_D$, for the state of plane stress was determined from the dynamic stress intensity factor, K_{ID}, by using Freund's formula [*13–15*] as

$$\mathcal{G}_D = \frac{K_{ID}^2(t)}{2G} \frac{\beta_1(\beta_2^2 - 1)}{(1 + \beta_2^2)^2 - 4\beta_1\beta_2} \tag{1}$$

where

$$\beta_1^2 = 1 - (C/C_p)^2,$$
$$\beta_2^2 = 1 - (C/C_2)^2,$$

G = dynamic shear modulus of Homalite-100, and
C, C_p, and C_2 = crack velocity, plate wave velocity, and distortional wave velocity, respectively.

The generality of this relation was discussed by Nilsson [16] who showed that once the dynamic stress intensity factor is determined by some means, such as dynamic photoelasticity, then the dynamic energy release rate can be computed for a moving crack in a finite body.

Fracture Dynamics of Single-Edge-Notched Plate

Four specimens with crack arrest at 70 to 98 percent of the 10-in. (254 mm) plate width were analyzed by dynamic photoelasticity and dynamic finite element method. Figure 2 shows the crack velocities measured during the dynamic photoelasticity experiments and the idealized crack

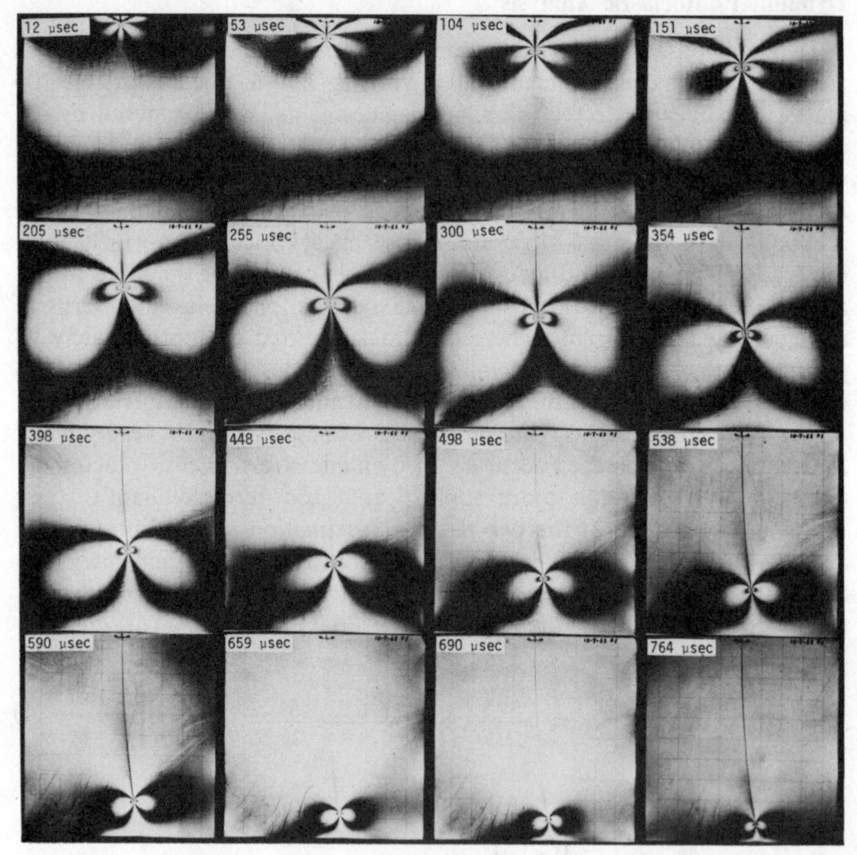

FIG. 1—*Isochromatic patterns of dynamic crack propagation for Specimen B14.*

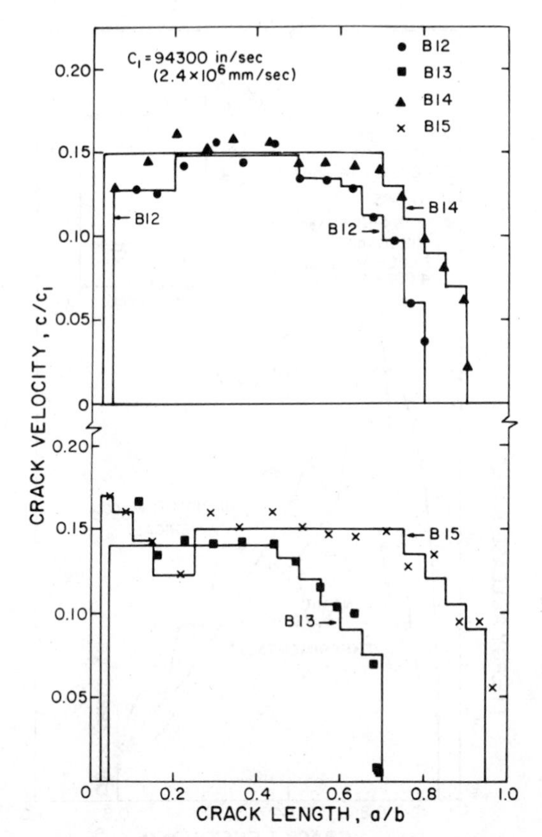

FIG. 2—*Crack velocities used for numerical analysis along with experimental data in Specimens, B12, B13, B14, and B15.*

velocities used in the dynamic finite element analysis. The small fluctuations in crack velocities in the former were ignored in prescribing the crack velocities in the latter since the more accurate crack velocity measurements by Döll [*17*] indicated that in general the crack velocity in such brittle materials as glass does not fluctuate appreciably.

Figures 3 through 6 show the static strain energy release rates and dynamic energy release rates in the four specimens. Note that the two coefficient procedure was used in place of the more accurate four coefficient procedure [*7*] in reducing the dynamic photoelastic data of Specimens B12, B14, and B15. The four coefficient procedure was also used in analyzing the last four frames of dynamic photoelastic patterns for a more accurate assessment of the dynamic stress intensity factor at crack arrest in these three tests. These dynamic stress intensity factors together with the crack velocities were then used to compute the dynamic energy release rates.

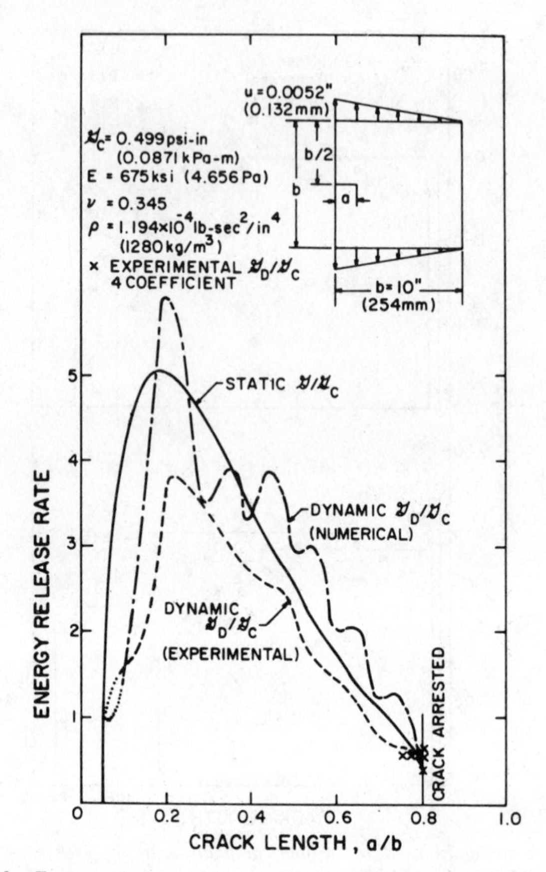

FIG. 3—*Energy release rates in an edge-notched-tension Specimen B12.*

Table 1 shows the measured and calculated dynamic energy release rate at crack arrest in terms of the static critical strain energy release rate. Also shown are the averaged dynamic energy release rates which were obtained by dividing the sum of the total dynamic energy release rates by the newly created crack surface during rapid fracture. The crack arrest dynamic energy release rates, both determined by dynamic photoelasticity and by dynamic finite element analysis, were reasonably close to 50 percent of the critical strain energy release rate except for Specimen B15. In terms of crack arrest stress intensity factors, this arrest value corresponds to about 70 percent of the static fracture toughness of Homalite-100.

Discussions

The changes in dynamic energy release rates, determined experimentally

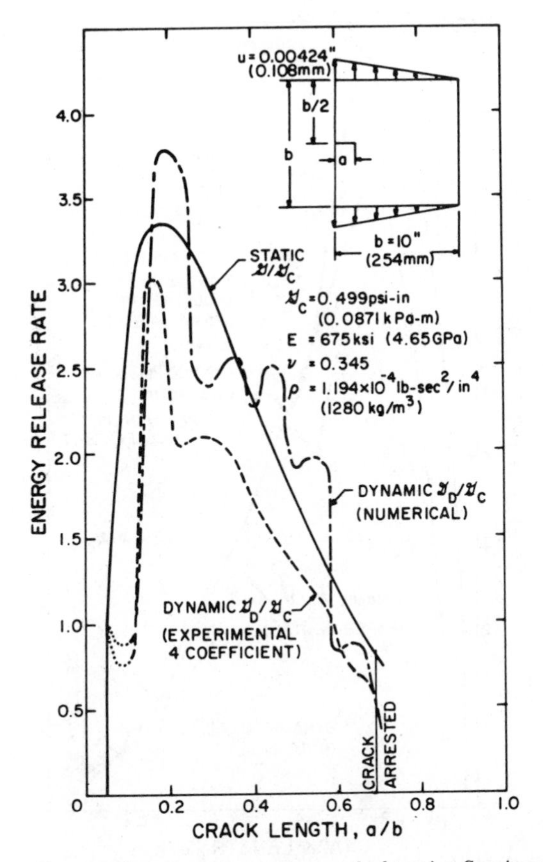

FIG. 4—*Energy release rates in an edge-notched-tension Specimen B13.*

and numerically as shown in Figs. 3 through 6, are remarkably similar when one considers the uncertainty in modeling the prescribed fixed gripped boundaries of the photoelastic model. The numerically determined maximum dynamic energy release rates were larger than the corresponding experimental values and oscillated about the static values which were also determined by finite element analysis. The differences between the numerically and experimentally determined dynamic energy release rates again can be explained by the uncertain boundary conditions in the photoelastic model.

Both the numerically and experimentally determined dynamic energy release rates were very close to the corresponding static values in the field of decreasing static strain energy release rate indicating that static analysis could be used to evaluate the crack arrest results in this type of specimen with decreasing stress field. Results from crack arrest experiments involving impacted stringer reinforced, pretensioned plates, and wedge-

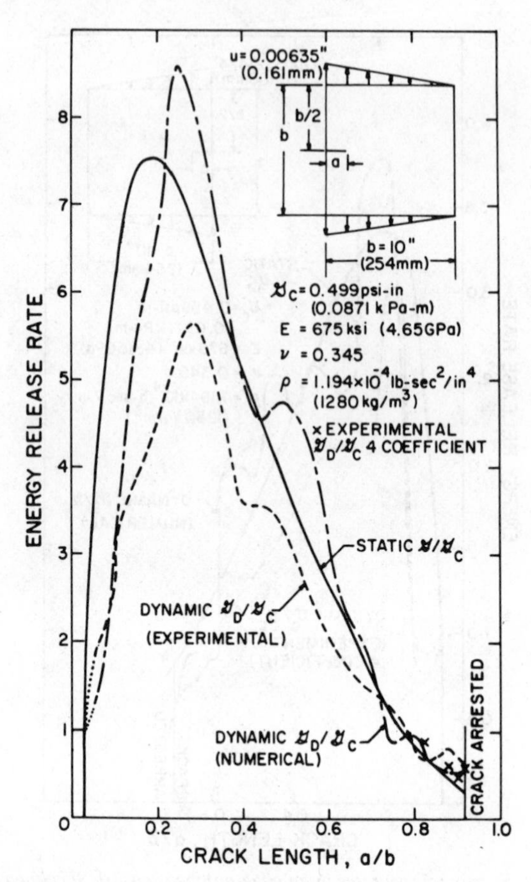

FIG. 5—*Energy release rates in an edge-notched-tension Specimen B14.*

loaded DCB specimens machined from the same Homalite-100 plates, however, yielded crack arrest dynamic energy release rates of 81 and 25 percent, respectively, of the critical strain energy release rates and are substantially different from the corresponding static strain energy release rates [*7*]. The foregoing conclusion regarding the equivalency of static versus dynamic analysis at crack arrest is, therefore, a problem dependent conclusion applicable only to a restrictive class of dynamic fracture specimens.

The initial drop in dynamic stress intensity factor and hence in the dynamic energy release rate immediately after the onset of crack propagation was predicted by Irwin [*18*]. Although this phenomenon is more or less noticeable in three of the four specimens, this downward dip is very pronounced in Specimen B13 in Fig. 4. The only possible cause for this distinct initial dip in dynamic energy release rate was that the starter crack

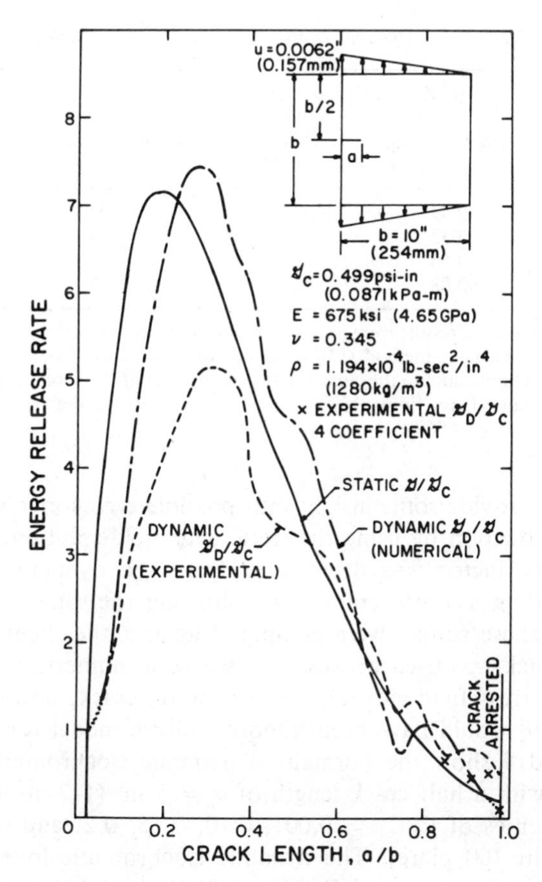

FIG. 6—*Energy release rates in an edge-notched-tension Specimen B15.*

was closer to an ideal crack than the other three specimens, thus initiating crack propagation at a lower static stress intensity factor. On the other hand, the slight bluntness in the starter cracks in the other three specimens caused the crack to be overdriven at the initial stage of crack propagation, thus obliterating the small initial dip in dynamic energy release rate.

The reasonable agreements in computed and measured dynamic energy release rates suggest that the lower crack arrest stress intensity factors for Homalite-100, as well as the fluctuations in dynamic stress intensity factors obtained by the authors in their previous experiments, are reasonable. The discrepancies between the University of Maryland and the University of Washington results could be thus due to causes other than mere experimental inaccuracies. One such cause could be the use of static near field solutions by both groups to compute the dynamic stress intensity factor from measured dynamic isochromatics.

TABLE 1—*Dynamic energy release rate at crack arrest.*

	$\mathcal{G}_D/\mathcal{G}_C$ At Crack Arrest		$\mathcal{G}_{avg}/\mathcal{G}_C$ At Crack Arrest	
Specimen No.	Dynamic Photo-elasticity [a]	Dynamic FEM [b]	Dynamic Photo-elasticity [a]	Dynamic FEM [b]
B12	0.49	0.46	2.07	2.90
B13	0.52	0.35	1.49	2.00
B14	0.56	0.53	2.77	3.70
B15	0.08	0.125 [c]	2.62	3.47

[a] Dynamic photoelastic results were obtained by using the four coefficient procedure.
[b] Dynamic finite element method (FEM) results were obtained from a computer model with arrest crack length equal to the closest half inch interval of the actual arrest crack length.
[c] Extrapolated value from finite element method results where the crack length at arrest was $a/b = 0.98$.

In order to provide some insight into possible errors involved in photoelastic data reduction by using the static near field solution, the dynamic stress intensity factor was determined from the dynamic isochromatic field surrounding a Yoffe crack [*19*] following the same data reduction scheme, and these results were compared against the theoretical results. The Yoffe crack was used because of its ease in numerically determining the dynamic stress field surrounding a running crack, although the Broberg crack [*20*] would have been a more realistic model for such studies. Figures 7 and 8 show the normalized dynamic isochromatic lobes of a Yoffe crack with a half crack length of $a = 5$ in. (127 mm) propagating at crack velocities of $C/C_1 = 0.001$, 0.10, 0.15, 0.2, and 0.25 in an infinite Homalite-100 plates. The dynamic isochromatic lobes for the extremely low crack velocity of $C/C_1 = 0.0001$ should be essentially equal to the static solution and were used to estimate the accuracy of our data reduction scheme using dynamic photoelastic patterns. The dynamic isochromatic lobes surrounding a Yoffe crack propagating at higher crack velocities were then used to determine the dynamic stress intensity factors following Bradley's procedure [*3*] and were compared with the theoretical dynamic stress intensity, K_{ID}, which is defined as [*13*],

$$K_{ID} = \lim_{r \to 0} \sqrt{2\pi r}\, \sigma_{yy}(r, \theta = 0) = \sqrt{\pi}\, \sigma \sqrt{a} \qquad (2)$$

where

r and θ = polar coordinates with references to the moving crack tip as shown in the legends of Figs. 7 and 8,
$\sigma_{yy}(r, \theta)$ = y component normal stress as shown in the legends of Figs. 7 and 8,
a = half crack length of a Yoffe crack, and
σ = applied load at infinity.

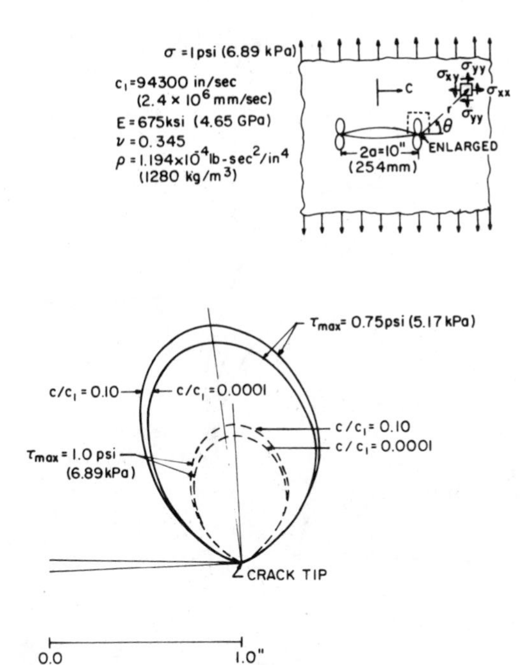

FIG. 7—*Isochromatic lobes from Yoffe's solution.*

Note that the dynamic stress intensity factor, as defined by Freund for the Yoffe crack, is independent of the crack velocities and is equal to its static counterpart of $K_I = \sqrt{\pi}\, \sigma \sqrt{a}$. This dynamic stress intensity factor differs with the decreasing dynamic stress intensity factors with increasing crack velocities in the Freund crack [*13*] and Broberg crack [*20*].

Table 2 shows a tabulation of the dynamic stress intensity factors computed by Bradley's procedure using the two inner and outer lobes of isochromatics and the corresponding theoretical results for various crack velocities. The good agreement between the theoretical static stress intensity factor and those obtained from the two inner and outer lobes of isochromatics of a Yoffe crack moving at an extremely low crack velocity of $C/C_1 = 0.0001$ indicates that Bradley's procedure is fairly reliable if the actual isochromatic lobes can be accurately located as shown in Figs. 7 and 8.

The differences between theoretical dynamic stress intensity factors and the dynamic stress intensity factors determined by Bradley's procedure increase with increasing crack velocity with an estimated total error of 27 percent at the highest observed crack velocity of $C/C_1 = 0.25$. The additional 17 percent error due to the use of larger isochromatic lobes, that is, the outer two lobes, indicates the added error due to the use of a static

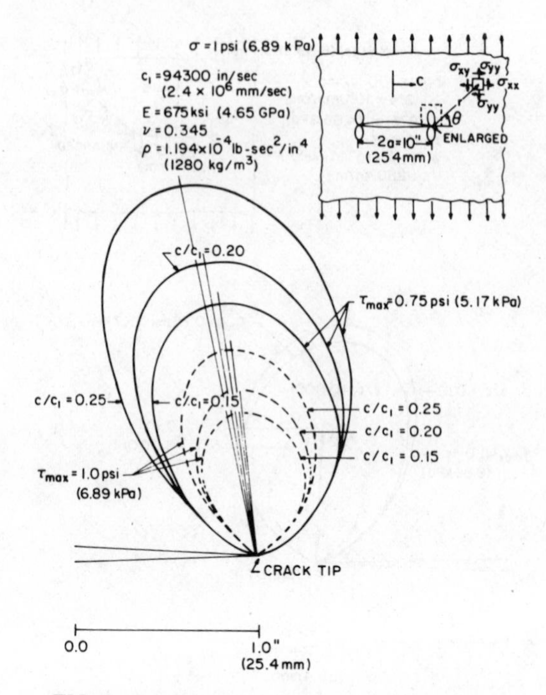

FIG. 8—*Isochromatic lobes from Yoffe's solution.*

near field solution in a larger dynamic stress field. The sizes of the isochromatic lobes used in this error analysis are much larger than those used by the authors and their co-workers; thus, an attempt was made to obtain a more realistic estimate of the errors involved by plotting the results in Table 2 on a log-log sheet as shown in Fig. 9. The estimated idealized errors obtained by interpolating the curves in Fig. 9 range from 5 to 14 percent for the maximum crack velocity of $C/C_1 = 0.25$. This

TABLE 2—*Dynamic stress intensity factor of a Yoffe's crack.* [a]

Crack Velocity C/C_1	Dynamic Stress Intensity Factor K_{ID}/K_I Using Bradley's Procedure: Two Inner Lobes	Two Outer Lobes	Theoretical Values
0.0001	1.04	1.04	1.0
0.10	1.09	1.12	1.0
0.15	1.11	1.16	1.0
0.20	1.19	1.26	1.0
0.25	1.27	1.44	1.0

[a]All dynamic stress intensity factors are normalized by the corresponding static stress intensity factor $K_I = \sqrt{\pi}\,\sigma\sqrt{a}$.

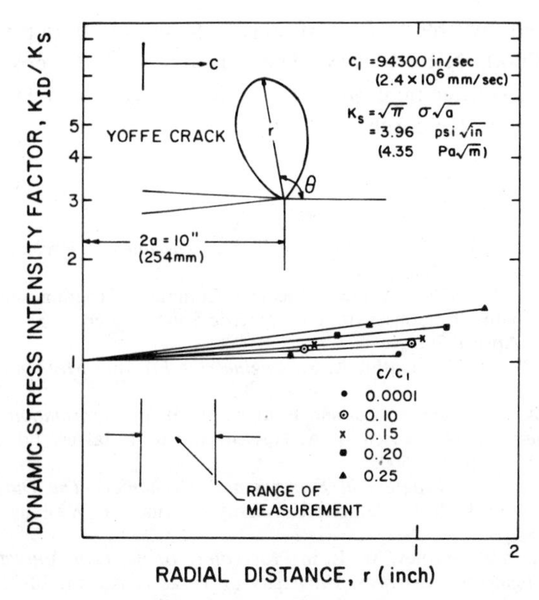

FIG. 9—*Variations in computed dynamic stress intensity factor with referenced distances.*

maximum possible error increases with the size of the isochromatic lobe and could be larger than all errors involved in reading the isochromatic fringes.

Conclusions

1. The quantitative agreements between the results obtained by dynamic photoelastic analysis and dynamic finite element method indicate that dynamic energy release rates during crack propagation and at crack arrest do fluctuate and vary with the imposed loading conditions.
2. The dynamic energy release rates at crack arrest in the three out of four experiments were approximately 50 percent of the critical static strain energy release rate of Homalite-100.
3. The use of static near field stresses in place of the dynamic near field stresses in computing the dynamic stress intensity factors could result in overestimation of these values. If the static stress field must be used in evaluating the dynamic photoelasticity results, the dynamic stress intensity factors should be computed by using the smallest isochromatics, preferably within 0.1 in. distance of the crack tip.

Acknowledgment

The results obtained in this investigation were obtained in a research contract funded by the Office of Naval Research under Contract No. N00014-76-C-0060, NR 064-478. The authors wish to acknowledge the support and encouragement of Drs. N. R. Perrone and H. Basdagas of the Office of Naval Research.

References

[1] Kobayashi, A. S., Emery, A. F., and Mall, S., *Experimental Mechanics,* Vol. 16, No. 9, Sept. 1976, pp. 321–328.

[2] Keys, S. W., "HONDO—A Finite Element Computer Program for the Large Deformation Dynamic Responses of Axisymmetric Solids," Report SLA-74-0039, Sandia Laboratories, April 1974.

[3] Bradley, W. B. and Kobayashi, A. S., *Engineering Fracture Mechanics,* Vol. 3, 1971, pp. 317–332.

[4] Kobayashi, A. S., Wade, B. G., and Bradley, W. B. in *Deformation and Fracture of High Polymers,* H. H. Kausch, J. A. Hassell, and R. I. Jaffee, Eds., Plenum Press, New York, 1973, pp. 487–500.

[5] Kobayashi, A. S. in *Progress in Experimental Mechanics—The Durelli Anniversary Volume,* V. J. Parks, Ed., Catholic University of America, Washington, D.C., 1975, pp. 83–98.

[6] Kobayashi, T. and Fourney, W. L. in *Proceedings of the 12th Annual Meeting of the Society of Engineering Sciences,* University of Texas at Austin, 20–22 Oct. 1975, pp. 131–140.

[7] Kobayashi, A. S. and Mall, S. in *Proceedings of the International Conference on Dynamic Toughness Testing,* London, 5–7 July 1976, pp. 259–272.

[8] Hahn, G. T., Hoagland, R. G., Kanninen, M. F., and Rosenfield, A. R. in *Cracks and Fracture, ASTM STP 601,* American Society for Testing and Materials, 1976, pp. 209–233.

[9] Hahn, G., Gehlen, R. C., Hoagland, R. G., Kanninen, M. F., Popelar, C., and Rosenfield, A. R., "Critical Experiments, Measurements and Analyses to Establish a Crack Arrest Methodology for Nuclear Pressure Vessel Steels," 4th Quarterly Progress Report, Task 62, Battelle Columbus Laboratories, Columbus, Ohio, BMI-1939, Nov. 1975.

[10] Crosley, P. B. and Ripling, E. J., *Journal of Basic Engineering, Transactions,* American Society of Mechanical Engineers, Vol. 91, Series D, No. 3, Sept. 1969, pp. 525–534.

[11] Crosley, P. B. and Ripling, E. J., *Journal of Pressure Vessel Technology, Transactions,* American Society of Mechanical Engineers, Vol. 97, Series J., Nov. 1975, pp. 291–298.

[12] Williams, M. L., *Journal of Applied Mechanics,* Vol. 24, No. 2, *Transactions,* American Society of Mechanical Engineers, 1957, pp. 109–114.

[13] Freund, L. B., *Journal of the Mechanics and Physics of Solids,* Vol. 20, 1972, pp. 129–140.

[14] Freund, L. B., *Journal of the Mechanics and Physics of Solids,* Vol. 20, 1972, pp. 141–152.

[15] Freund, L. B., *Journal of the Mechanics and Physics of Solids,* Vol. 21, 1973, pp. 47–61.

[16] Nilsson, F., *Journal of Elasticity,* Vol. 4, 1974, pp. 73–75.

[17] Döll, W., *International Journal of Fracture,* Vol. 11, 1975, pp. 184–186.

[18] Irwin, G. R., private communication.

[19] Yoffe, E. H., *Philosophical Magazine,* Vol. 42, 1951, pp. 739–750.

[20] Broberg, K. R., *Arkiv för Fysik,* Vol. 18, 1960, pp. 159–192.

G. Yagawa,[1] *Y. Sakai,*[1] *and Y. Ando*[1]

Analysis of a Rapidly Propagating Crack Using Finite Elements

REFERENCE: Yagawa, G., Sakai, Y., and Ando, Y., "**Analysis of a Rapidly Propagating Crack Using Finite Elements,**" *Fast Fracture and Crack Arrest, ASTM STP 627,* G. T. Hahn and M. F. Kanninen, Eds., American Society for Testing and Materials, 1977, pp. 109–122.

ABSTRACT: An application of the finite element method to the rapidly propagating crack problem in two-dimensional domain is presented on the basis of the energy balance concept and the consistent mass formulation. The creation of the new crack surface is simulated by splitting the nodal points along the crack line successively. By introducing the Lagrange multiplier approach into the conventional finite element method of crack propagation analysis, the inconsistency in the method is avoided in that the crack grows by one element length at a time. Several numerical examples are given for rectangular plates made of polymethylmethacrylate (PMMA) with and without initial crack to show the applicability of the proposed method.

KEY WORDS: crack propagation, crack velocity, fracture properties, finite element, energy balance, Lagrange multiplier approach, polymethylmethacrylate, dissipation energy, Newmark's beta method

Nomenclature

- D Dissipation energy, Eqs 17 and 18
- D_{ijkl} Elastic modulus tensor defined in Eq 11
- E Young's modulus
- $\bar{F}_i$ Body force vector in V (Fig. 1), Eqs 1, 2, 5, 9, and 16
- K_{ij} Stiffness matrix defined in Eq 14
- $\hat{K}_{ij}$ Matrix defined in Eq 15
- M_{ij} Mass matrix defined in Eq 13
- N_{ij} Shape function matrix, Eq 10
- P_i External force vector defined in Eq 16
- S_σ Mechanical boundary (Fig. 1)
- S_u Geometrical boundary (Fig. 1)
- T Kinetic energy, Eqs 17 and 18

[1]Associate professor, graduate student, and professor, respectively, Department of Nuclear Engineering, University of Tokyo, Bunkyo-ku, Tokyo, Japan.

T_i Traction force vector defined in Eq 4
U Stored strain energy, Eqs 17 and 18
V Volume occupied by the body (Fig. 1)
V_e Volume occupied by the element
W Work done by the external forces, Eqs 17 and 18
$\dot{a}$ Crack velocity
d_i Nodal displacement vector, Eqs 10 and 12
h Time increment
n_i Unit vector perpendicular to the boundary
u_i Displacement vector defined in Eq 10
ϵ_{ij} Strain tensor defined in Eq 8
λ_2 Lagrange multiplier, Eqs 5 and 6
ν Poisson's ratio
ρ Density
σ_{ij} Stress tensor defined in Eq 11
$\delta(\ )$ Variation
$\Delta(\ )$ Increment
$(\dot{\ })$ Derivative with respect to time
$(\ )_{,i}$ Derivative with respect to coordinate i
$(\bar{\ })$ Prescribed value

During the last decade, there has been a growing trend to use the finite element method for analyzing various static and dynamic problems in solid mechanics, since any boundary condition is treated easily in the formulation [*1,2*].[2] In fracture mechanics applications, inertia effects often play an important role. For instance, the phenomena of unstable crack propagation are included in the category of moving-boundary value problems in dynamics, wherein both the effects of inertia and geometry change with time must be taken into account. The modelling of such behavior with the finite element method is performed generally by cancelling the internal forces at nodes along the advancing crack line successively with a step-by-step integration technique regarding time [*3*]. There exists a shortcoming occurring in this respect in that the location of the produced crack tip by the discrete method is incompatible with the presupposed one by just one element size at the most; in other words, the behavior of crack propagation by this method shows the stepwise or sudden increase of crack length by one element size, occurring at each arrival of the presupposed crack tip at the nodal point along the crack line. The reason for this is because the conformity of the displacement is invalidated between two nodal points adjoining each other in the conventional finite element formulation when either one of the nodal points is disconnected.

The primary purpose of this paper is to present the Lagrange multiplier

[2]The italic numbers in brackets refer to the list of references appended to this paper.

approach [4,5] avoiding the foregoing mentioned shortcoming of the finite element method regarding the analysis of rapidly propagating crack. In addition, the first law of thermodynamics is combined with the present numerical method to calculate the dissipation energy supplied in the dynamic process of crack propagation with which the crack velocity may be related [6]. Several example problems are solved involving the two-dimensional crack propagation in brittle material.

Finite Element Method for Rapidly Propagating Crack Problems

Let us consider the initially cracked body subjected to boundary force $\bar{T}_i$ on s_σ, body force $\bar{F}_i$ in V, boundary displacement $\bar{u}_i$ on S_u, each of which is a time dependent and prescribed value. The assumption is then made that a new crack starts its propagation from the initial crack tip into the solid at some moment with such velocity as the consideration of the inertia effects is meaningful, Fig. 1. The dynamic motion of the body is governed by the principle of virtual work which can be written with the tensorial notation as [4,7]

$$\int_V \sigma_{ij}\delta\epsilon_{ij}dV - \int_V \bar{F}_i\delta u_i dV - \int_{S_\sigma} \bar{T}_i\delta u_i dS + \int_V \rho\ddot{u}_i\delta u_i dV = 0 \qquad (1)$$

It can be easily proven that Eq 1 is equivalent to the equation of motion and the mechanical boundary condition which follow, respectively,

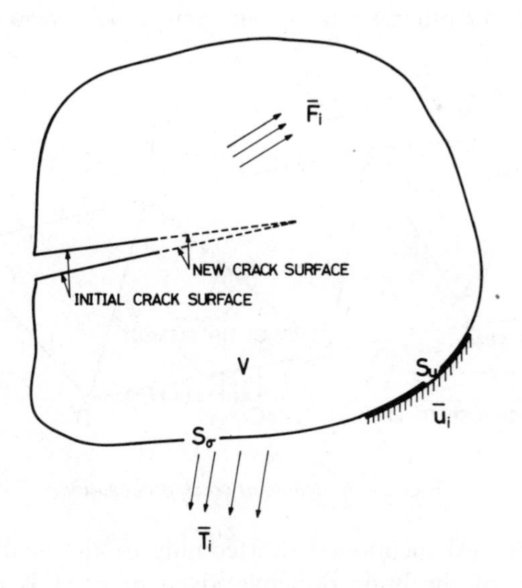

FIG. 1—*Continuum with propagating crack.*

$$\sigma_{ij,j} + \bar{F}_i = \rho \ddot{u}_i \quad \text{in } V \tag{2}$$

and

$$T_i = \bar{T}_i \quad \text{on } S_\sigma \tag{3}$$

with

$$T_i = \sigma_{ij} n_j \tag{4}$$

The phenomena of rapidly propagating cracks could be generally simulated by the finite element method based upon the preceding principle, along with the successive removing process of reaction force at the node located on the crack line; thus the new crack surface which satisfies the boundary condition $T_i = 0$ is being created step by step with the presupposed velocity. As explained briefly in the introduction of the present paper, a difficulty arises in this respect in that the inconsistency in length occurs between the actual length of propagating crack and the idealized one by the finite element model, Fig. 2. The inconsistency corresponds to the distance between the points C and D in the figure, which represent the actual crack tip and the idealized one at some instant, respectively, and after a period the former will arrive at the latter point.

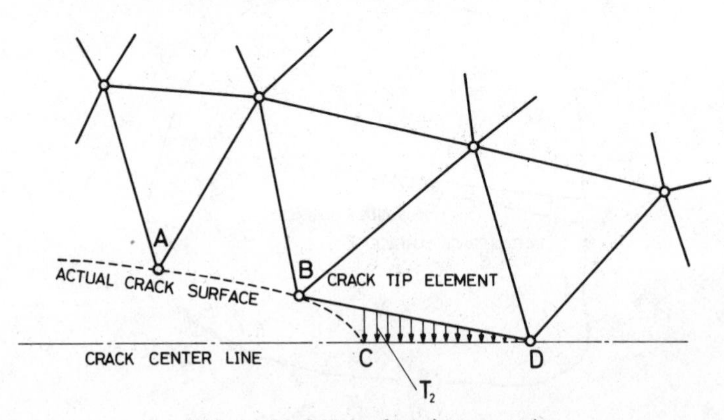

FIG. 2—*Modelling of crack propagation.*

To avoid the just mentioned shortcoming of the method of analysis, a modification of the basic principle given in Eq 1 is proposed in the present paper with the intention of making a correction in the gap along the boundary surface *CD* shown in Fig. 2, which can be written for Mode I crack growth as follows

$$\int_V \sigma_{ij}\delta\epsilon_{ij}dV - \int_V \bar{F}_i\delta u_i dV - \int_{S_\sigma} \bar{T}_i\delta u_i dS + \\ + \int_V \rho\ddot{u}_i\delta u_i dV - \int_{CD} \delta[\lambda_2 u_2]dS = 0 \quad (5)$$

where the last term represents the integral spanning the segment *CD* shown in Fig. 2, λ_2 is the Lagrange multiplier, and u_2 the displacement along the edge *CD* of the crack tip element which is perpendicular to the crack centerline. By putting the variational calculation on Eq 5 with the aid of the Green-Gauss' theorem, we have the following equations

$$\lambda_2 = T_2 \quad \text{on } CD \quad (6)$$

and

$$u_2 = 0 \quad \text{on } CD \quad (7)$$

together with Eqs 2 and 3, where the infinitesimal theory of strain-displacement relation

$$\epsilon_{ij} = \frac{1}{2}(u_{i,j} + u_{j,i}) \quad (8)$$

is utilized. The introduction of Eq 6 back into Eq 5 leads to the modified principle of virtual work which follows

$$\int_V \sigma_{ij}\delta\epsilon_{ij} - \int_V \bar{F}_i\delta u_i dV - \int_{S_\sigma} \bar{T}_i\delta u_i dS \\ + \int_V \rho\ddot{u}_i dV - \int_{CD} \delta[T_2 u_2]dS = 0 \quad (9)$$

Here, it should be noted that the displacement only is the independent variable in this particular equation, whereas we can formulate such an alternative that λ_2 is also an independent variable.

In order to apply Eq 9 to the finite element formulation for the analysis of dynamic crack propagation, we shall express the displacement within an element in terms of its nodal values as

$$u_i = N_{ij}d_j \tag{10}$$

Using Eq 10 together with Eq 8 and the stress-strain relation

$$\sigma_{ij} = D_{ijkl}\epsilon_{kl} \tag{11}$$

in Eq 9, we finally obtain the finite element equation of motion pertinent to the present problem in the following form

$$M_{ij}\ddot{d}_j + (K_{ij} + \hat{K}_{ij})d_j = P_i \tag{12}$$

where

$$M_{ij} = \int_{V_e} \rho N_{ik}N_{jk}dV \tag{13}$$

$$K_{ij} = \int_{V_e} D_{klpq}N_{ki,l}N_{pj,q}dV \tag{14}$$

$$\hat{K}_{ij} = -\int_{CD} D_{k12q}(N_{ki,l}N_{2j} + N_{kj,l}N_{2i})n_q dS \tag{15}$$

and

$$P_i = \int_{V_e} \bar{F}_k N_{ki}dV + \int_{S_\sigma} \bar{T}_k N_{ki}ds \tag{16}$$

It is noted that integrals with respect to both surfaces CD and S_σ appearing in Eqs 15 and 16 should be applied only to the relevant element boundaries. The standard assemblage procedure in Eq 12 yields the finite element equation of the motion of the whole structure.

Energy Balance Relation

The thermodynamic equilibrium for an elastic body subjected to external loads requires

$$\dot{W} = \dot{U} + \dot{T} + \dot{D} \tag{17}$$

or

$$\Delta W = \Delta U + \Delta T + \Delta D \tag{18}$$

Combining Eq 17 or 18 with the results of the finite element dynamic analysis regarding the crack propagation, we can estimate easily the variation of $\dot{D}$ or ΔD with time.

Numerical Analysis

Two-dimensional numerical analyses are carried out with reference to the dynamic crack propagation in plane-stress condition for polymethylmethacrylate (PMMA) at room temperature. Young's modulus, Poisson's ratio, and density of the material are assumed to be 320 kg/mm^2, 0.4 and 1.18×10^{-6} kg/mm^3, respectively, and the plate thickness is 3 mm. The Newmark's beta method [8] is adopted with the beta parameter of one sixth to solve Eq 12 for the relevant problems. The usual triangular element with constant strain is used to idealize the structures.

Results and Discussion

In order to study the effectiveness of the proposed variational principle and its application to the finite element crack propagation analysis, one half of the rectangular plate symmetric with respect to the centerline *PQRS* is taken as the first example problem with the several element discretizations as depicted in Fig. 3. Let the uniform displacement $\bar{u}_2 = 0.3$ mm in the longitudinal direction be statically applied at the top and bottom of the plate, then let the crack be initiated and propagated with the constant velocity $\dot{a} = 500$ m/s across the centerline *PQ* in the figure.

The calculated time variations of the longitudinal opening displacement at point *P* in Fig. 3 are shown in Figs. 4 and 5 using the M-2 and M-3 mesh discretizations depicted in Fig. 3, respectively. The time increment h is chosen 0.25 μs throughout the calculation in each figure, so that 80 time steps are required to complete the calculation of the crack propagation with constant velocity $\dot{a} = 500$ m/s from points *P* to *Q* in Fig. 3. In both figures, the curves by the present method are compared with the results by the conventional finite element method. Both curves calculated by the latter method in these figures show a rather wavy tendency in which the number of waves seems dependent on the size of elements located along the crack line. However, this unreasonable result, which could be a kind of error caused by the finite element discretization, is corrected considerably with the use of the proposed method, as can be recognized by comparing both curves in each figure.

The influence of mesh size on the time variation of the dissipation energy is calculated by the present method and shown in Fig. 6, from which we can see that the mesh size has a fairly significant influence on the dissipation energy versus time curve within the range of the mesh sizes chosen in Fig. 3.

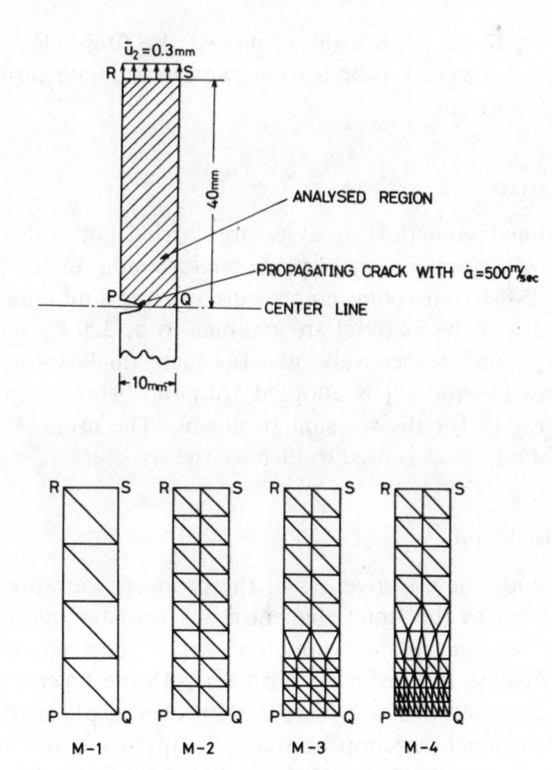

FIG. 3—*Rectangular plate and the mesh subdivisions of one half of the structure.*

Next, we shall consider a more realistic structure having an initial side crack as shown in Fig. 7 with the mesh discretizing the upper half of the structure *PQRS* because its symmetry with respect to the centerline along the crack is assumed. Here, the crack initiation criterion based on the linear fracture mechanics is utilized; the new crack begins its propagation from the initial crack tip as the static stress intensity factor resulting from the external displacement $\bar{u}_2$ reaches the fracture toughness of the material, 4.0 kg·mm$^{-3/2}$ [9]. The same time increment used in the previous problem is employed in this example.

Figure 8 depicts the time variations of the crack opening shapes under dynamic propagation for three different crack velocities, where the ordinate represents the difference between the total crack opening displacement and the initial one. It is worth noting that the crack shapes are sharpened, in general, as the crack velocity increases. It is also interesting to note that the crack tip has a tendency to keep a constant form with its propagation provided the velocity is unchanged.

The dynamic stress distributions along the crack propagation in the loaded direction are given in Fig. 9 as functions of time and the distance

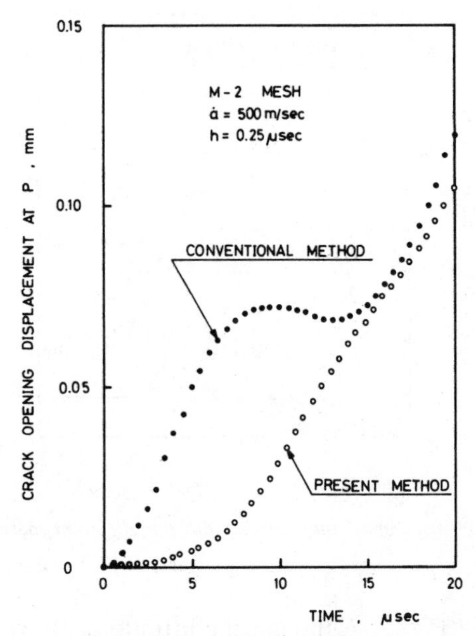

FIG. 4—*Crack opening displacement versus time curves for M-2 mesh,* ȧ = *500 m/s,* h = *0.25 μs.*

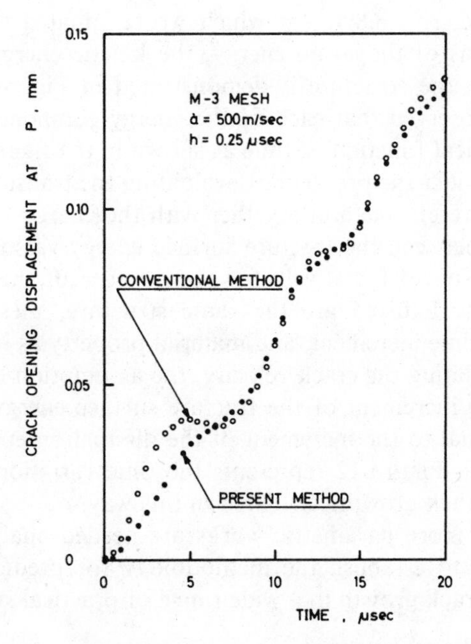

FIG. 5—*Crack opening displacement versus time curves for M-3 mesh,* ȧ = *500 m/s,* h = *0.25 μs.*

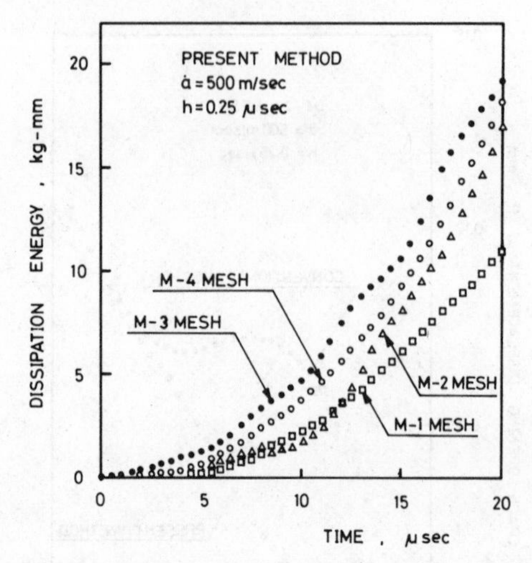

FIG. 6—*Dissipation energy versus time curves for four different meshes,* ȧ = *500 m/s,* h = *0.25 μs.*

from the point *P* in Fig. 7. Although the infinite stress values are impossible to obtain at the crack tip because of the approximate property of the finite element numerical method, the figure shows the group of curves where the stresses at the crack-tip element increase with the crack propagating to the time, $t = 68$ μs, at which we terminated the calculation. The time variations of the strain energy, the kinetic energy, and the dissipation energy in the structure is demonstrated in Fig. 10, from which it can be easily observed that each of the energy components behaves as a nearly monotonical function of time as shown in the figure.

Finally, we consider the problem of evaluating the transient crack velocity by using the present method together with the energy balance concept and the relation between the fracture surface energy versus the crack velocity which is assumed tentatively for the purpose of the calculation as shown in Fig. 11. Utilized are the same structure, mesh idealization, initial condition, time increment, and material property as in the preceding problem. In calculating the crack velocity, the assumption is made in each time step that the increment of the fracture surface energy consumed by the material is equal to the increment of the dissipation energy calculated from Eq 17 or 18. Figure 12 represents the time variations of the crack velocity and the crack growth calculated in this way.

It appears that more parametric works are needed analytically as well as experimentally to establish the methodology for predicting the crack velocity and the crack growth in a wide range of practical structures.

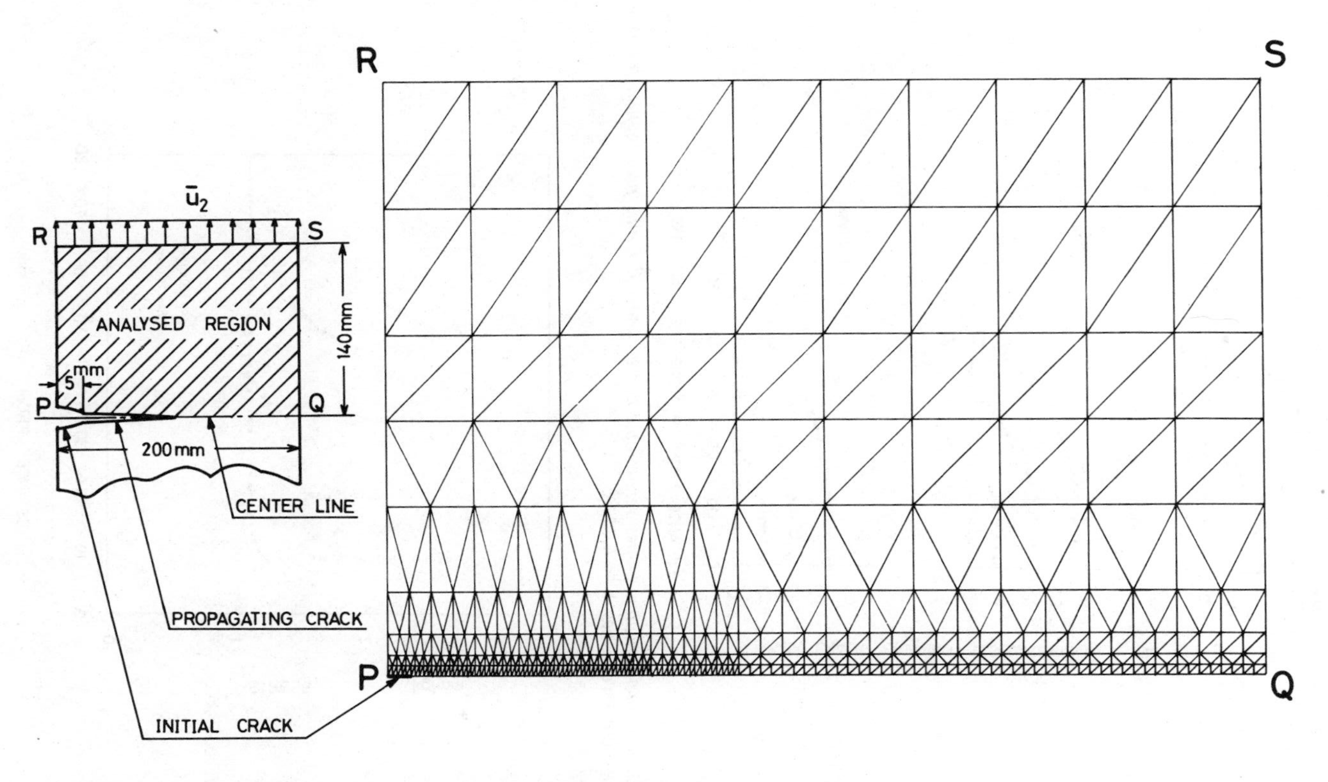

FIG. 7—*Rectangular plate and the mesh subdivision of one half of the structure, number of elements = 698, number of nodes = 468.*

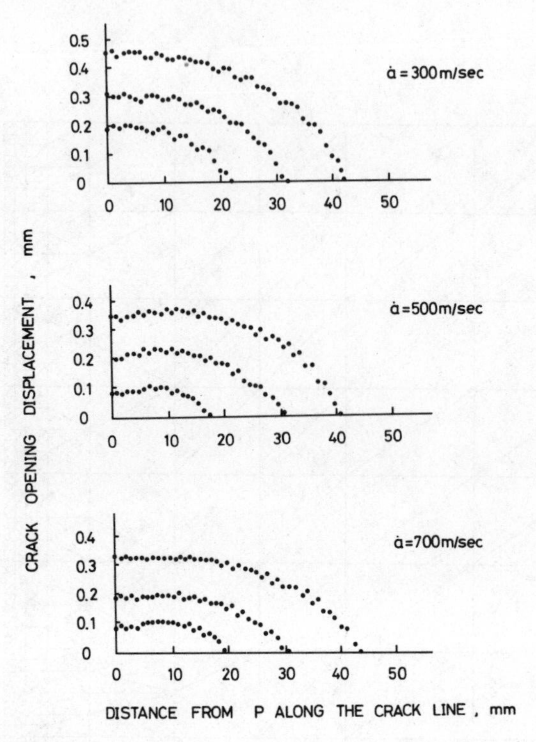

FIG. 8—*Crack opening shapes versus time curves under dynamic propagation for three different crack velocities,* h = *0.25 μs.*

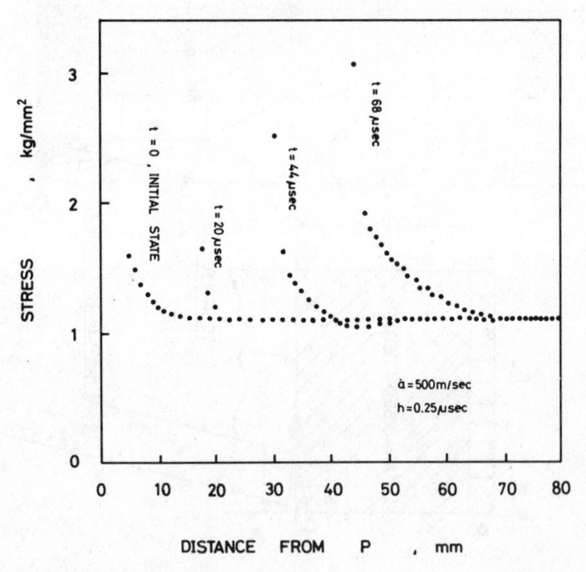

FIG. 9—*Stress distributions along the crack propagation in the loaded direction versus time curves,* ȧ = *500 m/s,* h = *0.25 μs.*

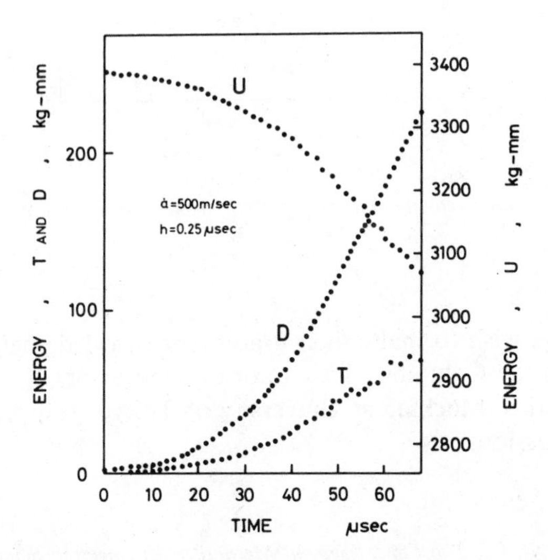

FIG. 10—*Strain energy, kinetic energy, and dissipation energy versus time curves,* ȧ = *500 m/s,* h = *0.25 μs.*

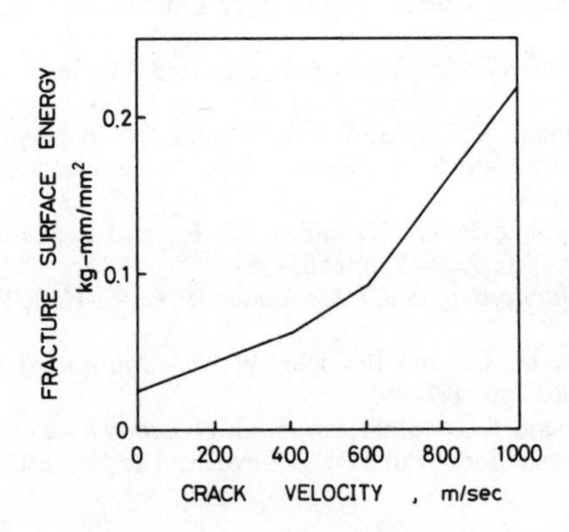

FIG. 11—*Fracture surface energy versus crack velocity curve assumed tentatively for the calculation.*

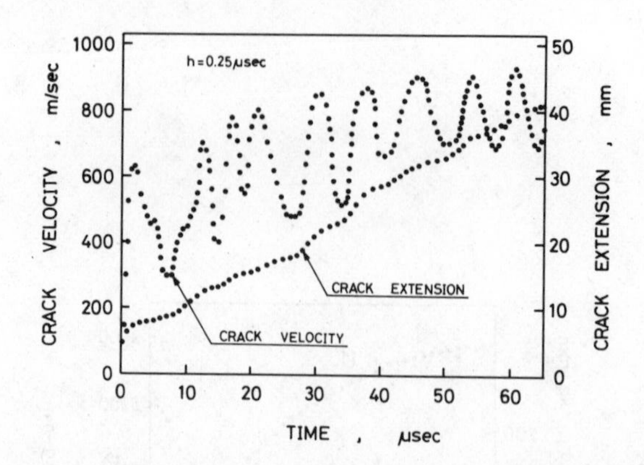

FIG. 12—*Crack velocity and crack growth versus time curves,* h = *0.25 μs.*

Acknowledgments

The authors wish to make their grateful acknowledgment to Dr. G. T. Hahn at Battelle-Columbus Laboratories, Professors T. Kanazawa, H. Okamura, and S. Machida at University of Tokyo, respectively, for their valuable discussions.

References

[1] Zienkiewicz, O. C., *The Finite Element Method in Engineering Science,* McGraw-Hill, London, 1971.

[2] Przemieniecki, J. S., *Theory of Matrix Structural Analysis,* McGraw-Hill, New York, 1968.

[3] Ando, Y., Yagawa, G., and Sakai, Y., *Transactions,* 3rd International Conference on Structural Mechanics in Reactor Technology, London, United Kingdom, Sept. 1975, L7/1.

[4] Washizu, K., *Variational Methods in Elasticity and Plasticity,* 2nd edition, Pergamon, London, 1975.

[5] Yagawa, G., Nishioka, T., Ando, Y., and Ogura, N. in *Computational Fracture Mechanics,* E. F. Rybicki and S. E. Benzley, Eds., American Society of Mechanical Engineers, 1975, pp. 21–34.

[6] Hahn, G. T., Hoagland, R. G., Kanninen, M. F., and Rosenfield, A. R., *Engineering Fracture Mechanics,* Vol. 7, 1975, pp. 583–591.

[7] Fung, Y. C., *Foundations of Solid Mechanics,* Prentice-Hall, Englewood Cliffs, N.J., 1965.

[8] Chang, S. P., Cox, H. L., and Benfield, W. A., *Journal of the Royal Aeronautical Society,* Vol. 66, 1962, pp. 457–460.

[9] Carlsson, J., Dahlberg, L., and Nilsson, F. in *Dynamic Crack Propagation,* G. C. Sih, Ed., Noordhoff International Publishing, Leyden, The Netherlands, 1973, pp. 165–181.

J. A. Aberson, [1] *J. M. Anderson,* [1] *and W. W. King* [1]

Singularity-Element Simulation of Crack Propagation

REFERENCE: Aberson, J. A., Anderson, J. M., and King, W. W., "**Singularity-Element Simulation of Crack Propagation,**" *Fast Fracture and Crack Arrest, ASTM STP 627,* G. T. Hahn and M. F. Kanninen, Eds., American Society for Testing and Materials, 1977, pp. 123–134.

ABSTRACT: Finite-element simulations of rapid crack propagation are presented. An earlier analysis of a crack extending in an infinite body is reviewed, and an unsuccessful attempt to take advantage of a crack-tip singularity element is discussed. Plausible stress-intensity factors are obtained for both constant speed and accelerating cracks in finite sheets; the results are compared to those obtained by other investigators.

KEY WORDS: crack propagation, fracture properties, finite elements, accelerating cracks

Recent mathematical studies of two-dimensional problems of rapid crack propagation in linearly elastic bodies have produced fundamental information about the behavior of semi-infinite cracks in infinite bodies and the nature of stresses and deformations near the tip of a running crack, for example [*1-6*].[2] Extensions of these analyses to problems in which finite dimensions cannot be ignored are likely to be quite difficult; hence, approximate or numerical methods will continue to play significant roles in studies of such problems. Prominent among numerical techniques are the finite-difference [*7-9*] and finite-element [*10,11*] methods. In this paper the writers present results of a continuing investigation, initiated in Ref *11*, on the finite-element simulation of rapid crack propagation.

The finite-element analysis of a crack propagating in an infinite body [*11*] is reviewed. In that work the crack-tip stress singularity was not taken into account explicitly. Hence the analysis of Ref *11* is modified in an attempt to exploit a special crack-tip singularity element which has

[1]Assistant professor and associate professors, respectively. School of Engineering Science and Mechanics, Georgia Institute of Technology, Atlanta, Ga. 30332.

[2]The italic numbers in brackets refer to the list of references appended to this paper.

performed well in stationary-crack elastodynamic problems. Since the results of this modification are not encouraging, the method of Ref *11* is applied to two problems studied by Kobayashi et al [*10*]. It is of particular interest to note that, while the writers and Kobayashi et al employ the same basic scheme for simulating crack propagation, different techniques are used for extracting stress-intensity factors from the numerically determined stresses and displacements.

Crack Propagation in an Infinite Body

In Ref *11* the writers have presented a finite-element analysis of a problem to which Broberg [*12*] has obtained an exact solution. We now recapitulate the principal features and results of Ref *11* since they are closely related to the present work.

Broberg's problem is that of an infinite body in equilibrium with a uniform uniaxial tension, σ, prior to crack propagation. A crack grows symmetrically, from an initial length of zero, at constant rate 2*c*, each tip moving at speed *c*. Broberg's analysis revealed (1) that the ratio of dynamic stress-intensity factor to static stress-intensity factor depends only upon the crack propagation speed and (2) that this ratio decreases monotonically from unity at zero crack speed to zero when the crack speed is that of Rayleigh waves.

The finite-element model of one quadrant of a rectangular region is depicted in Fig. 1. Each element of the model is a constant-strain triangle,

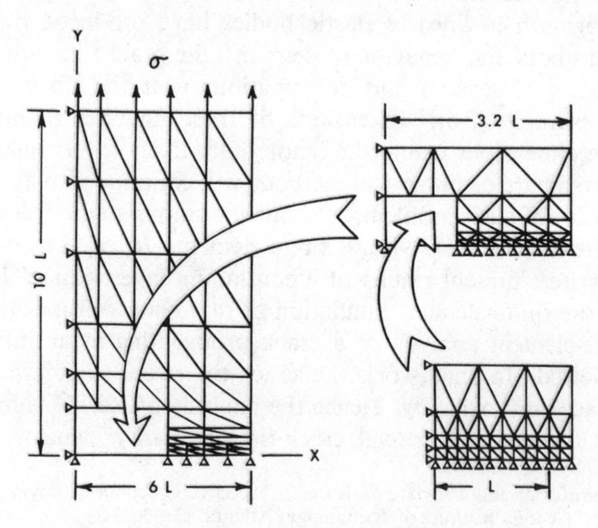

FIG. 1—*Finite-element model of Broberg's problem.*

and the base of the model coincides with the trajectory of the moving crack tip. The characteristic length, L, is the largest half length of the crack, and the smallest distance between nodes is $L/10$. Material properties were chosen so that $c_1/c_2 = 2$, where c_1 and c_2 are the propagation speeds of longitudinal and transverse waves, respectively. Crack speeds of $c/c_2 = 0.2, 0.4, 0.6$, and 0.8 were considered; thus, the rectangular region is of sufficient size to simulate, for the time interval of interest, the infinite space of Broberg's problem.

Crack propagation was simulated by the sequential removal of restraints on the nodes at the base of the finite-element model. The computational procedure was as follows:

1. Nodal displacements for the equilibrium configuration of the uncracked body (all base nodes restrained against vertical displacement) were determined.
2. With these nodal displacements as initial values and with all initial nodal velocities zero, the equations of motion were integrated numerically for the model with Node 1 (base nodes numbered 1,2,3,. . . from left to right) unrestrained and the other base nodes restrained. Integration was terminated at the time corresponding to the crack-tip's arrival at Node 2.
3. Displacements and velocities at the end of the first interval of integration were taken as initial values for the second interval during which Nodes 1 and 2 were unrestrained. This process was repeated for time intervals during which the crack tip is imagined to be running between successive nodes.

It can be seen that the numerical procedure was one in which a sequence of transient problems, each associated with a stationary crack, were solved. Except at the end of each integration interval, the apparent crack length in the finite-element model at any instant was greater than that of the continuously expanding crack which was being simulated.

Stress-intensity factors were computed using the nodal displacements occurring at the times at which the crack tip coincided with the apparent crack tip of the finite-element model. Near-tip nodal displacements were matched to a four-term series of eigenfunctions [*11,13,14*] appropriate to a crack propagating at constant speed. One of these four functions expresses the asymptotic form[3] ($r^{-1/2}$) of stresses at the crack tip and, hence, is related to the stress-intensity factor. Coefficients in the four-term series were determined by a least-squares matching of the series representation of the displacement field to the 13 displacement components computed for the nodes shown by filled circles in Fig. 2. The stress-intensity factors,

[3]The asymptotic form has been proven valid also for an accelerating crack [*5*].

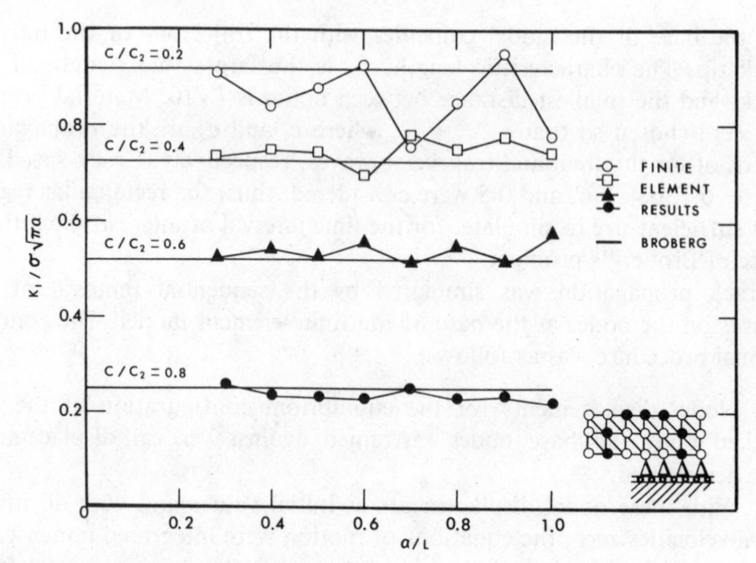

FIG. 2—*Stress-intensity factors for Broberg's problem using running-crack eigenfunctions.*

K_I, resulting from these calculations are plotted against crack half length, a, in Fig. 2; the maximum error is about 15 percent.

Use of a Singularity Element

Finite-element analyses of problems of stationary cracks have been facilitated by the use of special crack-tip elements which incorporate several of Williams' eigenfunctions appropriate to a stationary crack in a linearly elastic body [*15,16*]. The eight-node element shown in Fig. 3 employs the first 13 terms of a series of Williams' eigenfunctions for crack-opening modes of deformation, and the writers have used this element for successful analyses of the elastodynamics of bodies with stationary cracks [*17*]. It should be noted that the running-crack eigenfunctions utilized in the preceding section reduce to Williams' functions at zero propagation speed. While the singularity element incorporates the correct asymptotic form of stresses and displacements for a stationary crack rather than a running crack, this deficiency is in itself not likely to be serious for most applications since these near-tip distributions are essentially the same for $c/c_2 < 0.2$ [*14,18*]. It is, therefore, reasonable to assume that finite-element analyses of crack propagation problems might be improved by utilization of such singularity elements. To that end we modify the analysis of the preceding section in an attempt to take advantage of the existing singularity elements.

The geometry of the eight-node singularity element allows it to be sub-

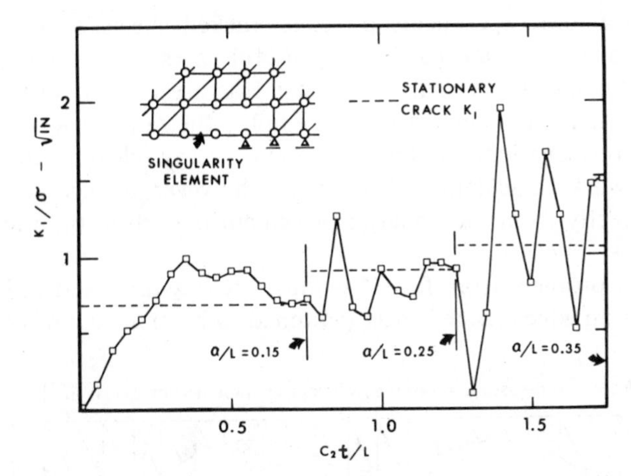

FIG. 3—*Stress-intensity factors from the singularity-element simulation of Broberg's problem.*

stituted for six triangles in the model (Fig. 1) of Broberg's problem. Following the procedure of the preceding section, calculations have been performed for the first three nodal releases in the simulation of this problem for $c/c_2 = 0.2$. In this scheme the singularity element was advanced one nodal spacing with each nodal release. The time dependence of the stress-intensity factor given by the singularity element during the first three intervals of "propagation" are shown in Fig. 3. During the first interval, the stress-intensity factor varies in the manner appropriate to the sudden appearance of a stationary crack in an infinite body [*17*]. However, the high-frequency and erratic oscillation of the stress-intensity factor during the second and third intervals precludes the association of the results of this analysis with the behavior of the continuously extending crack. The reasons for this oscillation, which was not reduced by an order-of-magnitude reduction in integration step size, are not clear, but we surmise the excitation of a high-frequency mode of vibration because of the simulation process. That is, at each nodal release a portion of the structure, previously represented by two triangles, is represented subsequently by a portion of the singularity element and vice versa. Hence nodal displacements (and velocities) at the end of an interval of time integration are imposed as initial conditions for the next interval for a model whose local stiffness has been constituted differently. Therefore, we must be pessimistic about the prospects for this approach.

Crack Propagation in Finite Sheets

Recently, Kobayashi et al [*10*] have presented finite-element analyses of two fast-fracture experiments on edge-cracked sheets of Homalite-100. These problems provide particularly useful cases for the comparison of different finite-element analyses of fast fracture in a finite body. While both the writers and Kobayashi et al employ the same process of simulating crack propagation, the latter compute energy-release rates through a near-tip "work" calculation.[4] The writers, however, deduce stress-intensity factors directly from the nodal displacement pattern in the finite-element model.

The first problem from Ref *10* is illustrated by the insert in Fig. 4, and consists of an edge-cracked sheet (assumed to be in a state of plane strain)

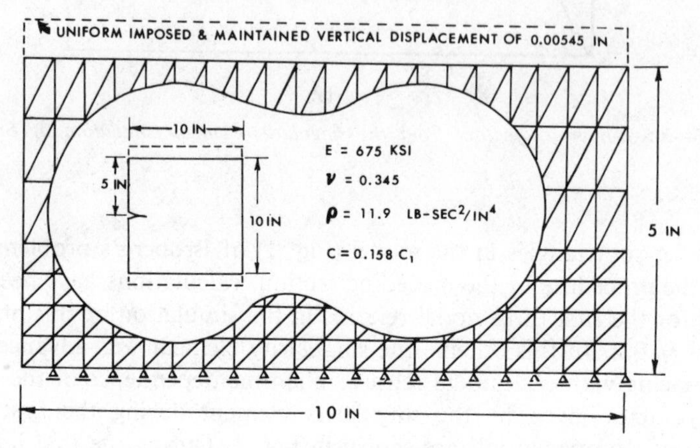

FIG. 4—*Finite-element model for the uniformly stretched rectangular sheet of Kobayashi et al* [10].

subjected to uniform time-independent displacements imposed on the edges parallel to the crack. The crack propagates from an initial length of 0.5 in. across the sheet at a constant speed of 14 900 in./s. The writers have employed the same finite-element grid, Fig. 4, as in Ref *10*; however, Kobayashi et al have used constant-strain quadrilateral elements while the writers have used constant-strain triangles. For the present work, stress-intensity factors for the running crack were deduced in exactly the fashion of Ref *11* which was reviewed in an earlier section.

Results of the analysis of this first problem are shown in Fig. 5 along with stress-intensity factors appropriate to quasi-static fracture; the latter were deduced using the eight-node singularity element. The static stress-intensity factor is supported by its relation to two well-known analytical results shown in the figure. That is, for very short cracks the stress-inten-

[4]It should be noted that both simulations preclude energy absorption at the crack tip. Consequently, apparent energy-release rates are in conflict with a global balance of energy in the finite-element model.

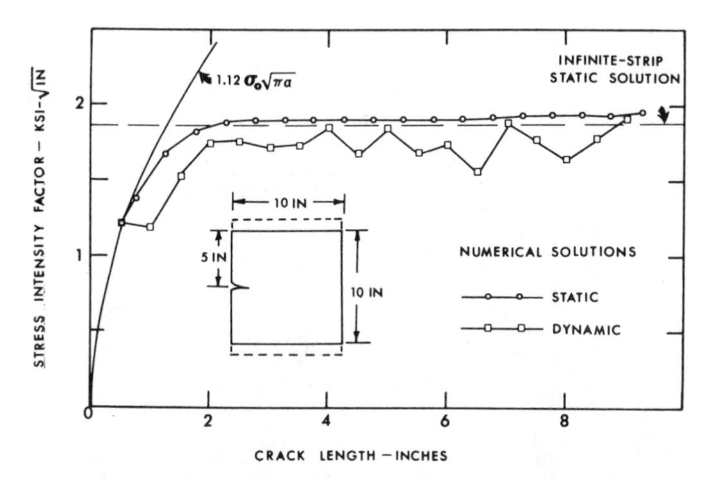

FIG. 5—*Static and dynamic stress-intensity factors for the uniformly stretched rectangular sheet.*

sity factor should be given accurately by 1.12 $\sigma_0\sqrt{\pi a}$ where σ_0 = 835 psi is the uniform stress which would exist were the sheet not cracked [*19*]. Over that range of crack lengths for which the stress-intensity factor is nearly constant, it is only slightly greater than that for a semi-infinite crack in an infinite strip subjected to uniform displacements on the edges [*20,21*].

Based upon the accuracy to be anticipated from the results of the study of Broberg's problem, it is reasonable to surmise that the dynamic stress-intensity factor (Fig. 5) is sensibly constant for most of the fracture process. While the dynamic stress-intensity factor is less than the static value at any given crack length, the reduction is only about one half that which occurs in the Broberg problem for the same crack speed.

In Figs. 6 and 7 comparisons of the present results with those of Kobayashi et al are shown. The present energy-release rates, both static and dynamic, are noticeably greater than those of Ref *10*. The present static result is supported by its relation to the "analytical average" shown in Fig. 6. This is the average strain-energy release rate for quasi-static fracture of the sheet starting with a vanishingly small crack, that is, the strain energy in the uncracked sheet divided by the width of the sheet.

The second problem reported by Kobayashi et al [*10*] is an edge-cracked finite sheet with linearly decreasing time-independent displacements imposed along the edges parallel to the crack faces. This case is depicted by the insert in Fig. 8 where the dotted lines illustrate the linear distribution of imposed displacements. This problem contrasts with the preceding one in that (1) the sheet was subjected to combined overall stretching and in-plane bending, whereas in the first problem it was placed in overall stretching only; (2) during propagation the crack tip accelerated as shown by the

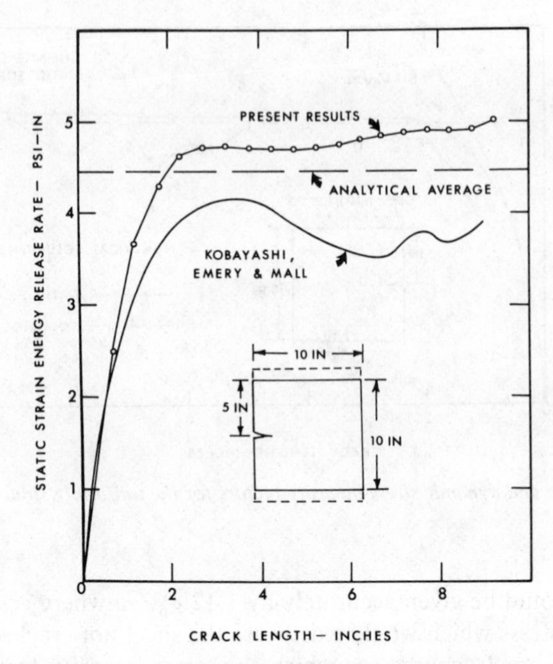

FIG. 6—*Static energy-release rates for the uniformly stretched rectangular sheet.*

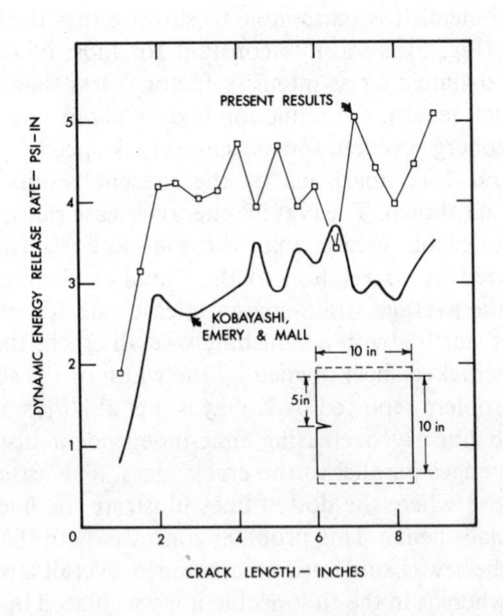

FIG. 7—*Dynamic energy-release rates for the uniformly stretched rectangular sheet.*

velocity profile in Fig. 8, while for the stretched case the crack velocity remained constant; and (3) the crack arrested at a final length of 7 in. (Fig. 8), but in the first problem the crack ran completely across the sheet.

The finite-element mesh of Fig. 4—with imposed linear displacements replacing the imposed uniform displacements—was used (as did Ref *10*) for solution of this second problem. The static and dynamic stress-intensity factors were computed in the same way as described for the previous problem. Results of these computations are shown in Fig. 8 where two interesting and potentially important features are observable. Firstly, the static and dynamic stress-intensity values are not separated significantly throughout the time that the crack is extending. And secondly, at the time of arrest the dynamic stress-intensity factor is very nearly the reported toughness of the test material [*10*].

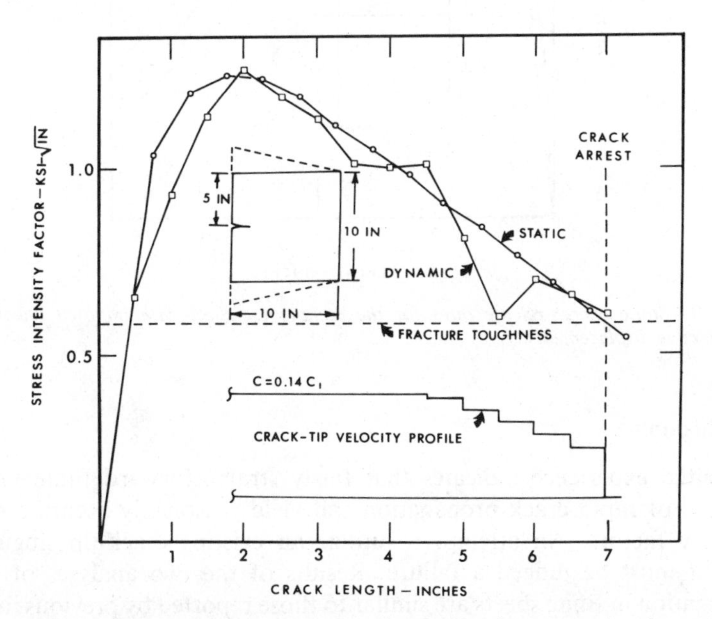

FIG. 8—*Static and dynamic stress-intensity factors for the rectangular sheet with imposed linearly decreasing edge displacements.*

Comparisons of the present results with those reported are displayed in Figs. 9 and 10. Although the comparisons reveal general qualitative agreement, just as for the first problem, energy release rates computed by the writers are again clearly larger than those previously reported. Such significant quantitative differences lead Kobayashi et al to observations about the fracture/arrest sequence which differ strongly from those listed by the writers.

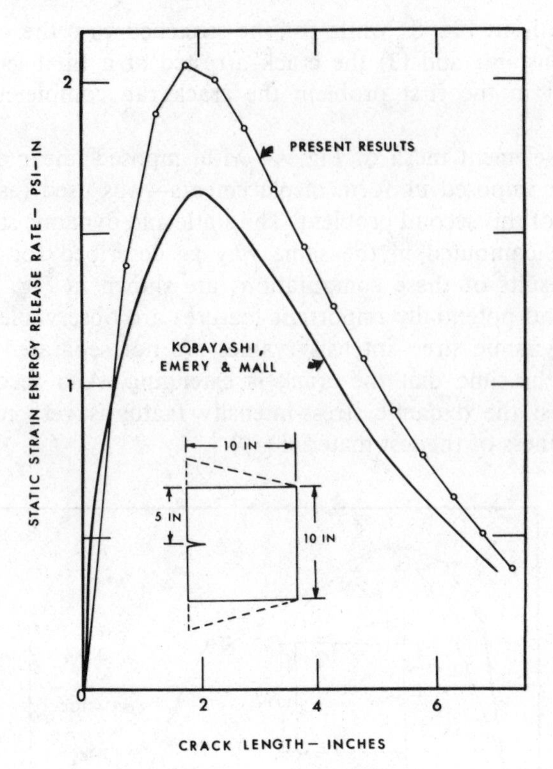

FIG. 9—*Static energy-release rates for the rectangular sheet with imposed linearly decreasing edge displacements.*

Conclusion

Limited experience indicates that fairly straightforward finite-element analyses of rapid crack propagation can yield reasonably accurate stress-intensity factors. An attempt to utilize an existing crack-tip singularity element must be judged a failure. Results of the two analyses of crack propagation in finite sheets are similar to those reported by previous investigators, although there are significant quantitative differences which lead to markedly different conclusions concerning crack arrest. As might be expected, dynamic and static stress-intensity factors for the finite-sheet problems are not related in the same manner as in either the infinite-body problem solved by Broberg [*12*] or that solved by Freund [*22*].

Substantial numerical experimentation is required before the finite-element method becomes highly reliable for crack propagation problems. In the absence of analytical solutions to problems involving finite bodies, independent studies by a number of investigators are needed to establish guidelines for mesh sizes and time-integration steps for accurate and economical computations.

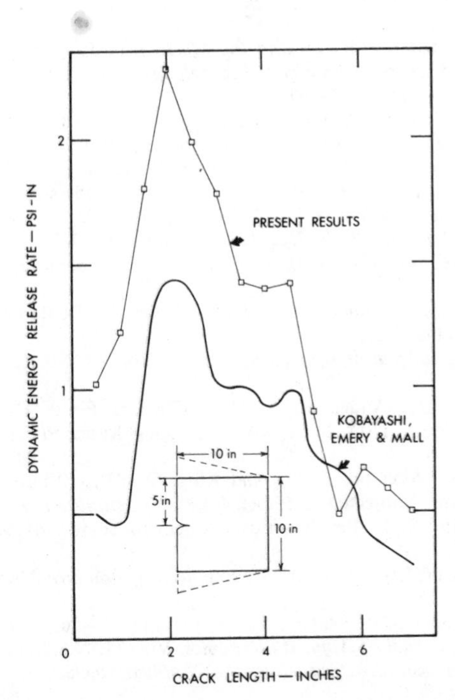

FIG. 10—*Dynamic energy release rates for the rectangular sheet with imposed linearly decreasing edge displacements.*

Acknowledgment

The authors wish to acknowledge gratefully the aid of J. F. Malluck who developed the computer program for extracting stress-intensity factors from the numerically determined nodal displacements of the finite-element models.

References

[*1*] Achenbach, J. D. in *Mechanics Today,* Vol. 1, S. Nemat-Nasser, Ed., Pergamon, London, 1972, pp. 1–57.

[*2*] Freund, L. B., *Journal of the Mechanics and Physics of Solids,* Vol. 22, 1974, pp. 137–146.

[*3*] Kostrov, B. V., *International Journal of Fracture,* Vol. 11, No. 1, Feb. 1975, pp. 47–56.

[*4*] Achenbach, J. D. and Bazant, Z. P., *Journal of Applied Mechanics,* Vol. 42, No. 1, March 1975, pp. 183–189.

[*5*] Nilsson, F., *Journal of Elasticity,* Vol. 4, No. 1, March 1974, pp. 73–75.

[*6*] Freund, L. B. and Clifton, R. J., *Journal of Elasticity,* Vol. 4, No. 4, Dec. 1974, pp. 293–299.

[*7*] Shmuely, M. and Alterman, Z. S., *Journal of Applied Mechanics,* Vol. 40, No. 4, Dec. 1973, pp. 902–908.

[*8*] Shmuely, M. and Peretz, D., *International Journal of Solids and Structures,* Vol. 12, 1976, pp. 67–79.

[9] Wilkins, M. L. in *Shock Waves and the Mechanical Properties of Solids, Sagamore Army Materials Research Conference Proceedings,* Vol. 17, Syracuse University Press, Syracuse, N.Y., 1970, pp. 387–394.
[10] Kobayashi, A. S., Emery, A. F., and Mall, S., "Dynamic Finite Element and Dynamic Photoelastic Analyses of Two Fracturing Homalite-100 Plates," ONR Technical Report No. 23, University of Washington, Seattle, Wash., Dec. 1975.
[11] King, W. W., Malluck, J. F., Aberson, J. A., and Anderson, J. M., *Mechanics Research Communications,* Vol. 3, No. 3, 1976, pp. 197–202.
[12] Broberg, K. B., *Arkiv för Fysik,* Vol. 18, 1960, pp. 159–192.
[13] Rice, J. R. in *Fracture,* Vol. II, H. Liebowitz, Ed., Academic Press, New York, 1968, p. 235.
[14] Malluck, J. F., *Crack Propagation in Finite Bodies,* Ph.D. thesis, Georgia Institute of Technology, Atlanta, Ga., 1976.
[15] Williams, M. L., *Journal of Applied Mechanics,* Vol. 24, No. 1, March 1957, pp. 109–114.
[16] Aberson, J. A. and Anderson, J. M., "Cracked Finite Elements Proposed for NASTRAN," NASA TMX-2893, NASA Langley Research Center, Hampton, Va., Sept. 1973.
[17] Anderson, J. M., Aberson, J. A., and King, W. W., "Finite Element Analysis of Cracked Structures Subjected to Shock Loads," *Computational Fracture Mechanics,* E. F. Rybicki and S. E. Benzley, Eds., American Society of Mechanical Engineers, New York, 1975.
[18] Bradley, W. B. and Kobayashi, A. S., *Engineering Fracture Mechanics,* Vol. 3, 1971, pp. 317–332.
[19] Wigglesworth, L. A., *Mathematika,* Vol. 4, 1957, pp. 76–96.
[20] Knauss, W. G., *Journal of Applied Mechanics,* Vol. 33, No. 2, June 1966, pp. 356–362.
[21] Rice, J. R., discussion of Ref 20, *Journal of Applied Mechanics,* Vol. 34, No. 1, March 1967, pp. 248–249.
[22] Freund, L. B., *Journal of the Mechanics and Physics of Solids,* Vol. 20, 1972, pp. 129–140.

M. Shmuely[1]

Effect of Poisson's Ratio on Crack Propagation and Arrest in the Double-Cantilever-Beam Specimen

REFERENCE: Shmuely, M., **"Effect of Poisson's Ratio on Crack Propagation and Arrest in the Double-Cantilever-Beam Specimen,"** *Fast Fracture and Crack Arrest, ASTM STP 627,* G. T. Hahn and M. F. Kanninen, Eds., American Society for Testing and Materials, 1977, pp. 135–141.

ABSTRACT: A recently proposed finite difference scheme for treating fast propagation and arrest in the double-cantilever-beam (DCB) specimen, which has so far yielded satisfactory results when compared with experimental measurements related to steel and epoxy resin, is here applied to a variety of materials, distinguished in the analysis by their Poisson's ratio only. It is shown that higher Poisson's ratios imply higher ratios between the initiating stress intensity factor and the dynamic material toughness when the same amount of crack growth is considered. The relation between the crack length at arrest and the crack speed, with the latter given with respect to the shear wave velocity, was found to be essentially independent of changes in the material when geometrically similar DCB configurations are considered.

KEY WORDS: fracture properties, numerical analysis, crack propagation, crack arrest

A finite difference scheme for treating fracture initiation and fast crack propagation and arrest in the double-cantilever-beam (DCB) specimen was recently proposed [*1–3*].[2] The computer program was so constructed that essentially the same scheme is employed in solving both the static (initiation) and the dynamic (crack extension) problems. Thus, the validity of the scheme may be verified by referring to results drawn from either the static or the dynamic solutions.

In as much as the static solution is concerned, the numerically derived stress intensity factors were found to be close to those reported in the literature, and, for a variety of specimen geometries, the compliances

[1]Associate professor, Faculty of Mechanical Engineering, Technion-Israel Institute of Technology, Haifa, Israel.

[2]The italic numbers in brackets refer to the list of references appended to this paper.

calculated were in good agreement with those obtained experimentally [2]. A good matching was also found between a photoelastic analysis and the numerically calculated and plotted stress fields [3].

Satisfactory results were obtained from the dynamic solution as well. In accordance with experimental findings, both the crack length at arrest (a_a) and the crack speed (V) have been found to be single valued increasing functions of the ratio K_q/K_d between the initial and dynamic stress intensity factors (K_q and K_d, respectively) with the a_a – V dependence curve close to the measured one [2]. In addition, for each of the two materials, steel and epoxy resin, good agreement was found between the analytically derived and experimentally found K_q/K_d ratios [3–5].

In this paper, the investigation is extended to include a variety of materials by spanning a wide range of values of Poisson's ratio, which is the only parameter introduced in the otherwise similar scheme to distinguish one material from the other.

In all cases investigated, a fracture stress criterion was assumed. However, it is shown that the same results would have been obtained had the fracture been controlled by an energy criterion. The last criterion is based on the local density of the energy field in the crack-tip region, close to the criterion used by Sih in his S-theory on fracture initiation [6]. Here, compared with the S-theory, averages rather than stationary values of the energy density are considered. (The stress criterion was preferred due to numerical convenience.)

Elastic Equations and Numerical Data

A detailed description of the finite difference approximations employed and the structure of the final numerical scheme is given in Refs *2,3*. A brief account is given here of the equations used and the numerical data chosen.

Assuming an elastic medium under plane-strain conditions, the governing equations are

$$(C_1^2 - C_2^2)U_{k,ki} + C_2^2U_{i,kk} = U_{i,tt} + \alpha U_{i,t} \qquad i,k = 1,2 \qquad (1)$$

In Eqs 1, C_1 and C_2 are, respectively, the dilatational and distortional wave velocities of the material considered, U_l stands for the displacement vector components in the l direction, t is the time, and the ordinary tensor notation for differentiation and summation is used. We let α in Eqs 1 be different from zero and positive, as implied by the dynamic relaxation method, when seeking the static solution. By letting α be zero, Eqs 1 reduce to the elastic equations of motion, by which the dynamic state is controlled.

For the fixed grips case, a solution of Eqs 1 is sought satisfying the following boundary condition (Fig. 1)

$$
\begin{aligned}
\sigma_{yy} = \sigma_{xy} = 0 \quad &\text{on } y = 0 \quad \text{for } 0 \leqslant x < a_0 + e \\
\sigma_{xx} = \sigma_{xy} = 0 \quad &\text{on } x = 0, L + e \quad \text{for } 0 \leqslant y \leqslant H \\
\sigma_{yy} = \sigma_{xy} = 0 \quad &\text{on } y = H \quad \text{for } 0 \leqslant x \leqslant L + e \\
U_y = \sigma_{xy} = 0 \quad &\text{on } y = 0 \quad \text{for } a_0 + e < x \leqslant L + e \\
U_y(x_0, y_0) &= \delta \quad \text{for } t \geqslant 0
\end{aligned}
\tag{2}
$$

where δ denotes the constant deflection at the point of load application.

The problem has been formulated so that all physical quantities are given relative to the specimen height H, the dilatational wave velocity C_1, and the material density ρ. A value of 1 is substituted in the scheme for these last mentioned constants. For the problem to be completely defined (Eqs 1 and 2), the values of L, a_0, δ, and C_2 should be provided. Given the specimen geometry, L and a_0 are defined in terms of H. The deflection δ, which, due to the linearity of the equations involved, may be arbitrarily chosen, is taken to be equal to H. The value of C_2, however, depends on the Poisson's ratio ν of the material considered and is defined in terms of C_1 according to the relation $C_2 = C_1(1 - 2\nu)^{1/2}/(2 - 2\nu)^{1/2}$. This means that for any given geometry, different materials are distinguished in the scheme by their corresponding different Poisson's ratio only. Starting with a Poisson's ratio of 0.250 and increasing it by 0.025 at a time, 7 different cases were examined, in the last of which, instead of $\nu = 0.400$, we take $\nu = 0.392$ corresponding to the Poisson's ratio of the epoxy resin studied in Ref 5. The proportions of the specimen geometry used in the analysis, the same for all cases, were $H/a_0/L = 1.0/1.0/4.8$.

The mesh size used in the numerical solution, the results of which are described hereafter, was $H/15$. This particular mesh size was found to

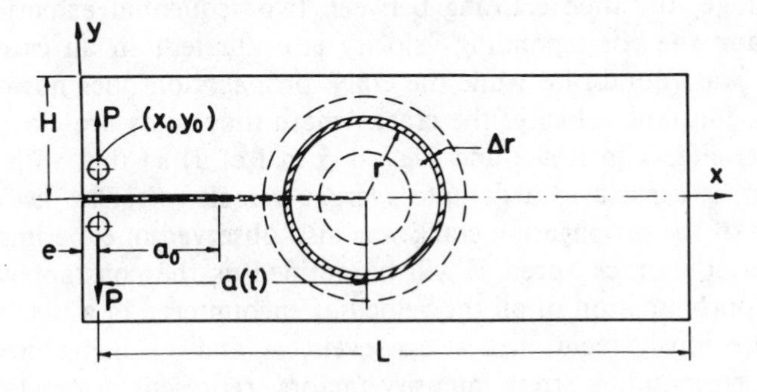

FIG. 1—*The DCB specimen configuration.*

be the largest possible mesh size which, except for the crack end shape [3], yields results which show no significant differences from those obtained with denser grids. A larger mesh size is chosen, since the resulting cuspated crack end shape obtained, in contrast to the steeper sloped shapes (closer to the analytical elliptic profile) obtained with smaller mesh sizes [3], happens to yield dynamic solutions which are closer to reality.

Dynamic Solution and Results

The simulation of a fracture process runs as follows. Given a Poisson's ratio, we first solve the static problem. This is accomplished by solving Eqs 1 with $\alpha > 0$, subjected to conditions (Eqs 2). The solution is assumed to approximate the static state when, at every grid point, the displacement variation between two successive iterations does not exceed 10^{-4}. At this stage, the displacement field is recorded on a disk ready for the start of the dynamic process.

In the dynamic solution α is reduced to zero and conditions (Eqs 2) are adjusted continuously to account for the growing crack. A fracture stress criterion is assumed according to which the crack extends by one mesh size whenever the cleavage stress at the grid point lying on $y = 0$, next to the tip reaches a predetermined critical value σ_c.

At least for the static case, by investigating a variety of crack lengths, this σ_c was shown to be proportional to the stress intensity factor; it is here assumed that this proportionality still exists in the dynamic case as well, that is, σ_c being proportional to the dynamic stress intensity factor K_d.

Starting each time with the previously mentioned static displacement field recorded back from the disk, solutions are obtained for different σ_c, taken to be smaller or equal to the stress level ahead of the crack tip at initiation (σ_q) and kept constant during each run. The crack is assumed to be arrested when a relatively long time passes after the last extension, with the stress level ahead of its tip remaining below σ_c. During the propagation stage, the time elapsing between two sequential extensions is recorded and the corresponding velocity is evaluated. In all cases investigated, it was found that while the crack propagation does not occur at a precisely constant velocity, the crack length-time plots are close to being linear (see Fig. 7 in Ref *2* and Figs. 4–5 in Ref *3*) so that with each run there can be associated a definite average velocity V. The just described behavior of the propagating crack was also observed in experiments [*4,5*]. Hereafter, the crack speed V will be defined as the constant value least square approximation of all the velocities encountered in a particular run.

The previously mentioned stress levels, σ_q and σ_c, being proportional to the corresponding stress intensity factors, represent in practice K_q and K_d, respectively, with the last one taken to be the average of the dynamic stress intensity factors encountered in a given experimental run. While in practice, for a given DCB configuration and material constants, different cases are effected by initiating fracture with different levels of K_q, resulting in corresponding changes in the K_d; in the analysis, rather than the separate values of σ_q and σ_c, it is the ratio σ_q/σ_c (that is, K_q/K_d) that counts.

Figure 2 illustrates that both a_a and V are single valued functions of σ_q/σ_c, the form of which is dependent on the Poisson's ratio of the material considered. Numerical results deviate by less than 7 percent from the averaged $a_a/a_0 - V/C_2$ relation described, which practically means that this relation is independent of the material considered.

In the course of propagation and for an arbitrarily chosen particular case $\nu = 0.300$ and $\sigma_q/\sigma_c = 1.5$, the flow of energy towards and out from the crack tip was studied. This was performed in the following manner. At each time step the strain (potential), kinetic and total energy densities, denoted hereafter, respectively, by $e_i = 1,2,3$, were calculated at all grid points lying inside the circle $r = H = 1$, the center of which coincides with the running crack tip (see Fig. 1).

The following formulae were used

$$e_1(r,\theta,t) = \frac{1}{2E}[(1 - \nu^2)(\sigma_{xx}{}^2 + \sigma_{yy}{}^2) + 2(1 + \nu)(\sigma_{xy}{}^2 - \nu\sigma_{xx}\sigma_{yy})] \quad (3)$$

with E standing for Young's modulus ($E = \rho C_2{}^2(3C_1{}^2 - 4C_2{}^2)/(C_1{}^2 - C_2{}^2)$)

$$e_2(r,\theta,t) = \frac{1}{2}\rho\left[\left(\frac{\partial U_x}{\partial t}\right)^2 + \left(\frac{\partial U_y}{\partial t}\right)^2\right] \quad (4)$$

$$e_3(r,\theta,t) = e_1(r,\theta,t) + e_2(r,\theta,t) \quad (5)$$

For $r = j\Delta r$, $j = 1,2, \ldots, 15$, with $\Delta r = H/15$ being the mesh size used in the scheme [3], the average densities

$$\bar{e}_i(r,t) = \frac{1}{\pi}\int_0^\pi e_i(r,\theta,t)d\theta \quad (6)$$

are obtained and finally the "accumulated energy densities" E_i defined by

$$E_i(r,t) = \int_0^r \bar{e}_i(q,t)dq \quad (7)$$

are evaluated.

Given any of the last mentioned variables (E_i), a special program was used to trace through the $r - t$ plane lines on each of which E_i obtains

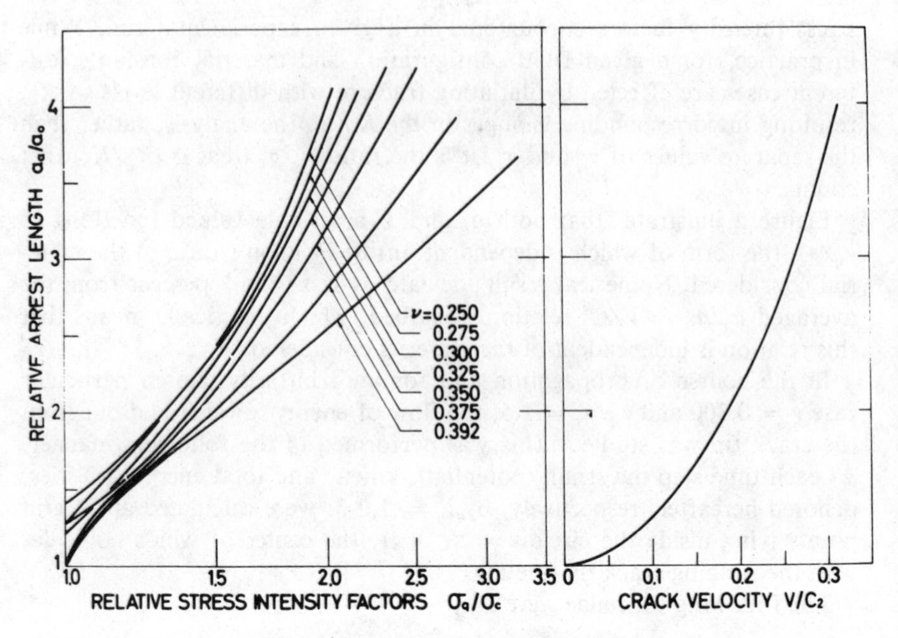

FIG. 2—*Results for different Poisson's ratios.*

a constant level, the increment between sequential levels of E_i being constant. These lines are then written on the CALCOMP plotter as shown in Fig. 3.

From Eq 7 and the way Fig. 3 was constructed, it follows that the convergence of the E_i constant lines down towards $r = 0$ indicates that the energy considered flows towards the crack tip, whereas if these lines diverge towards $r = R = 1$, the energy considered flows out. In as much as the strain energy density (Fig. 3*a*) is considered, we find that a constant number of E_i constant lines are accumulated below $r = \Delta r$ (that is, the smallest radius possible numerically) just before an extension of the crack by one mesh size $h = \Delta r$, occurs. This means that the rise of σ_{yy} ahead of the crack tip to the σ_c level is accompanied by a corresponding rise of the strain energy density there, each time reaching the same peak level. Hence, the final results will remain the same if the fracture criterion is chosen to be the just mentioned local crack-tip strain energy density level instead of σ_c. However, it should be noted that although the assumed constancy of the stress intensity factors infers the constancy of the strain energy density at the crack tip, the energy release rate G (that is, the decrease rate of the total energy) must not be constant. In fact, a detailed calculation of the energy distribution in the DCB specimen, in the course of a fast crack propagation controlled by a stress criterion [3], shows a rather complicated pattern of changes in G, which reflects the continuous interchange between the kinetic and the strain energy.

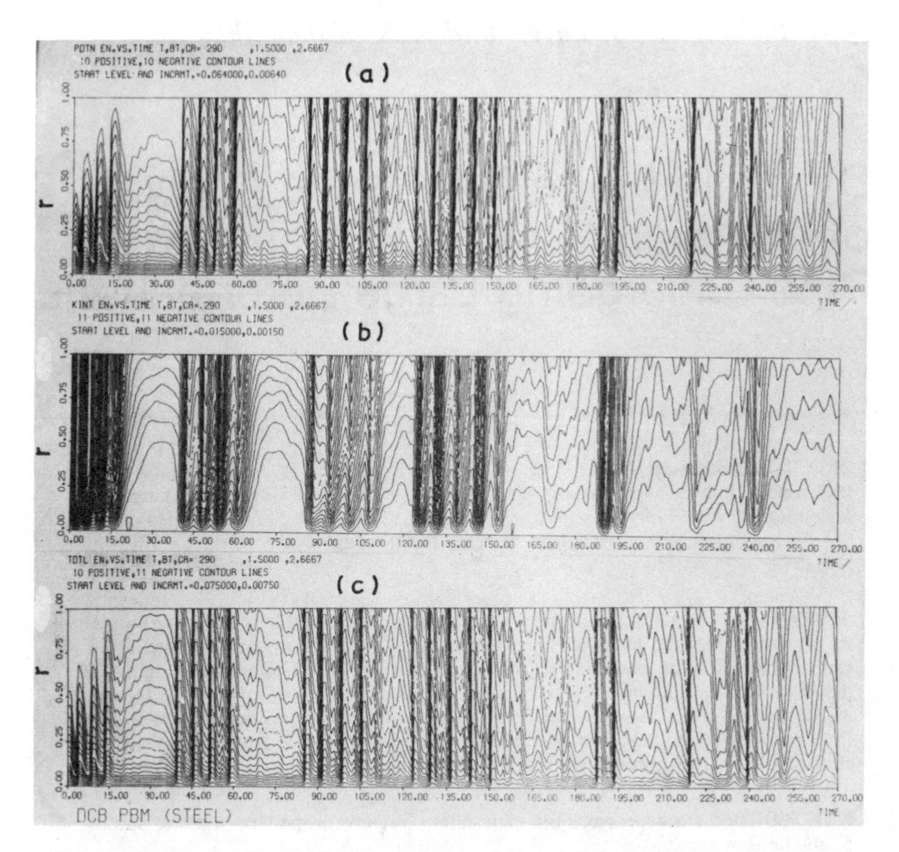

FIG. 3—*Energy density distribution with time:* (a) *strain energy,* (b) *kinetic energy, and* (c) *total energy.*

References

[1] Shmuely, M., *International Journal of Fracture,* Vol. 10, 1974, pp. 596–698.

[2] Shmuely, M. and Peretz, D., *International Journal of Solids and Structures,* Vol. 12, 1976, pp. 67–79.

[3] Shumely, M., "Analysis of Fast Fracture and Crack Arrest by Finite Differences," *International Journal of Fracture,* to be published.

[4] Kalthoff, S., Winkler, S., and Beinert, J., *International Journal of Fracture,* Vol. 12, 1976, and private communication.

[5] Hahn, G. T., Hoagland, R. G., Kanninen, M. F., Rosenfield, A. R., and Sejnoha, R., "Fast Fracture Resistance and Crack Arrest in Structural Steels," Project SR-201, "Fracture Arrest Study," Department of the Navy, 1973.

[6] Sih, G. C. in *Mechanics of Fracture,* Vol. 1, G. C. Sih, Ed., Noordhoff International Publishing, Leyden, The Netherlands, 1973, pp. XXI–XLV.

A. F. Emery,[1] *W. J. Love,*[1] *and A. S. Kobayashi*[1]

Dynamic Finite Difference Analysis of an Axially Cracked Pressurized Pipe Undergoing Large Deformations

REFERENCE: Emery, A. F., Love, W. J., and Kobayashi, A. S., "**Dynamic Finite Difference Analysis of an Axially Cracked Pressurized Pipe Undergoing Large Deformations,**" *Fast Fracture and Crack Arrest, ASTM STP 627,* G. T. Hahn and M. F. Kanninen, Eds., American Society for Testing and Materials, 1977, pp. 143–158.

ABSTRACT: An axial through crack was suddenly introduced into the wall of a pipe which was pressurized by either hot water or air. The crack tip was assumed to advance along the pipe according to a fracture criterion based upon the character of the deformation. For brittle elastic failure a maximum stress intensity factor was utilized, while for a plastic stress field, a maximum strain criterion was used. The fluid pressure in the pipe was calculated by a finite difference method in which the effect of the outflow through the crack was taken into consideration.

KEY WORDS: crack propagation, pipe lines, fracture properties, stresses, strains, plastic deformation

a	Radius of shell
A	Cross-sectional area for fluid flow
c_o, c_s, c	Dilatational and shear wave speeds, fluid speed of sound
E	Modulus of elasticity
f	Fluid friction term in Eq 1
$\hat{g}$	Base reactors for the undeformed shell
G	Mass flow rate, shear modulus
h	Half thickness of shell, enthalpy
k	Ratio of specific heats
M	Moment resultants
N, N_c	Force resultants, critical value for brittle failure
P, P°	Pressure, initial fluid pressure
Q	Shear resultant

[1]Professors of mechanical engineering, Department of Mechanical Engineering, University of Washington, Seattle, Wash. 98195.

r Radius
S Stress
t Time
T Shell surface tractions
u, v Displacements
V Crack-tip velocity
$\bar{V}$ Fluid velocity
$w, \bar{w}$ Radial displacement, average radial displacement
W Width of crack opening
x Axial coordinate
z Radial coordinate
α, β Rotations of shell midsurface
δ Half width of crack opening
ξ Generalized shell coordinate
ν Poisson's ratio
κ Shear stress modifier
ϵ Strain
θ Angle
ρ Density

Superscripts

$\partial^2/\partial t^2$
— Values associated with large deflections

Subscripts

1,2,3 Values associated with x, θ, r directions

The design and operation of high-pressure piping requires the ability to assess the proclivity to fracture of key components. Although the initiation and short-term growth of cracks may be estimated by using, as an upperbound, the peak pressures in the system, the crack growth in a rupturing pipe is affected strongly by the fluid pressure reduction associated with outflow through the crack. Under certain geometries, the pressure relief wave, generated by the pipe fracture, may reflect from the reservoir and actually raise the pipe pressure at the crack tip. At the same time, the free edges of the opening crack, termed the flaps, are subjected to a significantly reduced pressure which may decelerate the crack growth. Consequently, it is necessary to consider the simultaneous calculation of the pipe deformations and the fluid pressures if the dynamic characteristics of the crack are to be understood.

Emery et al *[1,2]* [2] have reported the analysis of fracture for elastic and plastic deformations for constant pressure and for coupled pressure-deformation calculations. These results have indicated that large deformation analysis is important only for elastic and not for plastic deforma-

[2]The italic numbers in brackets refer to the list of references appended to this paper.

tions. All of these calculations were for hot water pressurized pipes in which a modest outflow through the crack opening produced a very sudden pressure reduction to the fluid saturation pressure. The flaps were thus lightly loaded. In this paper, we treat the case of ductile tearing driven by an internal air pressure which decays slowly as the air leaks through the crack opening and also responds to dynamic changes in the cross-sectional area.

Fluid Pressure Modeling

The fluid is modeled by the one-dimensional equations of motion in which we assume that all the fluid properties are constant over a cross section and vary only with axial position and with time. The leakage out of the crack is treated by considering that the exiting fluid removes axial momentum and mass from the pipe, but causes no pressure variations across the cross section. Thus, the reaction pressure from the jet is neglected. For air and for steam, the reaction pressure is small compared to the pipe pressure. For hot water pressurization, the reaction pressure is greater, but liquid water leaks only during the initial times when the crack opening is small and the total reaction force is negligible. By the time that the crack opening area is large enough to require a consideration of the transverse pressure, the water has flashed to steam and the reaction pressure is small. The appropriate equations of fluid motion are the conservation of momentum plus the following equations which are derived from the energy equation by using the equation of state and the conservation of mass

$$-\frac{\partial p}{\partial t} = \underbrace{c^2\left[\frac{\partial G}{\partial x} + \frac{G}{A}\frac{\partial A}{\partial x}\right]}_{\text{compressibility}} - \underbrace{\frac{c^2}{h}\left[\frac{G}{\rho}\frac{\partial p}{\partial x} - G\frac{\partial h}{\partial x} + f\right]}_{\text{advection}}$$

$$+ \underbrace{\left[c^2 - \frac{c^2}{h}\left(h - \frac{G^2}{2\rho^2} - e' + \frac{\bar{V}G}{\rho}\right)\right]G_l\frac{W}{A}}_{\text{leakage}}$$

$$+ \underbrace{\left[c^2 - c^2\frac{(k-1)}{k}h\right]\frac{\rho}{A}\frac{dA}{dt}}_{\text{pipe expansion}} \tag{1}$$

$$-\rho\frac{\partial h}{\partial t} = c^2\left[\frac{\partial G}{\partial x} + \frac{G}{A}\frac{\partial A}{\partial x}\right] + \frac{c^2k}{(k-1)h}\left[\frac{G}{\rho}\frac{\partial p}{\partial x} - G\frac{\partial h}{\partial x} + f\right]$$

$$+\left[c^2 - \frac{c^2k}{(k-1)h}\left(h - \frac{G^2}{2\rho^2} - e' + \frac{\bar{V}G}{\rho}\right)\right]G_l\frac{W}{A} \quad (2)$$

where

k = ratio of specific heats (= 1.4 for air),
$\bar{V}$ = G/ρ if $G_l \geq 0$,
= 0 if $G_l < 0$,
e' = $h + G^2/2\rho^2$, and
G_l = leakage rate through the crack opening, which is calculated by considering the leakage to be an adiabatic expansion of the pipe fluid.

Although it is usual to write the one-dimensional fluid equations in terms of density, enthalpy, and velocity, the current equations of state for water-steam mixtures are best given in terms of p and h. A full discussion of these equations and their generalization for general fluids is given in Ref *3*. The coupling between the structural deformations and the fluid behavior are the terms G_l, the leakage rate, dA/dt, the cross-sectional area changes, and dA/dx, the connection of the pipe into the fluid reservoir.

Structural Deformations

The geometry of the cylindrical shell is shown schematically on Fig. 1, where u and v are the midsurface deflections in the axial and circumferential directs, w is the radial deflections, and α and β are the axial and circumferential rotations. Under the assumptions of small strains, but large deformations, the appropriate equations of dynamic motion, considering transverse shear are

$$A\ddot{u} + B\ddot{\alpha} = a\frac{\partial \bar{N}_{11}}{\partial x} + \frac{\partial \bar{N}_{21}}{\partial \theta} + a\bar{T}_1^N \quad (3a)$$

$$B\ddot{u} + C\ddot{\alpha} = a\frac{\partial \bar{M}_{11}}{\partial x} + \frac{\partial \bar{M}_{21}}{\partial \theta} + ha\,\bar{T}_1^M - a\bar{Q}_1 \quad (3b)$$

$$\left(A + \frac{B}{a}\right)\ddot{v} + B\ddot{\beta} = a\frac{\partial \bar{N}_{12}}{\partial x} + \frac{\partial \bar{N}_{22}}{\partial \theta} + a\,\bar{T}_2^N + \bar{Q}_2 \quad (3c)$$

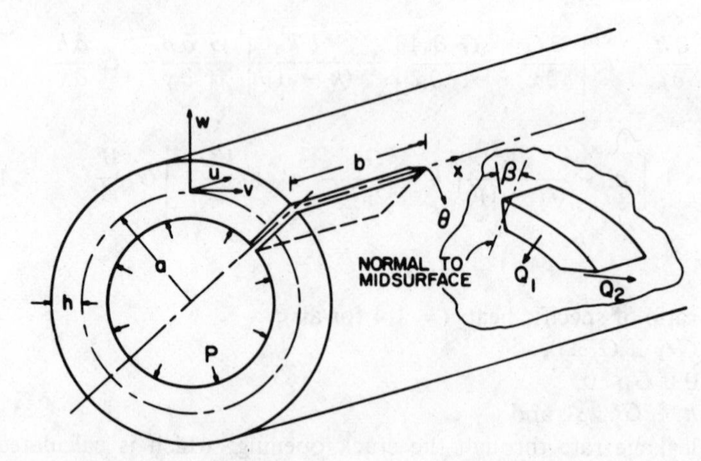

FIG. 1—*Schematic of a cylindrical shell showing the orientation of the crack, displacements and rotations.*

$$\left(B + \frac{C}{a}\right)\ddot{v} + C\ddot{\beta} = a\frac{\partial \bar{M}_{12}}{\partial x} + \frac{\partial \bar{M}_{22}}{\partial \theta} + ah\,\bar{T}_2{}^M - a\bar{Q}_2 \tag{3d}$$

$$A\ddot{w} = a\frac{\partial \bar{Q}_1}{\partial x} + \frac{\partial \bar{Q}_2}{\partial \theta} - \bar{N}_{22} + a\,\bar{T}_3 \tag{3e}$$

where

$$[A, B, C] = \int_{-h}^{h} \rho r[1, z, z^2]\, dz$$

and the force and moment resultants for large deflections ($\bar{N},\bar{M},\bar{Q}$) are defined in terms of the small deflection values (N,M,Q) as

$$\begin{Bmatrix} \bar{N}_{i1} \\ \bar{M}_{i1} \end{Bmatrix} = \left(1 + \frac{\partial u}{\partial x}\right)\begin{Bmatrix} N_{i1} \\ M_{i1} \end{Bmatrix} + \frac{1}{a}\frac{\partial u}{\partial \theta}\begin{Bmatrix} N_{i2} \\ M_{i2} \end{Bmatrix} + \alpha\begin{Bmatrix} Q_i \\ 0 \end{Bmatrix} \tag{4a}$$

$$\begin{Bmatrix} \bar{N}_{i2} \\ \bar{M}_{i2} \end{Bmatrix} = \frac{\partial v}{\partial x}\begin{Bmatrix} N_{i1} \\ M_{i1} \end{Bmatrix} + \left(1 + \frac{1}{a}\frac{\partial v}{\partial \theta} + \frac{w}{a}\right)\begin{Bmatrix} N_{i2} \\ M_{i2} \end{Bmatrix} + \beta\begin{Bmatrix} Q_i \\ 0 \end{Bmatrix} \tag{4b}$$

$$\bar{Q}_i = \frac{\partial w}{\partial x}N_{i1} + \left(\frac{1}{a}\frac{\partial w}{\partial \theta} - \frac{v}{a}\right)N_{i2} + Q_i \tag{4c}$$

The surface tractions for large deflections are given by

$$\begin{Bmatrix} \bar{T}_1{}^N \\ \bar{T}_1{}^M \end{Bmatrix} = \alpha\begin{Bmatrix} P \\ P \end{Bmatrix} - \frac{1}{h}$$

$$\times \left\{ \frac{\partial u}{\partial x} Q_1 + \frac{1}{a}\frac{\partial u}{\partial \theta} Q_2 + \frac{\partial w}{\partial x} \overset{0}{N_{11}} + \left(\frac{1}{a}\frac{\partial w}{\partial \theta} - \frac{v}{a}\right) N_{12} \right\} \tag{4d}$$

$$\begin{Bmatrix} \bar{T}_2^N \\ \bar{T}_2^M \end{Bmatrix} = \beta \begin{Bmatrix} P \\ P \end{Bmatrix} + \frac{1}{h}$$

$$\times \left\{ - \frac{\partial v}{\partial x} Q_1 - \left(\frac{1}{\alpha}\frac{\partial v}{\partial \theta} + \frac{w}{a}\right) Q_2 + \frac{\partial w}{\partial x}\left(N_{21} + \frac{M_{21}}{a}\right)\right.$$

$$\left. + \left(\frac{1}{a}\frac{\partial w}{\partial \theta} - \frac{v}{a}\right)\left(N_{22} + \frac{M_{22}}{a}\right)\right\} \tag{4e}$$

$$\bar{T}_3 = P$$

where

P = fluid pressure

and the small deflection force and moment resultants are

$$[N_{1j}, M_{1j}] = \frac{1}{a}\int_{-h}^{h} r S_{1j}\,[1, z]\, dz$$

$$[N_{2j}, M_{2j}] = \int_{-h}^{h} S_{2j}\,[1, z]\, dz$$

$$[Q_1, Q_2] = \int_{-h}^{h} \left[S_{13}\frac{r}{a}, S_{23} \right] dz$$

The Piola-Kirchoff stresses are related linearly to the Lagrangian strains by

$$S_{11} = \frac{E}{1 - \nu^2}(\epsilon_{11} + \nu\epsilon_{22}),\ S_{13} = \kappa G \epsilon_{13} \tag{5}$$

The Lagrangian strains are

$$\epsilon_{ij} = \frac{1}{2}\left(\tilde{g}_i \cdot \frac{\partial \tilde{u}}{\partial \xi_j} + \tilde{g}_j \cdot \frac{\partial \tilde{u}}{\partial \zeta_i} + \frac{\partial \tilde{u}}{\partial \zeta_i} \cdot \frac{\partial u}{\partial \epsilon_j}\right) \tag{6}$$

where g_i are the base vectors referred to the originally undeformed shell and $\partial u / \partial \xi_j$ is given by the covariant differentiation

$$\frac{\partial u}{\partial \xi_j} = g_\alpha u^\alpha |_j$$

A full description of the derivation of the large deflection equations and the underlying assumptions is given in Ref *4*. The stresses during plastic deformations are computed by using the von Mises yield criterion and an incremental strain theory.

Finite Difference Algorithm

The shell is divided into a series of nodal points by the mesh illustrated in Fig. 2 with the force and moment resultants defined at the points as indicated. The displacements and rotations are computed at the central nodal points. The pressures, enthalpy, and fluid mass flow rates are evaluated at the marked positions.

Fluid Algorithm

Because of the advection of fluid through the control volumes (Fig. 2), the finite difference algorithm is very sensitive to the particular differencing form used and manifests considerable phase shift and dissipation unless special care is taken. Although it is well recognized that upwind differencing strongly damps the fluid solution, Ref *5*, the errors so introduced are not likely to exceed those associated with a one-dimensional treatment of the flow, and, furthermore, the panacea for these errors is an algorithm which is too complex to be utilized in conjunction with the structural code. The spatial derivations in Eqs 1 and 2 are represented by

$$\frac{\partial f}{\partial x} = \frac{f(i+1) - f(i-1)}{2\Delta x}$$

where f is p, h, or A. Following the derivation of Ref *6*, the terms involving G are given in upwind difference form as

$$\frac{\partial G}{\partial x} = \frac{G(i) - G(i-1)}{\Delta x}, \quad G(i), G(i-1) \geq 0$$

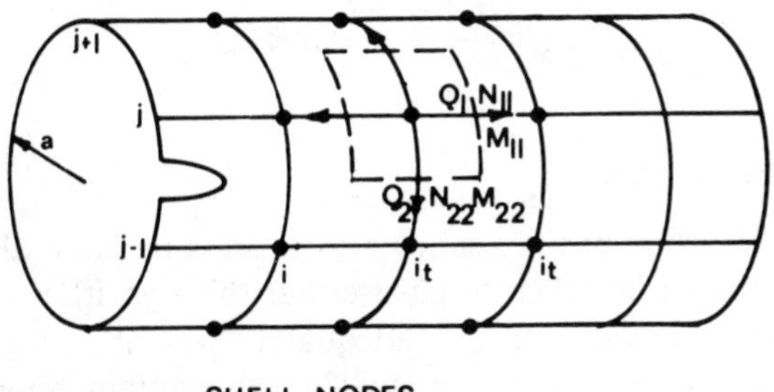

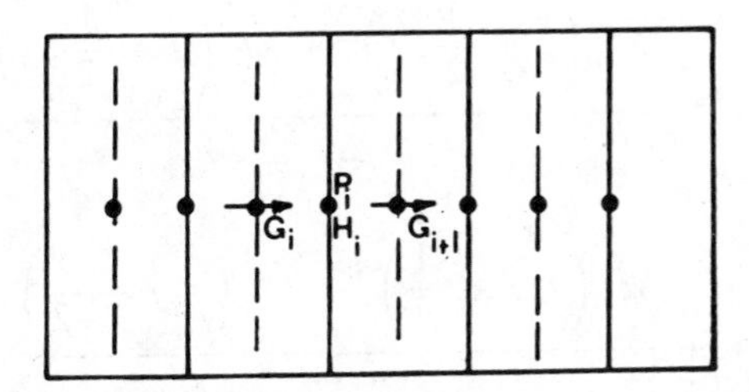

FIG. 2—*Schematic of the nodal network showing the location of the force and moment resultants and the fluid variables.*

$$= \frac{G(i + 1) - G(i)}{\Delta x}, \quad G(i + 1), G(i) \leq 0 \tag{7}$$

$$= \frac{G(i + 1) - G(i - 1)}{2\Delta x}, \quad G(i + 1) < 0, G(i - 1) > 0$$

$$= 0, \text{ otherwise}$$

These special difference forms preserve the correct advection nature and ensure conservation of mass and momentum, which Roache [7] has shown to be a necessary feature of fluid algorithms. The temporal derivative is given by

$$\frac{\partial f}{\partial t} = \frac{f(t + \Delta t) - f(t)}{\Delta t} = g(p, h, G, e', x, t)$$

where the right side of Eqs 1 and 2 is represented schematically by the functional g which is to be evaluated at the present time t. The stability of this explicit difference equation requires that we satisfy the usual Courant-Friedricks-Lewy condition

$$\left(\frac{|G|}{\rho} + c\right)\Delta t < \Delta x \tag{9}$$

Structural Deformations

The shell deformations are simpler to express in finite difference form, although care must be taken to ensure that the algorithm models the correct boundary behavior [*1*] and adequately describes the full range of those frequencies present in the shell which contain appreciable power [*8*]. The right hand side of Eq 3*b* is expressed as

$$\frac{\bar{M}_{11}\left(i + \frac{1}{2}, j\right) - \bar{M}_{11}\left(i - \frac{1}{2}, j\right)}{\Delta x}$$

$$+ \frac{\bar{M}_{21}\left(i, j + \frac{1}{2}\right) - \bar{M}_{21}\left(i, j - \frac{1}{2}\right)}{\Delta \theta}$$

$$+ ah\,\bar{T}_1{}^M(i, j) - a\,\frac{\bar{Q}_1\left(i + \frac{1}{2}, j\right) + \bar{Q}_1\left(i - \frac{1}{2}, j\right)}{2}$$

Similar expressions are used for the other equations. The time derivatives are expressed as

$$\frac{\partial^2 u}{\partial t^2} = \frac{u(t + \Delta t) - 2u(t) + u(t - \Delta t)}{\Delta t^2}$$

This set of explicit difference shell equations must satisfy the stability criteria of

$$\left.\begin{array}{l} c_0\,\Delta t < \min\,(2h, \Delta s) \\ \Delta x > 2h \end{array}\right\} \qquad \Delta s = \sqrt{\Delta x^2 + a^2\,\Delta\theta^2} \tag{10}$$

Coupled Codes

When the codes are coupled, with the cross-sectional area change and crack opening computed by the structural code used as input into the fluid code, both codes must use the same time step. For liquid water, this is not a problem because the fluid sound speed is nearly equal to that of the shell. However, for air or for steam, the fluid sound speed is an order of magnitude less. Thus the fluid code should be able to use a time step which is ten times that of the shell code. However, because the fluid pressure responds to changes in the crack opening which the shell code supplies, the fluid computations must take place simultaneously. This state of affairs is unfortunate because the erroneous damping effect of the upwind differencing is a minimum when Δt is as large as possible. For water-steam mixtures, this effect is overshadowed by the uncertainty about the metastable equilibrium of the fluid and the inaccuracy of the properties. For air it means that any shock waves will be smeared out over six or more nodal points [9] and implies that the results will be indicative of fracture tendencies rather than a precise quantitative measure of the crack's behavior. However, uncertainties in the specification of a fracture criteria are likely to be more important than the inexactness in modeling sharp pressure transients.

Fluid Pressures

Figure 3 illustrates the pressure distribution for an axial crack moving at a constant speed in a pipe pressurized by hot water and by air. The crack shape was prescribed as a cusp shape given by

$$w = \min\left(w^0, \frac{w^0}{2}\left(1 - \cos\frac{\pi z}{l}\right)\right)$$

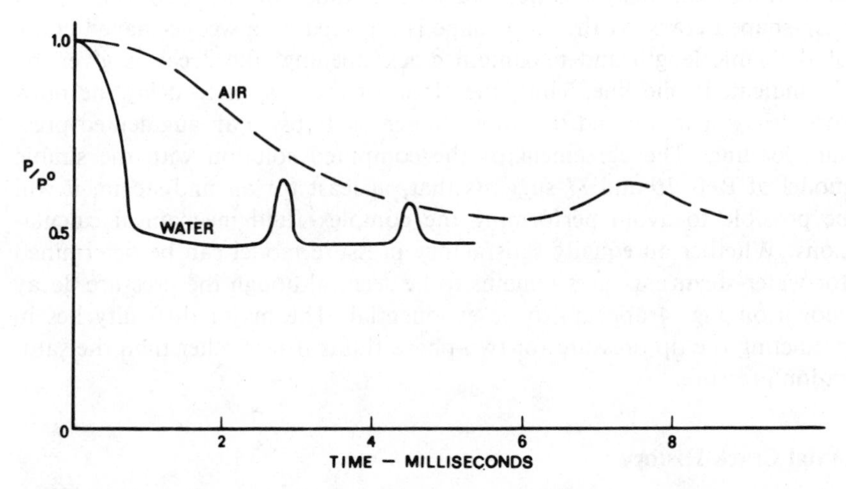

FIG. 3—*Crack-tip pressure for a constant crack speed for air and water pressurization* (V/c_s = *0.06, crack transition length = 5 diameters*).

where

z = distance behind crack tip,
l = crack transition, and
w^0 = maximum crack opening.

The crack transition length is the axial distance from the tip to the point of maximum opening.

The rapid decay of the pressure to the saturation value is seen easily. The pressure wave caused by reflection from the fluid reservoir is also evident. Whether this short time, high pressure pulse has a significant effect on the shell or the crack tip remains to be investigated. Kanninen [*10*] and Poynton [*11*] have suggested that the pressure at the crack tip can be estimated by modelling the crack discharge as the discharge from an open-ended duct whose end is moving at the speed V and for which the fluid velocity is sonic with respect to the end. The resulting tip pressure is then

$$\frac{p_{tip}}{p^0} = \left\{\frac{2}{k+1} + \frac{k-1}{k+1}\frac{V}{a}\right\}^{2k/(k-1)}$$

$$\cong 0.30 + 0.57\frac{V}{a} \text{ for } k = 1.3 \tag{11}$$

The algorithm used in this study produced a coefficient of V/a of 0.55 after the crack had moved through a starting distance of 5 to 6 diameters as shown on Fig. 3. Kanninen also suggested that the spatial pressure decay could be modeled by a simple exponential curve. Figure 4 shows their values for wedge-shaped cracks and those of the algorithm for a cusp-shaped crack. If the cusp shape is replaced by a wedge-shaped crack of the same length and maximum crack opening, the decay is given by the indicated solid line. Thus, the effect of the cusp is to delay the pressure decay spatially and to expose the crack flaps to an augmented pressure loading. The agreement of the computed solution with the simple model of Refs *10* and *11* suggests that, at least for air and steam, it will be possible to avoid performing the complex fluid mechanical calculations. Whether an equally satisfactory pressure model can be determined for water-steam mixtures remains to be seen, although the pressure decay shown on Fig. 4 appears to be exponential. The major difficulty lies in predicting the tip pressure for two-phase fluids if it is other than the saturation pressure.

Axial Crack History

A steel cylinder with a thickness to radius ratio of $h/a = 1/30$, which corresponds approximately to the shape used in the American Iron and

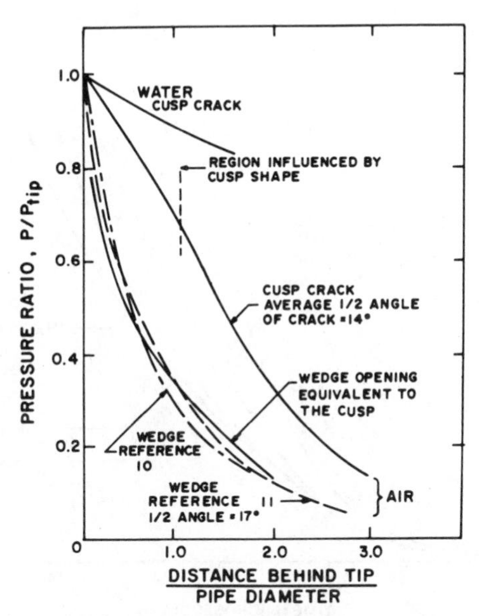

FIG. 4—*Spatial pressure distribution downstream of the crack tip for a constant crack speed for air and water pressurization* (V/c_s = *0.06, crack transition length = 5 diameters*).

Steel Institute tests [*12*] was divided by a mesh with $\Delta\theta = 9$ deg and $\Delta x/a\Delta\theta = \frac{1}{2}$. The shell was 8 radii long with an outgoing wave condition imposed at one end to simulate an infinitely long pipe and a plane of symmetry at $x = 0$. A half crack of length between $a/3$ and a was introduced at $x = 0$, with the crack edges initially fixed. The shell was pressurized with a pressure of p^0 and the crack edges suddenly released. Emery et al [*1,2*] discuss the behavior of the crack for brittle fracture and ductile tearing when the pipe was filled with hot water and in particular note that the initial length of the crack does not affect the results. Here we wish to discuss the effects of the pressurization by air, to comment upon a simplification proposed by Kanninen, and to suggest some simplifications in the calculations.

Ductile Tearing

The ductile fracture was computed by measuring the transverse strains at a point ahead of the crack and permitting the crack to extend whenever these strains exceeded a prescribed value. A critical strain value of 2 percent at $\Delta x/2$ ahead of the crack tip, based upon metallurgical estimates, was used. Although the value chosen affects the speed of the crack in an inverse way, the general characteristics of the deformation are applicable to any value. Figure 5 illustrates the crack extension history for brittle and ductile failure under constant fluid pressure and for large and small deflections.

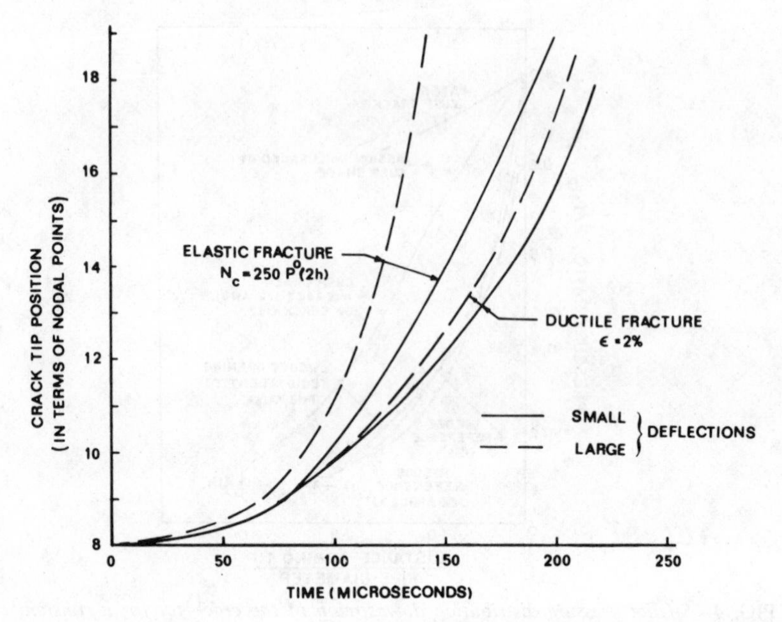

FIG. 5—*Crack-tip extension history for a constant pipe pressure for brittle and ductile failure, using small and large deflection calculations—initial pressure = 6.9 MPa, yield stress = 482.3 MPa.*

For brittle fracture the difference between large and small deflections is large. For ductile failure, because of the appreciable yielding around the crack, the flaps do not create a strong crack extending effect, and the difference between large and small deflection calculations is not significant. Since most piping is likely to fail in a ductile mode, it will not be necessary to describe the flap behavior accurately and crack computations should be possible with simple structural models. For most of these constant pressure calculations, significant yielding took place from about one half radius behind the crack tip to one quarter radius ahead of the tip. It should be pointed up that the crack opening and tip speed are independent of the initial crack length and thus of the pipe diameter and that the limiting speeds are constant fractions of the shear wave velocity.

Ductile Tearing with the Combined Codes

When the fluid escapes through the crack opening, the pressure near the crack tip will be reduced, and consequently the crack extension will be slower because of: (*a*) a reduced pressure at the crack tip and (*b*) a significantly reduced pressure on the flaps. To examine these effects, two fluid cases were considered: (*a*) air for which the pressure decay behind the crack tip is small and (*b*) a water-steam mixture. When a pipe is pres-

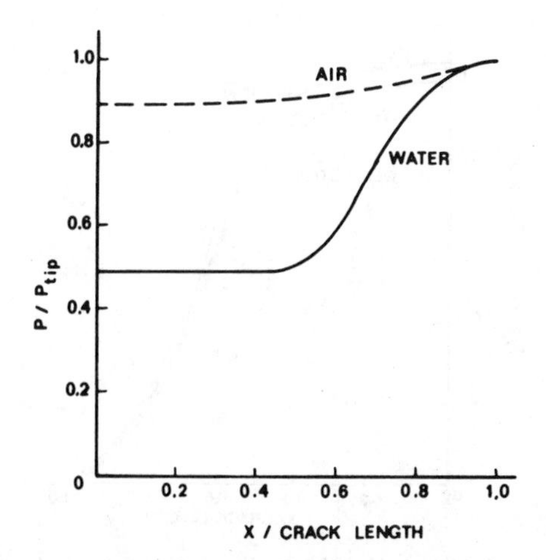

FIG. 6—*Pressure distribution downstream of the crack tip for air and water pressurization computed with the coupled code (using a reduced speed of sound for water)—initial pressure = 11.4 MPa, yield stress = 482.3 MPa.*

surized with water, the sound speed is so high that the pipe depressurizes to the saturation pressure before any significant crack growth can take place, unless the saturation pressure is high or the fracture toughness is low. In order to examine the effect of a strong axial pressure variation on the flaps, the speed of sound of the water was reduced artificially to approximately that of air. Thus, in both cases the wave speed in the fluid was approximately equal to the crack speed.

Figure 6 illustrates the pressure decay behind the crack tip for the two cases at a time for which the cracks are of the same length. The pressure decay for air is small because of the relatively small crack opening (12 percent of the pipe area) and because the outflow is choked. For water, the decay is very rapid and approximately one half of the flap area is at the saturation pressure and the half near the tip has a strongly spatially varying pressure. Because of this rapid pressure reduction for water, the crack driving forces for the two cases are significantly different. However, the crack opening shape for these two cases, as well as for a constant pressure small deflection case are virtually indistinguishable from one another as illustrated on Fig. 7.

In view of the difference in loading, and the difference in small and large deflection theory, this agreement strongly suggests that the flaps are not important in driving the crack, and their dynamic behavior should be amendable to a much simpler model. It must be recognized that the two cases do differ in absolute magnitudes, but not in character. For the conditions shown, the crack tip velocities are 0.136 C_s and 0.108 C_s for air and water, respectively. Previous numerical tests with constant pressures have shown that a nearly linear relationship exists between tip veloc-

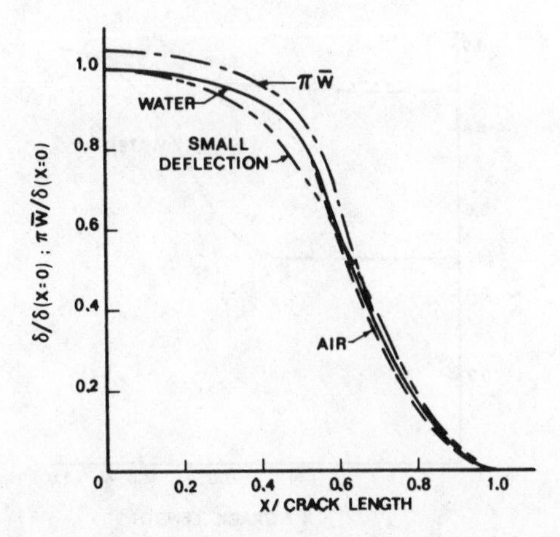

FIG. 7—*Computed and estimated crack opening shape for air and water pressurization.*

ity history and pressure. For these two cases of air and water, the tip velocities are also nearly linear but not with the pipe pressure but with the average pressure over that portion of the flaps between the tip and the inflection point in the curve for δ. This relationship also held for water computations, using the correct speed of sound, in which the entire uncracked pipe was at saturation pressure. Thus while it may not be necessary to model the pressure distributions on the flaps exactly, the pressure on the flaps near the tip does influence the crack motion. Freund [*14*] concluded, from the study of a simpler structural model, that only the total pressure force and its first moment should affect the crack motion. This finding is in agreement with the results shown in Fig. 7.

Kanninen [*10*] suggested that the half crack opening, δ, could be related to the average radial displacement, $\bar{w}$, by $\delta = \pi \bar{w}$. This assumption implied that the shell behind the crack tip is hinging about the side opposite the crack and undergoing no increase in circumferential length. This estimated value of δ is also shown on Fig. 7, and the agreement is excellent. Freund [*14*] pointed up that such an agreement should exist since shells deform in such a way as to minimize the extent of in-plane straining. This condition can be achieved in the cracked pipe by bending and in-plane axial extension, thus permitting the condition wherein $\delta = \pi \bar{w}$. This agreement existed for all crack lengths up to the time at which the crack flap deflections were so large ($\delta \cong a$) that the computations became unstable. Gas line experiments for nonbackfilled pipes [*13*] showed that long cracks had flaps which were scalloped in shape with a periodicity of the undulations of about 0.6 diameter. Just before the numerical predictions become unstable, similar undulations with a period of about 1 diameter began to exist. Unfortunately, it was not possible to carry out the computations to permit further examination of these effects.

Conclusions

The numerical studies for different pressure distributions on the free edges of axial cracks which are extending in a ductile stress field suggest, in agreement with Freund [*14*], that the pressure distributions on the flaps do not appreciably affect the crack's history. Consequently, it may be possible to model the dynamic motion of the flaps in a simpler and more qualitative way based upon Kanninen's suggestion that $\delta = \pi \bar{w}$ over the length of the flaps near the crack tip. By using such a simplified model and noting that the crack history can be well determined by using a constant pressure in the pipe, it appears that the fluid computation may be carried out independently of the structural calculations.

Acknowledgment

The work reported in this paper is sponsored by the Electric Power Research Institute under Contract No. RP231-1-1. The authors wish to thank Drs. C. Chan and A. Gopalakrishnan of the Electric Power Research Institute for their encouragement throughout the course of this research program.

References

[*1*] Emery, A. F., Love, W. J., and Kobayashi, A. S., *Journal of Pressure Vessel Technology,* American Society of Mechanical Engineers, Vol. 98, Feb. 1976, pp. 2–8.
[*2*] Emery, A. F., Love, W. J., and Kobayashi, A. S. "Fracture in Straight Pipes Under Large Deflection Conditions—Part I, Structural Deformations," to be presented at the 1976 IJPVPPME Conference, Mexico City and published in *Transactions,* American Society of Mechanical Engineers.
[*3*] Love, W. J., Emery, A. F., and Kobayashi, A. S. "Fracture in Straight Pipes Under Large Deflection Conditions—Part II, Pipe Pressures," to be presented at the 1976 IJPVPPME Conference, Mexico City and published in *Transactions,* American Society of Mechanical Engineers.
[*4*] Emery, A. F. and Cupps, F. J., "RIBSTEAK: A Computer Program for Calculating the Dynamic Motion of Cylindrical and Conical Shells," Report SLL 197, Sandia Laboratory.
[*5*] Fromm, J., "Numerical Solution of the Navier Stokes Equations at High Reynolds Numbers and the Problem of Discretization of Convective Derivatives," IBM Research Laboratory, San Jose, Calif., 1968.
[*6*] Forester, C. K. and Emery, A. F., *Journal of Computational Physics,* Vol. 10, No. 3, Dec. 1972, pp. 487–502.
[*7*] Roache, P. J., *Computational Fluid Dynamics,* Hermosa Publishers, Albuquerque, N. Mex.
[*8*] Emery, A. F. and Cupps, F. J., "The Finite Difference of the Dynamic Motion of Cylindrical Shells Including the Effect of Rotary Inertia," to be published in *International Journal of Earthquake Engineering and Structural Dynamics.*
[*9*] Richtmeyer, R. D. and Morton, K. W., *Difference Methods for Initial Value Problem,* Interscience, New York, 1967.
[*10*] Kanninen, M. F., Sampath, S. G., and Popelar, C., *Journal of Pressure Vessel Technology, Transactions,* Vol. 98, Feb. 1976, pp. 56–65.

[11] Poynton, W., "A Theoretical Analysis of Shear Fracture Propagation in Backfilled Gas Pipelines," *Symposium On Crack Propagation in Pipelines,* The Institute of Gas Engineers, Newcastle Upon Tyne, England, 1974.
[12] Ives, K. D., Shoemaker, A. K., and McCartney, B. F., "Pipe Deformation During a Running Shear Fracture in Line Pipe," ASME Paper No. 74-Mat-9 presented at the Pressure Vessels and Piping Conference, Miami, Fla., 1974.
[13] Poynton, W. A., Shannon, R. W. E., and Fearnehough, G. D., *Journal of Engineering Materials and Technology,* Oct. 1974, pp. 323–329.
[14] Freund, L. B., Parks, D. M., and Rice, J. R. in *Mechanics of Crack Growth, ASTM STP 590,* American Society for Testing and Materials, 1976, pp. 243–262.

Crack Arrest Determination Using the Double-Cantilever-Beam Specimen

J. F. Kalthoff,[1] *J. Beinert,*[1] *and S. Winkler*[1]

Measurements of Dynamic Stress Intensity Factors for Fast Running and Arresting Cracks in Double-Cantilever-Beam Specimens

REFERENCE: Kalthoff, J. F., Beinert, J., and Winkler, S., **"Measurements of Dynamic Stress Intensity Factors for Fast Running and Arresting Cracks in Double-Cantilever-Beam Specimens,"** *Fast Fracture and Crack Arrest, ASTM STP 627,* G. T. Hahn and M. F. Kanninen, Eds., American Society for Testing and Materials, 1977, pp. 161–176.

ABSTRACT: The influence of dynamic effects on the crack arrest process is investigated. For propagating and subsequently arresting cracks, actual dynamic stress intensity factors were measured applying a shadow optical technique in combination with a Cranz Schardin high-speed camera. The experiments were performed in wedge-loaded double-cantilever-beam (DCB) specimens machined from an epoxy resin (Araldite B). In the initial phase of crack propagation the measured dynamic stress intensity factors were found smaller; in the arresting phase, however, they were larger than the corresponding static values. After arrest the dynamic stress intensity factor oscillates with decreasing amplitude around the static stress intensity factor at arrest. Crack arrest toughness values determined according to a static analysis showed a dependence on the crack velocity prior to arrest, but the dynamic crack arrest toughness yielded a single value only, indicating that this quantity represents a true material property.

KEY WORDS: stress analysis, photoelasticity, crack propagation, crack arrest, fracture criterion, fracture properties

K_I^{stat} Statically determined stress intensity factor
K_I^{dyn} Dynamically determined stress intensity factor
K_{Ia} Crack arrest toughness in general
K_{Ia}^{stat} Statically determined crack arrest toughness
K_{Ia}^{dyn} Dynamically determined crack arrest toughness
K_{Ic} Fracture (initiation) toughness
K_{ID} Fracture toughness for a propagating crack
K_{Iq} Crack initiation stress intensity factor for blunted notches

[1]Physicists, Institut für Festkörpermechanik der Fraunhofer-Gesellschaft, Freiburg, Germany.

The crack initiation concept of fracture mechanics, corroborated by extensive theoretical and experimental investigations, is very well understood. Standardized methods have been developed and are applied successfully under widely different conditions. A crack arrest concept, however, is considerably less well developed, and generally accepted parameters to characterize the crack arrest process have not been established. Two points of view are current.

Crosley and Ripling [*1–3*] [2] assume that dynamic effects can be neglected and postulate that the crack-tip loading in the static condition following crack arrest provides an adequate description of the crack arrest condition. In this static analysis the crack arrest process is considered identical to the initiation process with the time scale being reversed. Dynamic effects (stress waves, structural vibrations) and their possible influences are not considered.

Hahn et al [*4–6*] analyzed the crack arrest process using an energy balance approach and concluded that a consideration of dynamic effects is essential. According to their approach, as the crack accelerates in the initial phase, kinetic energy is built up in the specimen which is subsequently available to contribute to the crack driving force at arrest.

The present investigation was undertaken to study the magnitude of the dynamic effects involved and their influence on the crack arrest process. Thus, actual dynamic stress intensity factors for arresting cracks were measured and compared with the corresponding static values.

Theoretical Implications

The experiments were performed on wedge-loaded double-cantilever-beam (DCB) specimens (Fig. 1). The cracks were initiated from blunted notches at initiation stress intensity factors K_{Iq} larger than the fracture toughness K_{Ic}. For this configuration the arrest process is illustrated for both approaches in Fig. 1. For simplicity the material resistance (in terms of the crack initiation toughness K_{Ic}, the toughness K_{ID} for a propagating crack, and the crack arrest toughness K_{Ia}) is assumed to be constant.

According to the static analysis the crack will arrest when the stress intensity factor K_I^{stat}, determined from the external loading conditions using the conventional static formulae, becomes less than the material resistance at an arrest length a_a^*.

According to the dynamic analysis the fracture behavior should be determined by a dynamic stress intensity factor K_I^{dyn} with the following crack length dependence: At the beginning of the crack propagation phase the dynamic stress intensity factor K_I^{dyn} should be smaller than the corresponding static value K_I^{stat} while at arrest it should be larger. This means

[2] The italic numbers in brackets refer to the list of references appended to this paper.

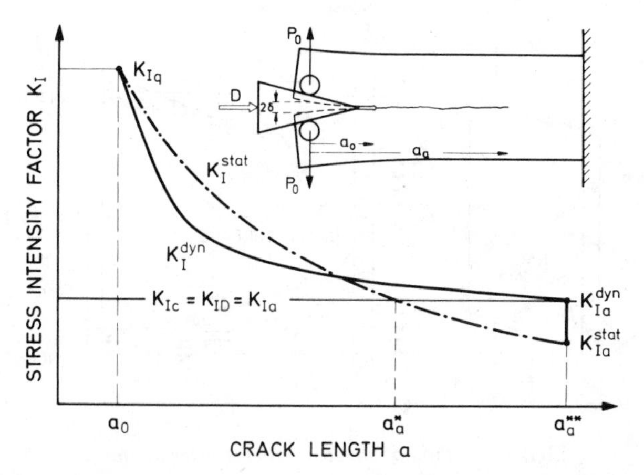

FIG. 1—*Schematic representation of crack arrest in the DCB specimen.*

that a crack can propagate even if K_I^{stat} becomes less than the material resistance. Consequently, an arrest length $a_a{}^{**}$ larger than $a_a{}^{*}$ results.

Crack arrest toughness data usually are evaluated from crack arrest experiments according to a static procedure. From their viewpoint of a dynamic analysis Hahn et al [*4–6*] conclude, therefore, that such statically determined crack arrest toughness values $K_{Ia}{}^{stat}$ are smaller than the true arrest toughness and do not represent a material property. A noncontroversial, exact interpretation of crack arrest experiments requires further knowledge of the actual physical conditions determining the arrest process.

Method of Shadow Patterns

Stress intensity factors for stationary or propagating cracks can be determined experimentally by shadow optical techniques. On this basis Manogg [*7*] developed the "method of shadow patterns" which was later extensively applied by Theocaris [*8*] under the name "method of caustics." The method can be applied in transmission or for nontransparent materials in reflection.

The underlying physical principle of this method is illustrated in Fig. 2. A notched specimen of a transparent material under external load is illuminated by parallel light. A cross section through the specimen at the position of the crack tip is shown on the right hand side of the figure. The stress intensification in the region surrounding the tip of the crack has the following two effects: it reduces the thickness *d* of the plate and alters the refractive index of the material. Consequently the area surrounding the crack tip—to use a very simple description—acts as a divergent lens which deflects the light outwards. This leads to the forma-

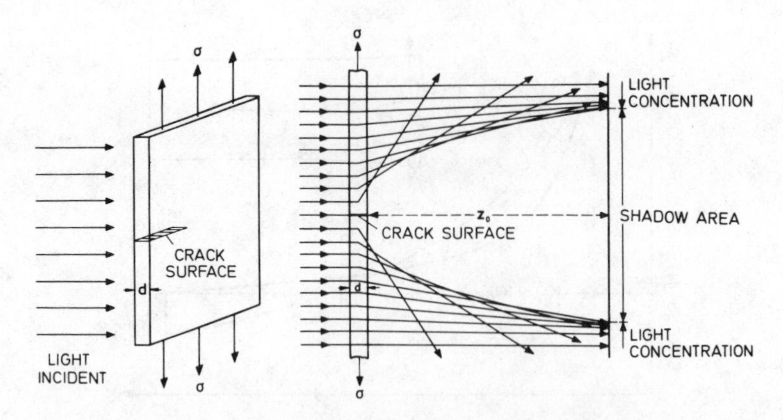

FIG. 2—*Method of shadow patterns after Manogg.*

tion of a shadow pattern bounded by bright light (the caustic) which may be observed on a screen placed behind the specimen. As can be seen from Fig. 2 the boundary between light and dark in this shadow pattern is determined neither by the light incident directly at, nor by that incident remote from the crack tip. Rather it is determined by a ring-shaped region around the crack tip whose radius depends on the distance z_0 between the screen and the specimen.

Assuming a stress distribution around the crack tip given by the Sneddon formula, Manogg calculated the shape of the resulting Mode I shadow pattern. Figure 3 shows the shadow patterns obtained for optically iso-

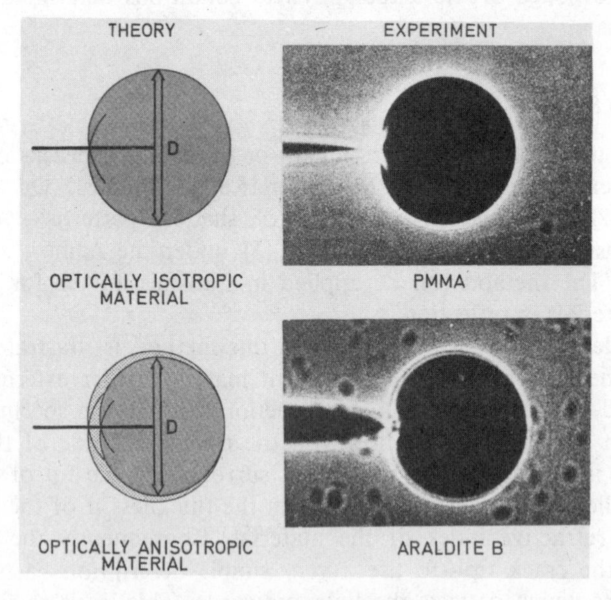

FIG. 3—*Shadow patterns.*

tropic and anisotropic materials compared to those experimentally observed. Good agreement is obtained in both cases. Only one caustic results for isotropic materials, while for anisotropic materials two are obtained. Quantitatively the diameter D of the caustic is a function of the stress intensity factor K_I and is given by

$$K_I = \frac{2\sqrt{2\pi}}{3 f_{o,i}^{5/2} c \cdot d \cdot z_o} D^{5/2}$$

where

K_I = Mode I stress intensity factor,
D = diameter of the caustic,
$f_{o,i}$ = numerical factor for outer/inner caustic,
c = photoelastic constant,
d = thickness of the plate, and
z_o = distance between specimen and image plane.

Table 1 shows numerical values of the factor $f_{o,i}$ and the photoelastic constant c for different materials. As can be seen from these values shadow patterns under plane-strain conditions are considerably smaller than those under plane-stress conditions. Furthermore, the splitting up of the double caustic for anisotropic materials is larger for plane strain than for plane stress. (In the case of Araldite B D_{outer}/D_{inner} = 1.085 for plane stress and 1.141 for plane strain). From the measured separation between the two caustics the actual state of stress of the ring-shaped region in the specimen can be experimentally determined and hence the corresponding $f_{o,i}$ values can be chosen.

Experimental Procedure

DCB specimens measuring 321 by 127 by 10 mm^3 with initial notches of length $a_o \approx 66$ mm were made from an epoxy resin (Araldite B). Araldite B was chosen because of the very small differences between the dynamic and the static material data (Clark and Sanford [9]); the elastic properties are: static (dynamic) Young's modulus E = 3380 (3660) MN/m^2, static (dynamic) Poisson's ratio ν = 0.33 (0.39), longitudinal wave speed ν_1 = 2500 m/s, transverse wave speed ν_2 = 1060 m/s (Soltész [10]). The acuity of the notch tip was varied by extending the notch over an additional short distance using specially prepared jewellers' saws of different thicknesses. The specimen was loaded in a testing machine by forcing a 20-deg wedge between the pins. The deflection 2δ of the beams was measured directly at the loading points using a specially designed clip gage.

Shadow patterns for propagating and subsequently arresting cracks were recorded with a Cranz Schardin high-speed camera. On technical

TABLE 1—*Elastic and shadowoptic constants for several materials.*

	Elastic Constants		Shadowoptic Constants					
			At Plane Stress			At Plane Strain		
Material	Young's Modulus, MN/m^2	Poisson's Ratio	c, m^2/N	f_o	f_i	c, m^2/N	f_o	f_i
Optical anisotropic								
Araldite B	3660	0.392	0.970×10^{-10}	3.31	3.05	0.580×10^{-10}	3.41	2.99
CR-39	2580	0.443	1.200×10^{-10}	3.25	3.10	0.560×10^{-10}	3.33	3.04
Plate Glass	73900	0.231	0.027×10^{-10}	3.43	2.98	0.017×10^{-10}	3.62	2.97
Optical isotropic								
PMMA	3240	0.350	1.080×10^{-10}	3.17		0.750×10^{-10}	3.17	

grounds divergent instead of parallel light was used; the distance between specimen and image plane was 1.4 m. The high-speed camera was triggered by the crack itself which, at the start of propagation, interrupted a laser beam to provide the trigger impulse.

Experimental Results

Cracks initiated at K_{Iq} values varying from 0.74 MN/m$^{3/2}$ to 2.56 MN/m$^{3/2}$ and propagating at velocities ranging from 15 to 320 m/s were investigated. The compressive stresses acting in the longitudinal direction of the specimen generated by the 20-deg wedge were sufficient to achieve straight-line crack propagation in more than 75 percent of all experiments.

Shadow Patterns

A series of shadow patterns photographed for a propagating and subsequently arresting crack is shown in Fig. 4. Only 6 out of the total of 24 pictures are reproduced here. The separation of the double caustic indicates that plane stress applied in all experiments. The center of the caustic marks the actual position of the crack tip. The corresponding crack lengths are given under each photograph.

Quantitative data obtained from such measurements are discussed in the following sections.

Velocity

In order to investigate the crack velocity history prior to arrest actual crack-tip positions are plotted as a function of time in Fig. 5. Only a few experiments, representative of different velocity ranges, are shown. The substantial linear regions at the beginning of the curves indicate constant velocities. As expected these maximum crack velocities v_{max} increase with the initiation value K_{Iq}, that is, with the amount of elastic energy stored in the specimen. Prior to arrest the crack velocity decreases from this maximum constant value (see also Fig. 6).

Dynamic Stress Intensity Factors

For the cracks considered in Fig. 5 stress intensity factors as a function of crack length are shown in the upper part of Fig. 6. Data from Specimens 21 and 35 were obtained under practically identical conditions to those for Specimen 4. The experimental points represent dynamic stress intensity factor values K_I^{dyn} evaluated according to the given equation from the shadow patterns. The very early phase of crack propagation was not investigated. The expected trend, however, is marked by the heavy

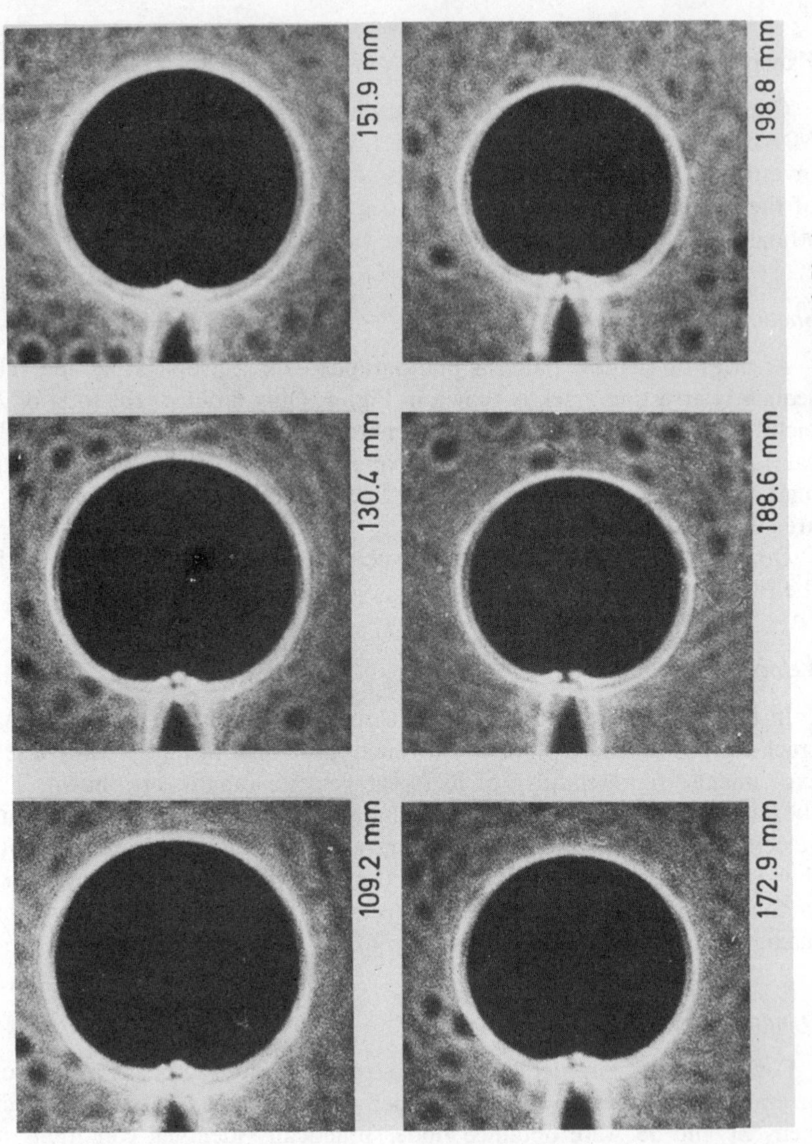

FIG. 4—*Shadow patterns for an arresting crack (picture interval: 73 μs).*

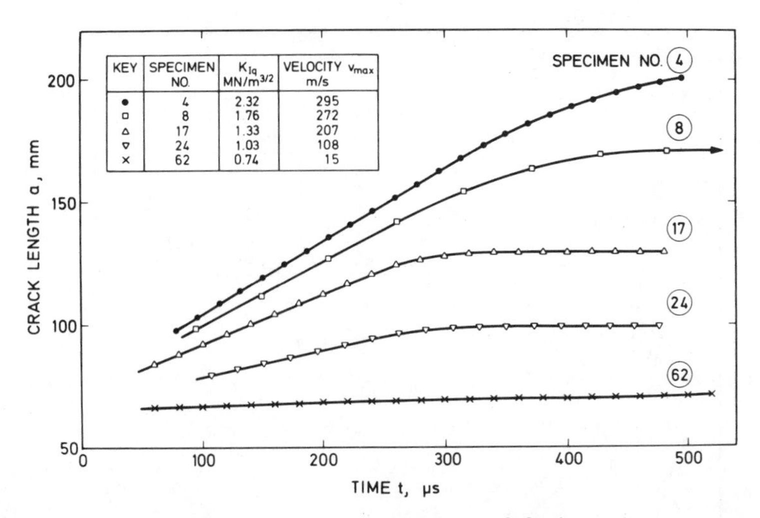

FIG. 5—*Crack propagation and arrest behavior.*

dashed lines. For comparison, curves of the static stress intensity factor K_I^{stat} are shown in the same diagram which were calculated from the measured deflection values 2δ at the loading points using the conventional stress intensity factor formula (Kanninen [*11*]). The crack velocities derived from Fig. 5 are shown in the lower part of Fig. 6. The same results as in Fig. 6, but plotted in a different form, are shown in Fig. 7.

The following characteristics of the crack arrest process can be deduced from these results:

1. At the beginning of the crack propagation phase the dynamic stress intensity factor K_I^{dyn} is smaller than the corresponding static value K_I^{stat}.

2. At the end of the crack propagation phase the dynamic stress intensity factor K_I^{dyn} is larger than the corresponding static value K_I^{stat}.

3. Only after arrest does the dynamic stress intensity factor K_I^{dyn} approach the static stress intensity factor at arrest K_{Ia}^{stat}.

Differences between the dynamic and the static stress intensity factor curves become smaller for cracks propagating at lower maximum velocities v_{max}, that is, the dynamic effects decrease with decreasing velocity as one might expect. Thus, for example, in Specimen 62 in which the crack propagated at a maximum velocity of only 15 m/s the dynamic stress intensity factors K_I^{dyn} scatter closely around the static curve K_I^{stat}. In fact, within the accuracy of the experimental technique both curves practically fall together, indicating that in this case dynamic effects were negligibly small.

The crack behavior subsequent to arrest was also investigated. In experiment No. 8 a relatively long time interval was selected between consecutive pictures which meant that the crack was photographed long after it had arrested. The results show that the dynamic stress intensity factor

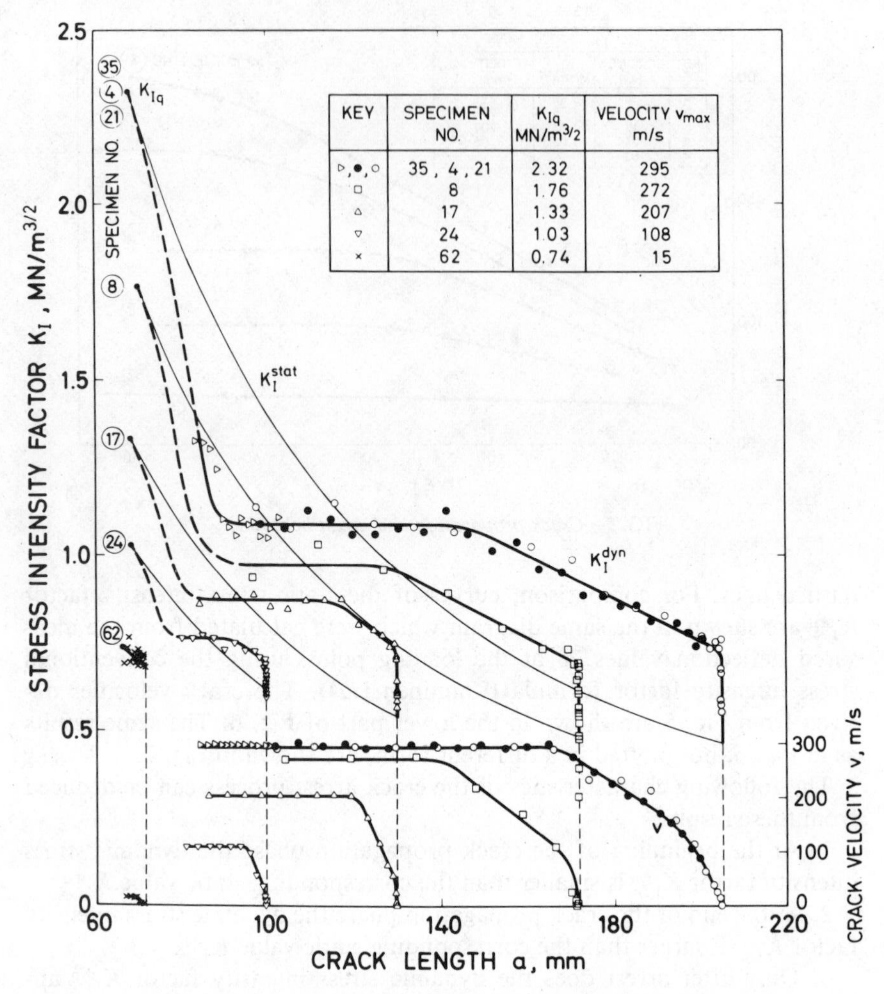

FIG. 6—*Stress intensity factors for arresting cracks.*

K_I^{dyn} decreases to less than the static stress intensity factor at arrest K_{Ia}^{stat} (Fig. 6) but subsequently increases again—which of course does not show up in this diagram. In order to analyse this behavior, measurements were carried out with triggering delay times larger than the crack propagation time. Results of two experiments, plotted as a function of time in Fig. 8, show a damped oscillation of the dynamic stress intensity factor K_I^{dyn} around the static value at arrest K_{Ia}^{stat}. The frequency of this oscillation has the same order of magnitude as that of a vibration of a cantilever beam corresponding to one half of the cracked specimen.

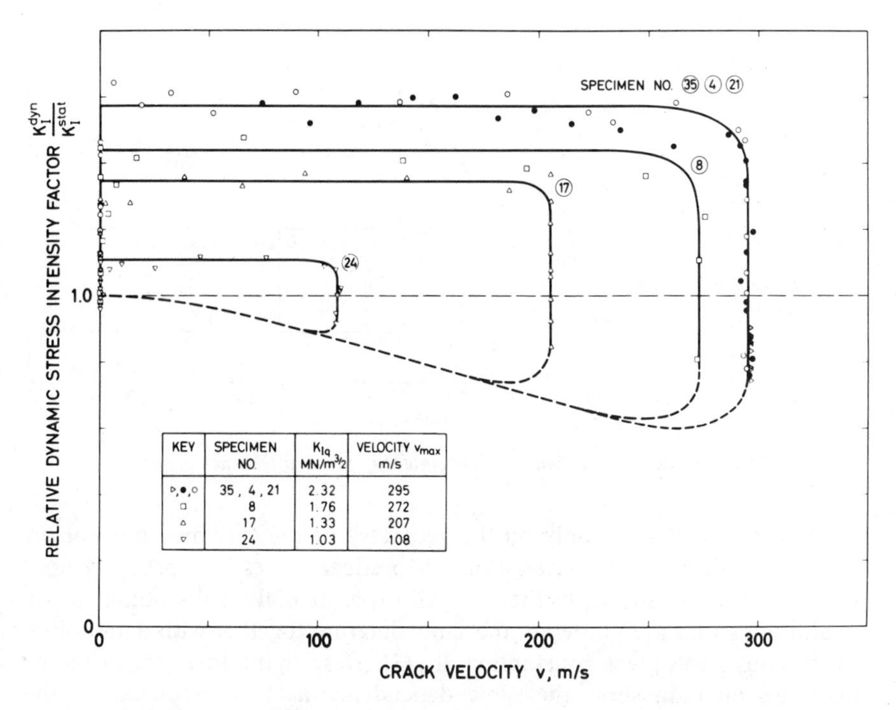

FIG. 7—*Normalized dynamic stress intensity factor for arresting cracks.*

Toughness Data

Crack arrest toughness values were determined from the experimental data and are shown in Fig. 9 together with the stress intensity factor curves of Fig. 6. The points $K_{Ia}{}^{stat}$ (full rhombi) are the crack arrest toughness values determined from the static analysis. These values depend on the crack velocities prior to arrest; the faster the crack the smaller the toughness value. The observed dynamic stress intensity factor at the moment of arrest represents the dynamically determined crack arrest toughness value which we have denoted $K_{Ia}{}^{dyn}$ (large open circles). These values are larger than the corresponding static values; furthermore, they scatter around a horizontal line and obviously—at least as these data show—do not depend on the crack velocity. The dashed line in the figure represents the average value of the initiation toughness K_{Ic} determined on CT specimens to be $K_{Ic} = 0.79 \pm 0.13$ MN/m$^{3/2}$.

Crack Velocity—Crack Length Relation

The theoretical calculations by Hahn et al [*6*] and by Shmuely [*12*] predict a unique relation between the length of the crack at arrest and crack

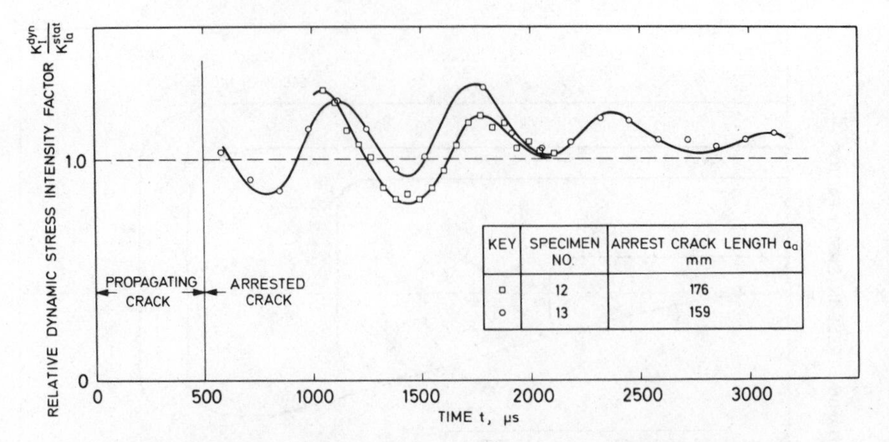

FIG. 8—*Oscillating dynamic stress intensity factor after crack arrest.*

velocity which depends only on the geometry of the specimen but not on the toughness of the material. Both theoretical curves in a properly normalized form are shown in Fig. 10. All experimental results obtained for Araldite B so far are plotted in the same diagram together with data points for various steels given by Hahn et al [*13*]. Despite the two very different materials all data show the same dependence as that predicted by the theoretical calculations.

Discussion and Conclusions

A shadow optical method for determining stress intensity factors has been described and applied to dynamically propagating and subsequently arresting cracks. A relation between the diameter D of the caustic and the stress intensity factor K_I was used, which was derived under the assumption of a static solution for the stress-strain field around the tip of a crack. An exact formula for propagating cracks of course requires the dynamic stress distribution ahead of the crack tip. Such a relation is currently being worked on by the authors. For the crack velocity range investigated, however, only small discrepancies are expected. This is supported by the fact that the shape of the caustic for a propagating crack differs insignificantly little from that for a stationary crack.

According to the method described actual dynamic stress intensity factors were measured for cracks before, at, and after arrest. At the beginning of the crack propagation phase, these values were found to be smaller than the corresponding static values, while at the end they were larger. This result agrees essentially with the predictions based on the theoretical results of Hahn et al [*4–6*] derived from their concept of recovered kinetic energy. Stress waves, carrying with them kinetic energy, emanate from

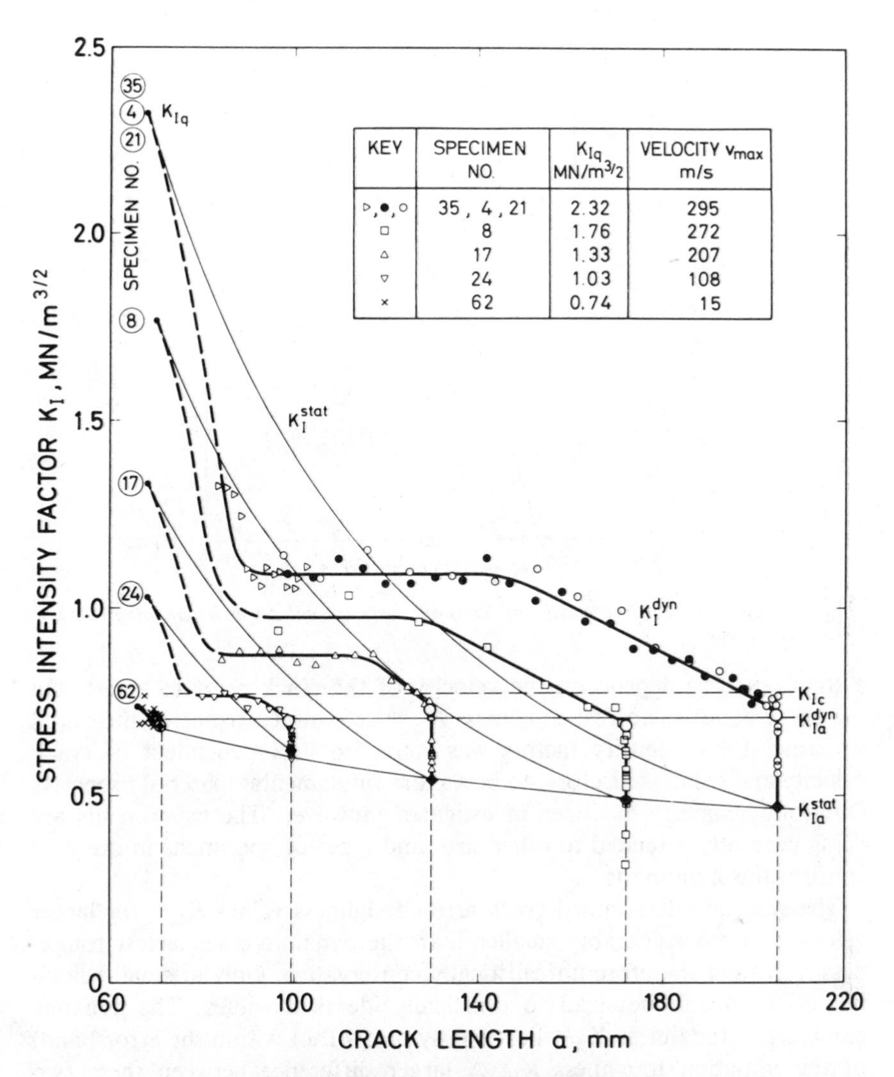

FIG. 9—*Crack arrest toughness values.*

the tip of the propagating crack and after being reflected at the finite boundaries of the specimen, contribute to the actual dynamic stress intensity factor characterizing the true stress intensification around the crack tip. The physical implications of these stress waves are demonstrated clearly by the observed oscillation of the dynamic stress intensity factor long after arrest.

The influence of these dynamic effects on the crack arrest process also manifests itself in the crack arrest toughness values evaluated from the experimental data. Crack arrest toughness values K_{Ia}^{stat} determined using

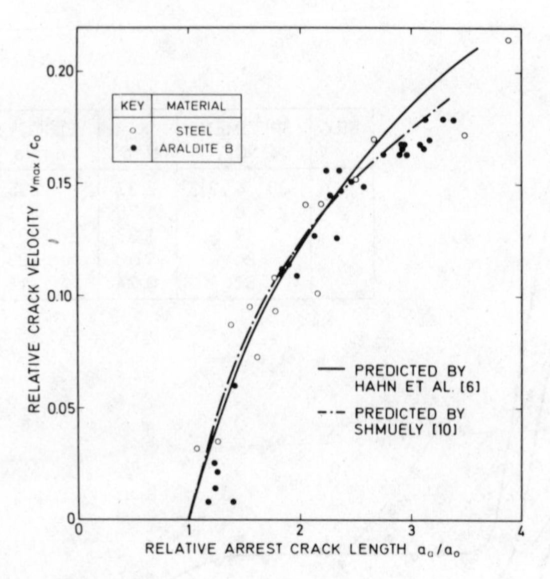

FIG. 10—*Relation between maximum constant velocity and crack length at arrest* (c_0 = *bar wave speed*).

a static analysis depend on the velocity of the crack prior to arrest. On the other hand, the arrest toughness K_{Ia}^{dyn} determined from the measured dynamic stress intensity factors was found to be independent of crack velocity and seems, therefore, to be a more fundamental material property. Only one geometry has been investigated, however. The experiments are being currently extended to other sizes and types of specimens in order to confirm this hypothesis.

The statically determined crack arrest toughness values K_{Ia}^{stat} for larger velocities are considerably smaller than the dynamic crack arrest toughness K_{Ia}^{dyn} and therefore unrealistically conservative. Only at small velocities do both analyses lead to practically identical values. The dynamic crack arrest toughness K_{Ia}^{dyn} lies slightly below (but within the error band) of the initiation toughness K_{Ic}. A larger difference between these two values is expected for more strain rate sensitive materials.

Various theoretical predictions are given in the literature for dynamic stress intensity factors K_I^{dyn} of propagating cracks in infinite media. Values calculated by Broberg [*14*], Freund [*15*], Nilsson [*16*], and others are less than the corresponding static stress intensity factors K_I^{stat} and decrease with increasing crack velocity. The experimental data of Fig. 7 show that these results—because of the effect of reflected stress waves—do not apply for decelerating cracks in finite specimens. Dynamic stress intensity factors larger than static values were also observed experimentally by Bradley and Kobayashi [*17*] and predicted theoretically for arresting cracks in strips of finite height by Nilsson [*18*].

The reported crack arrest data in Araldite B support the theoretically predicted existence of a material independent unique relation between crack arrest lengths and crack velocities. This correlation indicates the possibility of basing crack arrest safety predictions on inexpensive model experiments.

The results presented give experimental evidence that for fast propagating cracks in DCB specimens dynamic effects have an influence on the crack arrest process. The effects have to be considered in determining crack arrest toughness values and in applying a crack arrest safety analysis.

Acknowledgment

The authors are grateful to A. Wolf for his skillful experimental assistance. The work was funded by the Bundesministerium für Forschung und Technologie of the Federal Republic of Germany.

References

[1] Crosley, P. B. and Ripling, E. J., *Journal of Basic Engineering, Transactions,* American Society of Mechanical Engineers, Series D, Vol. 91, Sept. 1969, pp. 525–534.
[2] Crosley, P. B. and Ripling, E. J., *Nuclear Engineering and Design,* Vol. 17, No. 1, Aug. 1971, pp. 32–45.
[3] Crosley, P. B. and Ripling, E. J., *Proceedings,* Second International Conference on Pressure Vessel Technology, San Antonio, Tex., American Society of Mechanical Engineers, Oct. 1973, pp. 995–1005.
[4] Hahn, G. T., Hoagland, R. G., Kanninen, M. F., and Rosenfield, A. R. in *Dynamic Crack Propagation,* G. C. Sih, Ed., Lehigh University, Bethlehem, Pa., July 1972, Noordhoff International Publishing, Leyden, The Netherlands, Part VII, pp. 649–662.
[5] Hahn, G. T., Hoagland, R. G., Kanninen, M. F., and Rosenfield, A. R., *Proceedings,* Second International Conference on Pressure Vessel Technology, San Antonio, Tex., American Society of Mechanical Engineers, Oct. 1973, pp. 981–994.
[6] Hahn, G. T., Hoagland, R. G., Kanninen, M. F., Rosenfield, A. R., and Sejnoha, R., "Fast Fracture Resistance and Crack Arrest in Structural Steels," SSC-Progress Report on Project SR-201, Battelle Columbus Laboratories, Columbus, Ohio, 1973.
[7] Manogg, P., *Proceedings,* International Conference on the Physics of Non-Crystalline Solids, Delft, The Netherlands, 1964, pp. 481–490.
[8] Theocaris, P. S., *Journal of the Mechanics and Physics of Solids,* Vol. 20, No. 4, July 1972, pp. 265–279.
[9] Clark, A. B. J. and Sanford, R. J., *Experimental Mechanics,* Vol. 3, No. 6, June 1963, pp. 148–151.
[10] Soltész, U., Report 7/73 of the Institut für Festkörpermechanik, Freiburg, Germany, 1973.
[11] Kanninen, M. F., *International Journal of Fracture,* Vol. 9, No. 1, March 1973, pp. 83–92.
[12] Shmuely, M., "Analysis of Fast Fracture and Crack Arrest by Finite Differences," to be published in *International Journal of Fracture,* 1977.
[13] Hahn, G. T., Gehlen, P. C., Hoagland, R. G., Kanninen, M. F. Popelar, C., and Rosenfield, A. R., Fourth Quarterly Progress Report, Task 62, BMI-1939, Battelle Columbus Laboratories, Columbus, Ohio, Nov. 1975.
[14] Broberg, B., *Arkiv för Fysik,* Vol. 18, 1960, pp. 152–192.

[15] Freund, L. B., *Journal of the Mechanics and Physics of Solids,* Vol. 20, No. 3, May 1972, pp. 129–140 and 141–152.
[16] Nilsson, F., *International Journal of Fracture,* Vol. 8, No. 4, Dec. 1972, pp. 403–411.
[17] Bradley, W. B. and Kobayashi, A. S., *Experimental Mechanics,* Vol. 10, No. 3, March 1970, pp. 106–133.
[18] Nilsson, F., "Sudden Arrest of Steadily Moving Cracks," Rapport 18, Division of Strength of Materials and Solid Mechanics, The Royal Institute of Technology, Stockholm, Sweden, 1976.

R. G. Hoagland,[1] *A. R. Rosenfield,*[1] *P. C. Gehlen,*[1] *and G. T. Hahn*[1]

A Crack Arrest Measuring Procedure for K_{Im}, K_{ID}, and K_{Ia} Properties

REFERENCE: Hoagland, R. G., Rosenfield, A. R., Gehlen, P. C., and Hahn, G. T., "**A Crack Arrest Measuring Procedure for K_{Im}, K_{ID}, and K_{Ia} Properties,**" *Fast Fracture and Crack Arrest, ASTM STP 627,* G. T. Hahn and M. F. Kanninen, Eds., American Society for Testing and Materials, 1977, pp. 177–202.

ABSTRACT: New developments are described which offer a flexible procedure for measuring the fracture resistance values, K_{Im}, K_{ID}, and K_{Ia} which characterize the crack arrest behavior of materials. The procedure relies on a dynamically stiff, wedge-loading which limits dynamic energy exchanges between the test specimen and the testing machine. This makes it possible to interpret both small and large crack jumps without recourse to crack velocity measurements. The procedure is general and can be applied to ordinary and duplex rectangular and contoured double-cantilever-beam (DCB) specimens, and to compact and single-edge-notched (SEN) specimens when dynamic analyses for these shapes become available. The paper examines the virtues of the different specimen configurations, size and thickness requirements, possible upper and lower bounds on the size of the crack jump, and the problem of branching and side grooves. Measurements of specimen machine interactions are described. Results obtained for A533B steel with a series of rectangular DCB specimens illustrate the dependence of K_{Ia} on the size of the crack jump as well as the previously proposed relations between K_{Ia} and K_{Im} or K_{ID}. The results confirm that the K_{Im} (or K_{ID}) values obtained with the new procedure from static measurements of load point displacement and the crack length at arrest agree with values derived from crack velocity measurements. The experiments also illustrate that duplex DCB specimens with modest dimensions (400 by 140 by 50 mm) have the capacity for measuring K_{Im} and K_{ID} values in excess of 150 MPa·m$^{1/2}$.

KEY WORDS: crack propagation crack arrest, fractures (materials), fracture properties, fracture strength, fast fracture, crack velocity, cantilever beams, steels

Nomenclature

- B Specimen thickness
- B_n Net specimen thickness at the side grooves
- DCB Double cantilever beam

[1]Principal researchers, senior researcher, and manager, respectively, Battelle Columbus Laboratories, Columbus, Ohio 43201.

$\mathcal{G}$ Energy release rate
$\mathcal{G}_I$ Mode I energy release rate
H Beam height of specimen
K_a Stress intensity at arrest calculated assuming static equilibrium
K_c Critical stress intensity parameter for crack extension
K_D Propagating crack toughness ($K_D = \sqrt{ER_D/1 - \nu^2}$)
$K_{D,S}$ K_D of starter section
$K_{D,T}$ K_D of test section
$K_D(\Delta a_T)$ Propagating crack toughness for crack jump length in test section of Δa_T
$K_D(\bar{V})$ Propagating crack toughness for crack velocity $\bar{V}$
$\bar{K}_D$ K_D determined from energy balance
K_Q Stress intensity at crack initiation in blunt-notched DCB specimen
K_I Mode I stress intensity parameter
K_{Ia} Mode I K_a
K_{Ic} Mode I K_c
K_{ID} Mode I K_D
K_{Im} Minimum value of K_{ID}
NDT Nil ductility temperature
RTNDT Reference temperature nil ductility temperature
P Pin load
R_D Fracture energy (per unit crack area)
R_{ID} Mode I propagating crack fracture energy
R_{Im} Minimum value of R_{ID}
$R_{ID}(V)$ Velocity dependence of R_{ID}
V Crack velocity
$\bar{V}$ Average crack velocity
V_m Crack velocity associated with K_{Im}
a Crack length
a_o Initial crack length
Δa_T Crack length in test section
Δa_s Crack length in starter section
w Specimen width dimension (parallel to crack line)
σ_Y Yield stress
σ_{YD} Dynamic yield stress
ν Poisson's ratio

The criterion for crack arrest can be expressed simply in terms of the crack driving force and the minimum fracture resistance either in terms of energy or stress intensity[2]

[2]The crack driving force can be expressed either in terms of the energy release rate $\mathcal{G}_I$ or the stress intensity parameter K_I; the minimum fracture resistance in terms of the minimum

$$\mathcal{G}_{\mathrm{I}} < R_{\mathrm{I}m} \quad (1)$$

$$K_{\mathrm{I}} < K_{\mathrm{I}m} \quad (2)$$

By applying this criterion to calculations of the driving force and measurements of the resistance, it becomes possible to predict whether and where a running crack in a structure will arrest. Alternatively, the analysis can be used to design a crack arrester or to evaluate the fracture resistance from an instrumented run-arrest event in a laboratory specimen. The latter step is important because the quantity $K_{\mathrm{I}m}$ does not necessarily correspond with K_{Ic}, the resistance to the onset of crack extension.

Actual quantitative treatments of these concepts present difficulties. Rigorous calculations for structures or specimens with finite dimensions require a fully dynamic analysis of K_{I} along the lines discussed by Kanninen, Popelar, and Gehlen [*1*].[3] In this case, the value of K_{I} at arrest depends on the fracture resistance experienced along the entire-crack path—a resistance that can vary with crack velocity [*2-4*]. For this reason, the material property governing crack arrest length is not simple $K_{\mathrm{I}m}$, but the portion of the $K_{\mathrm{I}D}$ crack velocity curve sampled during the run arrest event. Examples of possible $K_{\mathrm{I}D}$ crack velocity curves are given in Fig. 1.

The difficulties of carrying out dynamic analyses and measuring $K_{\mathrm{I}D}$ values at different velocities are compounded by the complex shapes and large fracture resistance values of engineering structures [*5*]. For example, the fracture resistance values that enter the assessment of crack arrest in heavy walled nuclear pressure vessels are estimated to be $K_{\mathrm{I}D} \gtrsim 150$ MPa·m$^{1/2}$ [*6*]. The measurement of the $K_{\mathrm{I}D}$ crack velocity curve at this level of toughness with conventional ASTM Test for Plane-Strain Fracture Toughness of Metallic Materials (E 399-74) method would call for very large

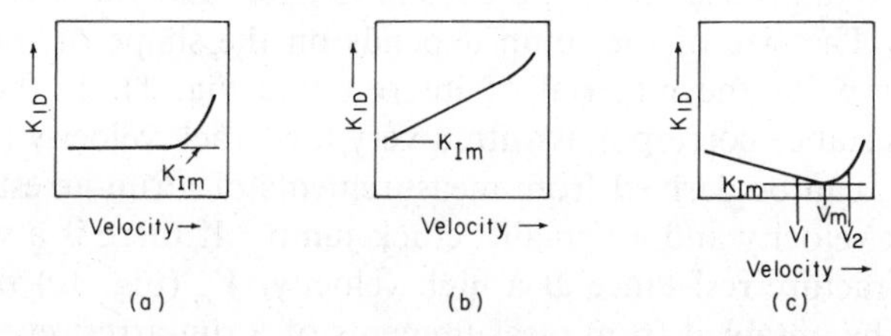

FIG. 1—*Possible fracture resistance* (K_{ID}) *crack velocity curves:* (a) *and* (b) *are examples where the minimum resistance* K_{Im} *corresponds with zero velocity, and* (c) *where* K_{Im} *corresponds with a high velocity.*

energy, $R_{\mathrm{I}m}$, of the variation of propagating crack fracture energy ($R_{\mathrm{I}D}$) with crack velocity, or the minimum toughness $K_{\mathrm{I}m}$ of the variation of propagating crack toughness ($K_{\mathrm{I}D}$) with crack velocity. The quantities $\mathcal{G}_{\mathrm{I}}$ and K_{I} and $R_{\mathrm{I}D}$ and $K_{\mathrm{I}D}$ are closely related (see list of symbols) and can be used interchangeably to express the driving force and resistance. To simplify the presentation, stress intensity values are used whenever practical in this paper.

[3]The italic numbers in brackets refer to the list of references appended to this paper.

specimens (comparable to 10T-15T compact specimens) as well as instrumentation to measure the crack velocity.

Simpler methods of analysis and testing will make it easier to use crack arrest concepts in practice. With this in mind, Irwin [7] has proposed that engineering calculations employ K_{Im} in place of the K_{ID} crack velocity curve. The substitution tends to understate the fracture resistance and is conservative. It will simplify calculations. It can also substantially reduce the number of K_{ID} determinations needed to characterize a material, and may eliminate the need for crack velocity measurements.

This paper describes new developments which offer a flexible procedure for measuring K_{Im}, K_{ID}, and K_{Ia} values. The procedure relies on a dynamically stiff, wedge loading arrangement which limits dynamic energy exchanges between the test specimen and the testing machine. This makes it possible to interpret both small and large crack jumps without recourse to crack velocity measurements. Results obtained for A533B steel with a series of rectangular DCB specimens confirm the viability of the new procedure and illustrate the relations among K_{Ia}, K_{Im} (or K_{ID}), and the size of the crack jump. The paper also touches on the virtues of different specimen shapes, specimen size and thickness requirements, possible upper and lower bounds on the size of the crack jump, and the problems of branching and side grooves. The large reduction in specimen size that can be achieved with duplex specimens is also demonstrated.

Specimen Configuration

Specimen Shape

The main factors affecting the choice of specimen shape are the size of the crack jump that must be accommodated and the stability of the crack path. The size of the jump depends on the shape of the K_{ID} crack velocity curve for the material of interest (see Fig. 1). If the minimum fracture resistance corresponds with a very low crack velocity (Fig. 1*a* and *b*), then K_{Im} can be derived from measurements of a run-arrest event with a low crack velocity and a "small" crack jump.[4] If there is a well defined minimum fracture resistance at a high velocity, V_m (Fig. 1*c*) then the K_{Im} value must be obtained from measurements of a run-arrest event embodying a velocity close to V_m and a "large" crack jump. For stiff, wedge loading and a given volume of test material the rectangular DCB shape accommodates the largest crack jump; the compact specimen is intermediate; and the single-edge-notched-bend (SENB) is least efficient of material in this respect (Fig. 2). The contoured DCB shape (Fig. 2*e*) has a slightly smaller K_{Im} measurement capacity than the rectangular DCB

[4]The crack velocity and the extent of the crack jump usually vary directly [*8–12*].

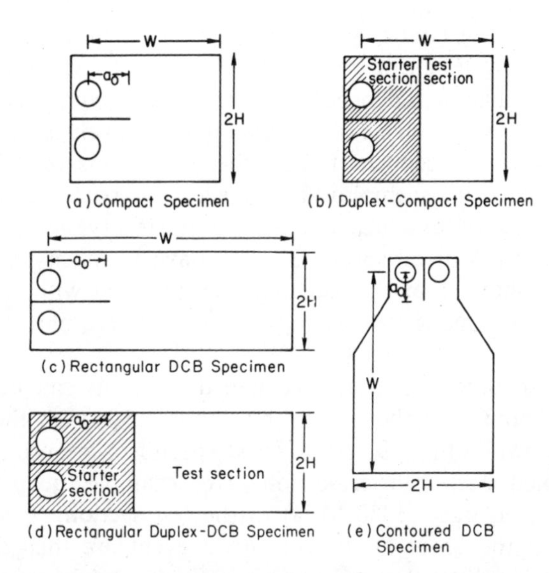

FIG. 2—*Schematic drawings of possible crack arrest specimens. The starter sections of duplex specimens are made of a hardened steel electron beam welded to the test section. The starting crack in duplex specimens is purposely blunted to obtain high* K_Q *values, and this eliminates the need for fatigue precracking.*

shape, and the contoured DCB shape offers no special advantage when K values are derived from displacement measurements under wedge loading. Another factor influencing shape is the tendency for the crack path to deviate from the axis of symmetry causing the arm of the specimen to break off before the crack can arrest. This tendency is strong in DCB specimens with small H/a ratios (see Fig. 2) and essentially absent in compact and single-edge-notch (SEN) geometry. The problem of crack path stability is currently overshadowed by the strong tendency for cracks to branch in A533B [*9,10,13*] and other lower strength grades [*11*], and this is discussed in a following paragraph. At this writing it is not yet clear whether the larger H/a ratio of the compact specimen suppresses branching. Deep side grooves are one device for restricting both branching and crack path instabilities that can be applied to both the compact and DCB geometry.

Size and Thickness Requirements

The K_{Im} measuring capacity of the specimens in Fig. 2 is limited by the onset of large-scale plasticity for the types of analysis discussed in this paper. The dimensions of the specimen, therefore, must remain large relative to those of the crack-tip plastic zone, which are a function of $(K_Q/\sigma_Y)^2$, where K_Q is the stress intensity at the onset of the run-arrest event and σ_Y is the (static) yield stress of the material surrounding the tip of the starting notch or crack. The K_Q value must be about 10 to 30 percent larger than K_{Im} depending on the crack jump distance requirement. Table 1 lists estimates of the maximum K_Q values that can be produced in different specimens having the yield stress of A533B steel, σ_Y = 500 MPa, which is employed in nuclear pressure vessels. Since the resistance values of practical interest for nuclear vessels are $K_{Im} \gtrsim 150$ MPa·m$^{1/2}$ [6], crack arrest specimens must have a capacity $K_Q \gtrsim 200$ MPa·m$^{1/2}$. Table 1 shows that this can only be obtained with extremely large conventional specimens (for example, a 600 by 720-mm compact specimen).

Table 1 also illustrates that specimen dimensions can be dramatically reduced by about ×7, the volume by about ×50, with the duplex configuration shown in Fig. 2*b* and *d*. These specimens are produced by welding a hardened steel "starter section" (for example, quenched and tempered 4340 steel, σ_Y = 1380 MPa) to the test section. Specimen size requirements at the onset of the run arrest event are then determined by the yield stress of the "starter section." Figure 3*a* shows an example of a 140 by 400 by 50.4-mm rectangular, AISI 4340/A533B duplex DCB specimen (No. DA-21) with two 15-mm-deep 45-deg side grooves which was successfully tested at −11°C (NDT + 18°C). A K_Q = 287 MPa·m$^{1/2}$ was applied without large-scale yielding, and this produced a 164-mm-long run-arrest event with a velocity of 690 ms^{-1} and K_D = 132 MPa·m$^{1/2}$ in the test section. A closeup of the arrested crack front, revealed by heat tinting followed by breaking off the arm is shown in Fig. 3*b*. The experience of the authors is that duplex specimens of this type are more costly to produce than ordinary specimens of the same size, but this is more than offset by the savings attending the reduction in size, and the elimination of the fatigue precracking step. Furthermore 600-mm-thick pressure vessel material is neither available nor representative with respect to microstructure.

The size and thickness requirements of the test section while the crack is running are reduced substantially because they depend on the ratio $(K_{ID}/\sigma_{YD})^2$ where $\sigma_{YD} \approx 2\,\sigma_Y$, is the dynamic yield stress of the test section appropriate for the high strain rate, for example, $\dot{\epsilon} > 10^5$ s^{-1}, existing within the running crack-tip plastic zone. This is borne out by results summarized in Fig. 4, which show the effect of specimen thickness on K_D values. The lack of a significant thickness dependence is interpreted as evidence that plane-strain conditions exist in all but one case. In terms of static yield strength the plane-strain thickness requirement for fast running cracks in A533B, inferred from these measurements is

$$B > 0.3 \left(\frac{K_{ID}}{\sigma_Y}\right)^2 \approx 0.3 \left(\frac{K_{Im}}{\sigma_Y}\right)^2 \tag{4}$$

TABLE 1—*Estimates of limiting* K_Q *values for various crack arrest specimens.*

Specimen Design	Ordinary[a] or Duplex	Specimen Dimensions, mm			K_Q (max), $MPa \cdot m^{-1/2}$		
		w	$2H$	a	No Side Groove	25% Side Groove	60% Side Groove
3T-compact[b]	ordinary	150	180	50	90	104	142
15T-compact[b]	ordinary	750	900	250	201	232	317
3T-compact[b]	duplex	150	180	50	250	289	395
Rectangular DCB[c]	duplex	380	140	83	250	300	411
Contoured DCB[c]	ordinary	284	101.6[d]	37.9	92	106	145

[a]The dimensions are calculated for a test material with a yield strength σ_Y = 500 MPa; the calculations for duplex specimens assume σ_Y, starter section = 1380 MPa.

[b]The dimension controlling the onset of yielding in the compact specimen is $(w - a)$. The limit load is $P_L = 0.172\, \sigma_Y Bw$, and $K_Q = 3.5P/Bw^{1/2}(1 - a/w)^{-1.5}$ [14,15]. Consequently the limiting dimension is $(w - a) \geq 2.8\,(K_Q/\sigma_Y)^2$.

[c]The dimension controlling the onset of yielding in a rectangular DCB specimen is $H \geq 1.5\, B_n/B\,(K_Q/\sigma_Y)^2$ [16]. For duplex specimens a slightly more conservative value $H \geq 2.0\, B_n/B\,(K_Q/\sigma_Y$, starter section$)^2$ is recommended.

[d]Linearly increasing to 203.2 mm at a = 127 mm.

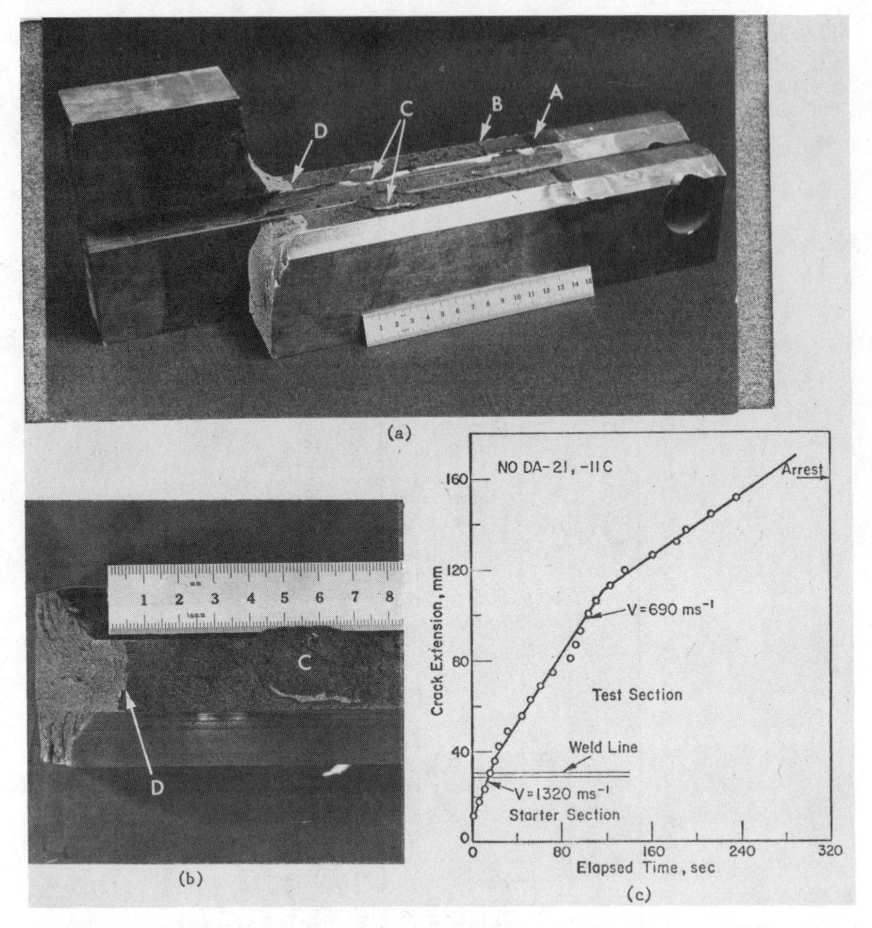

(*a*) Specimen after heat tinting fracture surface dark and breaking open at −78°C to expose fracture surface.
(*b*) Closeup of arrested crack front.
(*c*) Measurement of crack position versus time derived from resistance grid.

FIG. 3—*Example of an AISI 4340/A533B duplex DCB specimen* (*No. DA-21*) *tested at* −*11°C. The photographs show the position of the starting slot* (A), *weld line* (B), *knot-like perturbation* (C) *and unbroken ligament* (*untinted region near* (C) *caused by branching attempt and arrested crack front* (D). *Note that the reduction in crack velocity observed after about 120 mm of crack travel corresponds with the branching attempt* (C). *Additional test data can be found in Table 2.*

which is an order of magnitude smaller than ASTM Method E 399-74 requirement for essentially stationary cracks. Accordingly, the minimum thickness required to measure $K_{Im} \geq 150$ MPa·m$^{1/2}$ for A533B (σ_Y = 500 MPa) is $B \geq 27$ mm. Note that the quantity B stands for the full thickness of side grooved plates as opposed to the remaining ligament width B_n.

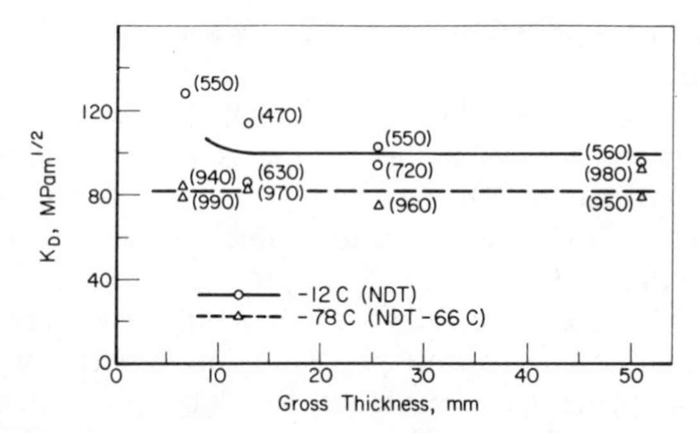

FIG. 4—*Effect of gross specimen thickness on* K_D *for A533B (BCL Plate) at −78°C and −12°C. Numbers in parenthesis are average crack velocity values.*

Crack Jump Length

The size of the crack jump needed for a meaningful, plane-strain resistance evaluation affects the size of the specimen and the choice of analytical approach. This is a separate consideration, first because the entire run arrest event does not proceed with a plane-strain crack front, second, because the analysis of the crack length at arrest provides a weighted average of the resistance along the crack path, and third, because materials are not completely homogeneous.

Crack arrest events occur in several stages:

Stage (i)—In ordinary specimens the initial extension proceeds from a point along the precrack front and gradually develops into the straight-fronted crack that is characteristic of plane-strain propagation (Fig. 5). As noted by Irwin [7], resistance during this period may depart from the plane-strain value. Figure 5 illustrates schematically that the extent of Stage (i) is comparable to the net specimen thickness B_n.

Stage (ii)—In the second stage the crack propagates with a plane-strain front. However, even here the resistance of anything but a homogeneous material will vary along the crack path, and the crack may arrest prematurely when it encounteres an atypical tough region. The measured

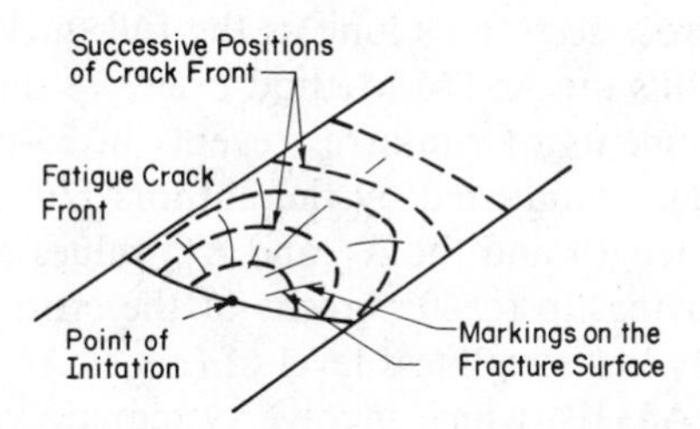

FIG. 5—*Schematic representation of stage* (i) *of run-arrest event based on fracture surface observations and crack velocity measurements.*

resistance will be more representative of an average as the crack samples more material.

Stage (*o*)—In duplex specimens, the crack first propagates through the starter section and the weld (the fushion zone is ~ 3 mm wide) before entering the test material. It may then experience Stages (i) and (ii). The fracture segment in the starter section, which is about 30 mm in the rectangular duplex DCB specimen shown in Fig. 4, is designed to contain the crack-tip plastic zone existing at the onset of the run arrest event.

Since the aim of crack arrest procedures is to obtain a representative measure of the plane-strain resistance, the Stage (ii) extension must be a significant fraction of the total jump in the test material.[5] It must also represent enough propagation, in absolute terms, to provide an adequate sampling. In view of the extent of Stage (i) a minimum jump requirement of $2B_n$ may not be unreasonable. For the 50-mm-thick duplex DCB specimen, this corresponds to a total jump size of from 70 to 130 mm depending on the depth of side grooves. As noted earlier and illustrated in the next section, jumps of this size do not lend themselves to a static K_{Ia} analysis but require the dynamic analysis approach discussed in the next section.

Side Grooves and Crack Branching

Side grooves that reduce the cross section of the specimen along the crack path can facilitate crack arrest measurements in a number of ways. As shown in Table 1, the side grooves increase the K_Q values, and thereby also the K_{Im} measuring capacity. Side grooves inhibit shear lip formation [*17*]. Finally, they tend to stabilize the crack path and, when deep enough, restrict branching (Fig. 6). These benefits are not without complications. The side grooves produce out-of-plane stresses and strains that gives the stress field of the propagating crack a three-dimensional character. This contribution is reflected in the shape of the arrested crack front in Fig. 3 which shows the crack front leading slightly (1 to 2 mm) at the side grooves. A number of systematic studies of the effect of side groove depth on K_{Ic} and K_{ID} measurements have been reported [*10,18–21*]. It appears that K_{Ic} values are not affected by groove depth equivalent to 60 percent of the cross section as long as the full thickness (in the absence of the grooves) fulfills the ASTM Method E 399-74 thickness requirement. Systematic measurements of run-arrest events in 25-mm-thick AISI 4340 steel DCB specimens, conducted by the authors [*10*] show that the crack velocity, the jump length and the K_{Ia} and K_{ID} values are all unaffected by side grooves occupying up to 60 percent of the cross section. These tests involved a relatively low toughness level of $(K_{ID}/\sigma_Y)^2 = 3.36$ mm. The results in Fig. 4 for A533B, which involve systematic variations of the side

[5]The lower resistance of the starter section of a duplex specimen is taken into account in the analysis and is not an issue here.

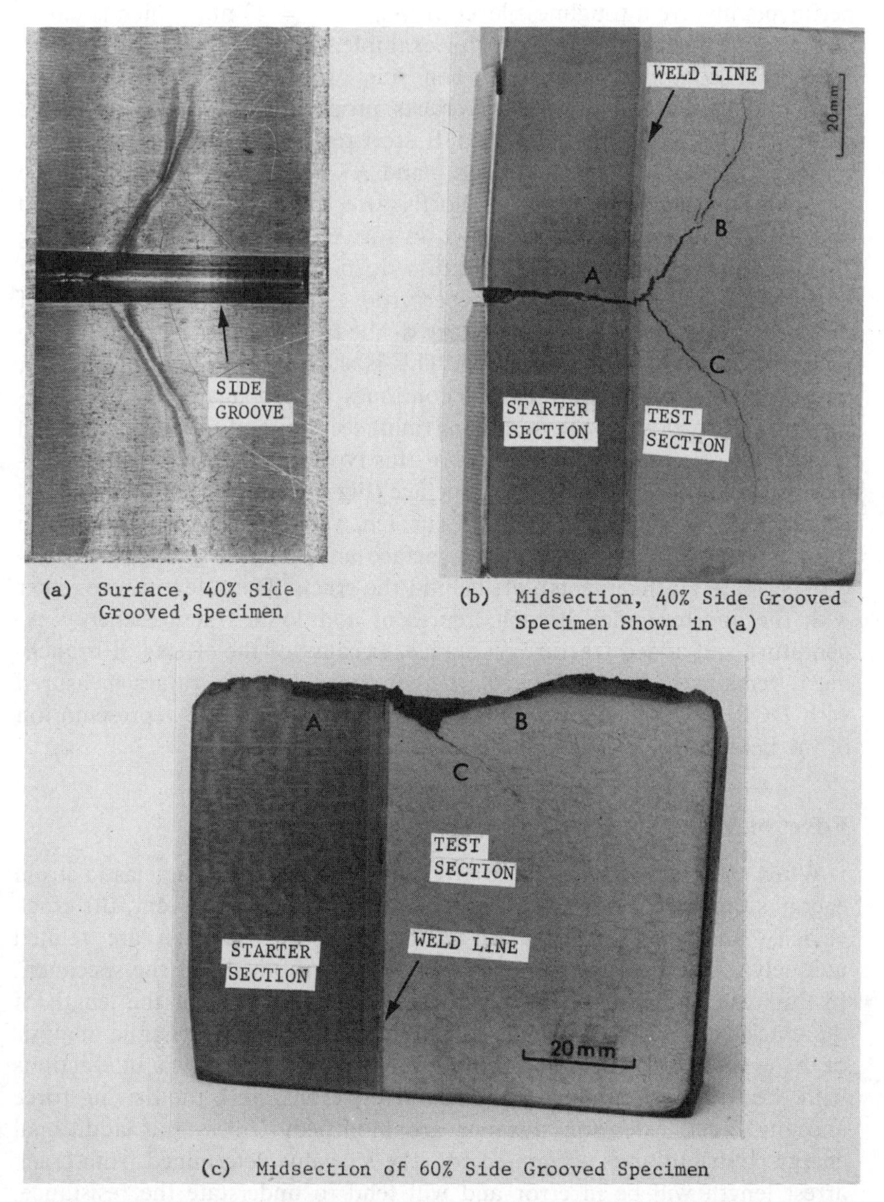

(a) Surface, 40% Side Grooved Specimen

(b) Midsection, 40% Side Grooved Specimen Shown in (a)

(c) Midsection of 60% Side Grooved Specimen

FIG. 6—*Examples of branching events in rectangular, AISI 4340/A533B duplex DCB specimens.* (a) *and* (b) *A 40 percent side grooved specimen* (*DA-13*) *tested at* $-12°C$, *and* (c) *A 60 percent side grooved specimen* (*DA-19*) *tested at* $1°C$. *The fractures propagated from left to right and the photos show the main crack* (A) *and the two branches* (B) *and* (C). *In the 60 percent side grooved specimen in* (c), *branch* (B) *continued to propagate and branch* (C) *arrested.*

groove depths from 2 to 15 mm, also show no effect on K_{ID}. These experiments involve a toughness level of $(K_{ID}/\sigma_Y)^2 = 49$ mm which is closer to the range of practical interest, for example, $(K_{ID}/\sigma_Y)^2 \gtrsim 90$ mm.

Another complication arises when side grooves are used to restrict branching. As noted previously, cracks propagating in rectangular and contoured DCB specimens of A533B steel tend to branch, greatly complicating the task of calculating K_{Ia} and K_{ID}. In duplex specimens, the branching events tend to occur shortly after the crack crosses the weld and enters the test section as shown in Fig. 6. Side grooves representing 25 and 40 percent of the cross section do not alter the branching event (see Fig. 6*a* and *b*). However, deeper grooves representing 60 percent of the cross section modify the trajectory of the two branches by encouraging them to run in the reduced section. This is shown in Fig. 6*c*. As a result, one of the branches prevails and continues to propagate, gradually regaining a path close to the minimum (mid) section, and the second branch is aborted. The branching attempts of this type are characterized by knot-like perturbations on the fracture surface (Fig. 3*a* and *b* show an example) which involves additional fracture surface, vertical shear lips that form the connection between perturbed surface and the side groove, and unbroken material (ligaments) left behind the crack. These features together with the aborted crack branch, represent additional fracture energy expenditure and added fracture resistance. Because of the effects of branching it remains to be established whether the K_{Ia} or K_{ID} values measured with DCB or other laboratory specimens are an accurate representation of the behavior of cracks in large structural components.

Effect of Method of Loading

When the crack driving force originates entirely from the elastic strain energy stored in the specimen at the onset of a run-arrest event, the crack velocity and crack propagation distance in the specimen are related uniquely to the fracture resistance K_{ID} and the geometry of the specimen. In this case, a measurement of either the crack velocity or the length of the crack at arrest is sufficient to determine K_D from a dynamic analysis of the event. When energy is allowed to enter the specimen via interactions with the test machine during the run-arrest event, both the driving force and the crack extension distance are modified. Unless this additional energy contribution is accounted for, the K_D value determined from crack arrest length will be in error and will tend to understate the resistance. The effects of the interaction produced by specific loading arrangements can be calculated with the existing dynamic analyses if the motion of the load points is known [*10*]. In practice, however, it may be difficult to characterize this motion accurately.

In this section results are presented which show that the load point motions are rather complex and that in some cases they become sufficiently large to cause additional crack extension. Specifically, experimental results for a relatively compliant tensile loading system are compared with results from a stiffer wedge loading method. While wedge loading reduces the amplitude of load point motion, significant amounts of energy are exchanged in both loading systems. Finally, a more dynamically stiff, wedge loading arrangement is described. This loading arrangement produces substantially smaller pin motions. A simplified procedure for evaluating K_D that neglects the specimen machine interaction can now be adopted for a wide variety of test conditions. This is discussed later.

Comparison of Tensile and Wedge Loading

Figures 7*a* and *b* show several test records of measured crack extension versus time for test on rectangular DCB specimens. Eddy current proximity detectors were used to monitor the motion of the specimen arms near the pinhole in these tests, and these results are also shown.

The records in Fig. 7*a* are from a 25.4-mm-thick ($B_n/B = 0.4$) ordinary A533B specimen tested at −78°C in a tensile loading arrangement. The compliance of the pullrod-grip-load pin train is 6.5 mm/MN which is not much less than 8.8 mm/MN, the specimen compliance prior to fracture. Propagation initiated at a load of 44.3 kN corresponding to a $K_Q = 60.6$ MPa·m$^{1/2}$. The crack extension occurs at essentially constant speed for a distance of 50 mm, halted for 200 μs, then extended another 15 mm before arresting. During the halt, relatively large movements of the pins were recorded indicating a correspondingly large energy input into the specimen. This energy eventually increased sufficiently to restart propagation.

That the propagation is unaffected initially by specimen-load machine interaction is brought out more clearly in Fig. 7*b*. These four records are of 25.4-mm-thick ($B_n/B = 0.4$) duplex 4340/A533B DCB specimens tested at −12°C. Only one arm of the specimen was monitored, and it must be assumed that the motion is symmetric. The specimens were wedge loaded using wedges having 11, 30, 80, and 110 deg included angles. The wedge loading method, in which a DCB specimen stands on end and a wedge is forced between pins inserted in the two ends of the specimen has been described in detail elsewhere [*8–12*]. The main element of the loading train, namely, the wedge (total thickness is 50.8 mm) and pins can be easily designed to have a compliance much less than that of the test specimen. Hence, the wedging method used in these experiments employs considerably stiffer loading elements than the tensile loading arrangement just described. While the fracture loads progressively increased with wedge angle the K_Q values at initiation were similar, 156, 177, 149, and 151 MPa·m$^{1/2}$, respectively. Because initiation stress intensities are similar, the initial crack velocities and crack lengths at which

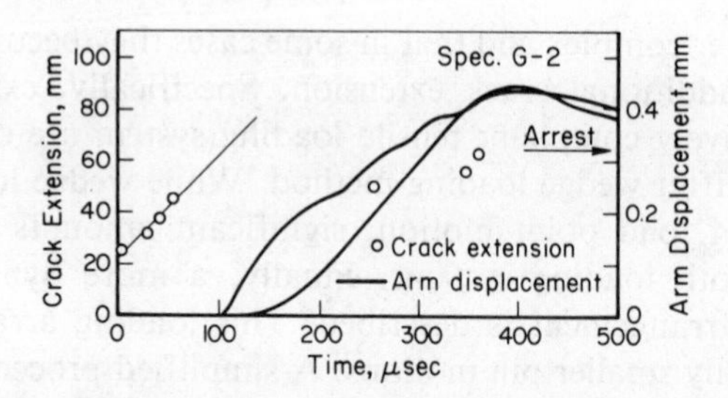

FIG. 7a—*Tensile loading in ordinary testing machine. Records of time rate of change of crack extension and arm displacement.* (a) *Ordinary A533B specimen tested at −78°C by tensile loading. Displacement of both arms are shown* (b). *Duplex 4340/A533B results tested at −12°C by wedge loading. The weld line is at 30 mm. Note scale change on AP-1 record. Also, in AP-1, arm motion was sufficient that the arm struck the displacement transducer at point indicated.*

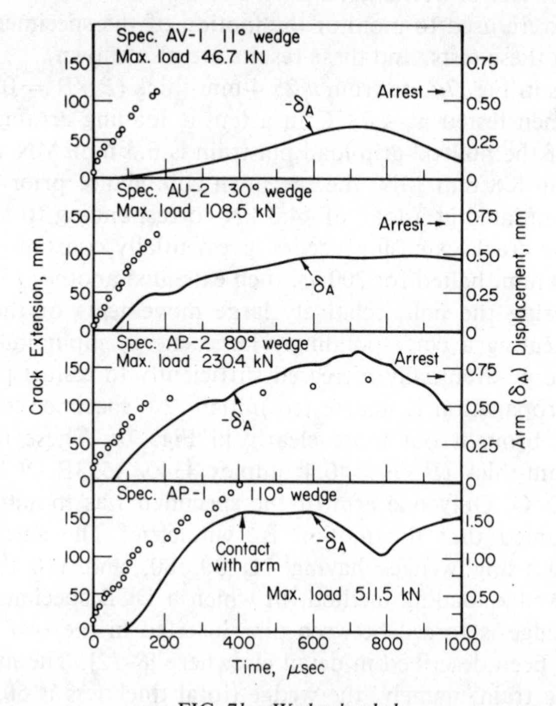

FIG. 7b—*Wedge loaded.*

rapid deceleration begins are alike in all cases. However, after a halt time of about 250 μs in Specimen AP-2 (80-deg wedge) and only 50 μs in Specimen AP-1 (110-deg wedge) additional propagation occurs, a consequence of an increased driving force due to specimen-load machine interaction during crack propagation.

Measurements also showed that the wedge advanced between the load pins in these tests. However, the extent of wedge motion was considerably less than would be needed to account for the arm motion. Thus, by inference, only a part of the work done on the specimen is supplied directly from the stored elastic strain energy in the loading mechanism. Subsequent tests have shown that the sudden release in compressive load applied to the specimen results in acceleration of the specimen off the lower platen of the machine. As a consequence, that part of the stored elastic energy in the specimen associated with the compressive stress acting parallel to the crack plane (which does not contribute to $\mathcal{G}$ initially) is first converted to kinetic energy, and then is reconverted to increase $\mathcal{G}$ as the specimen decelerates upon driving itself onto the wedge.

In summary the following conclusions may be drawn from a comparison of these tensile loaded and wedge loaded experiments.

1. The distance of propagation up to the point of the first halt is a reproducible quantity dependent upon the initiation conditions (that is, K_Q and the specimen crack length) and the resistance of the material to propagation.

2. While the wedge loading arrangement has the virtue of easily being much stiffer than tensile loading thereby reducing the work done on the specimen from the stored elastic energy in the test machine, the advantage has not been fully realized because of the freedom of movement of the test specimen.

Tie-Down Device

In Fig. 8 a loading arrangement is shown which utilizes the inherent stiffeners of wedge loading and, in addition, greatly reduces the translational degree of freedom available to the specimen in the wedge loaded results described previously. As before, the specimen is loaded by forcing a wedge between the pins. However, the counteracting force is supplied directly to the pins by supporting columns which are bolted to the lower platen of the test machine. The release of the strain energy in the loading pins is prevented from accelerating the specimen farther onto the wedge by the two beams placed a short distance (0.2 mm) above the pins. These beams are anchored to the supporting columns and thus constrain the vertical movement of the specimen. We refer to this arrangement as a "tie down" device.

Figure 9 shows the crack extension and pin motion records obtained from a 25.4-mm-thick duplex 4340/A533B specimen ($B_n/B = 0.4$) tested at -12°C. The load at fracture was 99.2 kN producing a K_Q of 168 MN/m$^{-3/2}$. Although the load at fracture was relatively high, the movement at the load points was substantially less than in the previous examples (compare specifically with Specimen AU-2 in Fig. 7*b*). In general,

FIG. 8—*Tie-down device. The specimen is supported by the pins on the side columns. Cooling is provided by cold nitrogen gas fed to the copper coils on either side of the specimen.*

recent tests show that the maximum amplitude of the load point movement is reduced by about one half to one third with the tie-down arrangement compared to the wedged-free specimen system described previously.

In summary, the wedge loaded-restrained specimen loading arrangement described here has adequately isolated the test specimen from the test machine. The advantages of this result become important in obtaining

K_{Im} from measurements of crack propagation distance coupled with predictions of a dynamic model.

Methods of Analysis

The K_D values of a material can be deduced from a dynamic analysis of instrumented run-arrest events in DCB specimens. The analysis is relatively easy to carry out for wedge loading, when the interaction between the specimen and the loading system is negligible. In this case, the K_D value can be obtained either from the crack velocity or from the crack length at arrest [8]. To illustrate this, tests were carried out on two heats of A533B steel using duplex specimens and the tie-down device, and these are described in detail in a companion paper [26]. The K_D values derived independently from the measured velocity, $K_D(\bar{V})$, and from the measured crack length at arrest $K_D(\Delta a)$ are in close agreement as shown in Fig. 10. The values based on the crack length appear to be slightly conservative (~10 percent). These findings indicate that K_{ID} or K_{Im} values can be derived from relatively unsophisticated "static" measurements of a DCB run arrest event:

(*a*) The load or displacement at the onset of propagation, which determine the initial stress intensity K_Q.

(*b*) The crack length at arrest which can be obtained unambiguously by the heat tinting method.

For a given specimen geometry, the dynamic analysis reduces to a single valued relation between the K_{ID}/K_Q ratio and the crack jump distance Δa, as shown in Fig. 11. The evaluation of K_{ID} values with the aid of Fig. 11 is therefore almost as simple as the calculation of K_{Ia}.

The K_a values displayed by these specimens are summarized in Fig. 12, and show a systematic variation with K_Q and the crack jump distance. For small penetrations with the test section, that is, 20 mm $\lesssim \Delta a \lesssim$ 80 mm, it is found that $K_a \approx 0.7\ K_D$. This result explains the apparent con-

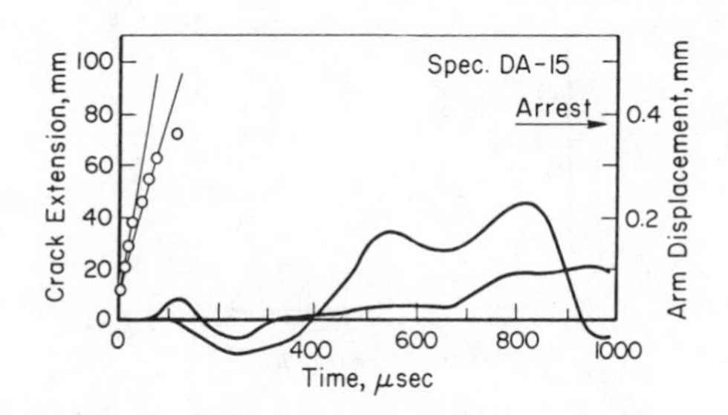

FIG. 9—*Crack extension and arm displacement records of a specimen tested using the tie-down device. Transducer outputs of the motion of both load pins are shown.*

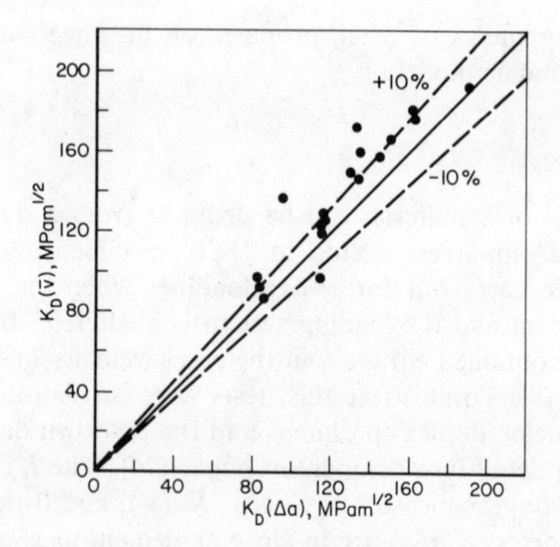

FIG. 10—*Comparison of* K_D *derived from measurement of crack extension in test section,* $K_D(\Delta a_T)$, *with* K_D *derived from crack velocity measurements,* $K_D(\bar{V})$ *in test section.*

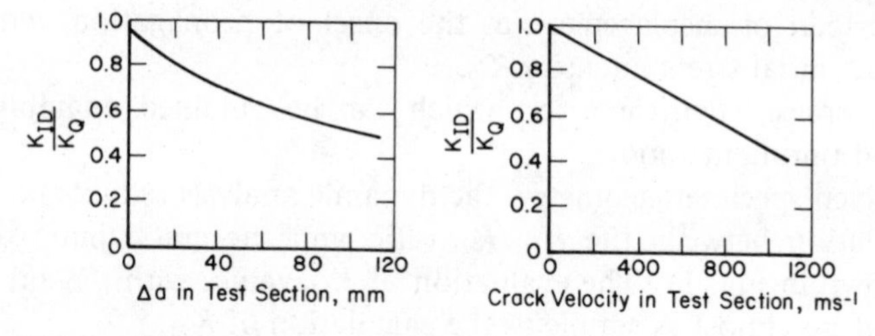

FIG. 11—*Calculated relation between the* K_{ID}/K_Q *ratio and the crack jump distance for wedge loaded, rectangular, duplex DCB specimens. The calculation is for the specimen dimensions given in Ref 26 in the absence of specimen machine interaction.*

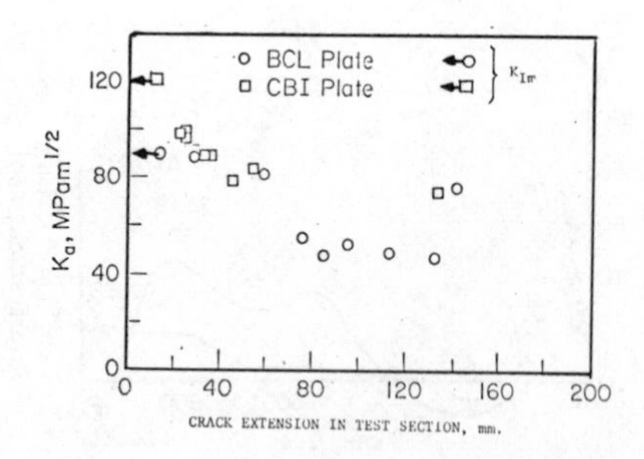

FIG. 12—*Variation of* K_a *with crack jump distance in A533B steel at 12°C. Measurements derived from wedge loaded duplex DCB specimens. Arrows show corresponding levels of* K_{Im}.

stancy of K_{Ia} reported by Ripling and Crosley [*23*]. For vanishingly small penetrations K_{Ia} approaches the K_D value for a small crack velocity which approximates K_m in this case. The results in Fig. 12, which are supported by the dynamic analysis [*26*], indicate that K_{ID} and K_{Im} values can also be deducted from K_{Ia} and a suitable correction factor for the relatively larger crack jumps that are unavoidable in duplex specimens.

Measurement Concepts

The design of a K_{Im} measurement procedure must, necessarily, take into account the shape of the K_{ID} crack velocity curve. Existing measurements for two heats of A533B steel are summarized in Fig. 13. While more work is needed to define the shape of the curve at the higher temperatures, the results illustrate the kinds of specifications that must be placed on the testing conditions:

1. When K_{ID} is independent of crack velocity, any measurement of K_{ID} also provides a measurement of K_{Im}. The only limitation on the crack

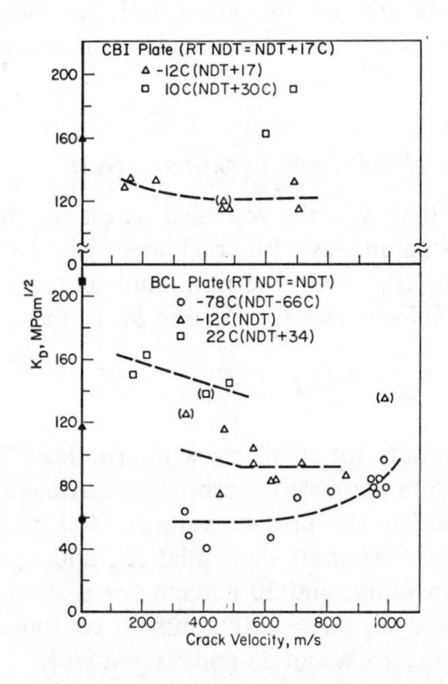

FIG. 13—*Dependence of fast fracture resistance,* K_D *with crack velocity and temperature for BCL and CBI lots of A533B steel. Bulk of the* K_D *results are determined from crack length at arrest except for tests where arrest did not occur in the specimen or where excessive energy input from the load system lead to additional crack extension. In these latter cases,* K_D *is based on crack velocity measurement.* K_{Ic} *measurements are located on the ordinate. Points where the crack velocity was not recorded were derived from the arrest length and enclosed by ( ).*

jump distance is the one connected with the use of static K_{Ia} interpretation.

2. When the K_{ID} value displays a shallow minimum at a finite velocity V_m, the measurement conditions can be defined by specifying suitable bracketing velocities, $V_1 \leq V_m \leq V_2$ within which K_{ID} values are an adequate approximation of K_{Im} (see Fig. 1*c*). The two velocities translate to a corresponding brack of allowable crack jump size. For example, the data at -12°C from the BCL and CBI plates suggests that 400 m/s $\leq V_m \leq$ 1000 m/s. For the duplex specimen the corresponding bracket on the crack extension distance in the test section would be 24 mm $\leq \Delta a_T \leq$ 146 mm. K_{Im} values can be derived from "such large" jump only by way of the dynamic analysis of arrest length method.

3. In the event K_{ID} increases at high crack velocities (as suggested by the measurements at -78°C) an upper limit must be placed on the size of the crack jump. For example, calculations [*26*] for rectangular duplex DCB specimen of the design used by the authors show that a limit on the crack jump of $\Delta a_T \leq 80$ mm will limit the crack velocity to $V \leq 800$ ms^{-1}.

These specifications along with the specimen size requirements attending K_{Im} values of practical interest provide a basis for judging the three difference instruments alien analysis strategies for interpreting laboratory run-arrest events.

Static Interpretation of the Crack Length at Arrest

It can be shown that K_{Ia}, the so-called arrest toughness,[6] approaches K_{Im} (the K value instantaneous with crack arrest) in the limit of an infinitestimal crack jump [*10*], when the minimum of the K_{ID} velocity curves occur at zero crack velocity (see Fig. 1*a* and *b*). In these cases:

$$K_{Ia} \approx K_{Im} \tag{3}$$

is a useful approximation for small crack jumps. The "small" jump must be defined in terms of a permissible error. Calculations for the rectangular DCB specimens used by the present authors (400 by 140 mm, with an initial slot length a_0 = 83 mm) show that K_{Ia} underestimates K_{Im} by 10 percent for a 20 mm jump, and 20 percent for a 30-mm jump. The corresponding figures for the (m = 0.052 mm^{-1}) contoured DCB employed by Crosley and Ripling are about 25 and 50 mm [*10*].

The small crack jump K_{Ia} approach can be applied to different specimen geometries, involves a relatively simple analysis and a minimum of instrumentation. In the case of contoured DCB specimens only the load

[6] Defined as the K value existing at the arrested crack tip after the system comes to static equilibrium.

existing statically after arrest must be measured; in other cases, either load or displacement and the crack length at arrest are needed. However, there are several reasons the small jump requirement may prove too restrictive:

1. Experience to date shows that it is difficult to produce a small crack jump above the NDT with anything but very thick specimens. This is illustrated in Table 2, which shows that even at low temperatures it is difficult to produce jumps consistently smaller than 50 mm in the contoured DCB. As a result, the K_a values consistently underestimate K_m. A systematic variation of K_a with jump size is reported elsewhere [*26*].
2. The larger K_m values of practical interest, for example, $K_m \gtrsim 150$ MPa$\cdot$m$^{1/2}$, will require much larger conventional specimens and are likely to involve relatively larger jumps. The use of duplex specimens preclude a "small" jump because the crack must propagate some distance in the "starter section." The crack must also propagate well beyond a weld to assure the measurements reflect properties of the test material.
3. As discussed earlier, the crack jump should probably exceed twice the specimen thickness to assure a representative two-dimensional place strain event. This would make it difficult to satisfy both a small jump requirement for K_{Ia}, and the minimum thickness requirement for plane strain. Note, that the K_a values reported on the 2nd and 3rd line entries of Table 2 (corresponding with Δa = 27 mm, 25 mm) do not satisfy the minimum crack jump requirement proposed here. The K_{ID} values derived from these two results also noticeably underestimate K_m.
4. Finally, the small crack jump K_{Ia} approach cannot be used when K_{Im} corresponds with a high crack velocity.

Dynamic Interpretation of the Crack Length at Arrest

"Large" crack jumps can be interpreted with a dynamic analysis but this is complicated by dynamic energy exchanges between the specimen and the testing machine. This paper describes a dynamically stiff, wedge loading arrangement that effectively prevents such interactions. This simplifies the analysis and makes it possible to infer K_{Im} or K_{ID} values directly from measurements of the load point displacement at the onset of the run arrest event and the extent of the crack jump. The K_{ID} value can be obtained in two ways:

(*a*) by deriving a correction appropriate for the crack jump distance from the dynamic analysis and applying this to K_{Ia} as illustrated in Table 2, or

(*b*) by calculating K_{ID} directly from K_Q and the crack length at arrest from results derived from the dynamic analysis.

TABLE 2—*Results of* K_a *measurements for two heats of A533B steel at −12°C from contoured DCB specimens* [a] [13,24,25].

Specimen No. (Measuring Laboratory)[b]	Heat	K_Q, MPa·m$^{1/2}$	Δa, mm	K_a, MPa·m$^{1/2}$	K_D, MPa·m$^{1/2}$ (from K_a value)[c]	K_m, MPa·m$^{1/2}$ (from Fig. 13)
B1 (MRL)	BCL	[90][d] 100	> 245[e]	...	...	
B2 (MRL)	BCL	[66] 73	27	[57][d] 63	70[f]	
B3 (MRL)	BCL	[69] 77	25	[62] 69	77[f]	
C2 (MRL)	BCL	[78] 87	55	[63] 70	88	
C3 (MRL)	BCL	[77] 86	48	[62] 69	86	
+ D[g] (BCL)	BCL	119	56	85	106	90
+ E[g] (BCL)	BCL	85	33	71	79	
+ G1 (BCL)	BCL	94	66	73	91	
E2[h] (MRL)	CBI	[101] 112	64	[77] 86	108 (−17°C)	120 (−12°C)

[a]The tests employed the 304.8 by 203.2 mm (m = 1.33 in.$^{-1}$) contoured DCB specimen described by Ripling [24] and shown in Fig. 2*e*. The specimens were 50.8 mm thick unless otherwise noted, and contained two 6.25-mm-deep side grooves. The test procedures used by the two laboratories were the same except that MRL employed a high loading rate.

[b]MRL = Materials Research Laboratory [13,24].
BCL = Battelle-Columbus Laboratories [25].

[c]The K_D values in this column were obtained directly from K_a by applying the appropriate dynamic correction calculated from the one-dimensional analysis for the particular contoured DCB geometry [10]:

Δa, mm	$\Delta a/a$	Corresponding Velocity, ms^{-1}	K_{Ia}/K_{ID}
25	0.67	~250	0.9
50	1.33	~400	0.8
75	2.00	~600	0.75

[d]The numbers in brackets were reported by Crosley and Ripling [13,24] and are based on their compliance calibration, but omit a $(1 - \nu^2)$ term that appears in the relation between compliance and K. The numbers outside of the brackets were calculated using relation employed in Hahn et al [10,25] which includes the $(1 - \nu^2)$ term and a compliance derivative that is about 13 percent larger.

[e]Crack failed to arrest.

[f]These values correspond with small jumps relative to the specimen thickness, for example, $\Delta a \sim B_n/2$, and for this reason may not reflect the resistance for a straightfronted, plane-strain run-arrest event. Also note that the probable crack velocity for these small jumps (see footnote *c*) is ~250 ms^{-1}, which is outside the range described by Fig. 13.

[g]Specimen 25.4 mm thick.

[h]Tested at −17°C.

These two procedures are essentially equivalent, and lead to the same results. A comparison of the last two columns of Table 2 illustrates that this is indeed the case. It should be noted that the calculations of the correction for K_a, or of the relations among K_D, K_Q, and Δa presuppose a knowledge of the shape of the K_{ID} crack velocity curve.

An approach based on stiff loading, the arrest length, and a dynamic analysis has many attractive features. For a given stress intensity at crack initiation, K_Q, this loading arrangement produces the smallest possible crack jump, and a jump size that is independent of the testing machine and reproducible from laboratory to laboratory. The instrumentation required is essentially the same as for the K_{Ia} approach and minimal. With the dynamic analysis the test result can always be interpreted regardless of the jump size. When the jump is small, results are interpretable by the K_{Ia} approximations. Finally, the dynamic analyses for contoured and rectangular DCB specimens have been worked out [*1,10*] and are not more difficult to apply than the static analyses of K_{Ia}. When two-dimensional models are completed [*1*] the same approach can be applied to compact and SEN geometries.

Dynamic Interpretation of the Crack Velocity

Dynamic analyses also make it possible to relate K_{ID} to the crack velocity of a particular run-arrest event and thereby deduce K_{Im}. The method has been used extensively by the authors [*8–12*]. It is has also been used here to validate the dynamic-crack-arrest-length approach. The principal advantage of the crack velocity method is that it does not require prior knowledge of the K_{ID} crack velocity curve. The relations between K_{ID} values and the initial crack velocity are relatively insensitive to the shape of the curve. Of course, a range of K_{ID} values must be explored to define K_{Im}. The crack velocity method has the advantage that it can be used to measure K_{ID} for a wide range of velocities and crack jumps. Its main drawback is that existing techniques for measuring the crack velocity are more difficult and do not lend themselves to routine laboratory use.

In the authors' view, a test method based on the dynamic interpretation of the crack length at arrest and the use of "duplex" specimens offers the most immediate prospects for a standardized test, capable of measuring K_{Im} values of practical interest. At the same time, the complications attending branching and the restricting of branching with deep side grooves or the use of alternate, less-branch-prone specimen shapes, require further study.

Conclusions

A methodology is advanced for determining the important crack arrest properties, K_{Im}, K_{Ia}, and K_{ID}. The major findings and conclusions on which this methodology is based are summarized as follows:

1. Of the specimen shapes considered the DCB geometry accommodates the largest crack jump distance for a given volume of material. Questions regarding crack path stability requirements remain.

2. Specimen size and thickness requirements are guided by: (*a*) $(K_Q/\sigma_Y)^2$ to preclude gross plastic deformation prior to crack propagation, and (*b*) $(K_D/\sigma_{YD})^2$ to maintain plane-strain conditions during propagation. The use of a hardened steel starter section in duplex specimens greatly reduce specimen sizes vis a vis (*a*) and experiments on side grooved DCB specimens suggest that $B > 0.3\ (K_{Im}/\sigma_Y)^2$ is an adequate propagating crack thickness requirement.

3. Considerations of the evolution of the crack front shape and also crack sampling during propagation suggest a minimum crack jump requirement of $2B_n$. This restriction may exclude a purely static K_{Ia} interpretation as an appropriate option for analyzing fracture results.

4. Side grooves are necessary to suppress shear lips and, in DCB specimens, should occupy more than 40 percent of the total thickness to restrict gross out-of-plane branching characteristic of the fracture behavior in A533B steel. Questions are raised regarding the three-dimensionality of the crack-tip stress field introduced by side grooves, but experimental evidence suggests this is not influencing. The interpretation of the added resistance conferred by small-scale branching attempts in laboratory specimens requires further study.

5. The crack jump distance may be increased depending on the nature of the loading system and the amount of energy input to the specimen during propagation. A tie-down device is described which greatly reduces the test machine specimen interaction even at high load levels. This result greatly facilitates dynamic interpretation of crack jump distance.

6. The value of K_D can be determined simply from a measurement of K_Q and the crack jump distance using reference curves generated by a dynamic one-dimensional analysis. From a group of A533B test results, K_D determined in this way agrees with the K_D determined from crack velocity measurements with the former being somewhat more conservative.

7. K_{Ia} is approximately equal to K_D in the limit of "small," low velocity crack jumps and can be converted to K_D for longer, higher velocity, propagation events via a dynamic analysis.

8. The procedure for ascertaining K_{Im} depends on the velocity dependence of K_D. It is simplest when K_D is independent of crack velocity as a crack jump length proviso is not required. A velocity dependent K_D introduces minimum or maximum velocities or both necessary to sample K_{Im} with corresponding limitations to the allowable crack jump distances in a test.

Acknowledgments

The authors are grateful for support given by the U.S. Nuclear Regulatory Commission, which sponsored this work. They with to thank E. K. Lynn, for his effective guidance, and T. U. Marston for substantial logistical support. The authors wish to thank their colleagues M. F. Kanninen and C. Popelar, as well as the other participants of the joint Nuclear Regulatory Commission/Electric Power Research Institute program: H. T. Corten, P. Crosley, J. W. Dally, A. Kobayashi, T. Kobayashi, E. J. Ripling, G. R. Irwin, and K. Stahlkopf for many useful ideas. Finally, the authors wish to acknowledge the important contributions of P. Mincer and R. Barnes who performed the laboratory work, and C. Pepper and L. Wall for their work on the manuscript.

References

[*1*] Kanninen, M. F., Popelar, C., and Gehlen, P. C., this publication, pp. 19–38.
[*2*] Eftis, J. and Krafft, J. M., *Transactions,* American Society of Mechanical Engineers, Vol. 87, Series D, 1964, p. 257.
[*3*] Hahn, G. T., Hoagland, R. G., and Rosenfield, A. R., "Fast Fracture Toughness of Steels," *Dynamic Fracture Toughness,* Welding Institute, Abington, Cambridge, England, 1976, p. 237.
[*4*] Kobayashi, T. and Dally, J. W., this publication, pp. 257–273.
[*5*] Kanninen, M. F., Mills, E., Hahn, G. T., Marschall, C. W., Broek, D., Coyle, A., Masabushi, K., and Itoga, K., "A Study of Ship Hull Crack Arrester Systems," to be published as a Ship Structure Committee report.
[*6*] Lynn, E. K. and Serpan, C. Z., U.S. Nuclear Regulatory Commission, private communication.
[*7*] Irwin, G. R., this publication, pp. 7–18.
[*8*] Hahn, G. T., Hoagland, R. G., Rosenfield, A. R., and Sejnoha, R., *Metallurgical Transactions,* Vol. 5, 1974, p. 475.
[*9*] Hahn, G. T., Hoagland, R. G., Kanninen, M. F., and Rosenfield, A. R., *Engineering Fracture Mechanics,* Vol. 7, 1975, p. 583.
[*10*] Hahn, G. T., Gehlen, P. C., Hoagland, R. G., Kanninen, M. F., Popelar, C., Rosenfield, A. R., and de Campos, V. S., NRC Report No. BMI-1937, Battelle Columbus Laboratories, Columbus, Ohio, 1975.
[*11*] Hahn, G. T., Gehlen, P. C., Hoagland, R. G., Kanninen, M. F., Popelar, C., and Rosenfield, A. R., NRC Report No. BMI-NUREG-1944, Battelle Columbus Laboratories, Columbus, Ohio, March 1976.
[*12*] Hahn, G. T., Hoagland, R. G., Kanninen, M. F., and Rosenfield, A. R., *Pressure Vessel Technology,* Part II, American Society of Mechanical Engineers, New York, 1973, p. 971.
[*13*] Crosley, P. B. and Ripling, E. J., Fifth Quarterly Report on "Crack Arrest Studies," to Electric Power Research Institute, Sept.-Dec. 1975.
[*14*] Wilson, W. K., *Engineering Fracture Mechanics,* Vol. 2, 1970, p. 169.
[*15*] Bucci, R. J., Paris, P. C., Landes, J. D., and Rice, J. R. in *Fracture Toughness, ASTM STP 514,* American Society for Testing and Materials, 1972, p. 40.
[*16*] Hahn, G. T., Gehlen, P. C., Hoagland, R. G., Kanninen, M. F., Popelar, C., and Rosenfield, A. R., NRC Report No. BMI-1939, Battelle Columbus Laboratories, Columbus, Ohio, Nov. 1975.
[*17*] Green, G. and Knott, J. F., *Metals Technology,* Sept. 1975, p. 422.
[*18*] Mostovoy, S., Crosley, P. B., and Ripling, E. G., *Journal of Materials,* Vol. 3, 1967, pp. 661–681.

[*19*] Kaufman, J. G., Nelson, F. G., Jr., and Holt, M., *Engineering Fracture Mechanics,* Vol. 1, 1968, p. 259.
[*20*] Hoagland, R. G., *Transactions,* American Society of Mechanical Engineers, Vol. 89, Series D, 1967, p. 525.
[*21*] Freed, C. N., Report 6654, Naval Research Laboratory, 1967.
[*22*] Hoagland, R. G. and Rosenfield, A. R., *International Journal of Fracture,* Vol. 10, 1974, p. 299.
[*23*] Crosley, P. B. and Ripling, E. G., Paper No. 75-PVP-32, American Society of Mechanical Engineers, 1975.
[*24*] Crosley, P. B. and Ripling, E. J., First Annual Report to Electric Power Research Institute, 1 Sept. 1974 to 1 Sept. 1975.
[*25*] Hahn, G. T., Gehlen, P. C., Hoagland, R. G., Kanninen, M. F., Popelar, C., and Rosenfield, A. R., NRC Fifth Quarterly Progress Report No. BMI-NUREG-1944, Battelle Columbus Laboratories, Columbus, Ohio, March 1976.
[*26*] Hahn, G. T., Hoagland, R. C., Marschall, C. W., and Rosenfield, A. R., "Crack Arrest and Its Relation to Propagating Crack Toughness," *Metallurgical Transactions,* in press.

P. B. Crosley[1] *and E. J. Ripling*[1]

Characteristics of a Run-Arrest Segment of Crack Extension

REFERENCE: Crosley, P. B. and Ripling, E. J., "**Characteristics of a Run-Arrest Segment of Crack Extension,**" *Fast Fracture and Crack Arrest, ASTM STP 627,* G. T. Hahn and M. F. Kanninen, Eds., American Society for Testing and Materials, 1977, pp. 203–227.

ABSTRACT: During a run-arrest segment of crack extension, the crack attains a high velocity shortly after initiating, and then decelerates in a continuous fashion to arrest.

Strain measurements made during the event show that over the early portion of the jump when the crack velocity is high, the specimen behavior requires a dynamic analysis. During the later portions of the jump, when the velocity is low, the specimen behavior is described adequately by an analysis that assumes a condition of static equilibrium. Hence, if the dependence of a on K for the test material is described by a gamma (Γ) shaped curve, the crack arrest toughness, K_{Ia}, is an adequate description of K_{Im}, the minimum toughness for stable crack extension.

KEY WORDS: crack propagation, steels, crack velocity, crack arrest, measurements, fracture properties

Nomenclature

- K Stress intensity factor
- K_{Ia} Static calculation of K after a run-arrest segment of plane-strain fracturing
- K_{Ic} Plane-strain fracture toughness
- K_{Im} Minimum value of K for a crack running in plane strain
- K_q Initiation toughness
- a Crack length
- $\dot{a}$ Crack velocity
- $\mathcal{G}$ Strain energy release rate

In 1965, Krafft and Irwin pointed up that there were two convenient transition points that could be used for characterizing the toughness of

[1]Principal scientist and director of research, respectively, Materials Research Laboratory, Inc., Glenwood, Ill. 60425.

materials: the value of K at which a stationary or slowly moving crack abruptly jumps ahead, and the value of K at which a running crack is arrested [*1*].[2] If the crack extends under a condition of plane strain, the first transition is identified as K_{Ic} and the second as K_{Ia}. In the same year, Irwin and Wells state "that arrests are simple reversals on the time scale of possible plane-strain initiations" [*2*]. This view of K_{Ia} suggests that it can be evaluated in a similar manner to K_{Ic}. Hence, methods for measuring it are relatively straightforward. Just as K_{Ic} is evaluated by measuring the load, P, and crack length, a, immediately prior to the stationary-to-running transition, K_{Ia} is based on measurement of P and a immediately after the running-to-stationary transition, and a more formal definition of K_{Ia} might be the value of K a short-time interval (about one millisecond) after a run-arrest segment of rapid crack extension. It is assumed that the test conditions permit establishment of a nearly static stress state in the test specimen in a time less than the just stated short-time interval.

This definition of K_{Ia} implies that it, like K_{Ic}, is a material property, that is, it is independent of the manner in which it is measured. Hahn et al have suggested that the measured value of K_{Ia} is specimen dependent on the basis of a one dimensional dynamic analysis, performed by Kanninen on the tapered-double-cantilever-beam (TDCB) and uniform double-cantilever-beam (UDCB) specimens [*3*]. This, of course, raises some question about the usefulness of K_{Ia}, and the ultimate decision of its usefulness, like that of any material characterization, must be based on experimental observations: if measurements made on test specimens satisfactorily predict the performance of structures, the measurement obviously has value. Testing large structures of a variety of shapes to evaluate the predictability of K_{Ia} is not feasible, however, so that its usefulness might be established, or at least the range of problems for which a K_{Ia} characterization has a predictive capability, might be established by comparing K_{Ia} with a characterization whose applicability is obvious.

Ideally, materials would be characterized by establishing the entire graph of $\dot{a} = f(K)$ for a crack extending under a condition of plane strain. Because it is helpful to characterize materials with a single value, the minimum value of K for stable crack extension, that is, K_{Im}, might be then identified. Hahn et al compared K_{Ia} as just defined with calculated values of K_{Im} (based on the Kanninen one-dimensional model) and found that K_{Ia} was not an adequate approximation of K_{Im}. The difference between K_{Ia} and K_{Im} (assuming two different $K - \dot{a}$ relationships) was less than 10 percent when the data were collected on TDCB specimens for which the ratio of initiation toughness, K_q, to K_{Ia} was less than about 1.3. The difference increased as the ratio K_q/K_{Ia} increased, however, as shown in Fig. 1 [*3*].

[2]The italic numbers in brackets refer to the list of references appended to this paper.

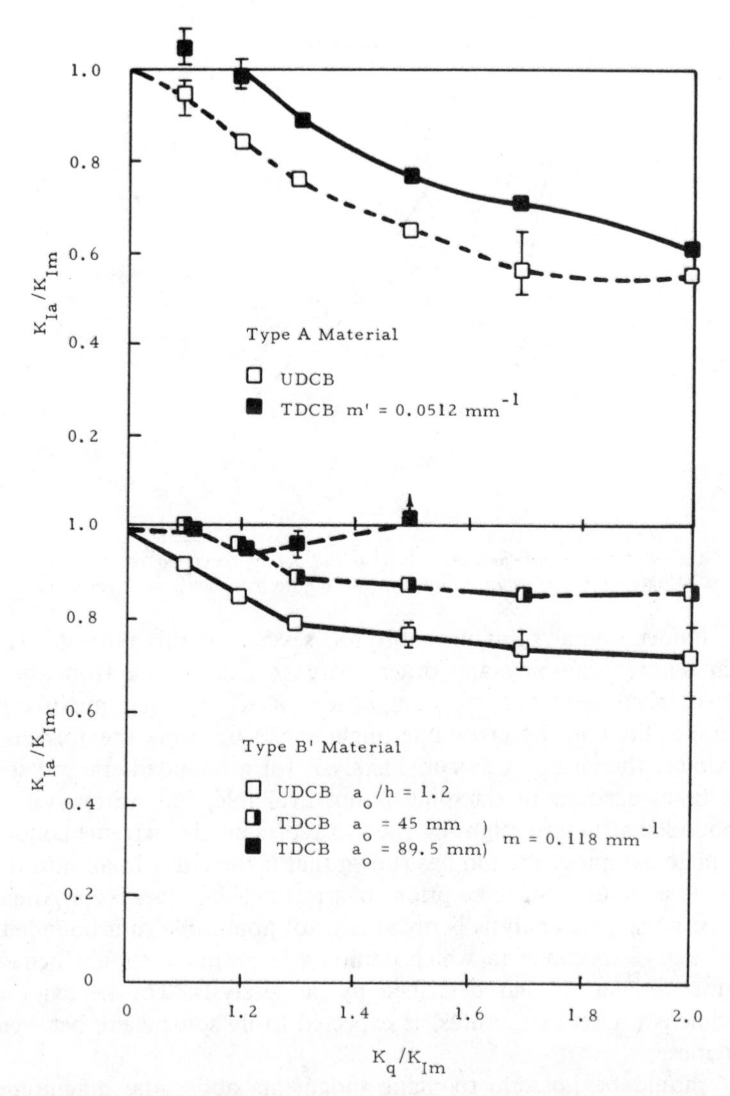

FIG. 1—*Calculated ratio of* K_{Ia}/K_{Im} *as a function of* K_q/K_{Im} *for two assumed* K-à *relationships and two specimen types according to Kanninen's one-dimensional dynamic analysis.*

The difference between K_{Ia} and K_{Im} is attributed to the dynamic response of the specimen. As shown schematically in Fig. 2, prior to the run-arrest segment, and at some time after the event, K can be evaluated on the basis of static calculations. Over the course of the event, and possibly a short time after it, however, the specimen is not in a condition of static equilibrium. The problem then becomes one of estimating the error in using K_{Ia}, as defined previously, to approximate K_{Im}.

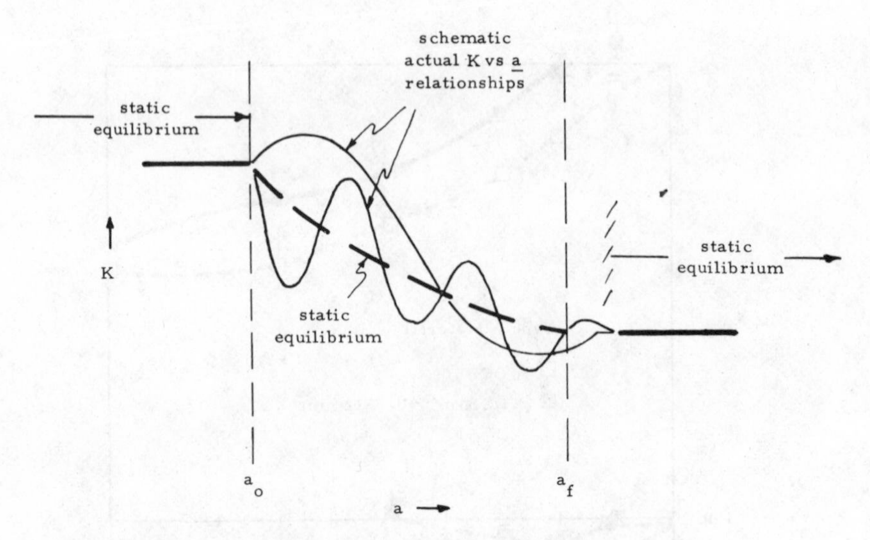

FIG. 2—*Schematic drawing showing that the actual specimen response might be considered as a dynamic disturbance superimposed on the specimen's static response.*

Kanninen's analysis is probably too severe for this purpose. His program ignores damping and other energy losses remote from the crack, and, as a consequence, his comparison of K_{Ia} and K_{Im} might represent an upper limit in the error one might make by using the former to approximate the latter. A dynamic analysis for a bounded cracked structure that takes account of damping is not available, but an analysis for an unbounded structure might be used to represent the extreme condition of complete damping. Freund has shown that if the crack in an infinite plane runs at a modest velocity prior to arresting, K_{Ia} does approximate K_{Im} [*4*]. Although his analysis is obviously not applicable to a bounded specimen, a real specimen in which damping is complete should behave in a manner similar to that described by his analysis. The behavior of test specimens (or real structures) is expected to lie somewhere between these extremes.

It should be possible to make judgments about the magnitude of a specimen's dynamic response and the influence of the latter on the value of K_{Ia} by making measurements on test specimens over the course of a run-arrest crack segment. It is such measurements that are the topic of this paper.

Materials and Procedure

Materials

The writer's interest in K_{Ia} is primarily for the use of A533B steel in thick-walled pressure vessels. Consequently, most of the data collected to date were obtained on this material. However, some data were also collected on a high-strength AISI 4340 steel and on bonded aluminum specimens as well. The purpose for making the latter measurements was not primarily for material characterization but in order to estimate differences between K_{Ia} and K_{Im}. This should depend only on the analysis and be independent of material as long as the test specimens are linearly elastic on a macrobasis. Hence, information collected on bonded aluminum specimens should be useful for making judgments on the behavior of steel specimens.

Surface Crack Velocity Measurements

The most obvious measurements to be made over a run-arrest segment of crack extension is crack velocity, and the simplest way to do this is to measure the crack front position versus time using a ladder gage on the specimen surface. Each rung of the ladder breaks as the crack passed under it, and this, in turn, causes a step in the output voltage measurement. On the basis of some preliminary tests, it was found that a thin uniform layer of a ductile insulator and conductor was needed. If the total layer were thin enough (of the order of 0.05 mm) it appeared to crack with the substrate even if it were more ductile than the latter. A number of coatings were tried, and the most promising insulating layer was a thin coat of varnish. Anthony, Chubb, and Congelton had previously found this to be satisfactory with a vapor deposited conductive layer, on smooth faced specimens [*5*]. For the face-grooved specimens used in this program, the conductive layer was made by spraying conductive paint onto a ladder shaped mask after the insulating layer had hardened. The crack jump length was small for the steel specimens tested on this program, so the distance between rungs has to be small (approximately 3 mm) to obtain a reasonable sensitivity in velocity measurements. Because the output voltage steps for these closely spaced rungs was not always distinct, each ladder gage was calibrated before the test was conducted. Calibration consisted of electrically breaking each rung by means of a switch in series with the rung so that the voltage change associated with breaking each rung was known. It was convenient to arrange the circuit associated with the ladder gage such that some arbitrary numbers of breaks (generally seven to ten) caused the voltage to increase, the next series caused it to decrease, etc. This had two advantages: first, breaking each rung caused a larger step in the oscilloscope record, and second, at the end of each series of steps where the voltage changed sign, the rung that had just broken was unequivocally identified. A typical calibration is shown in Fig. 3.

Effective Crack Velocity Measurements

The obvious uncertainty of evaluating crack velocities by making mea-

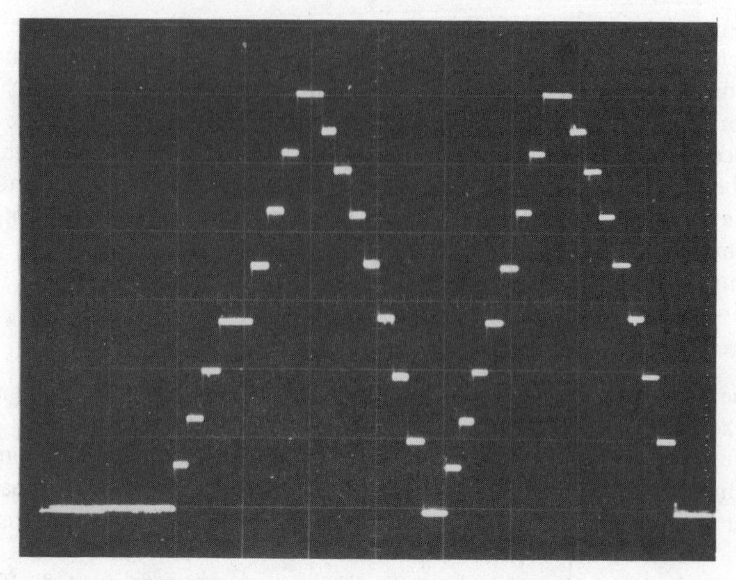

FIG. 3—*Calibration of ladder gage. Each horizontal line indicates one rung broken. The first eight rungs caused an increase in voltage, the next eight a decrease, etc.*

surements at the specimen surface is that one cannot be certain that the measurements are indicative of the crack velocity at cross sections other than the surface. A useful measure of crack length in fracture mechanics studies is the "effective crack length." Although this term is defined generally in terms of compliance, it can be thought of as an average value of a plus some plastic zone. Effective crack length might be measured in test specimens by placing strain gages at locations where strains are especially sensitive to crack-tip position, and measure the strain-time curve over the course of a run-arrest segment. One convenient measuring position is near the expected plane of crack extension to measure bending of the specimen arms, and another is on the neutral plane of the specimen arms to measure shear on either TDCB or UDCB specimens. Presumably, the output of gages placed anywhere on the specimen can be calculated for a condition of static equilibrium. It was more convenient, however, to measure the outputs of gages placed at specific locations with stationary cracks of different lengths directly, especially since a compliance calibration had to be made on $m = 52.4\ \text{m}^{-1}$ specimens.

One of the aluminum alloy specimens used for the compliance calibration was instrumented with strain gages, as shown in Fig. 4. Gages B1, B2, B3, and B4 were placed immediately above the face groove along the crack line to measure bending stress; and shear gages S1 and S2 were located midway between the crack line and the top edge of the specimens. The output of each gage was plotted against the output of the in-line load

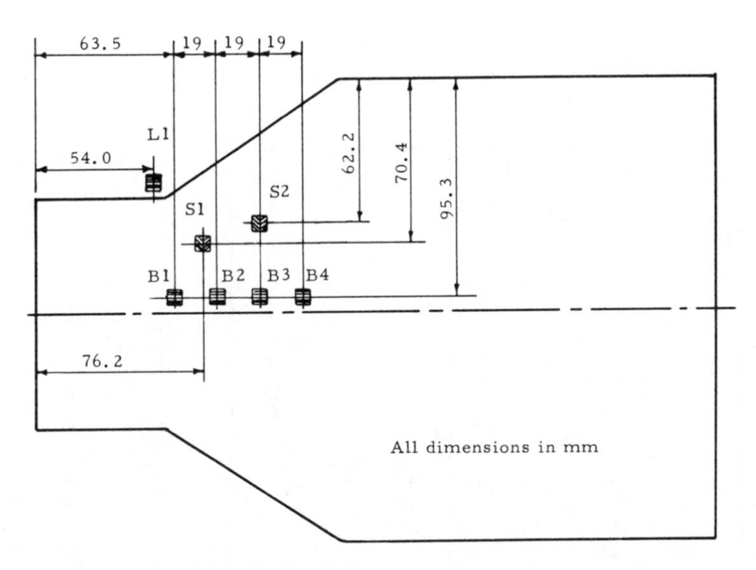

FIG. 4—*Location of strain gages on TDCB compliance calibration specimen.*

cell at each crack position that was sampled in the compliance calibration as described in Ref *6*.

The output of the shear gages, which were composed of two elements oriented at 45 and 135 deg to the *x*-axis (crack propagation direction), are given in Fig. 5. The plotted strain value, ϵ, is the difference between the strains on the two gage elements that is, $\epsilon = \epsilon(45 \text{ deg}) - \epsilon(135 \text{ deg})$. As the crack passes the gage position the strain changes from positive to negative. The change is somewhat more rapid for the gage located closer to the loading holes so that descending portions of the two curves are only approximately parallel and, hence, not uniformly displaced by the distance between the gages, 1 in. The curves are well-enough defined, however, that a monitoring of these gages during dynamic crack propagation should permit an estimate of average crack speed between the two gage positions.

The output of the four bending gages, B1, B2, B3, and B4, is plotted in Fig. 6. The curves for gages B2, B3, and B4 have essentially the same shape and are displaced along the crack length axis by amounts corresponding to the gage spacing, 19 mm. The output of each gage shows a distinct drop, reaches a minimum at a crack position of about 2.5 mm short of the gage position, and then increases rapidly. The output levels of the three gages are comparable when the crack is well past the gages. The output of the first gage, B1, shows a rapid increase at a crack length corresponding with the same behavior in the other gages; the output levels of gage B1, however, are different from the other gages.

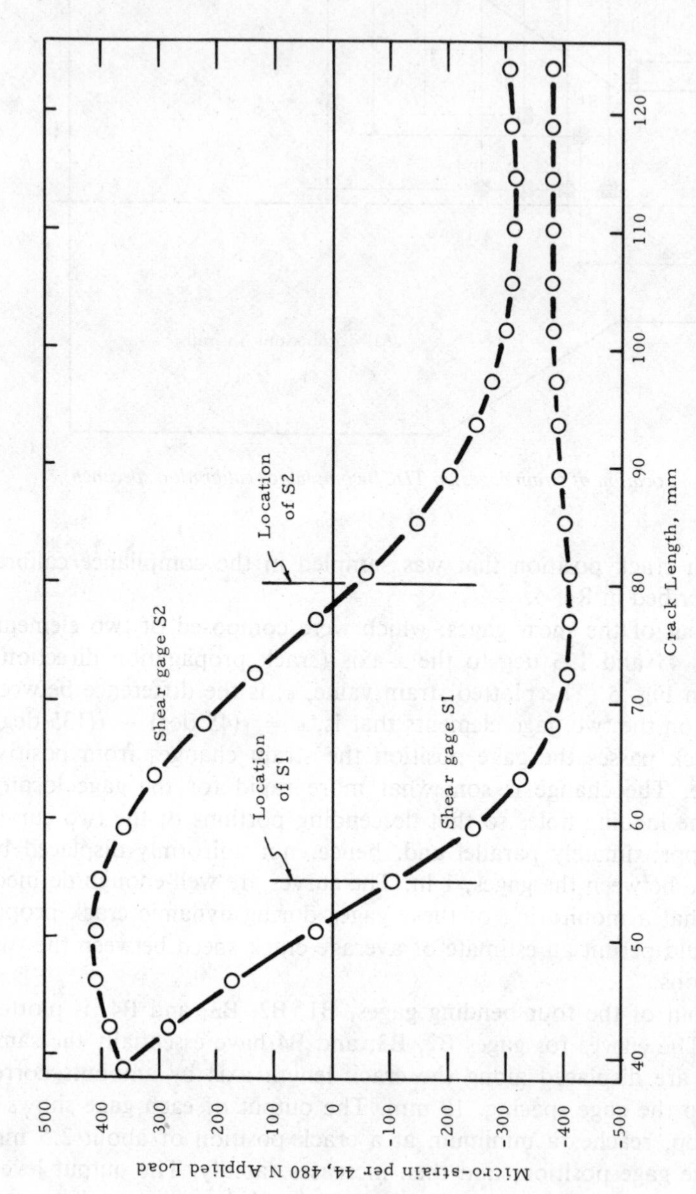

FIG. 5—*Output of shear gages on aluminum specimen as a function of crack length. Output* = $\epsilon(\pi/4) - \epsilon(3\pi/4)$.

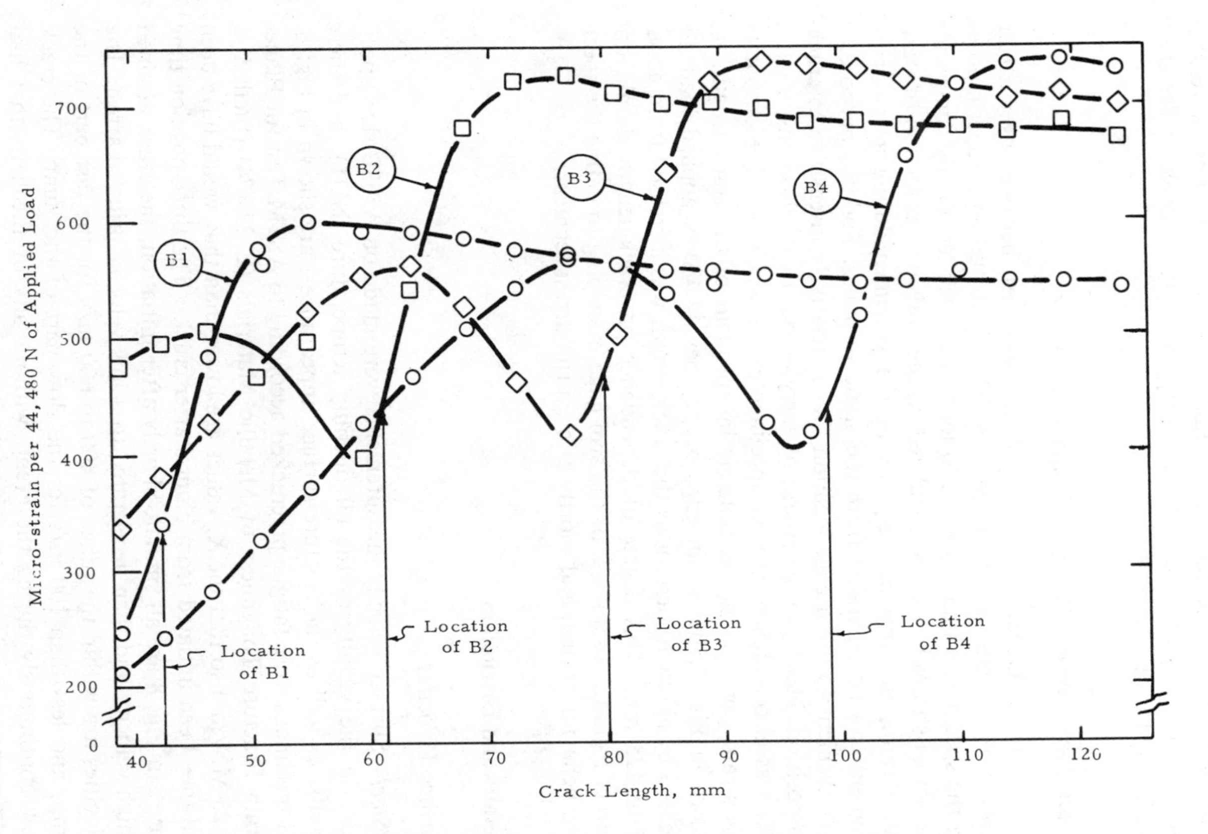

FIG. 6—*Output of bending gages on aluminum specimen as a function of crack length.*

The curves for the bending gages are more complex than those for the shear gage, and although the drop in output which occurs when the crack front passes each gage make the bending gages usable as a crack velocity monitor, the simpler shape of the shear gage output curves makes them preferable for this purpose.

Strain Measurement During a Run-Arrest Segment

As shown schematically in Fig. 2, the specimen behavior over a run-arrest segment can be considered as a dynamic disturbance superimposed on the specimen's state response to load and crack length. By comparing the actual strains to strains calculated on the basis of a condition of static equilibrium, the dynamic response of the specimen during a run-arrest segment can be separated from the static response. For this purpose, it is convenient to use a gage location that is relatively insensitive to crack-tip position. Hence, in the course of carrying out the calibrations, a gage, L-1, was also attached into the specimen arm (see Fig. 4). The output of this strain gage was not completely independent of the crack length. As shown in Fig. 7, the strain gage output per 44 480 N applied load decreased by about 10 percent as the crack length was increased from about 40 to 125 mm. This degree of dependence on crack length should not detract from the usefulness of the arm gage in helping to define the specimen behavior during, and shortly after, a run-arrest segment.

Results and Discussion

Surface Velocites

Steel—Surface velocity measurements were made on A533B steel specimens in the vicinity of the nil ductility temperature (NDT), and these results, as well as the fracture surface appearances, are shown in Fig. 8. All specimens were fatigue precracked according to ASTM Test for Plane-Strain Fracture Toughness of Metallic Materials (E 399-74) (final K_{max} = 25 MN/m$^{3/2}$) so that the K_q values are lower than they would have been had they been initiated from blunt starter cracks. The three-position time curves in Fig. 8 are all similar. Shortly after initiation, the crack attained a high velocity and then decelerated to a low velocity prior to arrest. The velocities are within the range of 400 to 600 m/s for the fast part of the jump, and less than 100 m/s for the slow part of the jump. The crack grew continuously during the event, without any of the halts that had been reported previously [7]. In addition, the time over which the crack grew slowly was appreciable, that is, in excess of 100 μs, depending on the manner in which one selects the arrested crack length. At arrest, the crack front was further advanced near the midplane than at the surface (see

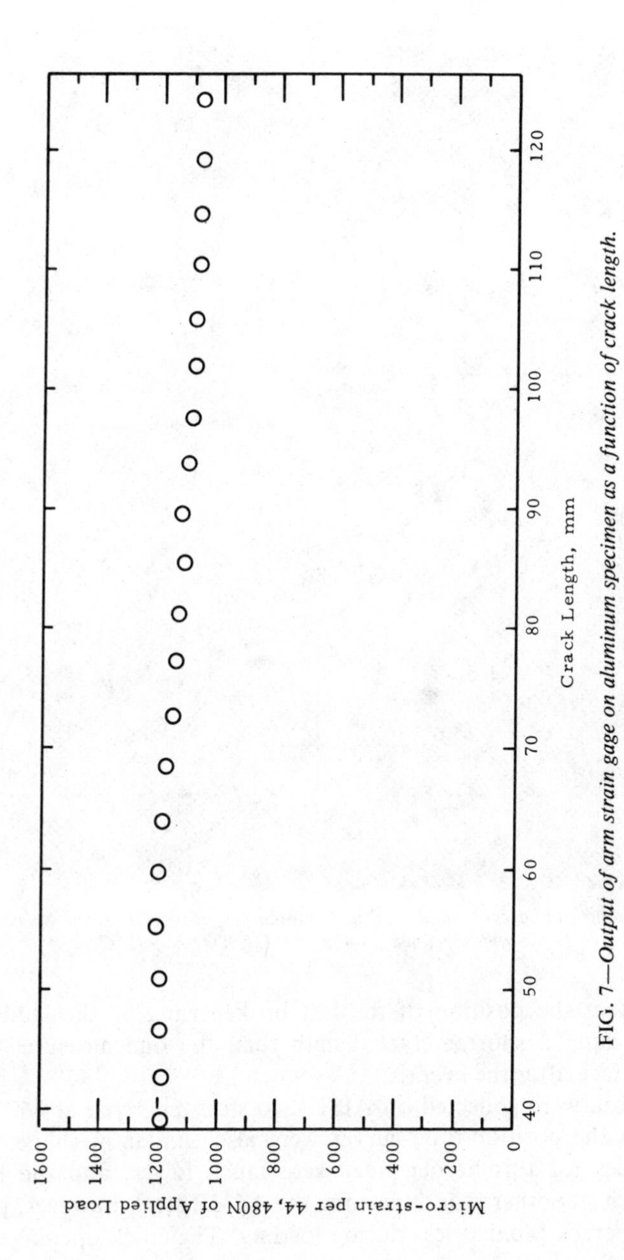

FIG. 7—*Output of arm strain gage on aluminum specimen as a function of crack length.*

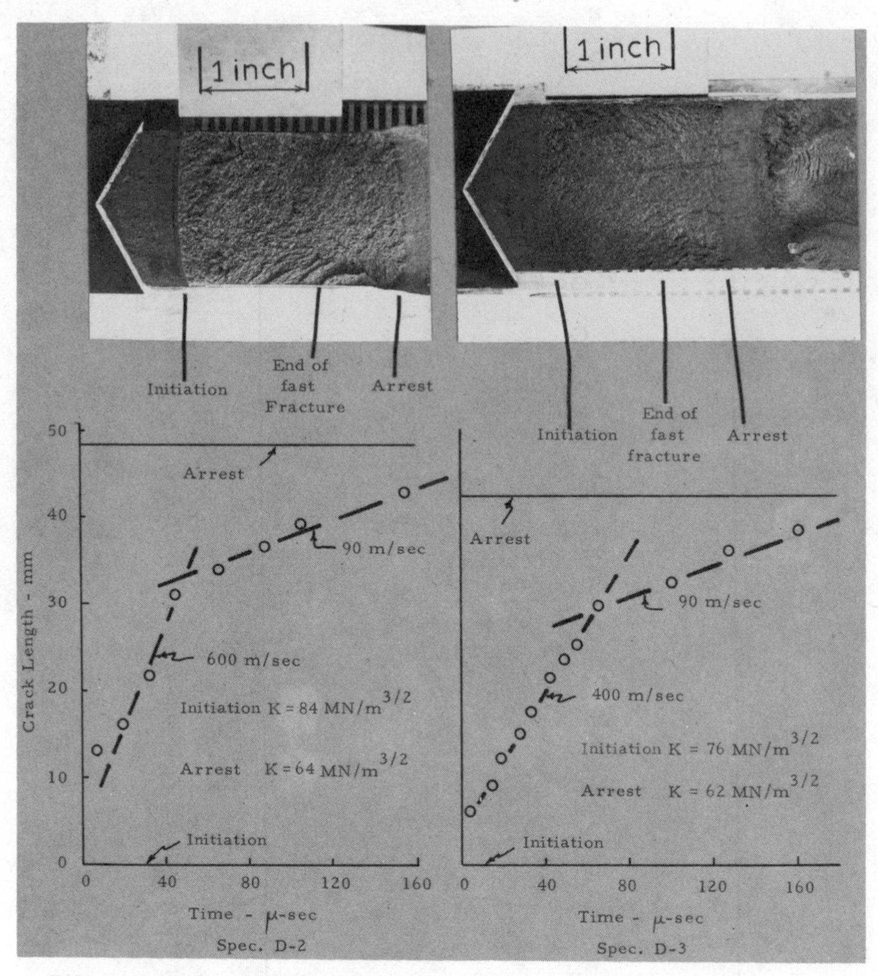

FIG. 8—*Fracture appearance and position-time curves of A533B steel. Specimens D-2 and D-3 tested at −12°C, and Specimens D-4 at −4°C (NDT × −12°C).*

Fig. 8) so that the position of the last broken rung of the ladder gage always indicated a shorter crack length than the one measured on the fracture surface after the event.

Similar data were collected on AISI 4340 steel tempered at 460°C. (R_C = 40), and the position-time curves were also similar in shape, Fig. 9. The velocities for this harder steel were much lower, and the fracture surface much smoother than it was for the A533B steel, however, possibly because the crack blunted less during loading. The crack opening stretch, δ, is proportional to the square of the ratio of K_q to the yield strength. Hence, the ratio of the crack-tip radius for the two steels would be about 2 or 3 to 1 at the time the crack began rapid extension. For the 4340 tests,

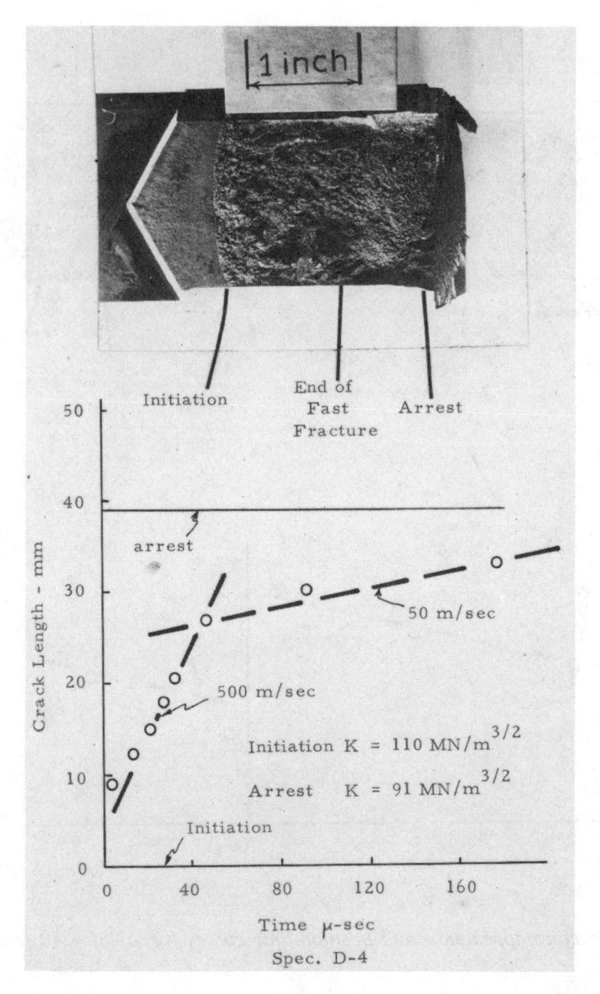

FIG. 8—*Continued.*

the crack jump distance was small so that it was not possible to stop the machine head displacement after the first "pop." Hence, the arrested crack length had to be estimated from compliance and surface markings on the fracture surface.

Again the crack was found to extend continuously with no evidence of halts. Although the amount of slow crack extension for the two steels was similar, because the crack extended so much slower in the hard steel than in the softer one, the time required for slow crack growth was about five to ten times longer in the latter than in the former.

Bonded Aluminum—It was not possible to use high ratios of K_q to K_{Ia} for the steel specimens and still arrest the crack because of the high ratio of machine to specimen compliance. Bonded aluminum specimens,

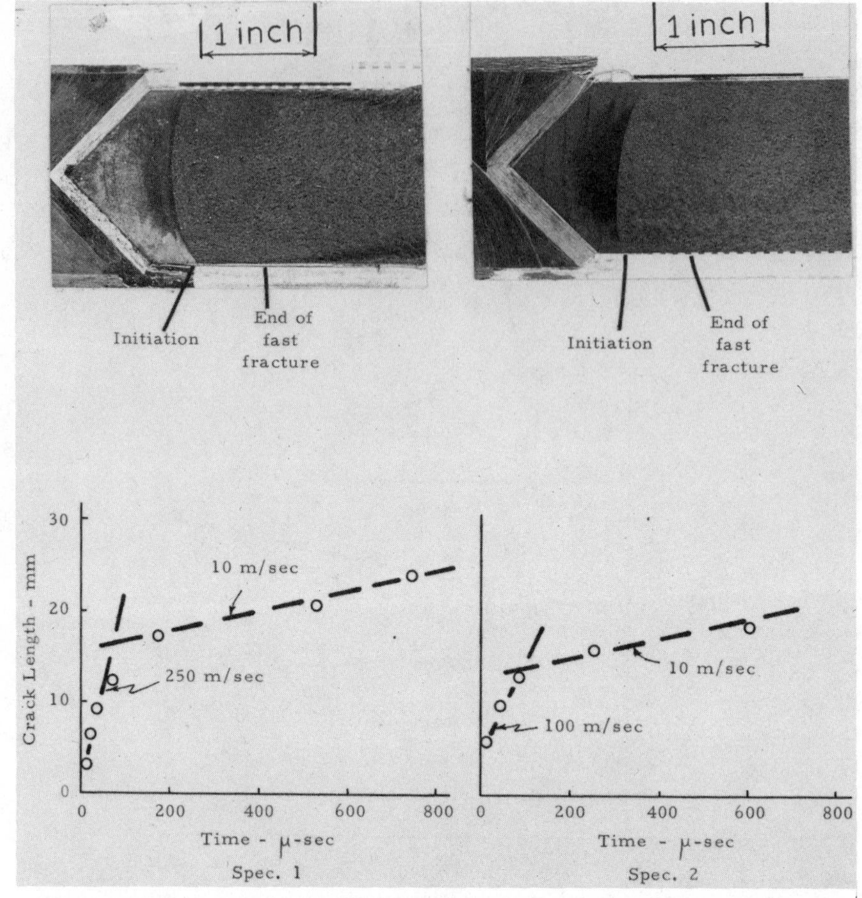

FIG. 9—*Fracture appearance and position-time curves for ANSI 4340 tested at* $-18°C$ ($R_C = 40$).

prepared as described in Ref *8*, did allow for very high values of K_q/K_{Ia} (actually $\mathcal{G}_q/\mathcal{G}_{Ia}$) so that some tests were run on this material as well. The crack-tip position time curves obtained on this material are shown in Fig. 10. Unfortunately, the toughness of the adhesive for slow running cracks was so low that the extending crack did not break the ladder gage and, as a consequence, velocity data just prior to arrest were not obtained. The previously reported velocity prior to arrest was about 1 m/s [*8*]. Of course, the crack length over which the crack ran rapidly was large because of the initial blunt crack.

Arm Gage Readings

Steel—The load-time records for the three A533B steel specimens are shown in Fig. 11*a*, and these are identical in shape to those reported pre-

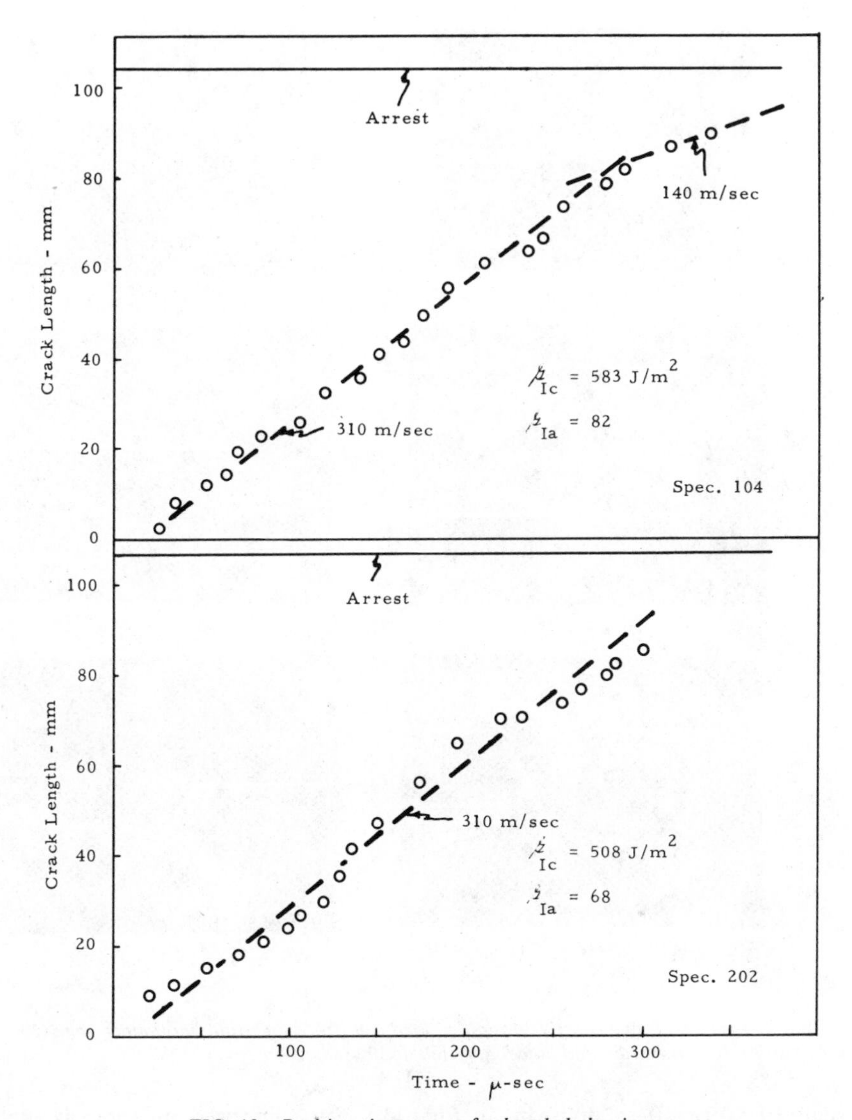

FIG. 10—*Position-time curves for bonded aluminum.*

viously [*3–8*]. The initiation and arrest toughness for Specimens D2 and D3 which were tested at −12°C (NDT = −12°C) were similar; K_{Ic} = 84 and 76 MN/m$^{3/2}$, and K_{Ia} = 64 and 62 MN/m$^{3/2}$, respectively. The values of K_{Ic} and K_{Ia} for Specimen D4, which was tested at a slightly higher temperature, −7°C, were somewhat higher, K_{Ic} = 110 and K_{Ia} = 91 MN/m$^{3/2}$.

The arm strain gage outputs are shown on a plot of voltage versus time on a time scale of 100 μs/division in Fig. 11*b*, and a somewhat finer time

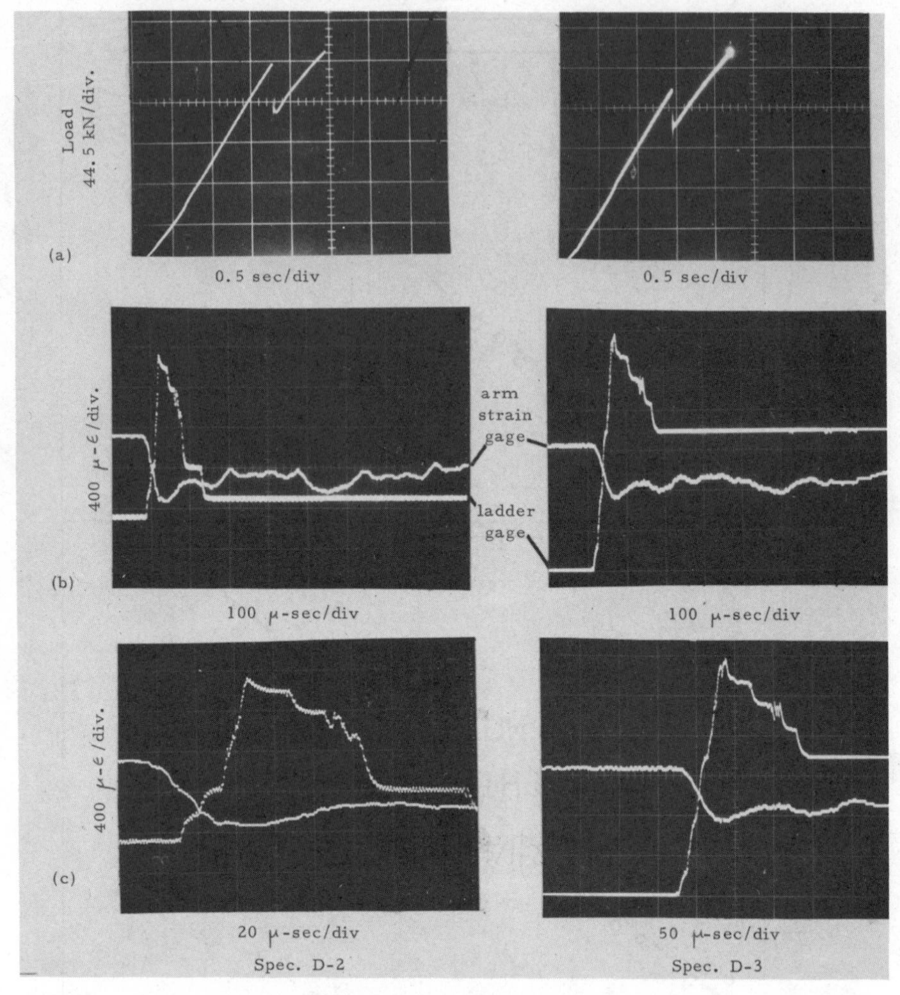

FIG. 11—(a) *Load-time curve from in-line load cell.* (b) *Arm strain and ladder gage* (*100 μs/division*). (c) *Arm strain and ladder gage* (*20 or 50 μs/division*).

scale of 50 or 10 μs/division, in Fig. 11*c*. Superimposed on these is the ladder gage output on which the velocity data of Fig. 8 were obtained. Although these time scales are too coarse for resolving breaking of the individual rungs (the time scale was expanded to 10 μs/division for obtaining the crack velocity curves) the crack surface velocity is proportional to the slope of the ladder gage output; the sign of the slope, as stated previously, is not important. Nevertheless, it is apparent for the three specimens that the strain on the arm gage drops abruptly over the time interval of fast crack extension, and then oscillates with a low amplitude and a period of 50 to 150 μs. This low amplitude oscillation starts before crack extension is complete and continues after arrest.

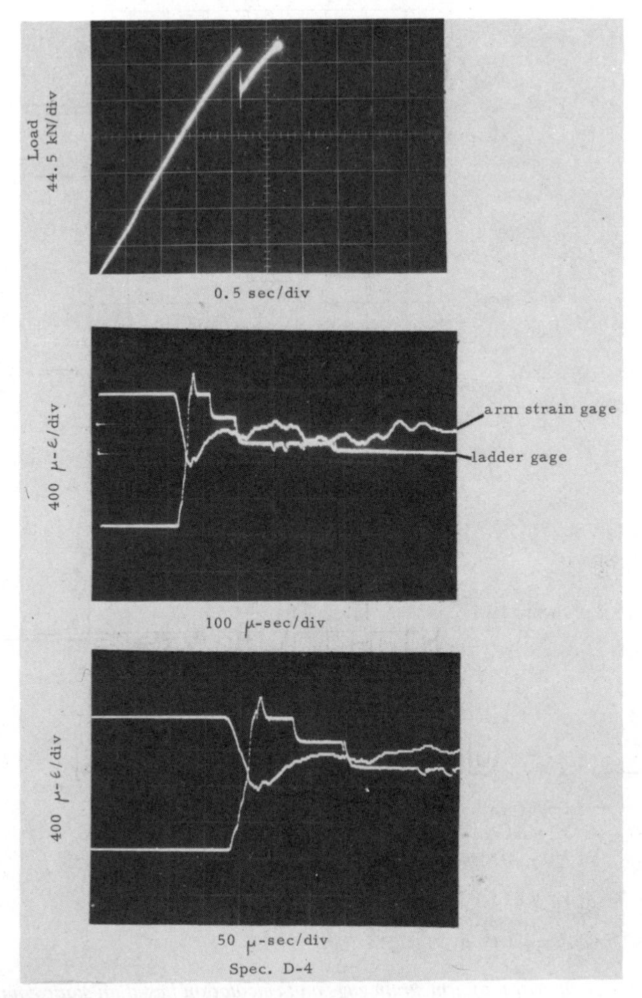

FIG. 11—*Continued.*

The arm gage output for the three A533B specimens was compared with a strain calculation, at the gage position, based on a condition of static equilibrium, Fig. 12. The three comparison figures are similar. Early in the event, the actual strain drops much faster than predicted by the static calculation, and the largest difference between the actual and static strains occurs at the end of fast crack extension. While the crack extends slowly, however, the strain in the arm increases, and then oscillates with a low amplitude about its eventual static value, suggesting that a static calculation of K near the end of a run-arrest segment of crack extension is an adequate approximation of the actual value of K.

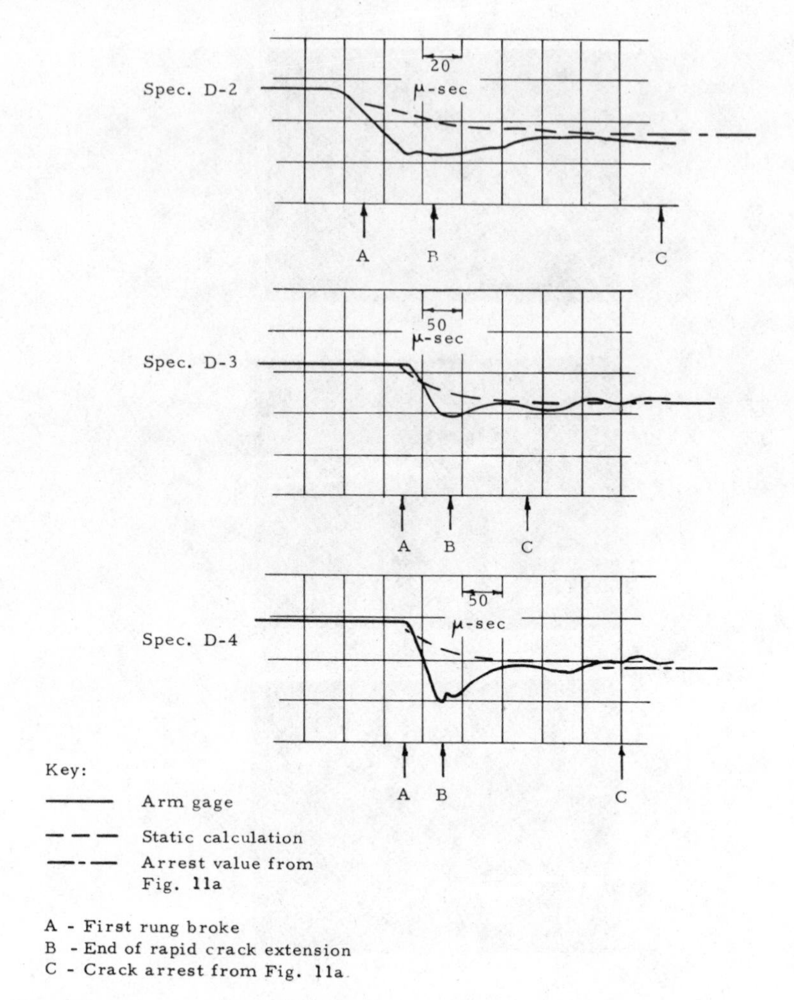

FIG. 12—*Comparison of arm strain gage and calculation based on static equilibrium.*

Similar tests were run on the AISI 4340, Fig. 13, but, because the difference between initiation and arrest was less for this steel than for the A533B, static calculations of strain were not conducted.

Bonded Aluminum—The arm gage data obtained on steel, like the surface velocity measurements, had to be based on modest ratios of K_q to K_a. The bonded aluminum specimens which made it possible to use a high ratio of initiation to arrest toughness were also strain gaged in order to collect arm strain gage data. A tracing of the strain-time curve for the two test specimens is shown in Fig. 14. These curves had a somewhat different shape than those obtained on the steel in that a peak occurred

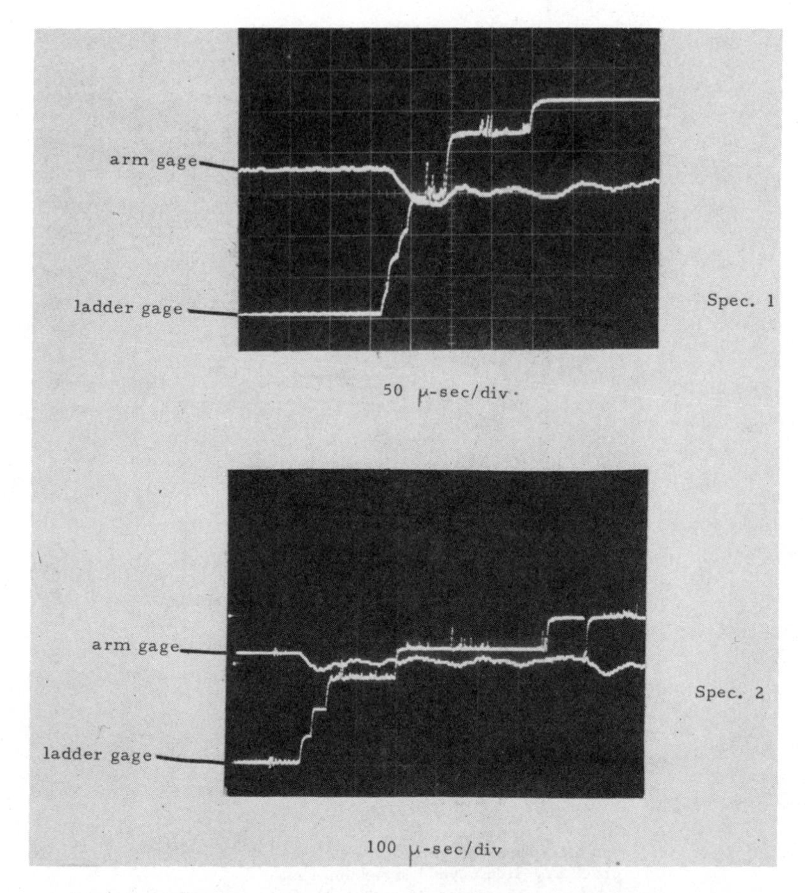

FIG. 13—*Arm gage and ladder gage record for AISI 4340 steel* (R_C = *40*).

shortly after initiation. After the peak, the voltage dropped rapidly, much like that obtained on the steel. Whether the peak is a result of the fact that the bonded aluminum specimens had a much higher compliance ($dC/da = 3.24 \times 10^{-5}$ versus 5.55×10^{-8} N^{-1} for the steel specimens), or was due to the larger difference between initiation and arrest toughness is not known. Nevertheless, in comparing the actual strains with those based on a static calculation, it was found that the dynamic portion of the specimen response was again dissipated long before the run-arrest segment was complete. As was the case with steel, during slow crack extension, near the end of the event, a static calculation of toughness is adequate even though the ratio of initiation to arrest toughness ($\mathcal{G}_q/\mathcal{G}_{Ia}$) was about 7:1 (or K_q/K_{Ia} about 2.5:1).

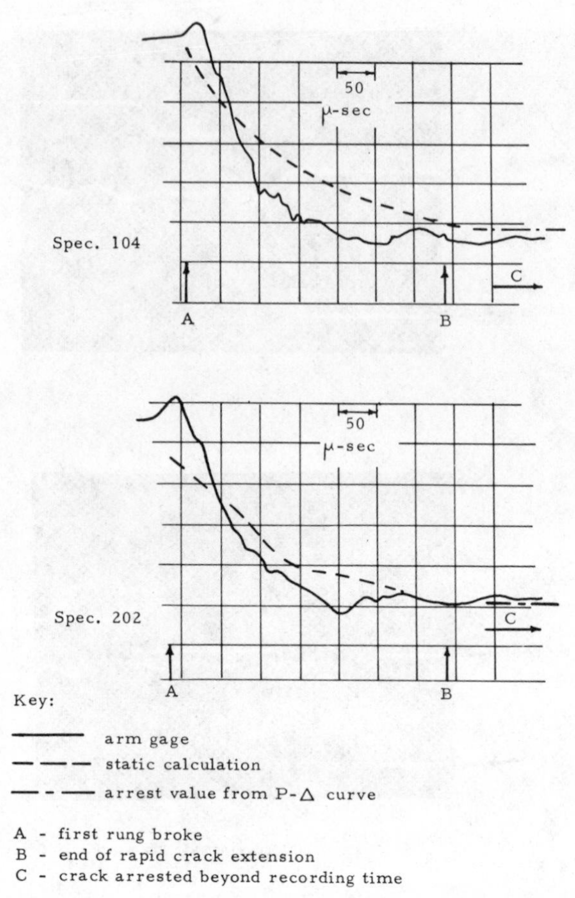

FIG. 14—*Comparison of arm strain gage and calculations based on static equilibrium.*

Shear Gage Reading

Steel—Shear strains were measured on only one steel specimen to date. For this specimen the fracture appearance and crack position versus time curve using both the ladder gage and shear gages are shown in Fig. 15. The toughness, both K_{Ic} and K_{Ia}, and crack jump length was somewhat larger for this specimen than for the other two tested at $-12°C$; nevertheless, the overall crack position time profile obtained with the ladder gage was similar to those shown in Fig. 8. A number of position time points could also be obtained with the shear gages using the calibration shown in Fig. 5: point a_1 is the crack length and the time at which Gage 1 crossed zero; a_2 is where (voltage on Gage 1) = $-$(voltage on Gage 2); a_3 where Gage 2 crossed zero; and a_4 where (voltage on Gage 1) = 2 (voltage on Gage 2). The crack velocity for the fast portion of crack extension is

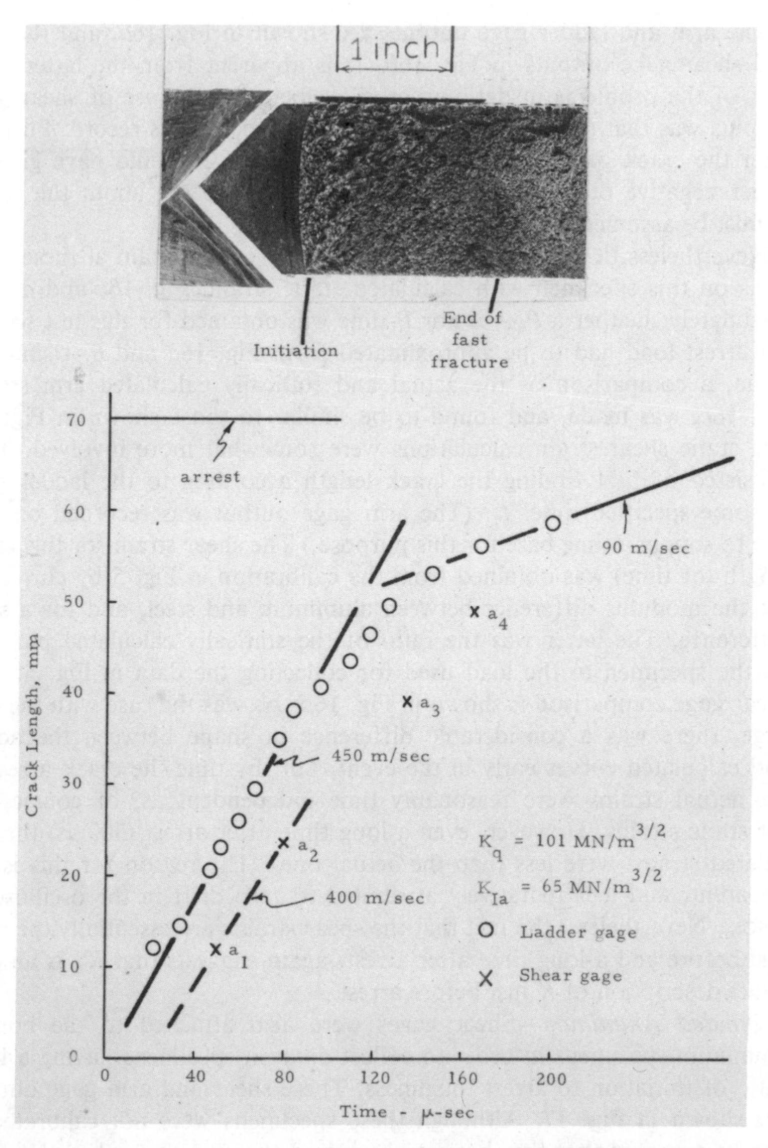

FIG. 15—*Fracture appearance and position-time curve of A533B steel (Specimen F-3, tested at −12°C).*

similar for the two methods of measuring it (450 versus 400 m/s). The reason the shear gage data lies to the right of the ladder gage data is not obvious, it may, however, be a result of the fact that the static calibration of Fig. 5 is not adequate for the fast running portion of a crack jump. In addition, if effective velocity is to be obtained with shear gages, it will be necessary to monitor more than two gage positions.

The arm and ladder gage outputs are shown in Fig. 16*a*, and the arm and shear gage outputs in Fig. 16*b*. It is apparent from the latter, that part of the problems in defining crack velocity by the use of shear gage outputs was that too insensitive a scale was used for this record. Further, after the crack passed both gage positions, Gage 1 should have given a larger negative output than Gage 2. Since the two are about the same, it must be assumed that some zero drift occurred.

Nevertheless, it was possible to compare the actual strain at these positions on this specimen with calculated static strain, Fig. 16*c* and *d*. Unfortunately, neither a $P - \Delta$ nor P-time was obtained for this test so that the arrest load had to be approximated from Fig. 16*a* and *b*. Using this value, a comparison of the actual and statically calculated arm strain, Fig. 16*c*, was made, and found to be similar to those shown in Fig. 12. The static shear strain calculations were somewhat more involved. They consisted of first finding the crack length according to the ladder gage at some specified time, t_1. (The arm gage output was recorded on Fig. 16*b* to supply a time base for this purpose.) The shear strain for this crack length (or time) was obtained from the calibration in Fig. 5 by correcting for the modulus difference between aluminum and steel, and for a scale difference. The latter was the ratio of the statically calculated pin load on the specimen to the load used for collecting the data in Fig. 5. This shear gage comparison is shown in Fig. 16*d*. As was the case with the arm gage, there was a considerable difference in shape between the actual and calculated curves early in the event, but, by time the crack arrested, the actual strains were reasonably time independent as, of course, are the static strains. However, even a long time after arrest (300 μs) the calculated strains were less than the actual ones. The reason for this is not apparent, and it is tentatively attributed to zero drift in the oscilloscope traces. Nevertheless, the fact that the shear strains are essentially the same just before and a long time after arrest, again suggests that K_{Ia} is an adequate description of K just before arrest.

Bonded Aluminum—Shear gages were also attached to the bonded aluminum specimens in order to collect data on specimens having a large ratio of initiation to arrest toughness. These shear and arm gage outputs are shown in Fig. 17. Although these specimens were not calibrated, it can be assumed that the shear strain passed through zero when the crack tip was directly below the shear gage. Using this assumption, the effective crack velocity for Specimen 104 was about 360 m/s, and for Specimen 202, 320 m/s, both of which are in close agreement with the values in Fig. 10.

The time at which rapid crack extension was completed for these two specimens is also shown in Fig. 17, and crack arrest occurred long after these records were completed. Nevertheless, it is apparent that even with

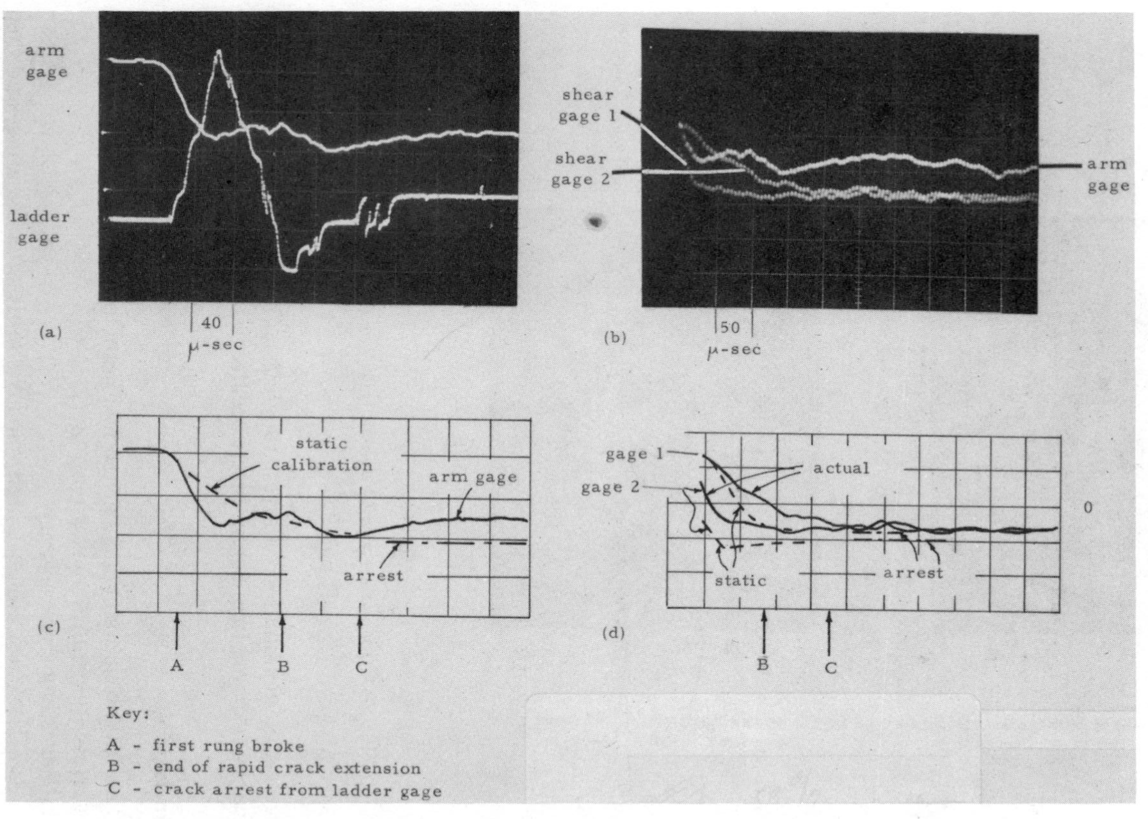

FIG. 16—*Comparison of actual and statically calculated strains.* (a)(c) *Arm gage.* (b)(d) *Shear gages.*

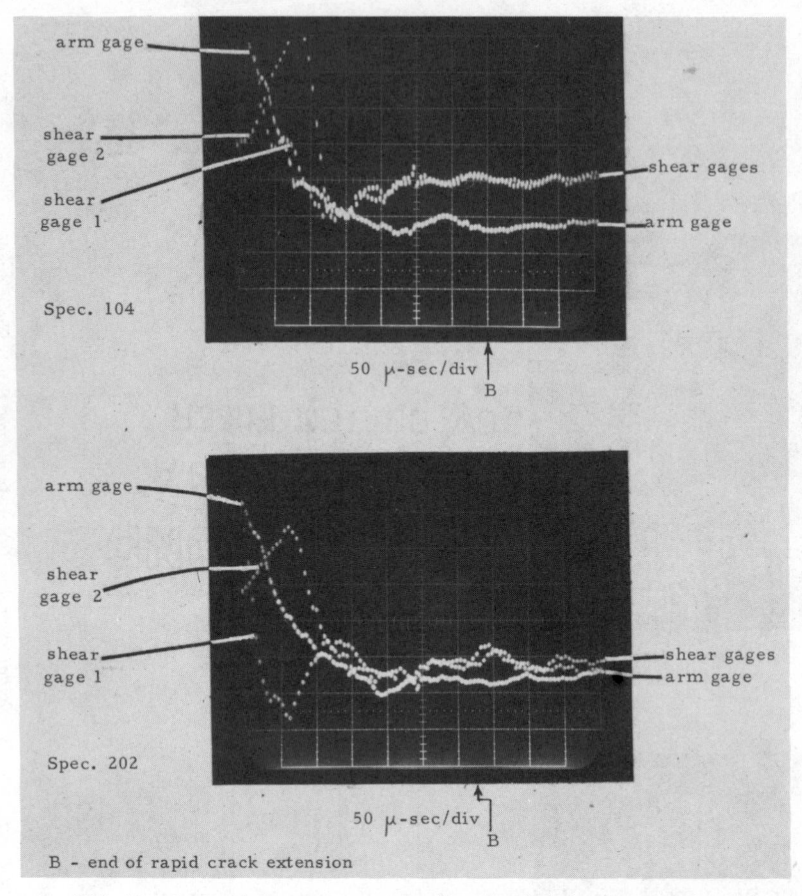

FIG. 17—*Arm and shear gages outputs from bonded aluminum specimen.*

large ratios of initiation to arrest toughness, the shear strains exhibit no dynamic response long before arrest occurs.

Conclusions

The following comments can be made on specimen behavior during a run-arrest segment of crack extension:

1. Regarding crack velocity
   (*a*) The crack attains a high velocity shortly after initiating, and then decelerates in a continuous fashion to arrest.
   (*b*) The crack velocity appears to increase for materials as the ratio of $K^2/\sigma ys$ is increased.
   (*c*) As the initiating crack is made blunter, the initial velocity is in-

creased, and persists over a longer portion of the run-arrest segment.

2. Regarding dynamic response of specimen
   (*a*) It is convenient to consider the total specimen behavior as a dynamic disturbance superimposed on a static response to the applied load. Strains can then be measured at various positions on the specimen, and compared with calculations of strains, based on a condition of static equilibrium, for these same locations. In this way the dynamic and static responses can be separated.
   (*b*) Early in a run-arrest segment, dynamic effects are so large that static calculations do not describe the specimen behavior. During the latter part of the event, prior to arrest, however, the dynamic effects are modest, and the actual behavior is described adequately by static calculations.
   (*c*) Since static and actual values of strain are approximately equal near arrest, K_{Ia} is an adequate description of K just prior to arrest.
   (*d*) If the dependence of $\dot{a}$ on K is described by a gamma (Γ) for the test material, K_{Ia} is an adequate identification of K_{Im}.

Acknowledgments

This paper describes work done for the Electric Power Research Institute (EPRI) on Contract No. RP 303-1. Comments by Dr. K. E. Stahlkopf and, more recently, Dr. T. U. Marston, of EPRI, were helpful. The many discussions the authors had with Professor G. R. Irwin and Dr. S. Mostovoy are gratefully acknowledged.

References

[1] Krafft, J. M. and Irwin, G. R. in *Fracture Toughness Testing and Its Application, ASTM STP 381,* American Society for Testing and Materials, 1965, p. 114.

[2] Irwin, G. R. and Wells, A. A., *Metallurgical Reviews,* Vol. 10, No. 38, 1965, p. 223.

[3] Hahn, G. T. et al, "Critical Experiments, Measurements and Analyses to Establish a Crack Arrest Methodology for Nuclear Pressure Vessel Steels," Report BMI-1937, Battelle Columbus Laboratories, Columbus, Ohio, Aug. 1975.

[4] Freund, L. B., *Journal of the Mechanics and Physics of Solids,* Vol. 20, 1972, Part 1, p. 129, Part 2, p. 141.

[5] Anthony, S. R., Chubb, J. P., and Congleton, J., *Philosophical Magazine,* Vol. 22, No. 180, 1970.

[6] Crosley, P. B. and Ripling, E. J., this publication, pp. 372–391.

[7] Hahn, G. T. et al in *Cracks and Fracture, ASTM STP 601,* American Society for Testing and Materials, 1976, pp. 209–233.

[8] Mostovoy, S., Crosley, P. B., and Ripling, E. J. in *Cracks and Fracture, ASTM STP 601,* American Society for Testing and Materials, 1976, pp. 234–244.

S. J. Burns[1] *and C. L. Chow*[1]

Crack Propagation with Crack-Tip Critical Bending Moments in Double-Cantilever-Beam Specimens

REFERENCE: Burns, S. J. and Chow, C. L., "**Crack Propagation with Crack-Tip Critical Bending Moments in Double-Cantilever-Beam Specimens,**" *Fast Fracture and Crack Arrest, ASTM STP 627,* G. T. Hahn and M. F. Kanninen, Eds., American Society for Testing and Materials, 1977, pp. 228–240.

ABSTRACT: Rapidly wedged, double-cantilever-beam (DCB) specimens have a critical bending moment as a propagating fracture criterion in the limit of the Bernoulli-Euler beam theory. The magnitude of the critical bending moment is calculated from a fully dynamic analysis of crack propagation. The shear force in the beam at the constant displacement rate end of the DCB specimen, multiplied by the square root of the loading time, is related to the critical bending moment. Experimental measurements of the time dependence of the shear force have been used to calculate the specific fracture surface energy versus crack velocity. The crack velocity in a single specimen decreases with increasing time, it varies by a factor of five and is typically 0.01 of $\sqrt{E/\rho}$. Details of the experimental measurements for brittle and ductile fractures, including stress intensity values versus crack velocity, are described.

KEY WORDS: cantilever beams, crack propagation, fracture properties, stress intensity, shear force, bending, crack velocity

The critical stress intensity factor for a propagating crack, K_{ID}, is a function of the crack velocity, the temperature of the test specimen, and the material tested. K_{ID} values in the literature have been measured in double-cantilever-beam (DCB) specimens by experimentally observing the crack length as a function of time or the stress intensity factors before and after crack propagation [*1,2*].[2] The object of this paper is to report on measurements of K_{ID} obtained by recording the time dependence of the shear force in DCB specimens that have been rapidly wedged open.

All reported K_{ID} values in the literature are found by comparing specific parameters calculated from dynamic mechanics analysis of a propagating crack, with a prescribed specimen geometry and loading [*3,4*], to experi-

[1]Associate professor and research assistant, respectively, Department of Mechanical and Aerospace Sciences, University of Rochester, Rochester, N.Y. 14627.

[2]The italic numbers in brackets refer to the list of references appended to this paper.

mental measurements of the same parameters. In the rapidly wedged DCB specimen the crack velocity decreases as the crack length increases; so, measured K_{ID} values are often recorded over an order of magnitude in crack velocities from a single specimen [*1*].

K_{ID} values in the literature frequently show significant experimental scatter. Part of the experimental scatter is affected directly by the difficulty of absolute measurements of the crack length. In the simple static DCB specimen with a fixed opening at the load end, the specific fracture surface energy, R, depends on the fourth power of the crack length. Thus, a 10 percent error in the measured crack length gives a 40 percent error in R. The approach used in this paper is to apply experimentally a constant rate opening on the end of the DCB specimen and measure experimentally the shear force near the load end as a function of time. The R values during crack propagation are computed from the time dependence of the shear force as calculated from the dynamic mechanics analysis of the rapidly wedged DCB specimen [*3*]. For plane-strain fracture $R = K_{ID}^2/E\ (1 - \nu^2)$ when the crack speeds are slower than several percent of the sound speed; however, if crack speed is very large, then K_{ID} is not simply related to the measured R value. In an infinite solid the analysis of Broberg [*5*] or Freund [*6*] relates R to K_{ID}.

The fracture criterion in DCB specimens in the limit of the Bernoulli-Euler beam theory, with the beam built in at the crack tip is a critical bending moment, M^*, at the crack tip. In general, the value of M^* may depend on the crack velocity, $\dot{l}$.

$$M^* = (R(\dot{l})WEI)^{1/2} \tag{1}$$

where

W = width of the crack,
E = Young's modulus, and
I = moment of inertia of one arm of the beam about the neutral axis.

This paper describes in detail how the critical bending moment and thus $R(\dot{l})$ may be deduced during crack propagation. In static beam theory the bending moment at the crack tip is given by the shear force at the load end times the crack length.

In rapidly wedged, dynamic crack propagation the value of the bending moment is determined by the shear force times the square root of the time subsequent to the contact of the wedge with the specimen.

The Procedure Section formally relates the shear force to the specific fracture surface energy. Also included are the shear force measurement techniques. The Experimental Results Section describes the experimental measurements on rapidly wedged DCB specimens and the interpretation of these measurements. K_{ID} versus crack velocity data are also presented in this section. In the Conclusion Section the general findings are summarized.

Procedure

Relating the Shear Force to the Specific Fracture Surface Energy

The analytic solution for crack propagation in rapidly wedged DCB specimens is found in Ref *3*; the solution is restricted to the slender Bernoulli-Euler beam theory with constant specific fracture surface energy. The beam is considered built in at the crack tip. The initial condition, during rapid wedging, is zero crack length at zero time. The displacement of the neutral axis of the beam, $y(x,t)$ is also given in the analytic solution [*3*]. In $y(x,t)$, x is the distance from the load end of the beam to a point along the beam; t is the time subsequent to the contact of the wedge with the beam. The shear force in the beam, $Q(x,t)$ is computed from the third derivative of $y(x,t)$ by

$$EI\frac{\partial^3 y}{\partial x^3}(x,t) = Q(x,t) \tag{2}$$

A dimensionless shear quantity is formed from $Q(x,t)$.

$$\frac{Q(x,t)\sqrt{t}}{(EI)^{1/4}\,(\rho A)^{3/4}V_e} \equiv Q_N(x,t)\sqrt{t} \tag{3}$$

where

ρ = density of the beam,
A = cross sectional area of the beam, and
V_e = constant end loading velocity of the beam.

It is now noted that $Q_N(x,t)\sqrt{t}$ for $x = 0$ is only a function of R, the beam geometry, modulus, and density. $Q_N(o,t)\sqrt{t}$ will be given as a function of a dimensionless crack propagation parameter, η_l, where

$$\eta_l \equiv \frac{1}{4}\left[\frac{\rho A}{EI}\right]^{1/2}\frac{(l(t))^2}{t} \tag{4}$$

$l(t)$ is the crack length at the time t. It should be noted that when the time for the DCB specimen to break completely is known, and when the final crack length is known, then η_l is known for that time. It follows from Eq 4 that when η_l = constant, the crack velocity, $\dot{l} = l(t)/2t \propto 1/l$. Now, Fig. 1 is $Q_N(o,t)\sqrt{t}$ plotted versus η_l as calculated from Ref *3*. Figure 2 relates R to η_l during crack propagation. In this second figure R is given

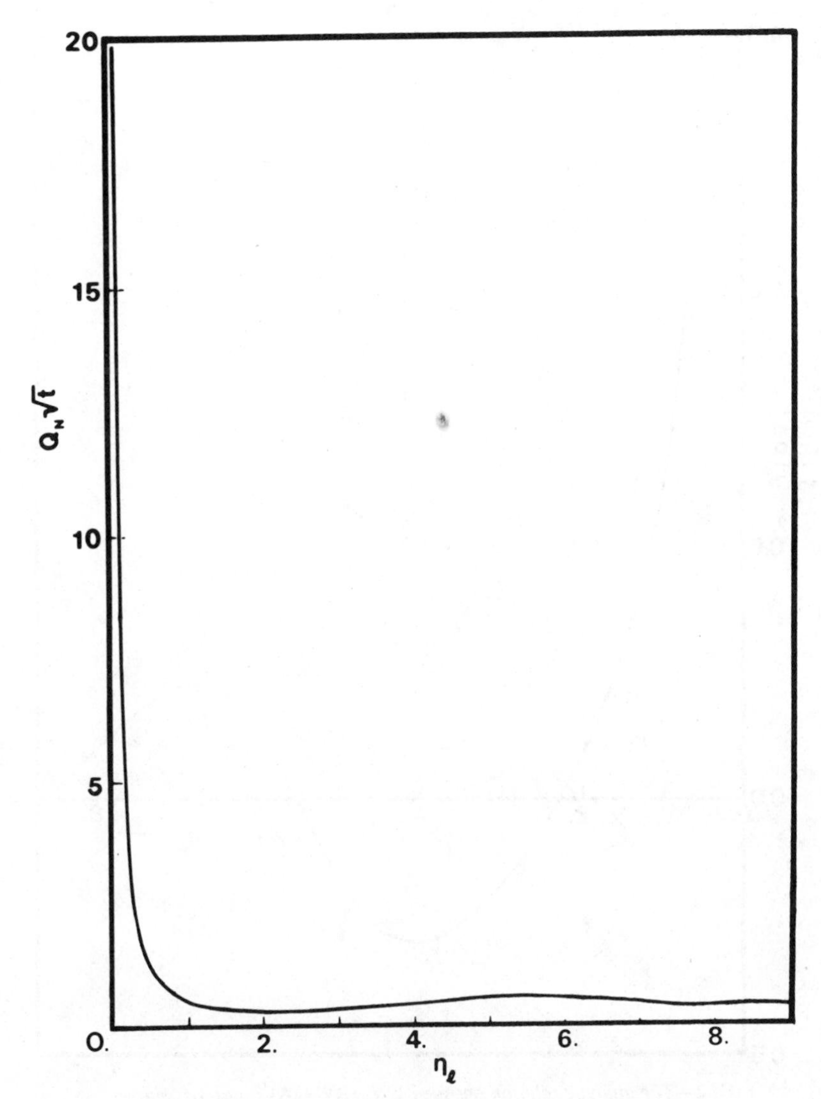

FIG. 1—*The analytic relation between* $Q_N\sqrt{t}$ *and* η_1 *is shown.*

in the dimensionless parameter $1/V_e[RW/\rho A]^{1/2}$. Figure 2 follows directly from Ref *3*.

The specific fracture surface energy, R, during crack propagation is calculated from experimental data by measuring the shear force at $x = 0$ as a function of time in the DCB specimen. From these data $Q\sqrt{t}$ is formulated. Note that ideally $Q\sqrt{t}$ and thus $Q_N\sqrt{t}$ is a constant when R is constant. Figure 1 relates the constant value of $Q_N(o,t)\sqrt{t}$ to the

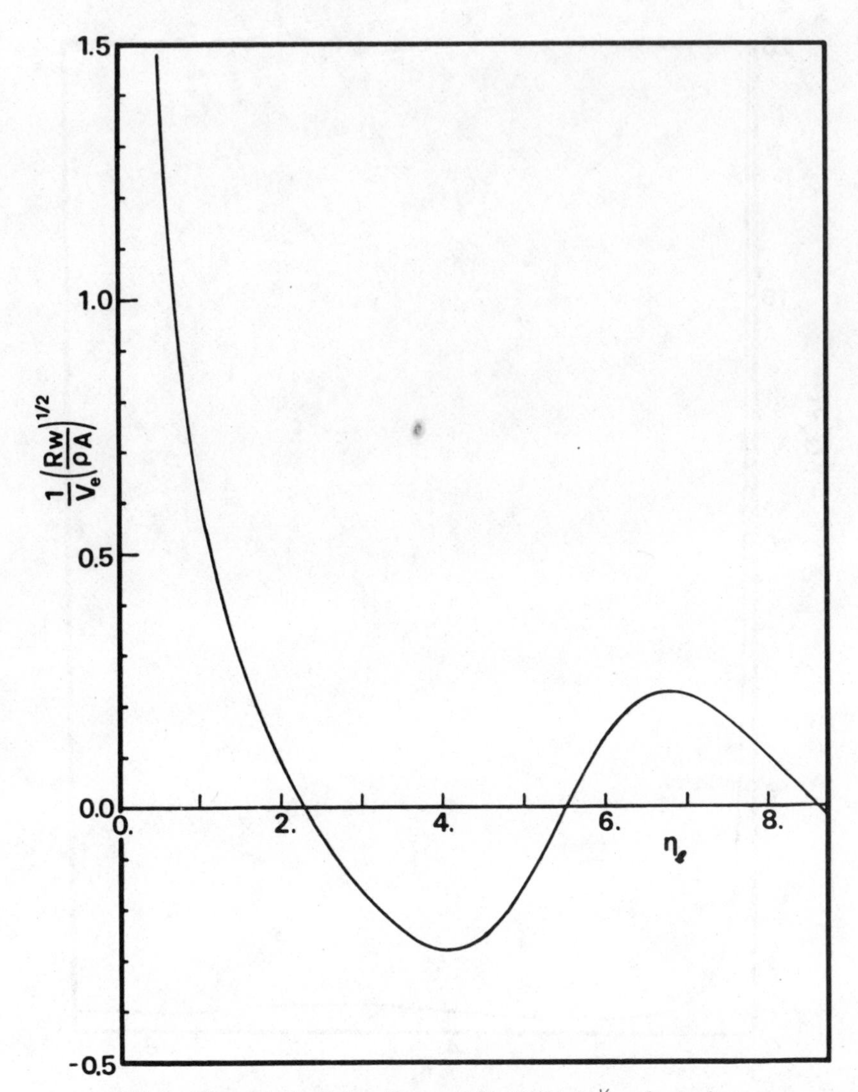

FIG. 2—*The analytic relation between* $1/V_e(RW/\rho A)^{1/2}$ *and* η_1 *is shown.*

constant value of η_l. R during the crack propagation is found from Fig. 2 since η_l is known.

One benefit of measuring the shear force to obtain the critical stress intensity factor during crack propagation, K_D, is that in the slow crack propagation limit K_D is proportional to $(Q_N\sqrt{t})^{2/3}$. Thus, the error in measurement of Q to 5 percent and t to 1 percent should give K_D accurate to 4 percent. In principle, a shear force measurement gives a more accurate determination of K_D than the direct measurements of the crack length. A second advantage to measuring R from $Q\sqrt{t}$ during crack propagation is that zero time, that is, when the wedge first contacts the specimen, is determined with reasonable accuracy. This follows immediately since $Q(o,t)$ rises very rapidly when the wedge first contacts the specimen. A simple extrapolation of $Q(o,t)$ to zero shear force determines zero time.

A third benefit to this method of measuring R during crack propagation is that the electronic hardware for measuring the shear force versus time is the same as that used in the American Society for Testing and Materials K_{Id} programs [7]. Although the interpretation of the data is quite different.

The formal theory of Ref *3* restricts $Q_N(o,t)\sqrt{t}$, η_l, and R to be exactly constant during crack propagation. However, it has been shown by comparing static and quasi-dynamic solutions of rapidly wedged DCB specimens, that are not restricted to R = constant, that for $\eta_l < 1$ that R may depend on $\dot{l}$ during crack propagation [3]. With this restriction on η_l, $Q_N(o,t)\sqrt{t}$ may also depend on t during crack propagation.

Experimental Measurements of the Shear Force

Details of the rapid wedge loading machine and the design of the specimens have been reported elsewhere [8,9]. The wedge loading machine is designed to give rigid loading of the DCB specimen with a constant applied deflection rate. This is achieved by a massive, 300 kg, hammer free falling approximately 2 m. The side grooved specimen is typically 7.0 by 2.5 by 40 cm. It is designed to be a slender beam that remains essentially elastic during the fracture test.

The shear force is measured on the DCB specimen by recording the shear strain on the neutral axis of the beam with a 90-deg rosette strain gage. The 90-deg rosette gage is placed so it is primarily sensitive to shear forces in the beam and insensitive to axial forces. The gage is located near the load end of the DCB specimen. The gage is placed as near to the neutral axis as possible and approximately a distance equal to one half the height of the beam away from the load point. Thus, the gage is midway between the load point and the initial crack length in the DCB specimen. The signal from the gage is recorded using a vertical amplifier, plug-in unit on an oscilloscope. The nominal rise time of the electronic system is 60 μs with a frequency response of 6 kHz. The shear force measurement versus time is recorded photographically using a triggered single sweep of the oscilloscope.

Absolute values of the deflection on the oscilloscope are calibrated to shear force values by statically loading the specimen with a negative shear force as measured with a load cell on a tensile machine. The gage output must be linear in the shear force. The response of the gage has been checked to be linear in the shear force although the slope of the response curve depends partially on the loading arrangement. If the gage were to measure the strain at a point (as opposed to a finite area) on the neutral axis of a beam very far from the load point the gage response should be insensitive to the loading arrangement. For the loading arrangement used during our crack propagation tests the load point is only one half the beam height away from the gage, so that the detail geometry of the contract of the wedge to the beam can give differences as large as 20 percent between the calibrated static force and the dynamically measured shear force. It is also important to have the wedge contact the DCB specimen in the midplane. A very thin piece of shimstock between the wedge and DCB specimen is ideal for this purpose. The shear force testing of rapidly wedged DCB specimens is self-calibrating (as will be discussed in the next section).

The photographic record of the shear force versus time during the fracture of a specimen, is processed by electronically digitizing the Q trace and replotting $Q\sqrt{t}$ versus t.

Experimental Results

$Q_N\sqrt{t}$ *versus* t *in Titanium Alloy*

The theory for determining R during crack propagation and the experimental procedures for recording the shear force, Q, during crack propagation were outlined in the previous section. Figure 3 shows Q versus t for a specimen of Ti-6A1-4V fractured at room temperature. This material has been investigated for dynamic fracture using direct measurements of crack length versus time [*9*]. Figure 3 shows several characteristic features of a Q versus t curve for rapidly wedged DCB specimens. The value of Q is zero prior to the wedge contacting the specimen on the left of the figure. The shear force then rises very rapidly after the wedge contacts the specimen. Q at the end of the loading curve reaches a maximum value and then Q decreases with time. The start of crack propagation is identified with the maximum value of Q on the far left of Fig. 3. This point corresponds to the intersection of the nearly smooth rising Q versus t curve and the decreasing part of the Q versus t curve after crack propagation. The Q trace is not smooth but shows small amplitude oscillations. At much later times, on the right of Fig. 3 the value of the shear force first rises rapidly and then decreases very rapidly to zero. Although not shown in Fig. 3 at longer times the shear force continues to oscillate about the zero value with several mixed frequencies. At very long times a single frequency is achieved, and the amplitude of the signal decays as time increases.

The time when the wedge first fully contacted the specimen is determined from the intersection of the zero Q value and the extrapolated

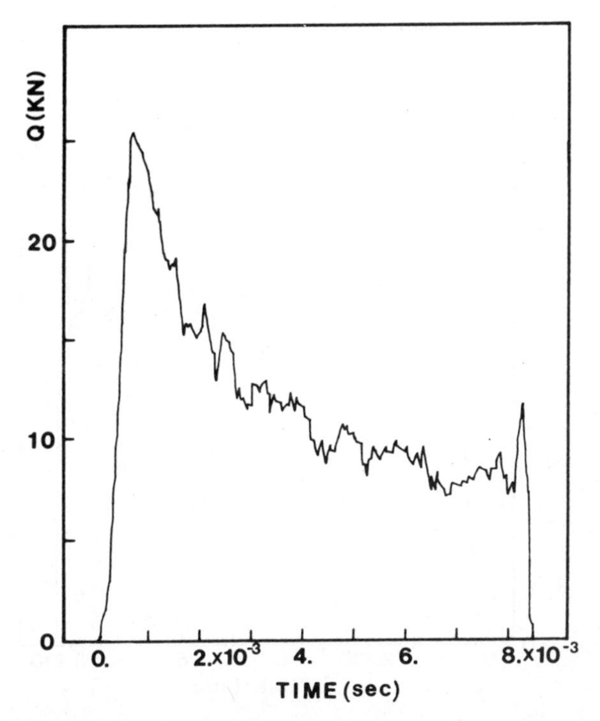

FIG. 3—*An experimental measurement of* Q *versus* t *for a titanium alloy specimen fractured at room temperature. The scale of the ordinate is determined from the final fracture point in Fig. 4 (see text).*

intersection of the rapidly rising shear force curve on the left of Fig. 3. Having defined zero time, $Q\sqrt{t}$ is now formed. $Q\sqrt{t}$ is the information necessary to determine R during the crack propagation. Figure 4 is $Q_N\sqrt{t}$ versus t for this specimen as computed from the digitized trace of Fig. 3 with the scale of the ordinate as determined next. $Q\sqrt{t}$ is proportional to $Q_N\sqrt{t}$, where $Q_N\sqrt{t}$ is dimensionless as given in Eq 3. On the far right of Fig. 4 just before $Q\sqrt{t}$ increases rapidly the specimen is fractured completely. At this point the crack length is the complete length of the specimen, and the time for the crack to propagate to this length is known from the abscissa value of t in either the Q or the $Q\sqrt{t}$ curves. Thus, at the end of the fracture η_l is known from the final crack length. At the end of the test $Q_N\sqrt{t}$ may now be determined from Fig. 1 since η_l is known for the final crack length. The scale of the ordinate axis in Fig. 4 is now determined. $Q_N(t)\sqrt{t}$ and $\eta_l(t)$ are determined throughout the entire test once the scale of the ordinate is chosen. As the crack approaches the entire length of the specimen, simple beam theory is not strictly applicable; thus, the final calibration point may introduce a systematic error of up to 5 percent in the absolute scale of the $Q_N(t)\sqrt{t}$ trace. It should be noted,

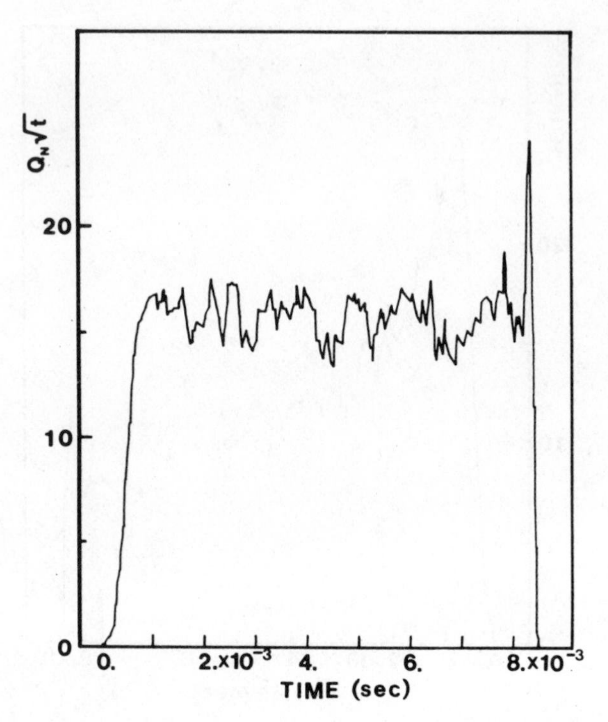

FIG. 4—*The experimental values of* $Q_N\sqrt{t}$ *versus* t *computed from the data in Fig. 3. The scale of the ordinate is defined from the final crack length.*

however, that the relative trends in K_D versus crack velocity curves are uneffected by minor adjustments in the scale of the $Q_N\sqrt{t}$ versus t curve. It probably would be more appropriate to calculate the scale of $Q_N \sqrt{t}$ curve by using a crack propagation gage near the midpoint of the DCB specimen.

It should be noted in Fig. 4 that $Q_N\sqrt{t}$ rises rapidly to a nearly constant value, and then oscillates with a period that increases slightly with time. On the extreme right of Fig. 4, $Q_N\sqrt{t}$ rises very rapidly and then goes to zero. It ultimately would become negative since Q becomes negative. The oscillations during crack propagation in $Q_N\sqrt{t}$ are nearly periodic and are thus believed to be associated with vibrations in the specimen. The surface of the fractured specimen showed no indications that the crack hesitated nor deviated from the fracture plane. In the analysis of the $Q_N\sqrt{t}$ data these oscillations will be considered not to contribute to the crack-tip bending moment and will be smoothed over in calculating the R data.

If the oscillations in Fig. 4 are not smoothed then the K_D values, when compared to the smoothed K_D values, throughout the fracture test does not vary by more than ± 5 percent. However, if the oscillations were interpreted as a rapid variation in η_l during an oscillation of $Q_N\sqrt{t}$ then the crack length would decrease and the crack velocity would be negative between oscillations. This is an unrealistic interpretation whereas vibrational modes in the DCB specimen are excited undoubtedly during the massive wedge impact. Thus, it is argued that the oscillations in $Q_N\sqrt{t}$, which are approximately of the same period as the free vibration of the beam, do not directly contribute to the crack tip bending moment nor do they represent periodic oscillations of the crack velocity. Thus, for the computation of K_D versus $\dot{l}$ as shown in Fig. 5, these oscillations have been removed and $\dot{l}$ is a smoothed crack velocity.

The K_D values of Fig. 5 have been corrected for the strain energy beyond the crack tip, that is, from slender to thick beam specimens. This is an important correction when the crack length is short and comparable to the beam height [*10*]. The K_D values recorded in Fig. 5 are about 50 percent larger than K_{Ic} in this material [*9*]. The fracture mode along the entire specimen is by ductile void coalescence. A plane-strain fracture condition is not achieved since the fracture surface is not flat. In addition, the calculated, static, plane-strain width as obtained from the dynamic K_D value and the static yield value is 50 percent larger than the measured fracture width.

$Q_N\sqrt{t}$ *versus* t *in Steel*

Figure 6 is Q versus t for a 1018 cold-rolled steel specimen. The specimen was fractured at −196°C. Q rises rapidly on the left of the figure and then decreases with time. On the right of the figure, Q increases and then goes to zero. Q then oscillates about zero with several frequencies. Figure 7 is $Q_N\sqrt{t}$ versus t as digitized from Fig. 6 following the same pro-

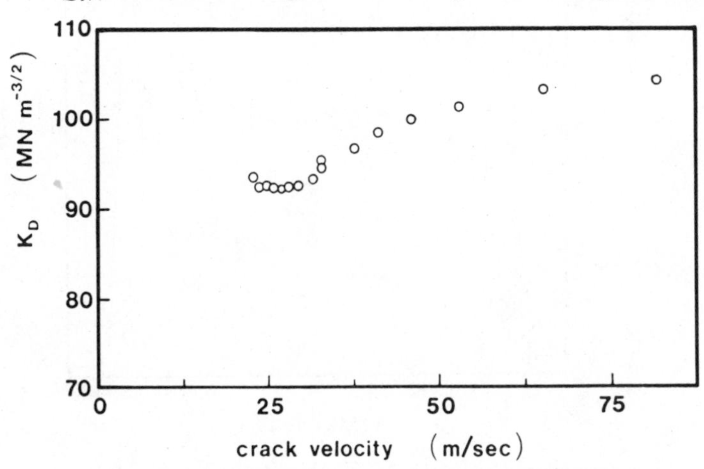

FIG. 5—K_D *versus crack velocity for titanium alloy as calculated from Fig. 4.*

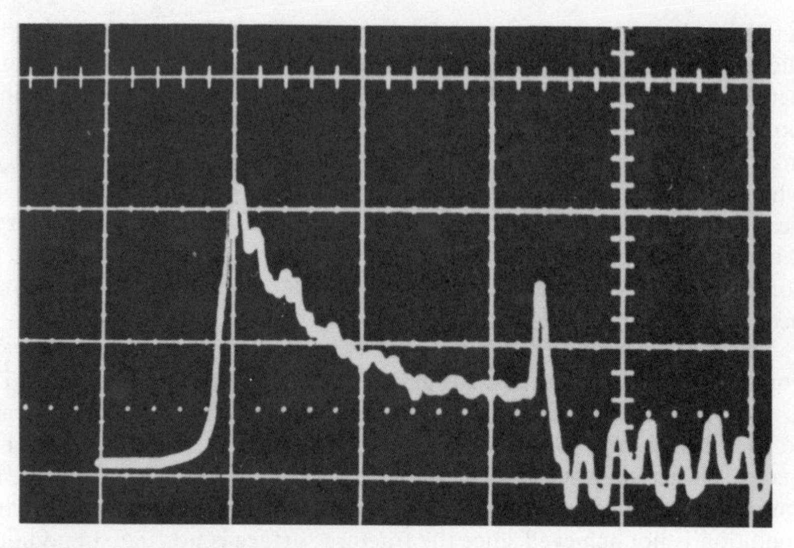

FIG. 6—*A photographic record of* Q *versus* t *for 1018 cold-rolled steel fractured at −196°C. The abscissa time axis is 2 ms/division.*

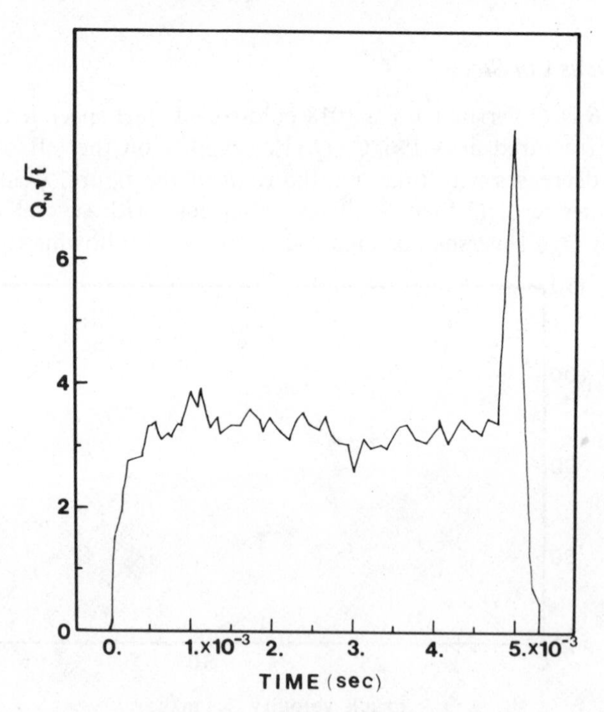

FIG. 7—*The experimental values of* $Q_N\sqrt{t}$ *versus* t *computed from the data in Fig. 6. The scale of the ordinate is defined from the final crack length.*

cedure used in Fig. 4. After rising rapidly during loading $Q_N\sqrt{t}$ varies slowly with time with small amplitude oscillations. Just before the large peak on the right of Fig. 7, the crack has broken the specimen completely. The time value just prior to this peak and the complete length of the broken DCB specimen and therefore the crack, is used to calculate η_l at this point. Figure 1 is now used to determine the scale of the $Q_N\sqrt{t}$ ordinate. The data in Fig. 7 are smoothed, and K_{ID} versus $\dot{l}$ is computed from the smoothed curve. This is shown in Fig. 8. The fracture mode of this specimen is brittle cleavage, and the fracture surface is very flat across the specimen. Plane-strain fracture values have probably been achieved. In addition to the flat fracture there is only a very small shear lip, and the width of the fracture is well in excess of 2.5 $(K_{ID}/\sigma_y)^2$ where σ_y is the static yield stress.

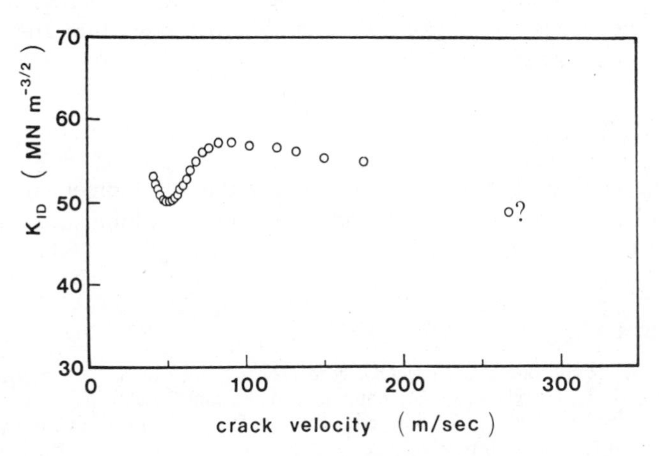

FIG. 8—K_{ID} *versus crack velocity for 1018 cold-rolled steel fractured at* $-196°C$ *as calculated from Fig. 7.*

Conclusions

The measured shear force in the rapidly wedged DCB specimen when multiplied by the square root of the time is a slowly varying function of time. Acoustic waves on the experimental data are small in amplitude but should be smoothed in analyzing $Q_N\sqrt{t}$. The determination of zero on the time axis is deduced from the shear force versus time curve. The crack velocities typically obtained using this test are a factor of two slower than the crack velocities in crack arrest specimens. In a single test the crack velocity varies by a factor of five and is typically 0.01 of $\sqrt{E/\rho}$ for the specimens and wedging machine used. The testing scheme has two self-consistency checks; first, the absolute shear force calibration obtained by loading the specimen in a tensile machine should be in reasonable agreement with the shear force calibrated from the end of the fracture test. Second, the initial crack length calculated from the extreme left side of the $Q_N\sqrt{t}$ curve should agree with the measured initial crack length in the actual DCB specimen. The stress intensity data during crack propagation as deduced from the $Q_N\sqrt{t}$ curve shows that the thick to slender beam correction is important for short crack lengths.

K_D data versus crack velocity in Ti-6A1-4V shows little rate dependence over the range of velocities tested. The K_D values obtained from the $Q_N\sqrt{t}$ data are, however, larger than K_{Ic} in this material but smaller than the K as calculated from the energy lost in a Charpy specimen and K as calculated from the load deflection energy in completing the fracture of a K_{Ic} test specimen [9]. The K_{ID} data versus crack velocity for the steel specimens, however, do show a rate dependence—the faster crack velocities have smaller K_{ID} values. In the range of crack velocities tested, the rate dependence is not a strong effect and is just larger than the estimated experimental scatter.

Acknowledgments

The authors are grateful for support for the development of this fracture test by the Energy Research and Development Administration through contract E(11-1)-2422.

References

[1] Burns, S. J. and Bilek, Z. J., *Metallurgical Transactions,* Vol. 4, 1973, p. 975.
[2] Hahn, G. T., Hoagland, R. G., Kanninen, M. F., and Rosenfield, A. R. in *Dynamic Crack Propagation,* G. C. Sih, Ed., Noordhoff International Publishing, Leyden, The Netherlands, 1973, p. 649.
[3] Bilek, Z. J. and Burns, S. J., *Journal of the Mechanics and Physics of Solids,* Vol. 22, 1974, p. 85.
[4] Kanninen, M. F., *International Journal of Fracture,* Vol. 10, 1974, p. 415.
[5] Broberg, K. B., *Arkiv för Fysik,* Vol. 18, 1961, p. 159.
[6] Freund, L. B., *Journal of the Mechanics and Physics of Solids,* Vol. 20, 1972, p. 141.
[7] American Society for Testing and Materials, Committee E-24, Task Force .03.
[8] Burns, S. J., *Proceedings of 12th Annual Meeting of Society of Engineering Science,* 1975, p. 121.
[9] Burns, S. J., "Crack Arrest in Titanium," Technical Report AFML-TR-75-101, Air Force Materials Laboratory, July 1975.
[10] Kanninen, M. F., *International Journal of Fracture,* Vol. 9, 1973, p. 83.

Material Response to Fast Crack Propagation

K. B. Broberg[1]

On Effects of Plastic Flow at Fast Crack Growth

REFERENCE: Broberg, K. B., "**On Effects of Plastic Flow at Fast Crack Growth,**" *Fast Fracture and Crack Arrest, ASTM STP 627,* G. T. Hahn and M. F. Kanninen, Eds., American Society for Testing and Materials, 1977, pp. 243–256.

ABSTRACT: The mechanism of energy dissipation near a fast running crack tip is studied. The presence of low-sound velocities in the plastic region should imply increased resistance to the energy flow from the elastic strain field at increasing crack-tip velocity. Numerical calculations indicate, however, that this is a rather weak effect in cases of small-scale yielding. On the other hand, increased resistance to ordinary plastic flow at increasing crack-tip velocity is found to be a strong effect. Increased resistance to plastic flow implies a smaller plastic region and thereby a smaller energy dissipation in this region. In the region where material separations are initiated, very different stress fields prevail at fast and slowly growing cracks. The implication on the morphology of material separation suggests that the associated energy dissipation should be much higher for very fast growing cracks than for slowly moving ones.

KEY WORDS: crack propagation, dynamics, fracture properties, plastic properties

Recent experiments by Paxson and Lucas [*1*][2] have shown that the energy dissipation near the tip of a fast growing crack increases very strongly with the crack-tip velocity. Thus at 70 percent of the Rayleigh wave velocity the energy dissipation is about 50 times the one for slowly growing cracks in polymethylmethacrylate (PMMA). The reason for this enormous increase is not clearly understood. One possible explanation could be sought in the fact that the sound velocities are very low near the crack tip. In some cases they are even lower than the crack-tip velocity. Such a situation should influence the energy flow to the near-tip region. It is, however, difficult to intuitively estimate the importance of this effect. A calculation based on a model, previously treated analytically by Broberg [*2*] has been carried out in order to get a quantitative estimate. Furthermore, some estimates are made regarding the significance of increased resistance to plastic flow at increasing crack-tip velocity.

[1]Professor, Lund Institute of Technology, Lund, Sweden.

[2]The italic numbers in brackets refer to the list of references appended to this paper.

A distinction will be made between the process region and the plastic region (outside the process region). In the process region material separations occur. The physical appearance of these separations, as is well known, can be of different kinds. In some cases holes are opened. The holes grow and coalesce with the main crack. In other cases microcracks are initiated. Both mechanisms, in general, are associated with considerable plastic flow on a microscale. As a consequence of material separations the process region is extended under the action of decreasing forces, that is, it can be characterized as a region that would be unstable under load-controlled conditions. The conditions *in situ* are, however, something between load and grip controlled.

The plastic region can be regarded as a continuum which would be stable even under load-controlled conditions. Near the process region formation of microseparations can occur, but these separations are not enlarged enough to cause decrease in the stresses at increasing strains.

Discussion of Possible Mechanisms of Energy Dissipation

Crack growth demands a certain amount of energy flow to the process region. This flow, which emanates essentially from the elastic region, is suppressed at higher crack-tip velocities due to low-sound velocities in the intermediate plastic region. Suppose, tentatively, that this effect is very strong. It is then obvious that the outer load (on the body) must be very high in order to transfer the energy required through the plastic region. Suppose further, tentatively, that the increased resistance to plastic flow at increasing crack-tip velocity is a very weak effect. Then it is obvious that the plastic region will be very large as the outer load becomes very large. Since energy is dissipated both in the plastic region and in the process region, the total amount of energy dissipated would be very large at high crack-tip velocities.

Suppose, on the other hand, tentatively, that the reverse situation prevails, that is, the suppression of the energy flow to the process region due to low-sound velocities in the plastic region is a weak effect and the resistance to plastic flow at increasing crack-tip velocity is a very strong effect. Then the plastic region will be very small at high crack-tip velocities. The experimentally found result that the total energy dissipation increases with the crack-tip velocity must then be attributed to increased energy dissipation in the process region.

It is not easy to intuitively estimate the net effect of the different phenomena appearing at high crack-tip velocities. From the preceding discussion it is obvious that a quantitative analysis—even though by necessity a very crude one—has to be made regarding the significance both of the low-sound velocities in the plastic region and of the increased resistance to plastic flow at increasing crack-tip velocities.

Estimation of Wave Velocities in the Neighborhood of the Process Region

The propagation velocity of plastic waves is given by the expression $[(d\sigma/d\epsilon)/\rho]^{1/2}$ in the case of uniaxial stress, σ. (ϵ is the strain and ρ the density.) Usually $d\sigma/d\epsilon \ll E$, the modulus of elasticity, at plastic deformation. Propagation velocities of plastic waves can be, therefore, much smaller than those of elastic waves.

At general triaxial deformations the stress wave pattern becomes more complicated in the plastic than in the elastic case. This fact depends on the anisotropy created by plastic flow and on the propagation velocity dependence on the magnitude of stresses and strains and on the previous loading history. However, two main groups of waves can be recognized. In one group dilatation is involved. In the other one the waves propagate without volume changes. A comparison may be made with the linear, elastic case. As is well known, two types of elastic waves exist, the irrotational one with propagation velocity

$$c_d = \{[K + (4/3)G]/\rho\}^{1/2}$$

and the equivoluminal one with propagation velocity

$$c_r = (G/\rho)^{1/2}$$

K is the modulus of compression and G the modulus of rigidity.

In the case of uniaxial stress in a linearly elastic body the modulus of elasticity

$$\frac{d\sigma}{d\epsilon} = E = \frac{9KG}{3K + G}$$

Transition from the elastic to the plastic region lowers $d\sigma/d\epsilon$ in many cases by a factor of the order of 100. The compressibility is, however, not substantially changed, except at very large dilatational strains. Thus, the drastic decrease of $d\sigma/d\epsilon$ is essentially the result of a drastic decrease of the rigidity. By comparison with the elastic case an estimation of the propagation velocity of the two main groups of plastic waves can be made. However, very little is known about material behavior at stresses and strains of the magnitude that prevails near the process region. Therefore, one has to resort to rather crude estimates.

In the one of the two main groups of plastic waves the propagation velocities can be estimated to be approximately

$$c_1 \approx (K/\rho)^{1/2} \approx 0.3\, c_d - 0.8\, c_d$$

The lower figure should be representative for very large and the higher one for very small dilatational strains. In the other group of plastic waves the propagation velocities should be of the order

$$c_2 \approx [(d\sigma/d\epsilon)/3\rho]^{1/2} \approx 0.01\, c_d - 0.1\, c_d$$

where $d\sigma/d\epsilon$ is the slope of the σ-ϵ curve in the case of uniaxial stress. The lower figure should be representative for very large and the higher one for small and moderate plastic shear strains.

So far the specific situation near the process region has not been considered. Since microseparations occur in this neighborhood, the compressibility should be considerably higher and the rigidity considerably lower than in the peripheral parts of the plastic region. The propagation velocities of waves in the neighborhood of a crack-tip, therefore, should be substantially decreased as the crack tip is approached. Naturally no accurate estimates are possible, but a study will be made based on the assumption that the propagation velocities in the neighborhood of the process region are typically of the order of

$$\begin{cases} c_1 \approx 0.3\, c_d \\ c_2 \approx 0.01\, c_d \end{cases}$$

Model Used

The model which will be used for investigation of the effect of low-sound velocities near the process region consists of a semi-infinite crack propagating in a thin layer (thickness $2d$) imbedded in an infinite plate, Fig. 1. The load consists of a normal stress $\sigma_y = -h(x - Vt)$ on the crack surfaces. Both the layer and the plate are supposed to be linearly elastic, but dissimilar. The crack-tip velocity is supposed to be supersonic with respect to both wave-propagation velocities in the layer, but subsonic with respect to both propagation velocities in the plate. More specifically: the wave propagation velocities in the plate are supposed to be c and kc, with $k^2 = 0.3$, and the wave propagation velocities in the layer are supposed to be κc and $k_1\kappa c$, with $\kappa = 0.3$ and $k_1\kappa = 0.01$, in agreement with the estimates made in the preceding section. The crack-tip velocity $V = \beta c_d$ where $\kappa < \beta < k$. The modulus of rigidity of the plate is $G = \rho k^2 c^2$, where ρ is the density. For the layer the modulus of rigidity is $G_1 = \rho_1 k_1^2 \kappa^2 c^2$, where ρ_1 is the density. The case $\rho_1 = \rho$ is regarded in the calculations and the normal stress on the surfaces is taken to be constant from the crack tip to a distance l from the tip and zero at larger distances.

The energy flow to the crack-tip region, the normal stress at the symmetry plane near the crack tip and the crack opening displacement have been calculated.

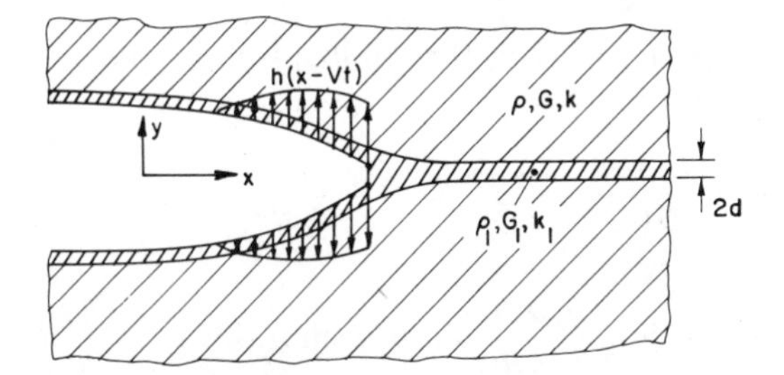

FIG. 1—*Semi-infinite crack propagating in an elastic layer with thickness* 2d *imbedded in an infinite elastic plate. The tip runs with constant velocity* V, *supersonic with respect to the layer and subsonic with respect to the plate. In the numerical calculations* h(x − Vt) *is taken to be constant for* − 1< x − Vt < 0.

The analytical solution to the problem [2] is expressed by the following formulas

$$\sigma_y = \frac{e^{-\theta}}{2} \int_0^\infty H(-q)R(q)dq$$

$$2v = \frac{2Ad}{G} e^{2\theta} \times \sigma_y$$

$$\frac{dU}{da} = 2[\sigma_y - h(-0)]v$$

where

σ_y = normal stress at the symmetry plane near the crack tip,
$2v$ = crack opening displacement,
dU/da = energy flow to the crack tip per unit of crack growth, and

$$H(q) = \frac{q}{d} \int_{-\infty}^{0} e^{-q(x/d)} h(x)dx$$

$$A = \frac{a_1(1 - a_2^2)}{4a_1a_2 - (1 + a_2^2)^2}$$

$$\theta = -\frac{1}{2\pi i} \int_0^\infty \left\{ \frac{d}{dq} \left[\ln \frac{N(iq)D(-iq)}{N(-iq)D(iq)} \right] \right\} \ln q \, dq$$

$$R(q) = -q^{-1/2} \frac{N(iq)D(-iq) + N(-iq)D(iq)}{|N(iq)| \times |D(iq)|}$$

$$\times \exp\left\{\frac{1}{2\pi}\int_0^\infty [s(ir) + s(-ir)] \ln\left|1 - \frac{q}{r}\right| dr\right\}$$

$$s(\alpha) = \frac{N'(\alpha)}{N(\alpha)} - \frac{D'(\alpha)}{D(\alpha)}$$

$$N(\alpha) = \cos b_1\alpha \cos b_2\alpha - \frac{a_2 b_1}{a_1 b_2} \sin b_1\alpha \sin b_2\alpha$$

$$D(\alpha) = 1 - \frac{G_1 A}{G b_1 (b_2^2 + 1)}\Big\{ [(b_2^2 - 1)^2 R_1$$

$$- 4b_1 b_2 S_2] (1 - \cos b_1\alpha \cos b_2\alpha)$$

$$- [(b_2^2 - 1)^2 S_2 - 4b_1 b_2 R_1] \sin b_1\alpha \sin b_2\alpha$$

$$+ \left[(b_2^2 - 1)^2 + 4\frac{a_2 b_1^2}{a_1}\right] \sin b_1\alpha \cos b_2\alpha$$

$$+ \left[(b_2^2 - 1)^2 \frac{a_2 b_1}{a_1 b_2} + 4b_1 b_2\right] \cos b_1\alpha \sin b_2\alpha\Big\}$$

$$R_1 = \frac{G b_1}{G_1 a_1 (1 - a_2^2)(b_2^2 + 1)}\Big\{ -4\left(\frac{G_1}{G}\right)^2 (1 - a_1 a_2)$$

$$+ 4\frac{G_1}{G}(1 + a_2^2 - 2a_1 a_2) + 4a_1 a_2 - (1 + a_2^2)^2 \Big\}$$

$$S_2 = \frac{G}{G_1 a_1 (1 - a_2^2)(b_2^2 + 1) b_2}\Big\{ \left(\frac{G_1}{G}\right)^2 (1 - a_1 a_2)(b_2^2 - 1)^2$$

$$+ 2\frac{G_1}{G}(1 + a_2^2 - 2a_1 a_2)(b_2^2 - 1) - [4a_1 a_2 - (1 + a_2^2)^2]\Big\}$$

$$a_1^2 = 1 - \frac{V^2}{c^2} = 1 - \frac{\rho k^2 V^2}{G}$$

$$a_2^2 = 1 - \frac{V^2}{k^2 c^2} = 1 - \frac{\rho V^2}{G}$$

$$b_1^2 = \frac{V^2}{\kappa^2 c^2} - 1 = \frac{\rho_1 k_1^2 V^2}{G_1} - 1$$

$$b_2^2 = \frac{V^2}{k_1^2 \kappa^2 c^2} - 1 = \frac{\rho_1 V^2}{G_1} - 1$$

The expression for $R(q)$ is here given in a more simple form than in the previous treatment [2]. The advantage of using ρ, ρ_1, k^2, k_1^2, G, and G_1 as constants describing the material behavior lies in the fact that the results obtained are then valid both for plane stress and plane strain.

The model used has the serious disadvantage of representing the rather uninteresting case of wedging of a semi-infinite crack. Most practical cases concern situations like the one of a finite crack in a large plate, subjected to loads on the plate edges. Thus, a more realistic, but still fairly simple model would be the one of a crack growing symmetrically in an infinite plate subjected to remote loads. Fortunately there is a simple connection between this model and the one of a semi-infinite crack. This connection will next be discussed.

For a semi-infinite crack in a homogeneous, infinite elastic plate, loaded by a stress $-\sigma_\infty$ on the crack surfaces from the crack tip to a distance l from the tip, the energy flow to the tip per unit of crack growth is [2]

$$\left(\frac{dU}{da}\right)_1 = \frac{1}{\pi} \times \frac{a_1(1 - a_2^2)}{G[4a_1 a_2 - (1 + a_2^2)^2]} \left[\int_0^\infty \frac{h(-z)}{z^{1/2}} dz\right]^2$$

where, in the case regarded

$$h(-z) = \begin{cases} -\sigma_\infty \text{ for } 0 < z < l \\ 0 \text{ for } \quad l < z \end{cases}$$

For a crack with length $2a$, growing symmetrically with constant crack-tip velocity V in an infinite plate, subjected to a remote stress σ_∞, the energy flow per unit of crack growth to each one of the tips is (Broberg [3])

$$\left(\frac{dU}{da}\right)_2 = \frac{\pi \sigma_\infty^2 a}{4(1 - k^2)G} w(\beta;k)$$

where

$$w(\beta;k) = \frac{2k^2(1 - k^2)(1 - \beta^2)^{1/2}[4k^3(1 - \beta^2)^{1/2}(k^2 - \beta^2)^{1/2} - (2k^2 - \beta^2)^2]}{\beta^2[g(\beta)]^2}$$

$$g(\beta) = [(1 - 4k^4)\beta^2 + 4k^4]K(\sqrt{1 - \beta^2})$$

$$- \frac{1}{\beta^2}[\beta^4 - 4k^2(1 + k^2)\beta^2 + 8k^4]E(\sqrt{1 - \beta^2})$$

$$-4k^2(1 - \beta^2)K(\sqrt{1 - (\beta/k)^2}) + \frac{8k^4}{\beta^2}$$

$$(1 - \beta^2)E(\sqrt{1 - (\beta/k)^2})$$

$$\beta^2 = 1 - a_1^2$$

and K and E are the complete elliptic integrals of the first and second kind.

Since

$$\int_0^{\infty} \frac{h(-z)}{z^{1/2}}\, dz = -2\sigma_{\infty} l^{1/2}$$

one obtains by putting $(dU/da)_1 = (dU/da)_2$

$$l = \frac{\pi^2}{16} \times \frac{w(\beta;k)\,[4a_1a_2 - (1 + a_2^2)^2]}{(1 - k^2)a_1(1 - a_2^2)}\, a$$

The result can be interpreted in the way that the stress-strain field in the near-tip region in the case of the finite crack is the same as that of the semi-infinite crack if the crack-tip velocities are the same and l is chosen according to the relation found. It is now evident that the solution obtained for the semi-infinite crack, travelling in a layer with low sound velocities can be transferred in the same way to the case of a finite crack, if the conditions

$$d \ll a \text{ and } d \ll l$$

are both satisfied. This has been done in the numerical calculations which, therefore, are intended to describe the case of a finite crack of length $2a$, growing symmetrically in an infinite plate. The propagation velocities of waves within a distance d from the crack tip are $0.3c$ (irrotational waves) and $0.01c$ (equivoluminal waves), where c is the propagation velocity of irrotational waves at greater distances from the crack tip.

Results of the Calculations

The results of the calculations are given in Table 1. A brief study of the table reveals that even though σ_y and v are very sensitive to the size d of the region of low-sound velocities, the energy flow dU/da is not. Thus, at a crack-tip velocity of $0.36c$ the energy flow dU/da is only about 13 percent smaller at $d/a = 0.01$ than at $d/a = 0$ (the reference case for which no decrease is assumed of the sound velocities as the crack tip is approached). The corresponding percentage figures for crack-tip velocities of $0.42c$ and $0.48c$ are 20 and 28 percent. The model cannot be used for crack-tip velocities less than $0.3c$ (with the elastic constants chosen here), but it is obvious that the relative deviation of dU/da for $d/a = 0.01$ from dU/da for $d/a = 0$ should be smaller the smaller the crack-tip velocity is.

The value $d/a = 0.01$ can be regarded as fairly representative for realistic cases since the linear dimensions of the dissipative region at small-scale yielding are less than some few percent of the crack length.

It should be noted that crack-tip velocities exceeding the lowest one in Table 1 ($0.36c$) are found rarely in experiments. Thus, the presence of low-sound velocities in the near-tip region should imply an influence on only the 10 percent level on the energy flow to the crack-tip region. This influence is obviously far too small to explain the remarkable increase of the total energy dissipation, found for instance by Paxson and Lucas [*1*], when large crack-tip velocities are approached.

Since the low-sound velocity region apparently cannot impede energy flow to the process region, a strong increase of the total energy dissipation with increasing crack-tip velocity (as found in experiments) should be due to a strong increase of the energy dissipation in the process region. Whether or not this increase is accompanied by a strong increase of the energy dissipation in the plastic region as well will be investigated in the next section.

Significance of Increased Resistance to Plastic Flow at Increasing Crack-Tip Velocity

In cases where the tip of an initially small crack accelerates to a high velocity the scale of yielding, even if initially large, will become small as the crack length increases. There are, of course, exceptions to this behavior. Thus, if significant length dimensions of the body (for instance the width of a plate or the diameter of a pipe) are not large enough, the case of small-scale yielding will not be reached. However, in the present investigation only cases of small-scale yielding are considered. Stresses above the static yield stress are then found in a crack-tip region that is small compared to the length of the crack and to other significant di-

TABLE 1—*Results of the calculations.*

$\frac{V}{c}$	$\frac{d}{a}$	$\frac{4(1-k^2)}{\pi\sigma_\infty{}^2 a} \times \frac{dU}{da}$	$\left(\frac{d}{a}\right)^{1/2} \frac{\sigma_y}{\sigma_\infty}$	$\frac{2Gv}{\sigma_\infty(da)^{1/2}}$
0.36	0	0.30198	0.3644	0.9299
	10^{-5}	0.300	0.365	0.923
	10^{-4}	0.296	0.366	0.908
	10^{-3}	0.285	0.370	0.863
	2×10^{-3}	0.279	0.374	0.839
	5×10^{-3}	0.271	0.382	0.795
	10^{-2}	0.264	0.394	0.751
0.42	0	0.18770	0.2169	0.9710
	10^{-5}	0.185	0.217	0.958
	10^{-4}	0.181	0.218	0.931
	10^{-3}	0.169	0.222	0.854
	2×10^{-3}	0.164	0.226	0.813
	5×10^{-3}	0.156	0.236	0.741
	10^{-2}	0.150	0.250	0.671
0.48	0	0.06627	0.0649	1.1454
	10^{-5}	0.0638	0.0653	1.096
	10^{-4}	0.0595	0.0667	1.001
	10^{-3}	0.0528	0.0759	0.781
	2×10^{-3}	0.0509	0.0835	0.684
	5×10^{-3}	0.0488	0.101	0.541
	10^{-2}	0.0476	0.124	0.429

mensions of the body (for instance the remaining ligament of a plate or the diameter of a pipe). Estimates of the size of such a region are then possible if the approximate value of the stress intensity factor can be determined. Such estimates show that the linear dimensions of the region with stresses above the static yield stress are generally smaller than about 10 mm, even for very tough materials. In many materials it is smaller than 1 mm.

Suppose the crack-tip velocity to be 500 m/s. Then a particle near the prospective crack path experiences stresses above the static yield stress during about 20 μs, if the linear dimensions of the region where such stresses occur is about 10 mm. The peak stress experienced depends on the distance between the particle and the crack path. The fact that the stress near the tip of a crack increase like $r^{-1/2}$ or slower (r being the distance from the crack tip) implies, for instance, that a particle at a distance of 2.5 mm from the crack path experiences a peak stress of about twice the static yield stress or less. The stress history for the particle will then be the one of stresses above the static yield stress during less than 20 μs with a peak stress of about twice the static yield stress or less. Such a stress history is not likely to produce substantial plastic flow. In several materials only flow on a microscale would appear, due to delayed yield phenomena. It is even difficult to imagine large amounts of overall plastic flow (in the ordinary sense) to take place during time durations of the order of some few microseconds, even if the stresses were several times the static yield stress. Other mechanisms, such as those by which separations occur in the material seem to be more likely. Such mechanisms are, however, characteristic of a process region.

So far the discussion has concerned a very fast running crack. Since the dynamic effects on the plastic region were found to be very strong, the question arises if substantial dynamic effects show up already at fairly low crack-tip velocities. It is obvious that for a sufficiently slowly growing crack the time effects on plastic flow should be very small in materials with negligible long-time creep. However, a quantitative analysis shows that the significant times involved are very small even for fairly low crack-tip velocities. Thus, an argument similar to the one previously used for fast running crack tips shows that stresses above the static yield stress may be experienced during times of the order of 0.1 s or less if the crack-tip velocity is about 0.1 m/s. Such a time duration may be short enough to substantially influence the development of plastic strains in, for instance, mild steel. At a velocity of about 1 m/s the time duration will be of the order of 0.01 s or smaller, certainly small enough to cause considerable reduction of the plastic strains in comparison to those expected in a static case under the same stresses.

The conclusion to be drawn from the discussion of time effects on plastic flow near a running crack tip would be that the energy dissipation in the plastic region (outside the process region) becomes smaller the higher the crack-tip velocity is. This effect becomes substantial already for very low crack-tip velocities (of the order of some few meters per second). Therefore, it should be expected to be very strong at high crack-tip velocities.

Morphology of Material Separations

From the preceding discussion the conclusion may be drawn that elastic stresses considerably larger than those causing plastic flow in a static case prevail in the neighborhood of a fast running crack tip. Whereas microseparations in static cases are initiated inside the plastic region, the presence of very high elastic stresses near the tip of a fast running crack could lead to material separation at weak spots, for instance at particle-matrix interfaces, without preceding plastic flow on a macroscale. The microseparations created grow towards coalescence with the main crack or with other material separations. Due to the extremely short times involved the formation and growth of one material separation does not substantially influence formation and growth of other ones even in a close neighborhood. Thus, many more separations will take place than at slow crack growth. The high stresses involved should favor formation of microcracks rather than of rounded voids in many materials, for instance base-centered-cubic crystals.

At very low crack-tip velocities microseparations, as mentioned, are initiated in the plastic region. Straight ahead of the crack tip the stress composition is approximately described by the relations

$$\sigma_x \approx 1.8\,\sigma_e \qquad \sigma_y \approx 3\,\sigma_e \qquad \sigma_z \approx 2.4\,\sigma_e \qquad \text{that is,} \quad \begin{cases} \sigma_x \approx 0.6\,\sigma_y \\ \sigma_z \approx 0.8\,\sigma_y \end{cases}$$

where σ_e is the von Mises effective stress. These relations can be found by using results obtained by Rice and Rosengren [*4*]. It is obvious that such a state of stress will favor growth of material separations preferably in the *x*- and *z*-directions. Recent calculations by Andersson [*5*] on void growth also indicate this behavior.

At high crack-tip velocities microseparations, as mentioned, are initiated in an essentially elastic region. The stress composition is then quite different from the one in the elastic case (and in the plastic region). Straight ahead of the crack tip the relation between the principal stresses are

$$\frac{\sigma_x}{\sigma_y} = \frac{2\beta^2(1 - k^2)(2k^2 - \beta^2)}{4k^3(1 - \beta^2)^{1/2}(k^2 - \beta^2)^{1/2} - (2k^2 - \beta^2)^2} - 1$$

$$\frac{\sigma_z}{\sigma_y} = \frac{\beta^2(1 - 2k^2)(2k^2 - \beta^2)}{4k^3(1 - \beta^2)^{1/2}(k^2 - \beta^2)^{1/2} - (2k^2 - \beta^2)^2}$$

Assuming the crack-tip velocity to be about 70 percent of the Rayleigh wave velocity gives for Poisson's ratio 0.35 approximately

$$\begin{cases} \sigma_x \approx 1.8\,\sigma_y \\ \sigma_z \approx \sigma_y \end{cases}$$

Such a state of stress should favor material separations growing preferably in the *y*- and *z*-directions, that is, in directions normal to the propagation direction of the crack. Naturally the directions would be somewhat changed at positions off the prospective crack path, but still the growth of the material separations should proceed in directions that are quite different from the average growth direction of the main crack. The simple (idealized) picture in the static case of material separations lined up along the prospective crack path and growing essentially in the plane of the main crack until they coalesce with the main crack seems, therefore, to be quite inadequate in the case of very high crack-tip velocities. It is obvious that growth of material separations in other directions than the average growth direction of the main crack implies a much more energy consuming mechanism.

Summary and Discussion

An investigation has shown that the presence of low-sound velocities near a fast running crack tip produces only a weak effect on the energy flow to the process region, that is, the region where material separations take place. On the other hand, the increased resistance to plastic flow (in the ordinary sense) at increasing crack-tip velocity has been found to be a very strong effect. The conclusion to be drawn is that the energy dissipation in the plastic region (outside the process region) decreases as the crack-tip velocity increases.

A study of the morphology of material separation indicates that formation of microcracks rather than rounded voids should be favored at high crack-tip velocities in many materials. Many more material separations should take place near the tip of fast growing than near the tip of slowly growing cracks, because of the very high elastic stresses that could prevail at high crack-tip velocities and because the short times involved suppress interaction between growing material separations. The growth directions of the material separations seem to change from being essentially coplanar with the main crack at low crack-tip velocities to being essentially normal to the direction of crack growth at high crack-tip velocities. Easy coalescence of the material separations with the main crack is, therefore, not possible in the high velocity case. As a result the energy dissipation in the near-tip region should be expected to be very high.

The investigations indicate that the energy dissipation decreases in the plastic region and increases in the process region with increasing crack-tip velocity. Substantial decrease of energy dissipation in the plastic region takes place at low crack-tip velocities, whereas substantial increase of energy dissipation in the process region takes place at high crack-tip velocities, according to simple estimates. Therefore, the net effect may be a decrease of the total energy dissipation with increasing crack-tip velocity until a certain velocity is reached, whereupon the total energy dissipation increases with the velocity.

Very little is known about material behavior near a nonmoving crack tip. The knowledge about the dynamic case is, naturally, even more rudimentary. Certainly different materials ought to show different behavior at very intense short-duration loading. The present investigations of energy dissipation mechanisms at fast running crack tips, therefore, should be regarded as attempts to take into account some factors that should influence these mechanisms. Other factors may be equally or more significant and may influence the energy dissipation mechanism in directions opposite to those found here. For instance, the significance of the high temperatures prevailing near fast running crack tips has not been investigated.

References

[*1*] Paxson, T. L. and Lucas, R. A., *Proceedings of an International Conference on Dynamic Crack Propagation,* Nordhoff International Publishing, Leyden, The Netherlands, 1973, p. 415.
[*2*] Broberg, K. B., *Proceedings of an International Conference on Dynamic Crack Propagation,* Nordhoff International Publishing, Leyden, The Netherlands, 1973, p. 461.
[*3*] Broberg, K. B., *Journal of Applied Mechanics,* Vol. 31, 1964, p. 546.
[*4*] Rice, J. R. and Rosengren, G. F., *Journal of the Mechanics and Physics of Solids,* Vol. 16, 1968, p. 1.
[*5*] Andersson, H., *Journal of the Mechanics and Physics of Solids,* 1976, to be published.

T. Kobayashi[1] *and J. W. Dally*[1]

Relation Between Crack Velocity and the Stress Intensity Factor in Birefringent Polymers

REFERENCE: Kobayashi, T. and Dally, J. W., "**Relation Between Crack Velocity and the Stress Intensity Factor in Birefringent Polymers,**" *Fast Fracture and Crack Arrest, ASTM STP 627*, G. T. Hahn and M. F. Kanninen, Eds., American Society for Testing and Materials, 1977, pp. 257–273.

ABSTRACT: An experimental investigation of the dynamic behavior of crack propagation in two birefringent polymers, Homalite-100 and KTE epoxy, is described. Photoelastic isochromatic fringe patterns associated with cracks propagating in center-pin-loaded, eccentric-pin-loaded, and crack-line-loaded single-edged-notched (SEN) specimens were recorded with a high-speed multiple spark camera. Experimental data were obtained in several tests for each polymer to cover cracks propagating from arrest to terminal velocity.

The size and shape of the isochromatic fringe loops were used to determine the instantaneous values of the stress intensity function K by matching analytical and experimental results. Analytical results for the fringe loop were obtained by employing a Westergaard stress function of the form

$$Z(z) = \frac{K}{\sqrt{2\pi z}}[1 + \beta'(z/a)]$$

together with a superimposed $\sigma_{ox} = \alpha'/\sqrt{2\pi a}$. Approximately 14 000 computer generated fringe loops were compared to the experimentally generated results, and values of the fitting parameters K, α', and β' were obtained.

Results obtained for $\dot{a}$ versus K show an inverted L relationship for both polymers. Crack propagation behavior with respect to the shape of $\dot{a}$ versus K curve is discussed.

KEY WORDS: crack propagation, fracture properties, dynamic fracture, dynamic photoelasticity, birefringent polymers, isochromatic fringe loop, stress intensity factor, crack velocity, crack arrest, toughness

The application of fracture mechanics to dynamic fracturing is relatively new and more complex than fracture initiation in static stress fields. Con-

[1]Assistant professor and professor, respectively, Mechanical Engineering Department, University of Maryland, College Park, Md. 20742.

siderable interest in dynamic fracture has developed in the decade since Krafft and Irwin [*1*][2] reviewed applications of fracture mechanics to dynamic fracturing. Recent studies involve: (1) Measurements of K_{Id} where the measurement of fracture initiation toughness is based on the stress intensity factor K at the instant prior to crack initiation. (2) Determination of the crack arrest toughness K_{Im} where the K value within 5 to 10 μs prior to or after arrest is used for the measurement. (3) Determination of K_D the instantaneous stress intensity factor where the K values are inferred by an energy balance from an analytical model.

In order to clarify many details associated with the much more difficult measurements of the instantaneous values of K observed during crack propagating and arrest, a whole-field experimental method which will provide K as well as a description of the stress field over the entire specimen is required. Instantaneous values of K can be determined by dynamic photoelasticity as demonstrated by the pioneering work of Wells and Post [*2*] and Irwin [*3*] and the more recent work of Kobayashi and his associates [*4–6*]. With this approach, the test specimens are fabricated from plates of transparent birefringent materials, and dynamic isochromatic fringes are recorded by using multiple-flash photography to observe K as the crack propagates and arrests.

This paper describes two materials which have been thoroughly studied using dynamic photoelasticity to characterize their fracture behavior. The materials are Homalite 100 which is a very brittle polyester commonly employed in dynamic photoelastic studies, and a modified epoxy, KTE, which is tougher but more rate sensitive than Homalite 100. The procedures followed in conducting the experiments and analyzing the data have been presented in detail. Finally the results obtained in terms of K versus crack velocity curves are given over a range of K with crack arrest on the low end and crack branching on the high end.

Description of Materials

Homalite-100,[3] a transparent birefringent polyester has been used in photoelasticity for the past 20 years because of its availability in large sheets with optical quality surface finish and its insensitivity to time-edge stresses. Clark and Sanford [*7*] have studied the material fringe value f_σ and have shown it to be nearly independent of loading rate. Kobayashi, Wade, and Bradley [*8*] have also examined the dynamic behavior of Homalite 100 and have shown that it is suitable for photoelastic investigations of crack propagation. The material has been selected for study because it is currently the polymer used most frequently in photoelastic

[2]The italic numbers in brackets refer to the list of references appended to this paper.
[3]Homalite-100 is commercially available from SGL Industries, Wilmington, Del.

studies of crack propagation and because it is one of the most brittle of the available birefringent materials.

The second material characterized in this study was a modified epoxy resin containing three components. The epoxy resin used was Epon 828, a low molecular weight (380) epichlorohydrin/bisphenol A resin manufactured by the Shell Chemical Co.[4] The curing agent, known as Jeffamine D-400, which is a polyoxypropyleneamine with a molecular weight of 400 was used to polymerize the epoxy. As the reaction is slow an accelerator A-398 was added to reduce the curing time. Both the curing agent and accelerator are produced by Jefferson Chemical Co.[5] The modified epoxy called KTE was prepared in sheets by casting in a closed mold.

The mechanical properties of both the Homalite-100 and the KTE epoxy were determined by conducting standard tension tests on a servo-controlled hydraulically actuated loading system at strain rates of 50×10^{-6} s^{-1}.

Static fracture toughness of the two materials was measured by employing a contoured-double-cantilever-beam (CDCB) specimen [*9*] as illustrated in the inset of Fig. 1. The CDCB specimen was subjected to a constant rate of crosshead displacement in a testing machine, and the load P and the displacement Δ of the loading pins were monitored on an x-y recorder. Typical load displacement curves from CDCB specimens from Homalite-100 and KTE epoxy are shown in Fig. 1. The critical strain energy release rate G_{Ic} was determined from

$$G_{Ic} = (P^2/2b)(dC/da) \tag{1}$$

where

P = load at crack initiation,
b = crack width, and
dC/da = slope of the compliance crack length function and a constant for the CDCB specimen configuration.

And, the fracture toughness was determined from G_{Ic} using

$$K_{Ic} = \sqrt{G_{Ic}E} \tag{2}$$

The elastic constants under dynamic conditions were determined by measuring the velocities of the dilatational and shear type stress waves. These measurements were made by photoelastically observing the stress waves propagate in a half-plane model dynamically loaded with a small explosive charge. The elastic constants are related to the velocities of the

[4]Shell Chemical Co., 1 Shell Plaza, Houston, Tex. 77002.
[5]Jefferson Chemical Co., P.O. Box 53300, Houston, Tex. 77052.

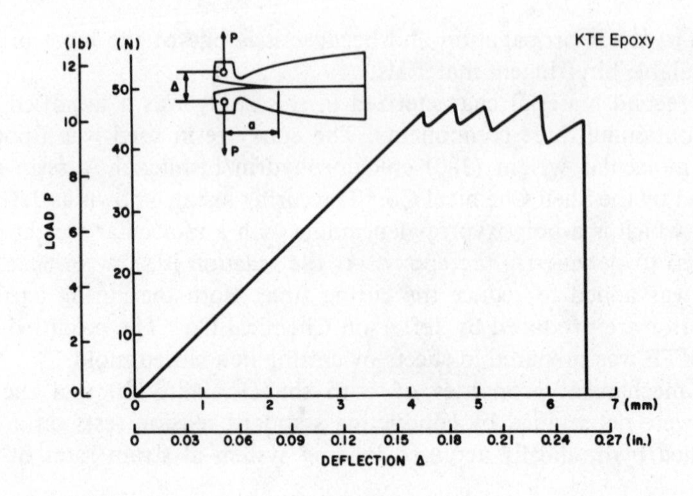

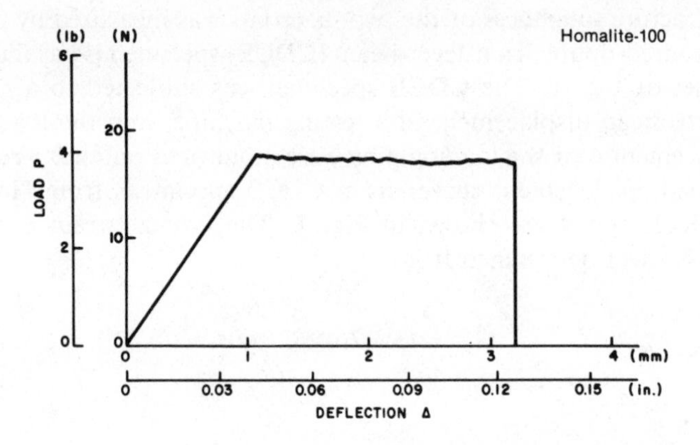

FIG. 1—*Load displacement curves for CDCB specimens of Homalite-100 and KTE epoxy.*

dilatational c_1 and shear c_2 stress waves through the well-known [*10*] relations

$$\mu = \rho c_2^2 \tag{3}$$

$$\nu = (k^2 - 2)/k^2 \tag{4}$$

$$E = 2(1 + \nu)\mu \tag{5}$$

where

μ = shear modulus,
ν = Poisson's ratio,
k = ratio of the wave speeds c_1/c_2, and
ρ = mass density.

It is estimated that the strain rates associated with these determinations of the elastic constants are of the order of 10^5 s^{-1}.

The material fringe value f_σ is the calibration factor which relates the optical response in terms of a fringe order N to stress field through the stress optic law [11]

$$2\tau_m = \sigma_1 - \sigma_2 = Nf_\sigma/h \quad (6)$$

where

τ_m = maximum in plane shear stress,
$\sigma_1 - \sigma_2$ = difference in the principal stresses, and
h = specimen thickness.

The determination of the material fringe value as a function of time under load is particularly important in dynamic studies since the crack velocities may range from near arrest to terminal velocity. Determination of f_σ for relatively long loading times was made with conventional static calibration techniques [11] with a disk in diametrical compression.

The measurement of f_σ under dynamic loading conditions was made by simultaneously measuring axial strain ϵ_a and fringe order N in a bar subjected to axial impact [12]. The value of f_σ is related to these quantities by

$$f_\sigma = Eh(\Delta\epsilon_a/\Delta N) \quad (7)$$

where

$\Delta\epsilon_a/\Delta N$ = slope of the axial strain fringe order relation.

Results for f_σ as a function of loading time over eight decades are given in Fig. 2 for both the Homalite-100 and KTE epoxy.

The results for all the mechanical and optical properties measured for these two photoelastic materials are given in Table 1.

Experimental Procedure

The local state of stress in the neighborhood of the crack tip was measured during crack propagation by employing dynamic photoelasticity to obtain instantaneous records of the fringe loops. The high-speed recording system employed is a Cranz-Schardin multiple spark camera which has been described previously [13]. The system is capable of 16 frames at framing rates which can be varied from 33 000 to 850 000 frames/s. For these experiments, the recording system has been fitted with lenses which provide a 12-in. (300-mm) diameter field. Initiation of the first eight and second eight spark gaps are on independent time controls in order to extend the observation interval for the camera. The time of each frame is

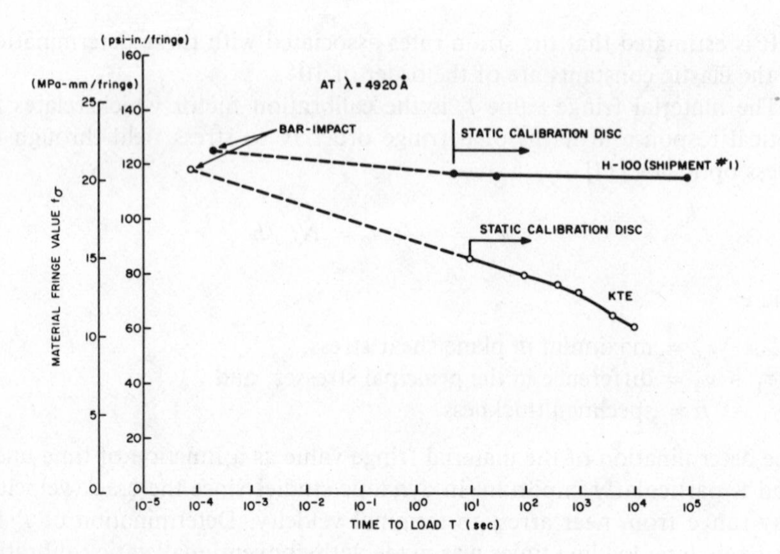

FIG. 2—*Material fringe value as a function of loading time for Homalite 100 and KTE epoxy* (λ = *4920* Å).

TABLE 1—*Mechanical and optical properties of Homalite-100 and KTE epoxy.*

	Homalite-100	KTE Epoxy
c_1 (in./s):(m/s)	84 700:2150	77 000:1970
c_2 (in./s):(m/s)	48 600:1230	44 700:1130
E_s (psi):(GPa)	560 000:3.86	437 000:3.01
E_d (psi):(GPa)	700 000:4.82	573 000:3.86
μ_d (psi):(GPa)	267 000:1.84	214 000:1.47
ν_d . . . : . . .	0.31	0.34
ρ(lb·s^2/in.^{4}):(Kg·s^2/m^4)	0.000112:122	0.000107:117
G_{Ic} lb/in.:J/m^2	0.33:57.8	2.65:464
K_{Ic} psi $\sqrt{\text{in.}}$:MNm$^{-3/2}$	405:0.45	1072:1.18
K_{Im} psi $\sqrt{\text{in.}}$:MNm$^{-3/2}$	380:0.42	770:0.85
$f_{\sigma s}$ psi·in./fringe:MN·mm/fringe [a]	121:21.1	85:14.9
$f_{\sigma d}$ psi·in./fringe:MN·mm/fringe [b]	125:21.9	118:20.7

[a]Static—10 s after application of load.
[b]Dynamic at a loading time of 200 μs both for γ = 4920 Å for spark gap light source with Kodak 4135 film and type K-2 filters.

established by monitoring the intensity of light output from the spark gaps with a high-speed photodiode and an oscilliscope.

A typical example of a set of 16 fringe patterns representing high velocity fringe propagation is shown in Fig. 3. An enlargement showing the detail of the isochromatic fringe loop at the crack tip is shown in Fig. 4. It is evident from these results that the size and shape of the fringe

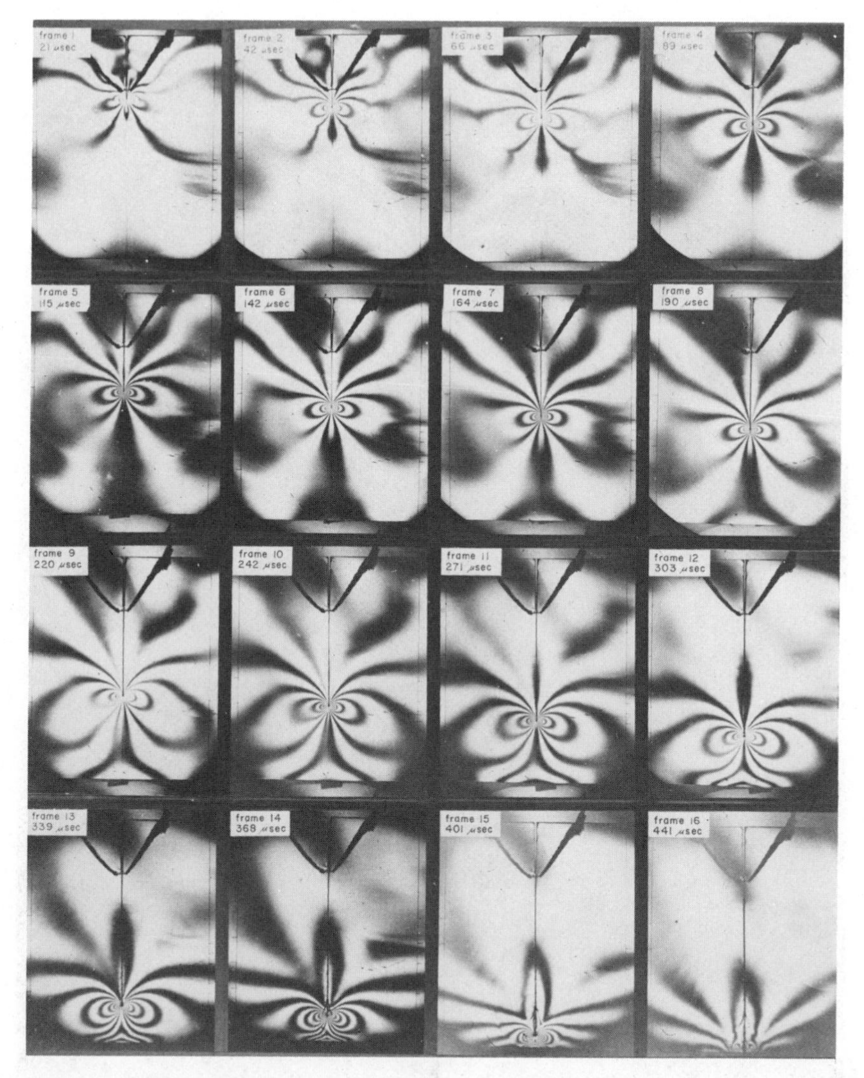

FIG. 3—*Complete set of 16 dynamic photoelastic fringe patterns showing high velocity crack propagation across a center-pin-loaded SEN specimen.*

loops which have been recorded in about 300 ns are sufficiently well defined to give instantaneous values of the stress intensity factor K. Also the tip of the crack can be defined so that the crack length can be established as a function of time during propagation.

Three different types of single-edge-notched (SEN) specimens were employed in the test program to determine the instantaneous stress intensity K as a function of crack velocity $\dot{a}$. The geometry of the SEN specimens

FIG. 4—*Enlargement of one isochromatic pattern showing state of stress as the crack attempts to branch.*

are presented in Fig. 5 for the center-pin-loaded (CPL), eccentric-pin-loaded (EPL), and crack-line-loaded (CLL) specimens. In all instances the specimens are relatively large so that any stress waves generated by the formation of fracture surfaces would disperse and attenuate before being reflected back into the neighborhood about the crack tip.

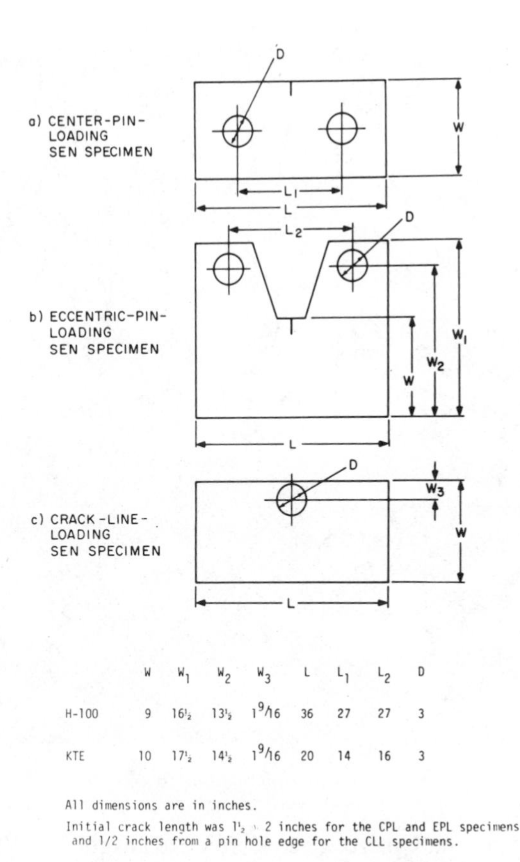

	W	W_1	W_2	W_3	L	L_1	L_2	D
H-100	9	16½	13½	1 9/16	36	27	27	3
KTE	10	17½	14½	1 9/16	20	14	16	3

All dimensions are in inches.

Initial crack length was 1½ to 2 inches for the CPL and EPL specimens and 1/2 inches from a pin hole edge for the CLL specimens.

FIG. 5—*Single-edge-notched specimens.*

In all instances, a starter crack was cut into the specimen with a bandsaw and then sharpened by scribing. For the SEN-CPL specimens, the load was increased slowly (manual control through a hydraulic cylinder) until the crack initiated. Initial crack velocities of 8 000 to 12 000 in./s (200 to 300 m/s) were typical. However, as K increased with crack length for the SEN-CPL specimen, the velocity of crack propagation increased as the crack extended until terminal velocity was achieved.

The SEN-EPL specimen was loaded in a similar fashion except that the pins had been moved to a location outboard relative to the edge of the specimen. This change in pin location resulted in a decrease in K as the crack extends during propagation. Usually the crack would be initiated with intermediate velocities, 8 000 to 12 000 in./s (200 to 300 m/s) and decrease to velocities of 3000 to 4000 in./s (75 to 100 m/s) as the crack extended.

The SEN-CLL specimen was loaded with a split-pin-loading fixture shown in Fig. 6 which applied a load to the crack line. The load was

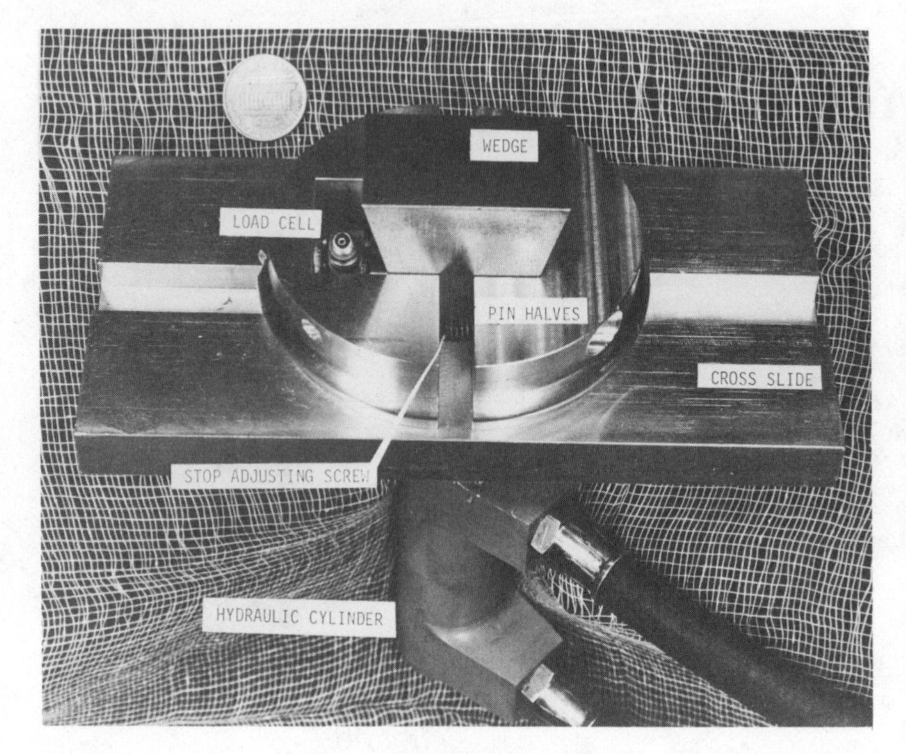

FIG. 6—*Split-pin loading fixture.*

measured with a small piezo electric force transducer. When the crack began to propagate, the split halves moved apart until they were constrained by an adjustable stop which limits their movement. As the crack extended in the SEN-CLL specimen, the K field decreased, and if the initiation velocity was not too high the crack arrested after propagating 3 or 4 in. (75 to 100 mm).

The high-speed recording system was sychronized to the propagating crack by using a strip of conducting paint across the path of the crack. When the crack interrupts this conductor a pulse is issued to electronic counters which activates the two banks of eight gaps each after preselected delay times. Typically, the recording interval ranges from about 300 to 1000 μs.

Analysis Methods

Two different methods were used in analyzing the data depending upon the shape of the isochromatic loops. When the fringe loops tilted too far forward and θ_m defined in Fig. 7*a* was less than 80 deg a three parameter method was employed. When $\theta_m \geqslant 80$ deg, Irwin's [*3*] two-parameter

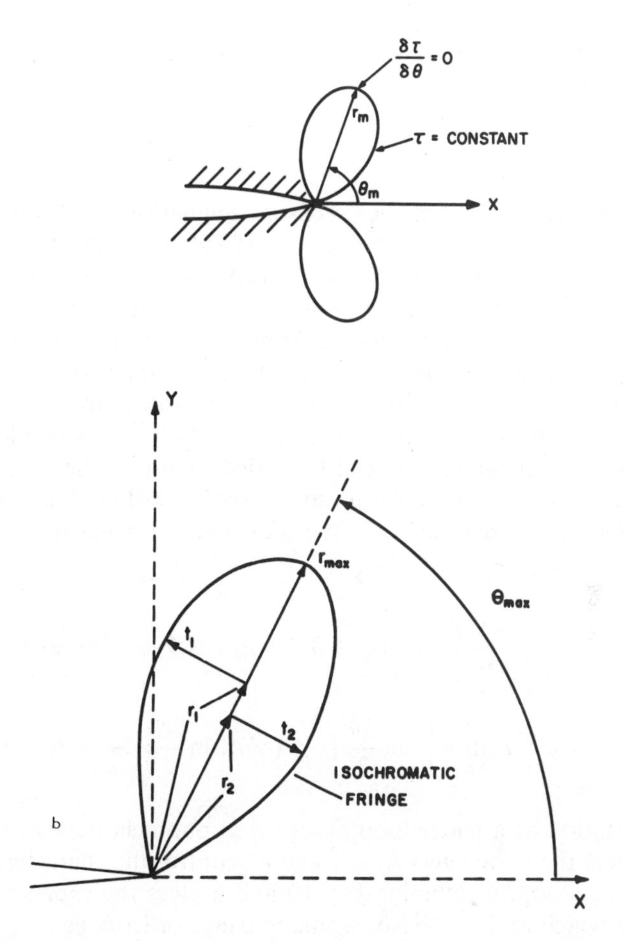

FIG. 7—*Characteristic shape of fringe loops. (a) Definition of* r_m *and* θ_m. *(b) Six measurements defining shape.*

method was used to determine K from the fringe loops. Irwin's equations are

$$K = \frac{Nf\sigma}{h} \frac{\sqrt{2\pi r_m}}{\sin \theta_m} \left\{ 1 + \left(\frac{2}{3 \tan \theta_m} \right)^2 \right\}^{-1/2} \left\{ 1 \pm \frac{2}{3} \frac{\tan (3\theta_m/2)}{\tan \theta_m} \right\} \quad (8)$$

where the positive sign corresponds to $\theta_m < 90$ deg and the negative sign to $\theta_m > 90$ deg. The symbol r_m is defined in Fig. 7*a*.

When θ_m was less than 80 deg a much more involved method of analysis was used where three fitting parameters were used to match experimental and theoretical results to obtain instantaneous K values. The theoretical fringe loops were developed in a static analysis where the Westergaard [*14*] stress function is

$$Z = K/\sqrt{2\pi z}\ [1 + \beta'(z/a)] \tag{9}$$

where

$z = re^{i\theta}$.

The $K/\sqrt{2\pi z}$ term describes the crack-tip singularity for a uniform thickness plate where the crack of length $2a$ is located centrally, and the in-plane boundaries extend to infinity. In order to more accurately analyze the SEN plate, the parameter β' was introduced into the stress function. The parameter β' was added to the stress function in order to model the effect of near field boundaries and boundary loading, thus extending to some degree the analysis of fringe loops further away from the crack tip. For completeness, a uniform stress, $\sigma_{ox} = \alpha' K/\sqrt{2\pi a}$ was added to the stress field. The parameter α' can be varied such that the stress σ_x at the far boundary is zero, thus creating stress free vertical boundaries.

Using Westergaard's methods, the maximum in-plane shear stress was derived as

$$\tau_m^2 = \frac{K^2}{8\pi r}\left[\sin^2\theta\,(1 - 2\beta'(r/a)\cos\theta + \beta'^2(r/a)^2) - 2\alpha'\sqrt{r/a}\sin\theta\left\{\sin\frac{3\theta}{2} - \beta'(r/a)\sin\frac{\theta}{2}\right\} + \alpha'^2(r/a)\right] \tag{10}$$

The description of a fringe loop observed in photoelastic tests is given by Eq 10 where the parameters K, α', and β' control the characteristic shape of the fringe loop. Combining Eqs 10 and 6 gives the expression for the position r which locates the isochromatic fringe order N as

$$\beta^2\sin^2\theta\, w^4 + 2\alpha\beta\sin\theta\sin\theta/2\, w^3 + \left(\alpha^2 + \frac{2\pi}{\gamma^2} - 2\beta\cos\theta\sin^2\theta\right)w^2 - 2\alpha\sin\theta\sin\frac{3\theta}{2}\, w + \sin^2\theta = 0 \tag{11}$$

where

$w = \sqrt{r}$,
$\gamma = Kh/Nf_\sigma$,
$\beta = \beta'/a$, and
$\alpha = \alpha'/\sqrt{a}$.

The parameters α, β, and γ where varied over the range anticipated, and solutions for the position r along the isochromatic loop were determined as θ was varied from 0 to 180 deg in 2 deg increments. Since the combination of parameters considered yielded 13 990 isochromatic loops with each loop defined by 91 points, a computer program FRACTURE was prepared to evaluate Eq 11 and to condition the results so that they are in a form which can be readily compared to the experimental findings.

Six measurements were made on each experimentally determined fringe loop to characterize its size, shape, and orientation as shown in Fig. 7*b*. These measurements are compared with the same measurements from the analytically determined fringe loops by evaluating the comparison function f_c

$$f_c = w_1|r_m - r_{me}| + w_2|\theta_m - \theta_{me}| + w_3|(t_1 + t_2) - (t_{1e} + t_{2e})| + w_4|(t_1 - t_2) - (t_{1e} - t_{2e})| + w_5|r_2 - r_{2e}| + w_6|r_1 - r_{1e}| \quad (13)$$

The values of the weighting coefficients w_1 through w_6 were selected to reflect the relative importance of the six different measurements in matching the analytical and experimental isochromatic patterns, that is

$$\begin{aligned} w_1 &= 0.627 \\ w_2 &= 0.565 \\ w_3 &= 0.439 \\ w_4 &= 0.251 \\ w_5 &= w_6 = 0.125 \end{aligned} \qquad |\sum_{i=1}^{6} w_i^2|^{1/2} = 1$$

A computer search is made to select the 13 solutions from 13 990 available which most closely match the experimental results. These 13 solutions are then examined manually to select the most consistent solution.

Stress Intensity Factor—Crack Velocity Relationship

Results for the stress intensity factor K at different crack velocities are shown in Figs. 8 and 9. Reference to Fig. 8 shows the K versus $\dot{a}$ relation for Homalite 100 as obtained from tests on seven different SEN specimens with either CCL or CPL loadings. These results correspond closely with a completely independent determination of the same curve by the authors [*15*] on a different lot of Homalite 100. The results show that there is a minimum value of K associated with crack arrest which is denoted here as K_{Im} = 380 psi $\sqrt{\text{in.}}$ (0.418 $\text{MNm}^{-1/2}$). Small increases in K above this minimum level result in very sharp increases in crack velocity until velocities of about 8000 in./s (200 m/s) are achieved. A transition region exists for velocities between 8 000 and 15 000 in./s (200 to 381 m/s) where the stress intensity factor must be doubled to produce this change in crack

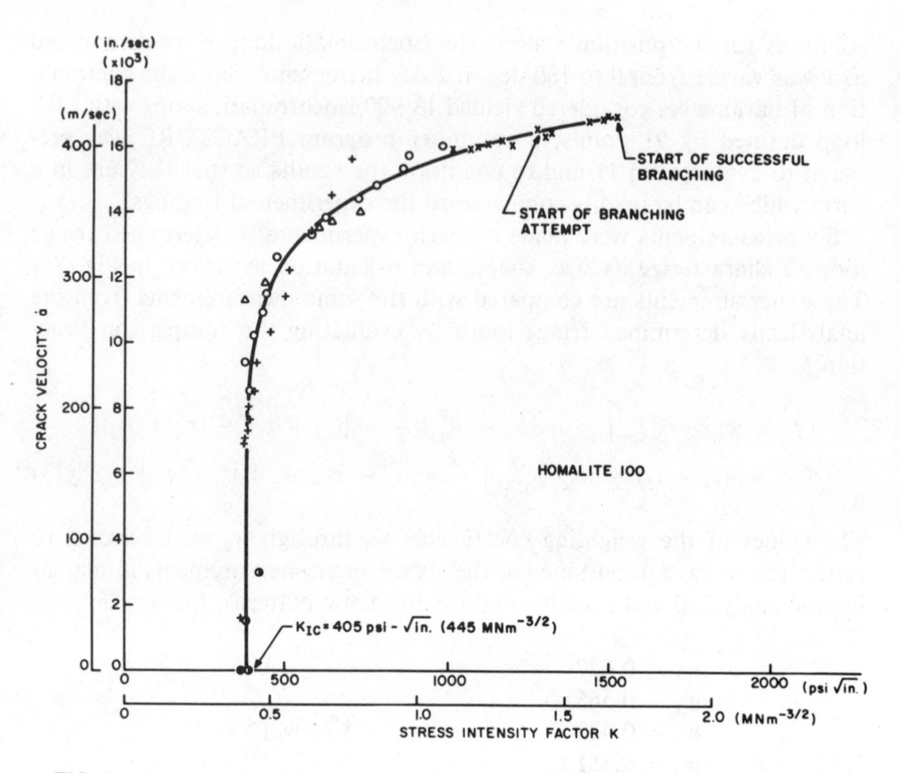

FIG. 8—*Crack velocity* ȧ *as a function of the instantaneous stress intensity factor for Homalite-100.*

velocity. There is some scatter in the data in this transition region due to errors in photoelastic measurements and analysis as well as errors in the velocity determinations. It is also possible that material variations account for some of the scatter. For higher velocities, 15 000 < $\dot{a}$ < 17 000 in./s (381 < $\dot{a}$ < 432 m/s), significant increases in the K are required to increase the speed. The value of K must be about doubled to achieve the last increase of 200 in./s (50 m/s) in crack velocity. The fracture surface is extremely rough in this high velocity region of crack propagation accounting for the large amounts of energy required to drive the crack. Branching begins to occur at about K = 1200 to 1300 psi $\sqrt{\text{in.}}$ (1.32 to 1.43 $\text{MNm}^{-3/2}$) and successful branching occurs at K = 1530 psi $\sqrt{\text{in.}}$ (1.68 $\text{MNm}^{-3/2}$) (about 4 times K_{min}) at a crack velocity of 17 000 in./s. This terminal crack velocity is 20 percent of c_1 and 35 percent of c_2.

The K versus $\dot{a}$ relation for KTE epoxy presented in Fig. 9 shows similar results for the tougher more viscous material. There are three features which aid in characterizing the dynamic crack propagation in this material. First, there is a terminal velocity of about 13 000 in./s (330 m/s) which is 0.30 times the shear wave velocity. This terminal velocity is achieved when

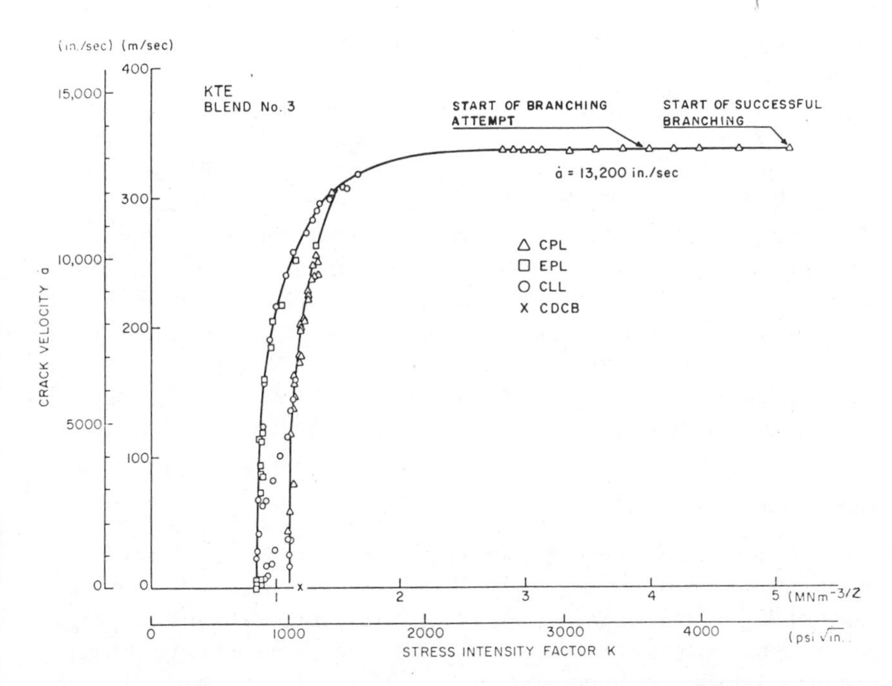

FIG. 9—*Crack velocity* ȧ *as a function of the instantaneous stress intensity factor for KTE epoxy.*

K = 1600 psi $\sqrt{\text{in.}}$ (1.76 MNm$^{-3/2}$), and further increases in K do not appear to drive the crack at higher velocities. As K is increased in this region it does result in rougher fracture surfaces, attempts to branch and finally successful branching occurs at K = 4650 psi $\sqrt{\text{in.}}$ (5.12 MNm$^{-3/2}$).

Second, there appears to be a minimum value of K below which cracks cannot propagate. This minimum value is denoted as the arrest toughness K_{Im} = 770 psi $\sqrt{\text{in.}}$ (0.85 MNm$^{-3/2}$) which is about one half the value of K associated with terminal velocity and about one sixth the value associated with successful branching.

Third, in the velocity range from near zero to about 12 000 in./s (305 m/s), there appear to be two branches in the $\dot{a}$-K relation. The lower energy branch is associated with decelerating cracks, and the higher energy branch is associated with both accelerating and decelerating cracks. Crossover from the higher energy to the lower energy branch was observed for both the EPL and CLL specimens when the initial crack velocity was below 12 000 in./s (305 m/s). From these limited observations, it appears that it is not possible for a crack to propagate on the lower energy branch without having first propagated for some distance on the higher energy branch. Further studies will be necessary to explain this phenomenon; however, it is similar to the behavior observed in linear polymers such as polystyrene and polymethylmethacrylate (PMMA) where crazing results in two branches for the $\dot{a}$-K relationship.

Results of the K_{Ic} determined by a CDCB specimen are also plotted in the Figs. 8 and 9. The value of K_{Ic} for Homalite-100 (405 psi $\sqrt{in.}$) is about 7 percent higher than that of K_{Im} (380 psi $\sqrt{in.}$); while the value of K_{Ic} for KTE epoxy (1072 psi $\sqrt{in.}$) is about 39 percent higher than the K_{Im} value (770 psi $\sqrt{in.}$). It is of interest to examine the crack propagation behavior in the CDCB specimens (Fig. 1) with respect to the relative values of K_{Ic} and K_{Im}. The closeness of K_{Ic} and K_{Im} values in Homalite-100 resulted in repeated small crack jumps (of the order of 0.025 in.) without a significant drop in the load, as shown in Fig. 1. On the other hand, a relatively large difference in the values of K_{Ic} and K_{Im} for KTE epoxy produced crack jumps of 0.2 ~ 0.7 in. in the CDCB specimen.

Conclusions

For Homalite-100 there appears to be a unique relation between the instantaneous stress intensity factor K and the crack velocity. A minimum value of K_{Im} = 380 psi $\sqrt{in.}$ (0.42 $MNm^{-3/2}$) is required to sustain propagation. Small increases in K above K_{Im} result in extremely large increases in $\dot{a}$ up to velocities of about 8000 in./s (200 m/s). When $K \approx 4K_{Im}$ branching occurs at a terminal velocity of about 0.35 c_2.

For KTE there appear to be two branches to the vertical stem of the K-$\dot{a}$ curve which probably is due to an interrelated shear and crazing fracture mechanism similar to that observed by Green and Pratt [16] for PMMA. For design purposes, the higher energy branch should be ignored and the lower K values used to predict fracture behavior. A minimum value of K_{Im} = 770 psi $\sqrt{in.}$ (0.85 $MNm^{-3/2}$) is required to sustain crack propagation. Again small increases in K above K_{Im} result in marked increases in $\dot{a}$ up to velocities of about 6000 in./s (150 m/s). When $K \approx 6K_{Im}$ branching occurs at a terminal velocity of 13 200 in./s (335 m/s).

Acknowledgments

The authors would like to thank E. K. Lynn and C. Z. Serpan of the Nuclear Regulatory Commission for their support on Contract No. AT(49-24) 0172 and for their encouragement to pursue these studies. We would also like to acknowledge the keen guidance provided by G. R. Irwin throughout this investigation.

References

[1] Krafft, J. M. and Irwin, G. R. in *Fracture Toughness Testing and Its Applications, ASTM STP 381,* American Society for Testing and Materials, 1965, pp. 114–128.

[2] Wells, A. and Post, D. in *Proceedings,* Society for Experimental Stress Analysis, Vol. 16, No. 1, 1958, pp. 69–92.
[3] Irwin, G. R., discussion to Ref *2*, *Proceedings,* Society for Experimental Stress Analysis, Vol. 16, No. 1, 1958, pp. 93–96.
[4] Kobayashi, A. S. in *Experimental Techniques in Fracture Mechanics,* Chapter 6, Monograph No. 1, Society for Experimental Stress Analysis, Iowa State Press, Ames, Iowa, 1973, pp. 126–145.
[5] Bradley, W. B. and Kobayashi, A. S. in *Proceedings,* Society for Experimental Stress Analysis, Vol. 27, No. 1, 1970, pp. 106–113.
[6] Kobayashi, A. S., Wade, B. G., and Maiden, D. E. in *Proceedings,* Society for Experimental Stress Analysis, Vol. 29, No. 1, 1972, pp. 32–37.
[7] Clark, A. B. J. and Sanford, R. J. in *Proceedings,* Society for Experimental Stress Analysis, Vol. 20, No. 1, 1963, pp. 148–151.
[8] Kobayashi, A. S., Wade, B. G., and Bradley, W. G. in *Deformation and Fracture of High Polymers,* H. H. Kansch, J. A. Haseele, and R. I. Jaffee, Eds., Plenum Press, New York, 1973, pp. 487–500.
[9] Ripling, E. J., Mostovoy, S., and Patrick, R. L., *Materials Research and Standards,* Vol. 64, No. 3, 1964, p. 129.
[10] Kolsky, H., *Stress Waves in Solids,* Oxford University Press, London, 1952.
[11] Dally, J. W. and Riley, W. F., *Experimental Stress Analysis*, McGraw-Hill, New York, 1965.
[12] Clark, A. B. J. in *Proceedings,* Society of Experimental Stress Analysis, Vol. 14, No. 1, 1956, pp. 195–204.
[13] Riley, W. F. and Dally, J. W., *Experimental Mechanics,* Vol. 9, No. 8, 1969, pp. 27–33N.
[14] Westergaard, H. M., *Transactions,* American Society of Mechanical Engineers, *Journal of Applied Mechanics,* 1939.
[15] Irwin, G. R., Dally, J. W., Kobayashi, T, and Etheridge, J. M., "A Dynamic Photoelastic Study of the Dynamic Fracture Behavior of Homalite-100," NUREG-75/107, U.S. Nuclear Regulatory Commission, Sept. 1975.
[16] Green, A. K. and Pratt, P. L., *Engineering Fracture Mechanics,* Vol. 6, 1974, pp. 71–80.

D. A. Shockey, [1] *L. Seaman,* [1] *and D. R. Curran* [1]

Computation of Crack Propagation and Arrest by Simulating Microfracturing at the Crack Tip

REFERENCE: Shockey, D. A., Seaman, L., and Curran, D. R., **"Computation of Crack Propagation and Arrest by Simulating Microfracturing at the Crack Tip,"** *Fast Fracture and Crack Arrest, ASTM STP 627,* G. T. Hahn and M. F. Kanninen, Eds., American Society for Testing and Materials, 1977, pp. 274–285.

ABSTRACT: This paper describes the initial development stages of a computational capability for fast fracture and arrest, based on treatment of plastic flow and microfracturing at the crack tip. The approach is to model the events occurring within the process zone, compute the associated energies, and thereby determine the fracture toughnesses of propagating and arresting cracks.

The model treats crack propagation as occurring by the nucleation, growth, and coalescence of microfractures in the plastically deforming material at the crack tip. It uses as input actual measurements from specimens fractured under stress wave loads. The dynamic stress history experienced by this material is calculated by a two-dimensional wave propagation code.

The approach was demonstrated by performing a computational simulation of a Battelle double-cantilever-beam crack arrest experiment and calculating the energies absorbed in plastic flow and microfracturing. Plastic work accounted for about 95 percent of the fracture toughness, but microfracture activity controls the amount of plastic work that is done and hence governs the toughness. Agreement between computed and observed crack velocity and arrest length is not yet satisfactory but should improve when a finer computational grid is used.

The approach offers an avenue for understanding fracture toughness on a microlevel by linking micromechanical material response to continuum toughness parameters.

KEY WORDS: crack propagation, microfracturing, crack initiation, fracture properties, crack arrest, stress intensity, velocity

The design technology that emerged in the 1950s from linear elastic fracture mechanics (LEFM) concepts has enabled us to resolve a wide variety of crack initiation problems. This success has encouraged re-

[1] Assistant manager, senior research engineer, and manager, respectively, Shock Physics and Geophysics Group, Poulter Laboratory, Stanford Research Institute, Menlo Park, Calif. 94025.

searchers to apply these concepts to problems of crack propagation and arrest, but the results have not been completely satisfying. For example, current attempts to develop a predictive capability for crack arrest by applying continuum fracture mechanics concepts have met with problems arising from kinetic effects in the process zone near the crack tip. Work by Crosley and Ripling [*1*][2] indicates that the stress intensity factor at crack arrest, K_{Ia}, is a material property; work by Hahn and co-workers [*2*] indicates that the geometry-dependent kinetic energy associated with a running crack influences crack arrest and suggests that K_{Ia} cannot be a material property. This discrepancy demonstrates a need to understand the nature of energy dissipation at the tip of a propagating crack.

This paper considers the various microevents that occur in the process zone at the tip of an advancing crack and describes an approach for computing the associated energies. It is hoped that the results will be useful in clarifying the meaning of toughnesses associated with running and arresting cracks.

Fracture Mechanisms and Models

Substantial evidence indicates that crack propagation occurs by microfracture activity in the region slightly ahead of the crack front [*3*]. Figure 1 shows the partially failed material at the tip of a crack in Fe-3Si steel. This photomicrograph was obtained by sectioning a double-cantilever-beam (DCB) specimen on a plane normal to the crack front. By removing successively thin layers of material from the sectioned surface, Hoagland et al [*4*] ascertained that the microfractures were linked with each other and with the crack front.

The inherent weak spots in materials are responsible for this mechanism of crack propagation. Favorably oriented grain boundaries and cleavage planes are common weak spots. Inclusions and second-phase particles also initiate microfractures either by interfacial debonding or by cracking of the particles themselves [*5,6*]. The weak spots in the path of the propagating crack can fail before the crack front arrives, because of the magnified stresses preceding the crack.

The details of this mechanism have not been quantitatively modeled. Crack propagation is treated usually as the movement through a homogeneous medium of a continuous crack front separating broken from unbroken material. This approach is computationally simple and often provides adequate results for design purposes. (For example, the toughness of a material with respect to crack initiation is a material property based on continuum considerations that has found considerable practical use.) In other instances, however, simplified continuum approaches have encountered difficulties as, for example, in describing crack arrest.

[2]The italic numbers in brackets refer to the list of references appended to this paper.

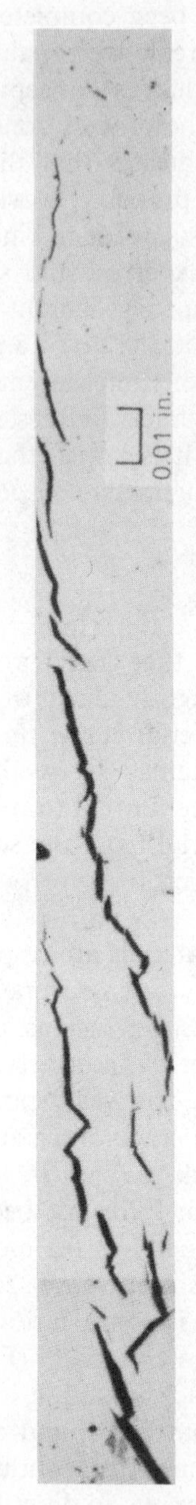

FIG. 1—*Microfractures near the crack tip of a DCB specimen of Fe-3Si Steel* [4].

The need to make simplifying continuum assumptions to obtain a mathematical solution is averted to a large extent by the availability of large computers. More realistic treatments of crack propagation are now possible. Unfortunately, most researchers using large computers to solve fracture problems tend to concentrate on making better representations of geometries and put little additional sophistication into modeling the fracture process. As a result, our understanding of the physical meaning of toughness and how toughness depends on microstructure, strain rate, temperature, and so forth, has not increased very rapidly. Insight into these areas can best be gained through computational models that describe the fracture process in a detailed and realistic way.

To derive theoretical expressions that would describe microfracture activity at the tip of a propagating crack accurately at present appears to be a major task. To be sure, a number of models for microfracture nucleation at inclusions or on cleavage planes, for plastic void growth, and the like, have been postulated, and all these models describe more or less well the situation for a given material under given load conditions (usually in the necking region of a tensile bar). Furthermore, certain nucleation and growth models might conceivably be combined to yield predictions of void size distributions for arbitrary load histories. However, the criteria used in the current models are based on a wide variety of parameters that may not be physically appropriate. For example, it is unclear whether inclusion/matrix decohesion is controlled by shear stress, shear strain, normal stress, or some combination. Furthermore, no satisfactory model for microfracture coalescence appears to exist. Thus, the development of a successful theoretical model of microfracture nucleation, growth, and coalescence would seem to lie some distance into the future.

An approach that may have higher chances of early success is the observational approach used to develop a predictive capability for fracture under short impulse loads [7]. The fracture damage produced by a tensile pulse is assessed quantitatively by counting and measuring the sizes of individual microfractures visible on polished cross sections of impacted specimens. Figure 2 shows microcracks produced in Armco iron by planar impact (note the similarity of the microfractures in Fig. 1). The large number of microfractures makes a statistical approach possible, and damage distribution functions are constructed. By correlating these data with the loading history, we obtain empirical expressions describing nucleation and growth rates. Thus, the approach is not concerned with mechanistic details of nucleation and growth, such as the size distribution or spacing of nucleation heterogeneities or with dislocation models describing how voids grow. Instead, the microfracture nucleation and growth laws are deduced directly from the measured microfracture data.

Application of this approach, known as the SRI NAG approach, to a

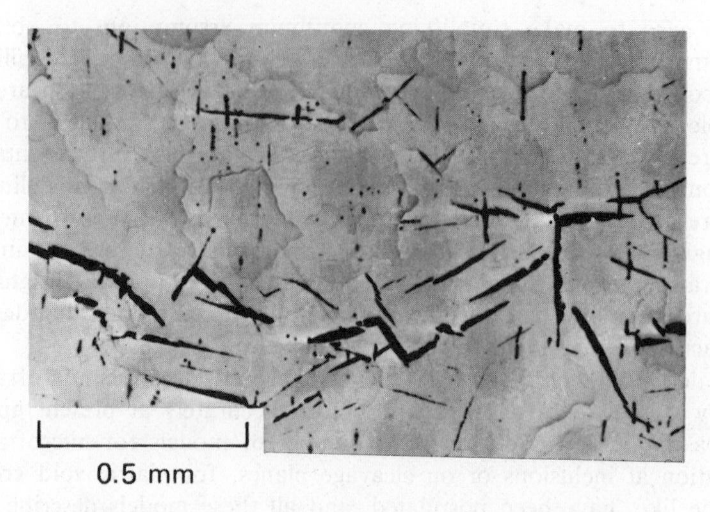

FIG. 2—*Microfractures in Armco iron produced by impact.*

variety of ductile and brittle metals and alloys [*7–10*] showed that microfractures nucleate and grow (NAG) according to the following expressions

$$\dot{N} = \dot{N}_0 \exp \frac{\sigma - \sigma_{no}}{\sigma_1} \tag{1}$$

$$\dot{R} = \frac{\sigma - \sigma_{go}}{4\eta} R \tag{2}$$

where the nucleation rate $\dot{N}$ is an exponential function of the tensile stress σ, and the growth rate $\dot{R}$ depends linearly on the stress and the size of the microfracture R. The remaining parameters act as material properties describing various aspects of micromechanical behavior. Their values are fixed by the fit to the data.

Computation of Crack Propagation and Arrest by Microfracturing at the Crack Tip

To determine whether the microfracture nucleation and growth functions extracted from plate impact experiments could be used to describe microfracture activity ahead of a propagating crack, we performed a computational simulation of an actual DCB crack arrest experiment by using the SRI NAG model and dynamic fracture data from plate impact experiments. A two-dimensional wave propagation code was used to compute the stress histories experienced by the material at the moving crack tip.

As a test case, we selected the DCB crack arrest experiment 3V-31 performed by Battelle Memorial Institute [*11*]. The specimen was a rectangular, notched plate of 4340 quenched and tempered steel with no side grooves. Specimen geometry and wedge loading arrangement are shown in Fig. 3. Loading pins were inserted in the holes at the notched end of the specimen, and a wedge attached to the crosshead of a tensile machine was forced downward between the pins. At constant crosshead speed, the load on the specimen increased monotonically until a sharp crack advanced from the blunted notch and propagated into the specimen. The crack ran about 75 mm at an average constant velocity of 435 m/s, then abruptly stopped. Wedge opening load and displacement at the onset of crack

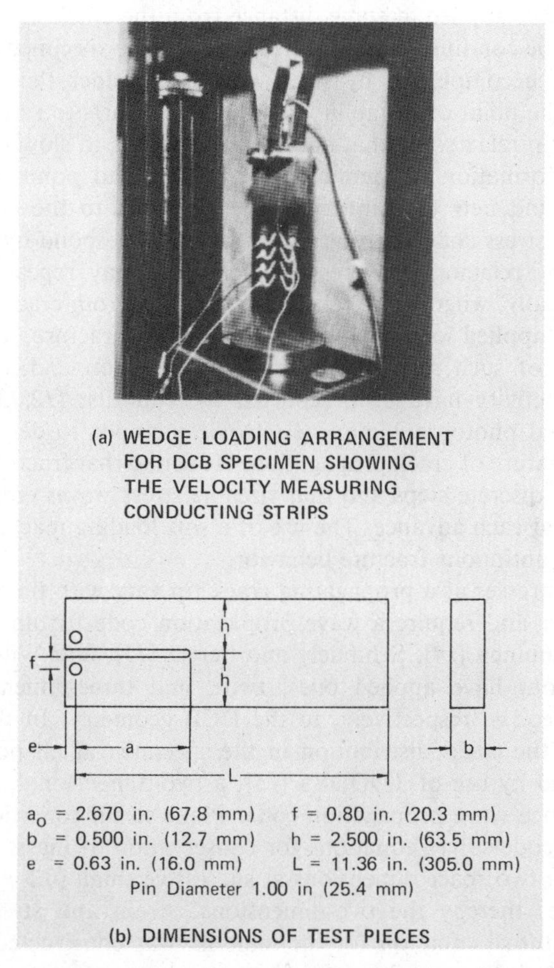

FIG. 3—*Wedge loading arrangement and specimen dimensions for the DCB crack arrest experiment* [11].

propagation were measured; crack velocities were measured by monitoring the breakage of a grid of conducting strips cemented across the expected crack path. Since the crack speed was orders of magnitude greater than the wedge opening rate, essentially fixed grip conditions prevailed. Reference *11* gives additional details.

The dimples on the fracture surfaces, Fig. 4*a*, were approximately equiaxed, and their diameters varied up to several micrometres. The absence of isolated voids beneath the fracture surfaces, Fig. 4*b*, and in front of the main crack tip indicates that voids form only in a very small zone ahead of the advancing crack tip and that all voids that nucleate become part of the main fracture.

Fast crack propagation through a material is clearly a dynamic process. Since the load is applied at some distance from the crack tip, stress information must be continually transmitted through the specimen as the crack runs. This is accomplished by stress waves. Consider the loaded DCB specimen at the point of instability. As the crack starts to run, the stresses at the crack tip relax somewhat and the crack tends to slow or stop. This unloading information is communicated to the load point by way of a stress wave, and new load information runs back to the crack tip and builds up the stress concentration. The crack may respond by accelerating again, thereby relaxing the stresses. This cycle may repeat itself many times. Eventually, when stress relaxation resulting from crack extension is such that the applied load can no longer maintain fracture, arrest occurs. Observations of such stop-and-go crack propagation and corresponding stress wave activity have been reported by Van Elst [*12,13*] who used ultrahigh-speed photographic and electronic methods to demonstrate the intermittent nature of crack propagation. He found that fracture proceeded in a series of discrete steps and that sizeable stress waves emanated from the crack tip at each advance. The use of a soft loading machine no doubt enhances discontinuous fracture behavior.

Thus, the stresses at a propagating crack tip vary with time in an oscillatory manner and require a wave propagation code for an accurate accounting. Kanninen [*14*], Schmuely and Peretz [*15*], and Wilkins (private communication) have applied one-, two-, and three-dimensional wave propagation codes, respectively, to the DCB geometry. In this work reported here, the stress distribution in the specimen at all points in time was calculated by use of TOODY3 [*16*], a two-dimensional, Lagrangian, finite difference wave propagation code. Plane-strain conditions were assumed. This code solves equations for conservation of mass, momentum, and energy in two space dimensions at successive small (0.5 μs) time steps and computes thereby the two-dimensional strain and stress states. A simple constitutive equation for the material was constructed using nonstandard round bar tensile data from specimens machined from the broken halves of the DCB specimen.

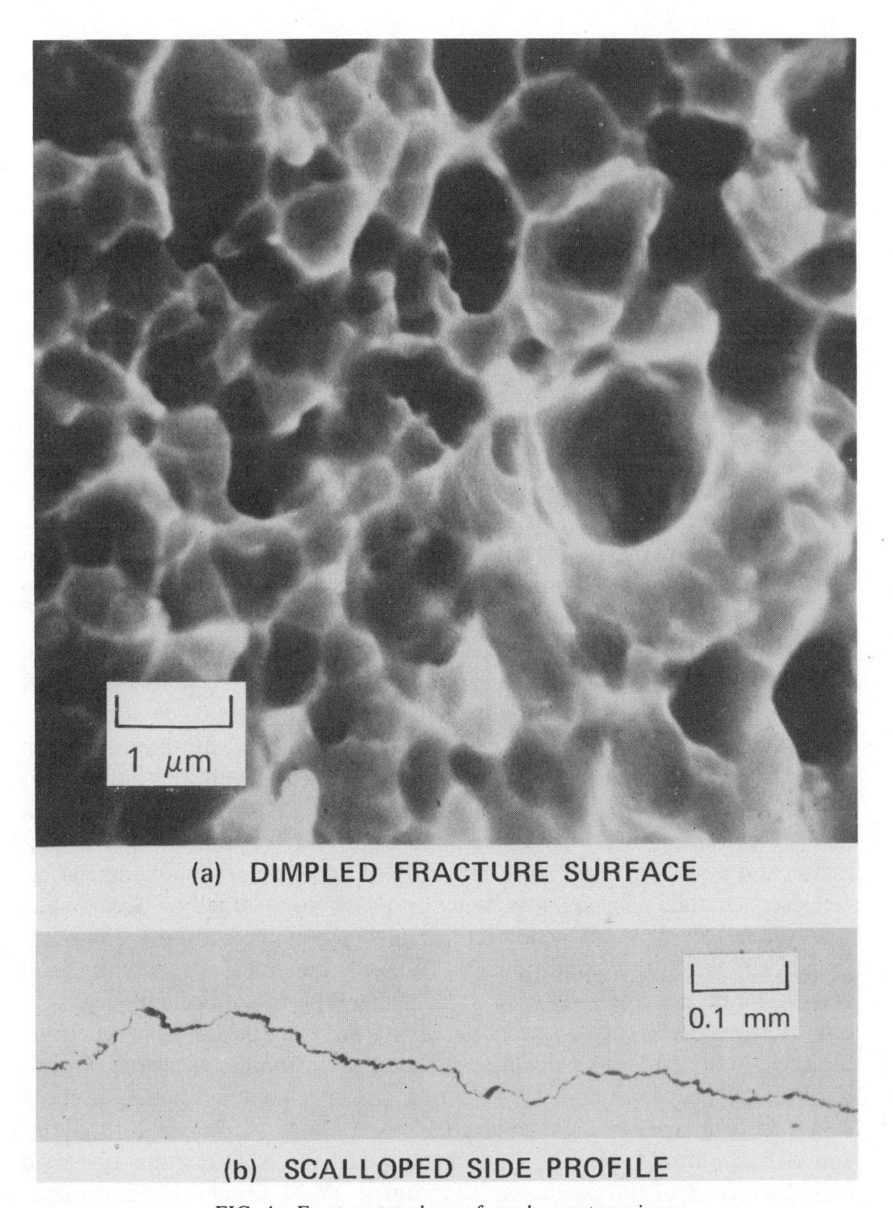

FIG. 4—*Fracture topology of crack arrest specimen.*

The computational grid consisted of a 16 by 50 array of 4.0 by 6.4-mm cells, as indicated in Fig. 5. Because of symmetry only half of the specimen had to be considered. We realized that a much finer grid with cell sizes of the order of the dimple size would be required for accurate results, but we chose the coarse grid of Fig. 5 to provide a less expensive demonstration of feasibility.

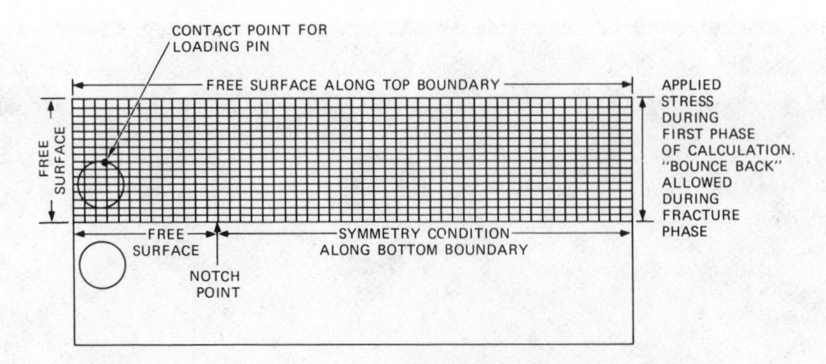

FIG. 5—*Grid scheme and boundary conditions used in computation.*

The computation was accomplished in two stages. First, the measured wedge opening displacements and forces were applied to the computational grid to obtain the elastic stress distribution in the specimen at the point of instability. The method of dynamic relaxation [*17*] was used to accomplish this in an economical time. When the static elastic solution was obtained to within about 1 percent, yielding was allowed to occur.

The second calculational stage began with instability of the blunted notch and continued until many microseconds after arrest. In this stage, stress wave activity was computed and allowed to dictate the stress state and fracture activity at the propagating crack tip. Nucleation and growth of voids was treated as occurring according to Eqs 1 and 2. Void nucleation and growth rate parameters for a similar steel under plate impact loading conditions were assumed applicable [*12*]. As microfractures nucleate and grow in a cell, the strength of the cell gradually decreases. Coalescence and, consequently, cell rupture were assumed to occur when the volume of all voids generated equaled the volume of the computational cell. When this condition was fulfilled, the crack advanced one cell length. Thus, the crack velocity is defined by the rate at which successive cells rupture. Reference *18* gives details of the computational procedures.

Crack branching was calculated as soon as instability occurred. In addition to a propagating fracture along the specimen midplane, a crack began to propagate at right angles to this fracture. Although bifurcation and trifurcation of fracture in similar specimens is frequently observed [*19*], the crack in the particular experiment 3V-31 simulated here propagated nominally on the specimen midplane. A second calculation was then performed for which off-axis cells were not permitted to fracture. The calculated crack ran 51.4 mm, about one third of the experimentally observed arrest length, in about 65 μs before stopping. The calculation was continued for an additional 100 μs after arrest to test whether reinitiation would occur. The propagation velocity was rather constant at 790 m/s, about 80 percent higher than measured. There were no significant periodic oscillations in macrocrack velocity from the periodic stress wave loading.

The energies absorbed by microfracturing and by plastic flow at the crack tip were calculated and printed out. The microfracturing energy was computed at each time step as the product of the average stress in the cell and the change in cell volume resulting from the nucleation and growth of microfractures during that time step. Similarly, the plastic energy was computed as the product of stress and plastic strain.

The variation with time of the elastic strain energy and the energies absorbed by plastic flow and by microcracking are shown in Fig. 6 for the material in the seventh computational cell from the notch point. As the crack tip approached and loaded this cell, the elastic strain energy rose sharply. Soon afterwards, plastic flow occurred, and the crack tip material began to absorb the elastic energy. Somewhat later, microfracturing began to occur and after about 25 μs ruptured the cell.

The results show that relatively little energy is absorbed in the microfracturing process; about 20 times as much as absorbed in plastic flow. However, it is the microfracturing activity that ruptures the cell and thereby controls the amount of plastic energy that is absorbed. Figure 6 shows the crescendo of microfracture activity shortly before the cell ruptures.

The rupture of this particular crack tip cell required 86 MN/m^2 of plastic work and only 3.3 MN/m^2 of microfracturing work. Thus, the fracture toughness derives largely from plastic flow at the crack tip. As-

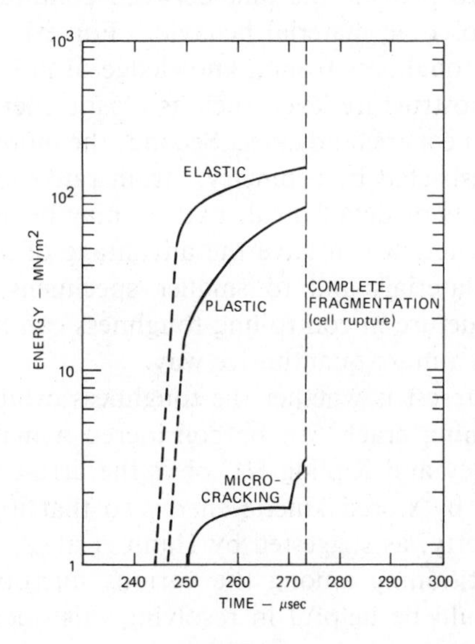

FIG. 6—*Energy partitioning in a computational cell in a DCB specimen as the cell is traversed by the crack.*

suming the radius of the plastic zone at the midplane of the specimen to be 10^{-4} m, the energy absorbed per unit crack extension can be computed and converted to obtain the fracture toughness for a propagating crack K_{ID}. The resulting value K_{ID} = 61 MN/m$^{-3/2}$ compares favorably with reported values [11] for static initiation toughness and arrest toughness of 54 and 68 MN/m$^{-3/2}$, respectively. In view of the coarseness of the computational grid and the approximate nature of the microfracture properties and constitutive relations, however, this result should be considered preliminary.

Discussion

We have demonstrated the feasibility of computing the energies absorbed at the tip of a propagating and arresting crack by treating the microevents that occur in the process zone. Agreement with experimental measurements of crack velocity and arrest length would be improved by using a finer computational grid to resolve more accurately the crack-tip stress concentration and to concentrate the fracture damage in a zone comparable in size to the process zone. This should decrease the macrocrack velocity and reduce the tendency to branch. A further improvement can be expected from the use of more accurate nucleation and growth properties and constitutive equations.

The motivations for using more detailed and physically realistic models to compute crack propagation and arrest are threefold. First, such approaches promise to provide the link between continuum mechanics parameters and microscopic material behavior. For example, being able to derive the fracture toughness from a knowledge of individual contributing factors on the microstructure level, such as plastic energy, and microfracture energy, would be a great advance. Second, the more detailed approach used here is not restricted by geometry, strain rate,[3] or even stress state. Therefore, the results of detailed calculations may be helpful in extending continuum approaches, which have the advantage of simplicity, to apply to more ductile materials and to smaller specimens. Finally, the role played by microstructure in controlling toughness can be studied and perhaps understood in a more quantitative way.

Of immediate interest is whether the toughness exhibited by a material in arresting a running crack can be considered a material property, as suggested by Crosley and Ripling [1], or if the arrest toughness is influenced significantly by stored kinetic energy so that it has little meaning as a material property, as suggested by Hahn et al [2]. An understanding of the energy partitioning among the various microprocesses occurring at crack arrest would be helpful in resolving this question. Such energy

[3]Simple trial calculations on a one-dimensional array of cells in tension indicate that the microfracture energy depends strongly on strain rate [18].

partitioning information can be obtained from detailed, physically realistic calculations such as described here.

Acknowledgment

Thanks are due to M. A. Austin who performed the stress wave calculations.

References

[*1*] Crosley, P. B. and Ripling, E. J., *Nuclear Engineering and Design*, Vol. 17, 1971, p. 32.

[*2*] Hahn, G. T., Hoagland, R. G., Kanninen, M. F., and Rosenfield, A. R., *Proceedings of Second International Conference on Pressure Vessel Technology,* San Antonio, Tex. 1973, p. 995.

[*3*] Crussard, C., Plateau, J. et al in *Fracture,* B. L. Averbach et al, Eds., Wiley, New York, 1959, p. 524.

[*4*] Hoagland, R. G., Rosenfield A. R., and Hahn, G. T., *Metallurgical Transactions,* Vol. 3, 1972, p. 123.

[*5*] Cox, T. B. and J. R. Low, Jr., *Metallurgical Transactions,* Vol. 5, 1974, p. 1457.

[*6*] Palmer, I. G. and G. C. Smith, *Proceedings of AIME Conference on Oxide Dispersion Strengthening,* American Institute of Mining, Metallurgical, and Petroleum Engineers, Bottom Landing, New York, June 1966, Gordon and Breach, New York, 1967.

[*7*] Barbee, T. W., Jr., L. Seaman, R. Crewdson, and D. Curran, *Journal of Materials,* Vol. 7, 1972, p. 393.

[*8*] Shockey, D. A., L. Seaman, and D. R. Curran, Final Technical Report AFWL-TR-73-12, Kirtland Air Force Base, New Mex., 1973.

[*9*] Shockey, D. A., Seaman, L., and Curran, D. R., et al, Final Technical Report on Contract DAAD05-73-C-0025, U.S. Army Ballistic Research Laboratories, Aberdeen, Md., 1973.

[*10*] Seaman, L. and Shockey, D. A., Final Technical Report AMMRC CTR 75-2, Army Materials and Mechanics Research Center, Watertown, Mass., 1975.

[*11*] Hahn, G. T., Hoagland, R. G., Kanninen, M. F., and Rosenfield, A. R. in *Dynamic Crack Propagation,* G. C. Sih, Ed., Noordhoff International Publishing, Leyden, The Netherlands, 1972, p. 649.

[*12*] Van Elst, H. C., *Transactions,* American Institute of Metallurgical Engineers, Vol. 230, 1964, p. 460.

[*13*] Van Elst, H. C. in *Dynamic Crack Propagation,* G. C. Sih, Ed., Noordhoff International Publishing, Leyden, The Netherlands, 1972, p. 283.

[*14*] Kanninen, M. F., *International Journal of Fracture,* Vol. 10, 1974, p. 415.

[*15*] Schmuely, M. and Peretz, D., *International Journal of Solids and Structures,* Vol. 12, 1976, p. 67.

[*16*] Bertholf, L. D. and Benzley, S. E., Research Report SC-RR-68-41, Sandia Laboratory, 1968.

[*17*] Otter, J. R. H., Cassell, A. C., and Hobbs, R. E., "Dynamic Relaxation," *Proceedings of the Institute of Civil Engineering*, Paper No. 6986, 1967.

[*18*] Shockey, D. A., Austin, M., Seaman, L., and Curran, D. R., Final Technical Report to Electric Power Research Institute, Palo Alto, Calif., Contract RP499-1-1, 1976.

[*19*] Hahn, G. T. et al, First Annual Progress Report on Task Agreement No. 62, BMI-1937 NRC-5, Battelle Columbus Laboratories, Columbus, Ohio, 1975.

G. Bullock[1] *and E. Smith*[1]

Effects of Grain Size and Temperature on Flat Fracture Propagation and Arrest in Mild Steel

REFERENCE: Bullock, G. and Smith, E., "**Effects of Grain Size and Temperature on Flat Fracture Propagation and Arrest in Mild Steel,**" *Fast Fracture and Crack Arrest, ASTM STP 627,* G. T. Hahn and M. F. Kanninen, Eds., American Society for Testing and Materials, 1977, pp. 286–300.

ABSTRACT: The paper presents results from an experimental program whose objective is the determination of the effects of grain size and temperature on flat fracture propagation and arrest in mild steel. Small laboratory test specimens, containing nitrided notches and surfaces so as to eliminate respectively the initiation barrier and shear lip formation, have been deformed by four-point bending. The onset of crack arrest has been correlated with the applied loading, and the fracture surface appearance during both propagation and arrest has been studied in detail; cleavage rather than ductile fracture is the predominent failure mechanism for a wide range of testing conditions. The results are discussed in relation to theoretical models describing the micromechanics of flat fracture propagation and arrest.

KEY WORDS: fracture properties, crack propagation, arresting (process), mild steels, grain size, temperature, cleavage

The prevention of unstable fracture initiation in engineering steel structures by the application of fracture mechanics principles is now an established procedure. However, because it is difficult to account for such factors as residual stresses, dynamic loading effects, change of material properties during service, subcritical crack growth by fatigue or stress corrosion, and indeed many other factors in situations where failure might have extremely serious consequences, it is desirable to have a fall-back position, and aim also to prevent extensive crack propagation, for in this way complete disintegration of the structure might be avoided.

Extensive investigations of service failures and also laboratory tests have both shown that crack propagation in mild steel proceeds in either a

[1]Undergraduate student and professor of metallurgy, respectively, Joint University/UMIST Metallurgy Department, Manchester, U.K.

flat fracture or a shear fracture mode. These modes are distinguishable by their speeds, flat fracture propagation usually being much faster than shear fracture propagation [*1*].[2] For a given material there exists a critical propagation transition temperature, above which fracture is of the slow shear type and below which fracture proceeds by the faster flat mode; this full-scale propagation transition temperature has been successfully correlated with the transition temperature determined from the Battelle drop weight tear test [*2*] provided the drop weight specimens and full-scale components have the same thickness. Since crack speed affects the extent to which the stresses can relax, it affects the way in which the structure loading influences the propagation phenomenon. Stress relaxation is more difficult with a high-crack velocity, and the maintenance of high-stress levels is therefore more likely if propagation is by the flat fracture mode. The loading pattern itself also plays a major role in the relaxation process; with a soft loading system the stresses within a structure will not relax irrespective of the crack speed, whereas with a hard loading system, a condition approached in many laboratory scale tests, the stresses can readily relax during crack propagation. For situations that are intermediate between these extremes, relaxation is easier the lower the crack speed, and consequently flat fracture is so dangerous in practice because it is associated with a high crack velocity, and this enables the stresses within a structure to be maintained at high levels, thereby encouraging the proparation process to continue. These considerations clearly show that a logical approach to minimize the risk of a catastrophic failure is to ensure that flat fracture never occurs. This will not automatically prevent catastrophic failure, since extensive shear fracture propagation can occur if the loading conditions are sufficiently exacting; nevertheless, it is a step in the right direction.

It is against this background of the importance of flat fracture in relation to the overall catastrophic failure problem that flat fracture propagation has been investigated. The long-term objective is the development of a comprehensive model of flat fracture propagation, which might be used as a guide for relating microstructural effects to dynamic fracture resistance; this would be of considerable assistance when selecting materials for engineering components, particularly if the relevant experimental data could be obtained from simple laboratory tests.

The particular aspect of the problem considered in the present paper is the micromechanics of flat fracture propagation and arrest, and how these phenomena are affected by temperature and microstructure in the form of grain size. These phenomena are deliberately studied without the complications introduced by shear lips, which are often associated with flat fracture propagation and arrest. Shear lip elimination can be achieved

[2]The italic numbers in brackets refer to the list of references appended to this paper.

by testing small laboratory specimens at very low temperatures, or their effects may be minimized by testing very thick specimens at temperatures closer to those of practical interest. However, the present investigation takes an alternative route in that it is based on the use of small Charpy notched specimens, whose surfaces are nitrided to eliminate shear lip formation and whose notches are nitrided to eliminate the initiation barrier, thereby allowing attention to be focussed on the propagation phenomenon. The authors have already used these procedures with Charpy specimens fractured under impact conditions, when shear lip elimination produced substantial decreases in both the impact and normalized impact energies [3]. Furthermore, the results showed that dynamic flat fracture resistance at a given temperature increased with decreasing grain size, while the failure mechanism was essentially 100 percent cleavage irrespective of the grain size and test temperature. The present investigation uses slow bend tests in order to study flat fracture arrest, and these show that for the particular mild steel investigated cleavage is essentially the sole failure mechanism during both propagation and arrest. The observations are discussed in relation to theoretical models describing the micromechanics of flat fracture propagation and arrest.

Experimental Procedures

The material investigated was a mild steel similar to the steels used for many structural applications, although it had a high-nitrogen and a low-carbon content since it was intended, for other parts of the investigation, to determine the extent of plastic deformation by means of Fry's etching method. The steel was cast as a 25 kg ingot at the Corporate Laboratories of the British Steel Corporation, Sheffield, and supplied as hot-rolled bar, approximately 15 mm square. The composition analysis was:

	C	N	Mn	Si	S	P
Percent	0.068	0.024	0.840	0.011	0.013	0.006

The as-received material's grain size was 25 μm, but to produce larger grain size (74 μm) material, the as-received material was strained approximately 15 percent and then heat-treated for 4 h in vacuum, followed by furnace cooling. The tensile properties for the two grain sizes studied were:

Grain Size	Proof Stress, 0.2%	Ultimate Tensile Strength	Elongation, %	Reduction of Area, %
26 μm	323 MN/m^{-2}	547 MN/m^{-2}	20	61
74 μm	260 MN/m^{-2}	445 MN/m^{-2}	20	66

The small and large grain size materials are hereafter referred to respectively as S- and L-materials.

Modifications were made to the standard Charpy specimen design in the light of some preliminary experiments. The 0.25 mm Charpy notch radius was too blunt, and specimens were machine notched to a depth of 1.5 mm, this being increased to 2.0 to 2.5 mm by hand sawing with a 0.2-mm-thick jeweller's saw blade (the specimen design is shown in Fig. 1).

The specimens were nitrided for 12 h in an ammonia atmosphere at 863 K, water-quenched, and tested in this condition as the nitride case is more brittle than when specimens are slowly cooled; the nitride case thickness was ~ 0.8 mm at the notch root and ~ 2.0 mm at the side surface.

The mechanical tests were carried out in a four-point bending jig attached to an Instron machine, with appropriate constant temperature baths surrounding the bending apparatus. The tests were conducted at a crosshead speed of 0.5 mm/min within the temperature range 248 to 353 K, the temperature during each test being constant to within ±1 K. A test was terminated whenever there was a load drop, since this indicated the propagation and arrest of a crack; there was complete load relaxation whenever crack propagation caused complete fracture.

After testing, the fracture surfaces were examined to see whether the features along the crack path and at arrest varied in a manner that could be attributed to grain size or temperature. Completely fractured specimens were slit longitudinally at midsection, one half being used for metallographic examination, the other half for fracture surface studies in the scanning electron microscope. Specimens containing arrested cracks were first longitudinally slit at midsection, one half being examined metallographically, the other half being fractured so that the surfaces could be examined.

Experimental Results

General Features

Fractures were of three types: complete fractures, long-arrested fractures (that is, arrest 1 to 4 mm from the compression surface), and short-arrested fractures (that is, arrest just outside the nitride layer); at low temperatures there were no long-arrested cracks, while at the highest temperatures there were only short-arrested cracks. The fracture surfaces of

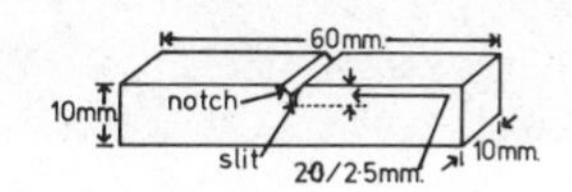

FIG. 1—*Details of test specimens.*

both S- and L-specimens were practically 100 percent crystalline even up to the arrest fronts, irrespective of the testing temperature.

The main general effect of increasing temperature was fewer complete fractures, and the occurrence of "kinked" arrest fronts formed by a crack running further in the nitride layer, before arrest, than in virgin material (Fig. 2). Except at the higher temperatures, arrest fronts in both S- and L-specimens were fairly straight.

Grain size had a significant embrittling effect, with arrest in S-specimens generally occurring at lower temperatures than in L-specimens, while long-arrested cracks were not observed in L-specimens.

Mechanical Test Results

When a notch embrittlement technique, such as nitriding, is used to facilitate crack initiation, the crack driving force cannot be controlled and it is therefore only natural that there should be appreciable scatter in

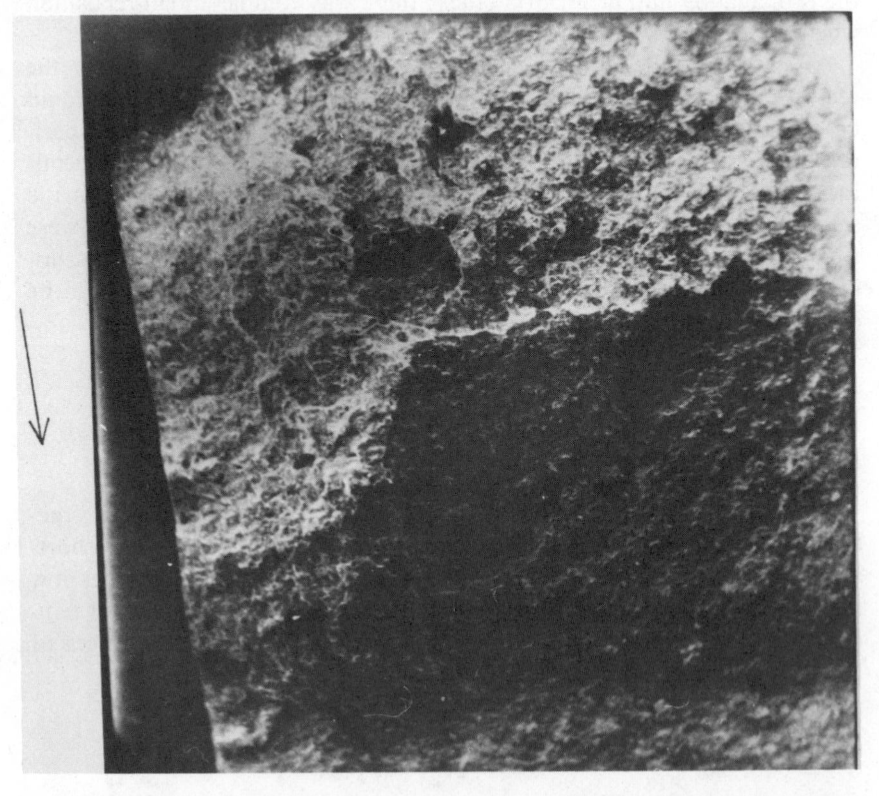

FIG. 2—*Fractograph of an S-specimen tested at 318 K, showing a typical fracture surface and a kinked arrest front* (×25).

the experimental results. This is of little consequence in the present investigation; indeed, it was desirable to measure the extent of crack growth for a wide range of driving forces, which were recorded in terms of the initiation stress intensity (K_i) as determined by Brown and Srawley's expression [*4*]. The extent of crack growth was expressed in terms of the dimensionless quantity $\Delta a/L$, Δa being the amount of crack growth and L the initial ligament depth of a notched specimen; this gives $\Delta a/L = 1$ for all complete fractures.

The S-specimen results are presented in Fig. 3 which shows that, in general, the K_i values for short- and long-arrested cracks are separated by a threshold K_i value. The term short refers to cracks for which $\Delta a/L < 0.4$, while the term long means that $\Delta a/L > 0.4$, the latter category including complete fractures; the distinction between short and long cracks was quite marked since $\Delta a/L$ for long cracks was rarely as low as 0.4 and then only at high temperatures (Fig. 3). The threshold K_i value is given by the broken line, which essentially separates, for temperatures up to 300 K, the highest and lowest K_i values for short and long cracks, respectively. Within this temperature range, there is no apparent temperature variation of K_i or $\Delta a/L$ for short cracks. Figure 3 shows considerable scatter in the higher K_i values, but there is no evidence for crack arrest being due to lower K_i values within this band. Despite the scatter, there is a definite trend for K_i to increase with temperature, presumably because of the increased ductility of the nitride layer at a notch root. Between 312 and 323 K, there is a very sudden decrease of $\Delta a/L$ from the typical long-crack value (~ 0.8) to a typical short-crack value (~ 0.15) despite an increasing crack driving force; this is clear evidence for a significant dynamic toughness increase within this temperature range. A further indication of increasing toughness with temperature is the arrest of long cracks above 294 K despite an increasing trend in K_i; below this temperature, all cracks that initiate at K_i values in excess of the threshold, propagate to complete failure.

The most important feature of the L-specimen results (Fig. 4) is the absence of long-arrested cracks, and another feature was the ease with which fracture could be reinitiated at an arrested crack front. Unlike the S-specimen situation, it is difficult to judge whether a threshold K_i value exists; however, increasing temperature would seem to cause a transition from complete fractures to short arrested cracks between 287 and 294 K, and despite the scatter, there is a trend for both complete fracture and arrested crack K_i values to increase with temperature. There is little variation in $\Delta a/L$ up to 318 K, which is an indication of increasing toughness since K_i is increasing. Above 318 K, $\Delta a/L$ rises with temperature, until there is a large drop to a low value at 353 K; this result is extra conclusive evidence for an increase in dynamic fracture resistance with increasing temperature.

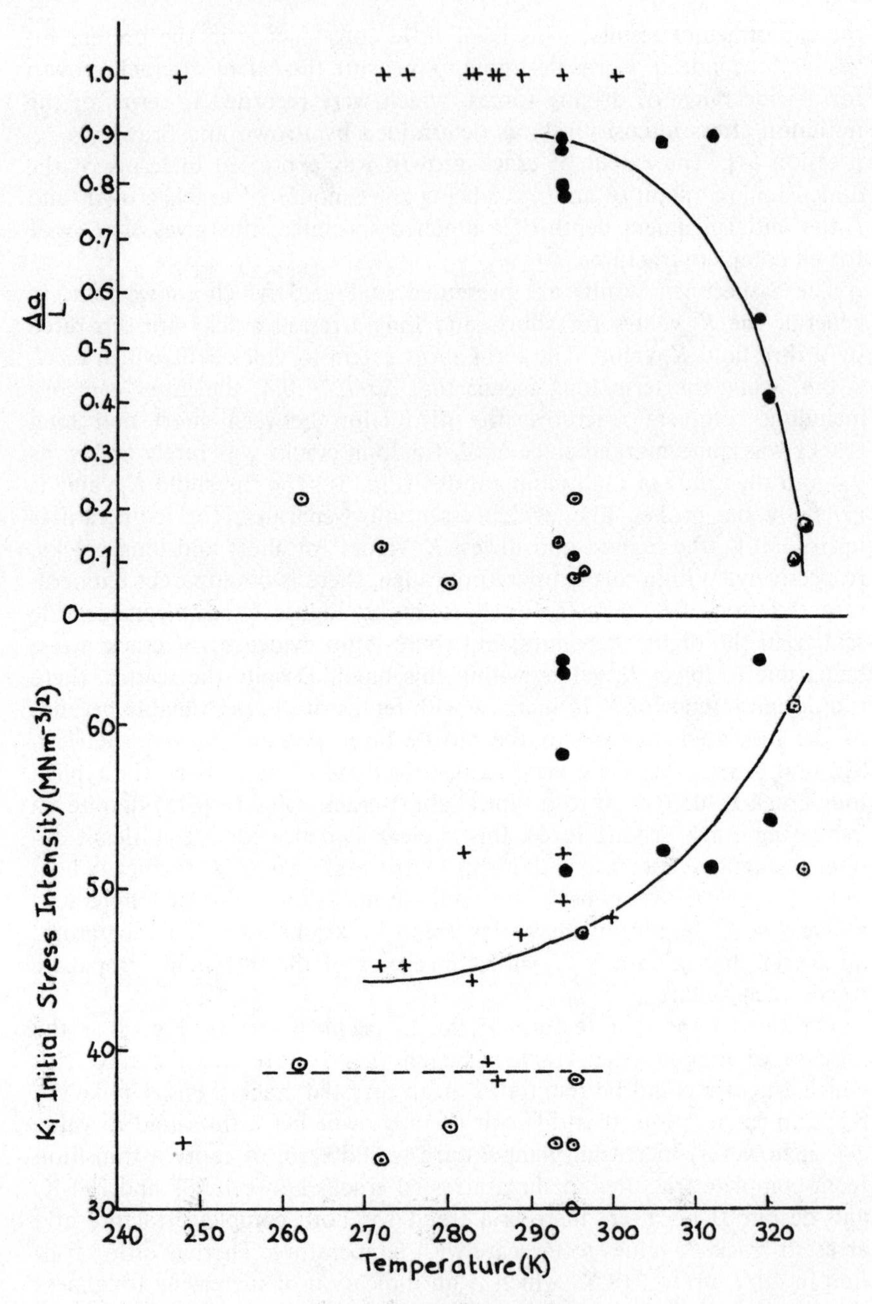

⊙ short arrested crack data points.
• long arrested crack data points.
+ complete fracture data points.
------ threshold K_i value.

FIG. 3—*Values of* K_i *and* $\Delta a/L$ *for S-specimens.*

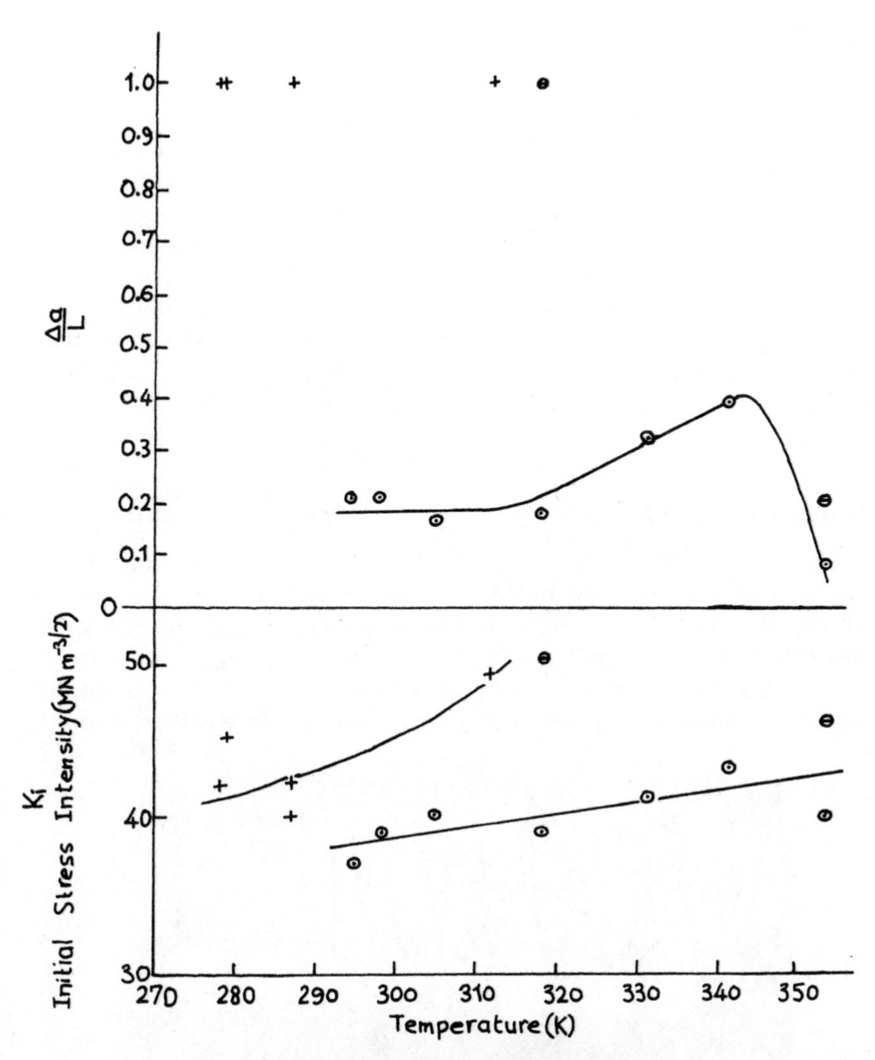

⊙ short arrested crack data points.
⊖ reinitiated crack data points.
+ complete fracture data points.
FIG. 4—*Values of* K_i *and* $\Delta a/L$ *for L-specimens.*

The embrittling effect of increasing grain size is demonstrated clearly by comparing the data for S- and L-specimens, the results from tests at and above room temperature being particularly illuminating. For example, at 312 K an L-specimen fractured completely at a K_i value below that for which cracks arrested in S-specimens, and for which $\Delta a/L$ values were rapidly decreasing as the temperature increased. Furthermore, in the region of 320 K, the $\Delta a/L$ values for S-specimens are similar to or less than the L-arrested crack values, despite their much greater K_i values.

Metallographic Observations of Fractures

Examination showed that all specimens fractured by cleavage, irrespective of the initial crack driving force (K_i) or testing temperature. As regards arrested cracks, unfractured links were observed in the vicinities of both short- and long-crack arrests in S-specimens (Fig. 5); with short cracks, the general trend was towards more extensive links as the temperature increased, while with long cracks the link size appeared to decrease as the temperature increased above 312 K, coinciding with the occurrence of kinked arrest fronts and progressively smaller arrested crack lengths.

The fracture surface profile was more regular with L-specimens than S-specimens (Figs. 6 and 7). There were no long-crack arrests in L-specimens but unfractured links were associated with arrested short cracks (Fig. 8).

Scanning Electron Microscope Observations of Fractured Surfaces

The aim of this aspect of the work was to determine the relative amounts of cleavage and ductile fracture associated with flat fracture propagation and arrest. Surface examinations were conducted with specimens that were fractured completely at room temperature subsequent to arrest, and it was anticipated originally that there might have been difficulties in distinguishing between links fractured before and after arrest.

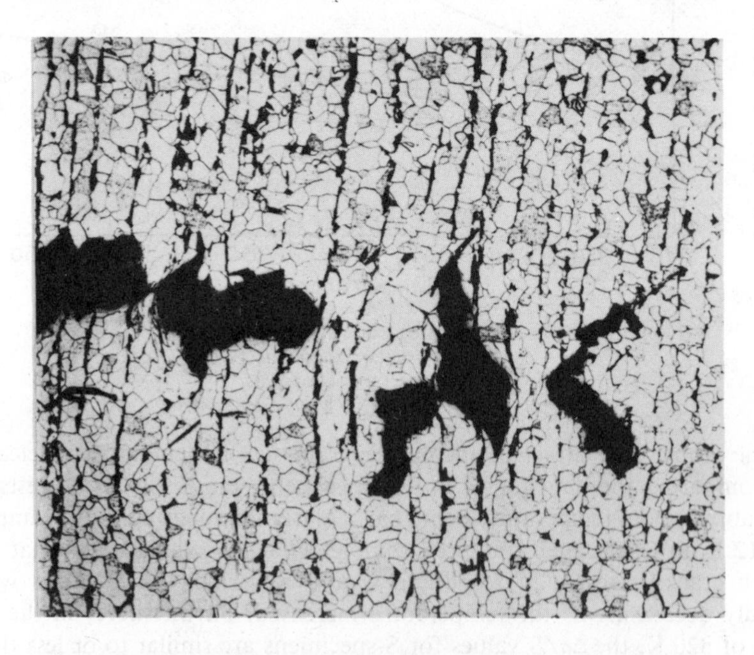

FIG. 5—*Link formation in S-specimen tested at 294 K (× 100).*

FIG. 6—*Fracture surface profile* (transverse section) *of S-specimen tested at 318 K* (×*170*).

In the event, however, this was no problem since ductile reinitiation of short cracks in S-specimens was associated with a strip of ductile fracture that was easily distinguishable from the prior arrest features, while brittle reinitiation of long cracks in S-specimens and short cracks in L-specimens left no markings on the fracture surfaces. This, in fact, meant that the arrest front was difficult to locate at higher magnifications, since temperature had apparently no effect on the microscopic fracture surface features during both propagation and arrest. The fracture mode was essentially 100 percent cleavage, although there were thin strips of ductile fracture, which presumably are due to tearing across boundaries separating grains that have cleaved (Fig. 9). When observed, ductile fracture was always confined to grain boundary regions, and there was less ductile fracture with L-specimens. Figure 10 shows the region near a short crack arrest in an L-specimen tested at 331 K, the arrest front being delineated by the out of focus region near the bottom of the figure; there is clearly very little evidence of ductile fracture.

Discussion

The preceding section's experimental results on flat fracture propagation and arrest in mild steel have been obtained with small laboratory

FIG. 7—*Fracture surface profile* (transverse section) *of L-specimen tested at 353 K* (×*120*).

test specimens without the complications introduced by the presence of shear lips, which have been eliminated by nitriding the specimen surfaces. Furthermore, in order to focus attention on the propagation phenomenon, initiation was facilitated by nitriding the notches. The important features of the results are: (*a*) the dominant role of cleavage as the failure mechanism throughout both the propagation and arrest stages of flat fracture; ductile failure processes seemingly play only a minor role and (*b*) grain size has a marked effect on the propagation process, in that dynamic flat fracture resistance decreases with increasing grain size, a conclusion that manifests itself particularly by an absence of long-arrested cracks in large grain size material. This grain size effect is in general accord with the Charpy impact results [*3*], mentioned previously, which showed that both the impact energy and also the normalized impact energy at a given temperature decreased with increasing grain size.

Cottrell [*5*] has emphasized that plane-strain fractures can propagate at low-stress levels because microcracks or holes are able to form and grow within a fracture process zone ahead of the propagating crack tip. An alternative view [*6*] is that the main crack bypasses locally tough regions, which subsequently fracture. In both cases, the crack-tip motion

FIG. 8—*Link formation in L-specimen tested in 305 K* (×*85*).

can be formally described by the climb of a group of edge dislocations; this type of fracture is referred to as a cumulative fracture [*5*], because the contribution to fracture, made by a dislocation moving through the material ahead of the crack, accumulates continuously with the distance travelled by the dislocation. Thus, the general picture is that flat fracture propagates in the present material by the formation of cleavage cracks in preferentially oriented crystals within a process zone at the crack tip, followed by the fracture of the remaining ligaments. However, an important feature of the present work is the observation that the ligaments also fracture by a cleavage mechanism, in other words by the same mechanism as that which is responsible for the formation of cracks surrounding the ligaments. Consequently, all the crystals in the process zone fracture by cleavage, and the heterogeneous nature of the process, that is, the formation and fracture of ligaments, is due to the relative ease by which cleavage cracks form in the differently oriented crystals at the crack front. Based on Tipper's work [*7*], Cottrell [*5*] envisaged the ligaments to fail by a plastic tearing mechanism, but this is certainly not the case with the present material, perhaps because cleavage is encouraged by the high-nitrogen content.

Since cleavage is associated usually with lower local strains than plastic

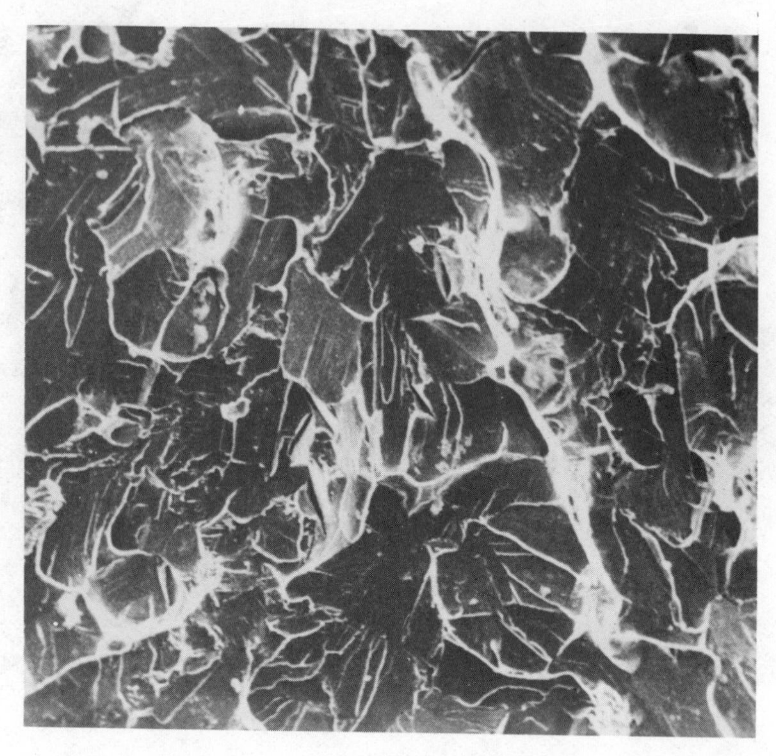

FIG. 9—*Fractograph showing cleavage facets with thin interfacet regions of ductile fracture in S-specimen tested at 318 K* (×*570*).

tearing, the ligament failure mode is important with regard to propagation and arrest phenomena; thus, other things being equal, continued propagation will be easier and arrest more difficult if the ligament failure mode is cleavage. Following Cottrell [*5*] and assuming σ_p to be the average failure stress of the discontinuous fracture process zone, and Φ_p the limiting plastic displacement at the crack tip, that is, Φ_p is the crack opening associated with ligament failure, the work per unit area of fracture is $\gamma_p = \sigma_y \Phi_p$. A change of ligament failure mode is likely to have a greater effect on Φ_p than σ_y, and Φ_p will be much lower for cleavage than for plastic tearing. Furthermore, in view of the well-known effect of grain size on the cleavage ability of mild steel in static tests [*8*], Φ_p should be smaller with large grain size material. Consequently, it is immediately seen why flat fracture propagation should be so easy at the relatively high-testing temperatures in the present investigation, and moreover why grain size has such a marked effect. However, it should be emphasized that the results described in this paper will not be truly representative of the behavior of typical mild steels when tested at the same temperatures, unless

FIG. 10—*Fractograph showing very little evidence of ductile fracture in L-specimen tested at 331 K* (×*125*).

the latter are embrittled by, for example, neutron irradiation or strain aging so as to promote the cleavage mode of failure at the expense of plastic tearing.

Conclusions

1. With the particular mild steel investigated, in which shear lip formation has been eliminated in small laboratory test specimens by nitriding the specimen surfaces, cleavage is essentially the only failure mode involved in both the propagation and arrest of flat fractures.

2. Increasing grain size has a deleterious effect on the dynamic fracture resistance, in that crack propagation is easier and arrest more difficult in coarse grain size material.

Acknowledgments

The authors thank the British Steel Corporation via their Corporate Laboratories (Dr. M. J. May) for financial support for the research described in this paper.

References

[*1*] Duffy, A. R., McClure, G. M., Eiber, R. J., and Massey, W. A., *Fracture,* H. Liebowitz, Ed., Academic Press, New York, Vol. 5, 1969, p. 159.
[*2*] Eiber, R. J., Duffy, A. R., and McClure, G. M. in *Proceedings of the Sixth Technical Conference,* T. G. Bradbury, Ed., Gordon and Breach, London and New York, p. 445.
[*3*] Bullock, G. and Smith, E., International Conference on Dynamic Fracture Toughness, London, July 1976, proceedings to be published.
[*4*] Brown, W. F. and Srawley, J. E., *Review of Developments in Plane Strain Fracture Toughness Testing, ASTM STP 463,* American Society for Testing and Materials, 1970, p. 216.
[*5*] Cottrell, A. H., "The 1963 Tewkesbury Lecture," University of Melbourne, Australia.
[*6*] Hoagland, R. G., Rosenfield, A. R., and Hahn, G. T., *Metallurgical Transactions,* Vol. 3, 1972, p. 123.
[*7*] Tipper, C. F., *Journal of the Iron Steel Institute,* Vol. 185, 1957, p. 4.
[*8*] Cottrell, A. H., *Transactions,* Metallurgical Society, American Institute of Mining, Metallurgical, and Petroleum Engineers, Vol. 212, 1958, p. 192.

L. S. Costin,[1] *J. Duffy,*[1] *and L. B. Freund*[1]

Fracture Initiation in Metals Under Stress Wave Loading Conditions

REFERENCE: Costin, L. S., Duffy, J., and Freund, L. B., "**Fracture Initiation in Metals Under Stress Wave Loading Conditions,**" *Fast Fracture and Crack Arrest, ASTM STP 627,* G. T. Hahn and M. F. Kanninen, Eds., American Society for Testing and Materials, 1977, pp. 301–318.

ABSTRACT: An experimental procedure is described for accurately establishing the dynamic fracture initiation properties of structural metals at extremely high loading rates. The apparatus is an adaptation of the Kolsky pressure bar (split-Hopkinson bar) in which a 1-in.-diameter round bar specimen with a prefatigued circumferential notch is loaded to failure by the rapidly rising tensile pulse resulting from an explosive detonation. Using the standard Kolsky technique, the average stress at the fracture site is measured as a function of time. Crack opening displacement is measured by optical means, as a function of time, thus yielding a complete load-displacement record for each test. From the data the critical value of the crack-tip stress intensity factor, K_{Ic}, at loading rates, $\dot{K}_I$ in excess of 10^9 psi $\sqrt{\text{in.}}$/s may be obtained. This is nearly two orders of magnitude faster than has been achieved by other standard techniques. Results are presented for dynamic tests conducted on SAE 4340 steel and 1020 cold-rolled steel, and these are compared to results from static tests performed on specimens of similar shape.

KEY WORDS: fracture initiation, fracture properties, experimental techniques, explosive loading, stress waves, strain rate, metals

Nomenclature

- δ_c Displacement due to presence of crack
- D Outside diameter of bar
- E Elastic modulus
- F Size function
- $\mathcal{G}$ Griffith energy release rate
- J J-integral
- K_I Crack-tip stress intensity factor
- $\dot{K}_I$ Crack tip loading rate
- K_{Ic}^e Equivalent fracture toughness

[1]Research assistant, professor of engineering, and professor, respectively, Division of Engineering, Brown University, Providence, R.I. 02912.

ν Poisson's ratio
P Applied load
R Radius of remaining circular ligament
R_{eff} Effective radius of remaining ligament
σ_{yp} Yield stress
t Time
θ Relative rotation angle between grid lines
W Fundamental Moiré fringe width
w Grid pitch

Because flaws are present in all engineering structures, whether occurring naturally or as a result of some fabrication process, it has become common practice to design against fracture initiated failures. In most cases the fracture initiation is regarded as occurring under static or quasi-static loading conditions. However, many loading conditions occur in practice which cannot be treated as quasi-static, and, in these cases, the inertia of the material as well as its rate sensitivity must be taken into account. A potential danger arises in the use of materials which exhibit high sensitivity to loading rate because this behavior can lead to a significant reduction in fracture toughness and thus to unexpected failures in service under dynamic loading.

Fracture initiation resulting from the application of dynamic loads has received considerable attention in recent years [*1–5*].[2] Most recent experimental work has employed hydraulic testing machines or similar mechanical devices to achieve rapid loading of a standard fracture specimen. With such apparatus, it is possible to determine the critical values of the stress intensity factor, K_{Ic}, for crack-tip loading rates of up to $\dot{K}_I = 10^6$ psi $\sqrt{\text{in.}}$/s. However, such a loading rate is still quite low when compared to loading rates associated with propagating cracks, nominally 10^{12} psi $\sqrt{\text{in.}}$/s [*2,4*].

A somewhat different approach to dynamic testing is the Charpy test which, because of simplicity and low cost, is perhaps the most widely used test for measuring dynamic fracture toughness properties. While loading times as low as 10 to 50 μs have been obtained in Charpy tests [*6–8*], resulting in loading rates one to two orders of magnitude faster than dynamic machine tests, the energy measurements resulting from the standard Charpy test are somewhat difficult to interpret in the framework of elastic or elastic-plastic fracture mechanics.

In the present work, an experimental procedure is described by means of which the dynamic fracture initiation properties of structural metals can be accurately established at extremely high loading rates. The experiment is, in part, an adaptation of the Kolsky pressure bar to dynamic

[2]The italic numbers in brackets refer to the list of references appended to this paper.

fracture testing. However, we have further modified the technique to allow for rapid tensile loading of a fatigue cracked specimen. This technique has the distinct advantage of achieving extremely high loading rates, while providing a load-displacement record which is directly comparable to those produced in a static test on a similar specimen. A determination of the loading rate sensitivity, under stress wave loading conditions, of the parameters usually used to characterize fracture initiation is therefore possible.

Experimental Apparatus

A schematic diagram of the apparatus is shown in Fig. 1. The specimen consists of a solid round bar, with a circumferentially fatigued precrack. Fracture of the specimen is produced by a tensile stress pulse initiated at one end by the detonation of an explosive charge. As the pulse passes through the precracked section, the section is loaded to fracture at an essentially constant rate. The incident pulse is of sufficient magnitude to fracture the precracked section while still on the rising portion of the pulse. Using explosive loading techniques we are able to achieve fracture within 20 to 25 μs after the arrival of the tensile pulse at the precracked section.

Specimen

The specimen consists of a solid round bar, 1 in. in diameter and 40 in. in length. A circumferential notch is machined into the bar, 26 in. from the loading end. The notch is machined so that its faces are parallel, and the root is sharp. A circumferentially uniform fatigue crack is grown

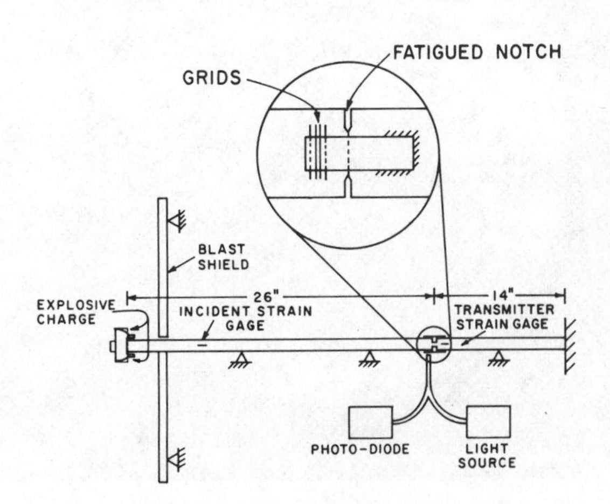

FIG. 1—*Schematic diagram of apparatus.*

in from the root of the notch, leaving an unfractured ligament slightly less than ½ in. in diameter. Fatiguing is accomplished in an apparatus designed by Mylonas and Hermann [*9*] which produces a concentric fatigue annulus. Figure 2 shows the prefatigued annulus on the fracture surface of a specimen.

Two sets of strain gages are attached to the specimen. The first set is placed 8 in. from the loading end. These gages are used to measure the incident pulse as it propagates down the bar toward the notch and are referred to as incident gages. Their location is such as to be sufficiently far from the loading end to ensure that the transients induced by the loading are not recorded, and far enough from the notch so that the reflections returning from the notch faces do not interfere with the measurement of the incident pulse.

The second set of gages, called the transmitter gages, is located 1 in. beyond the notch. These gages measure that portion of the pulse transmitted through the notched region. Kolsky [*10*] has shown that the transmitted pulse in his pressure bar experiments provides a direct measure of the average stress in the specimen. Generalizing the specimen to a region containing the notch, it becomes evident that the magnitude of the transmitted pulse is directly proportional to the average net section stress at the fracture site. Further analysis of the Kolsky pressure bar technique

FIG. 2—*Fracture surface of prenotched steel bar showing annular fatigue crack.*

indicates that when the pulse length is long compared to the notch width, the loading at the notched section may be viewed as quasi-static for purposes of analysis. Thus the results of stress analysis of circumferentially notched round bars may be employed, whether this analysis be elastic [*11*] or elastic-plastic [*12*]. The transmitter gages are located close enough to the crack so that no significant amount of dispersion of the pulse has occurred when the measurements are made, yet far enough away to ensure that measurements at the surface accurately reflect the character of the transmitted pulse. The outputs of the gages are recorded on an oscilloscope. An oscilloscope photograph of the incident, reflected, and transmitted pulses from a typical test is shown in Fig. 3.

Measurement of Crack-Opening Displacement

Accurate measurement of the crack-opening displacement as a function of time is achieved by using an optical device based on the phenomenon of Moiré fringes. Moiré fringes are produced when light passes through two transparent gratings mounted face to face with their rulings nearly, but not quite, parallel. Our device employs matched sets of grids that are produced photographically and fixed to the specimen so that any relative displacement between the outer edges of the notch causes an identical relative displacement between the two grids.

The first grid is produced by making a contact print of a master grid of the desired pitch (distance between rulings) on one end of a 1 in. by 3 in. high-resolution, glass photographic slide. The slide then serves as a master for the second grid which is produced directly on the specimen. In preparing the specimen, two narrow flat areas are machined on opposite sides of the bar extending approximately 3 in. to either side of the notch. Each of the flat areas accommodates a set of grids, one on the glass slide and one on the specimen.

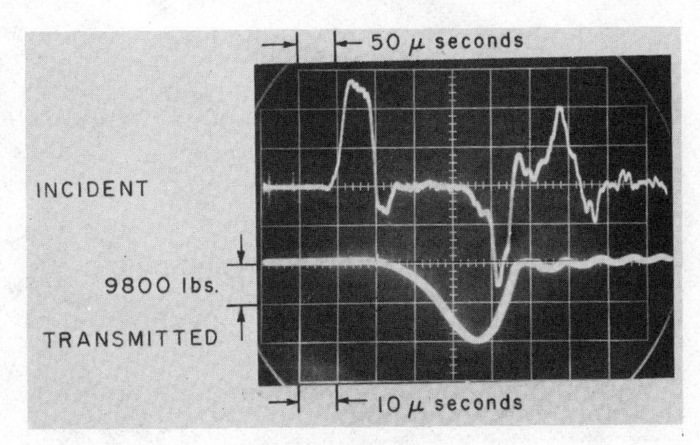

FIG. 3—*Oscilloscope traces showing incident and reflected pulses above, and transmitted pulse below.*

The grids on the specimen are located on the flats just before the notch on the incident side of the bar. They are produced using a photoresist process [*13*], which employs a special emulsion that can be spread directly upon the polished metal flat surfaces, allowing a contact print of the grid on the glass slide to be produced directly on the specimen. A jig, as shown in Fig. 4, is used to hold the glass slides in place on the specimen during this process. Once the matching sets of grids are produced, the glass grids, still held in the jig, are positioned over their counterparts on the specimen and cemented to the flat portion of the bar on the transmitter side of the notch. The jig is removed prior to testing, leaving the complete assembly as shown in Fig. 5. After the grids are mounted in the experimental configuration, light is supplied to the grids and returned to a photodiode through bifurcated fiber-optic tubes. The output of the diode is recorded on an oscilloscope.

In order to explain fully how the measurement technique works, it is first necessary to provide a few details of the theory of Moiré fringes. As mentioned earlier, Moiré fringes are produced by optical interference when light passes through two grids of similar pitch whose lines are nearly, but not quite, parallel. If the rulings are exactly parallel, the superimposed grids will appear of uniform brightness. But if the rulings are not quite

FIG. 4—*Jig used to position grid slides.*

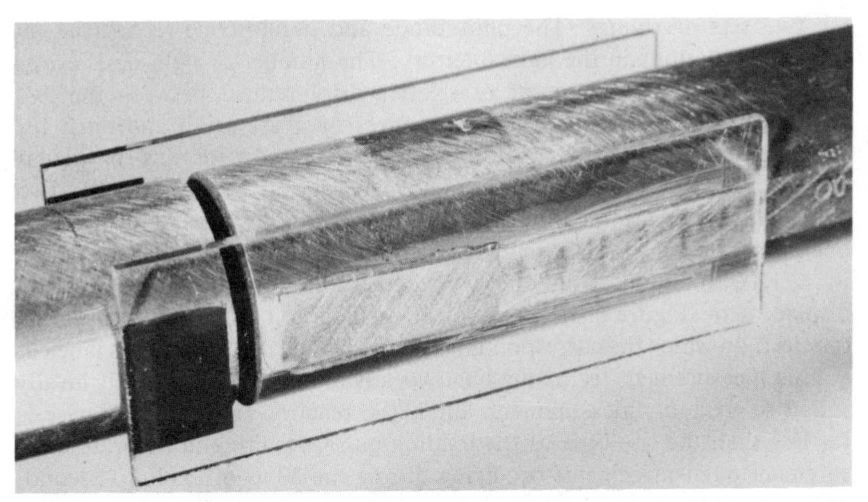

FIG. 5—*Optical extensometer mounted on specimen.*

parallel, the grids appear to be spanned by a number of equally spaced shadows or fringes which run perpendicular to the rulings. The width of these fringes, W, depends on the rotation angle between the two grids and is given by Guild [*14,15*] as

$$W = \frac{w}{\theta} \tag{1}$$

where

w = pitch of the grids and
θ = rotation angle between the rulings of the two grids.

The fringe width is significant, since it governs directly the strength of the output signal of the photodiode. The photodiode, with oscilloscope readout, responds only to changes in light intensity. To attain an output from the photodiode sufficient to record on an oscilloscope, it is necessary to maximize the variations in intensity caused by the fringes passing across the field of view. The field of view in this case is the portion of the grid covered by the end of the fiber-optic tube. This maximizing condition is achieved when the ratio of optic tube diameter to fringe width is one half, causing the intensity to change from complete shadow to complete light as the fringes move across the end of the tube. In practice a suitable fringe width is achieved by aligning the overlapping grids to the proper angle θ with the jig when cementing the glass slides in place.

When relative motion between the two grids takes place, the Moiré fringes move across the field in a direction perpendicular to themselves (parallel to the grid lines), at a speed independent of the angle between the two sets of rulings. The photodiode and oscilloscope record the resultant oscillations in the light intensity. The number of light-dark cycles recorded for a given amount of relative displacement between the two grids depends greatly on the circumstances of observation and must for all practical purposes be determined experimentally for any particular test arrangement. For our test arrangement, it was determined that two light-dark cycles are recorded when the grids are displaced a distance of one pitch relative to each other. In the dynamic tests we use grids of pitch w = 1200 μin./line. Thus one cycle corresponds to 600 μin. of relative displacement. Figure 6 shows a typical oscillograph from a dynamic fracture test, on which the corresponding crack-opening displacement is labeled.

This measurement technique has two advantages which make it ideally suited to dynamic measurement. First, the reaction time of the device is far less than the rise time of the loading pulse, resulting in accurate measurement of displacements occurring during the 20 μs of loading. Second, once the grids are in place on the specimen, no calibration of the device is required, since the relationship between fringe cycles and displacement, once established for the type of grids used and the experimental configuration, is fixed for all time. This is a definite advantage since the specimen and more specifically the notch tip need not be disturbed for calibration purposes prior to testing.

Explosive Loading Technique

The tensile pulse used to load the notched section of the bar is produced by detonating an explosive charge on a loading head attached to the end of the bar by a large bolt. The loading head (see Fig. 1) is shaped so that the compressional wave produced by the explosion is directed at the head of the bolt. Reflection of the compressional wave from the back face of

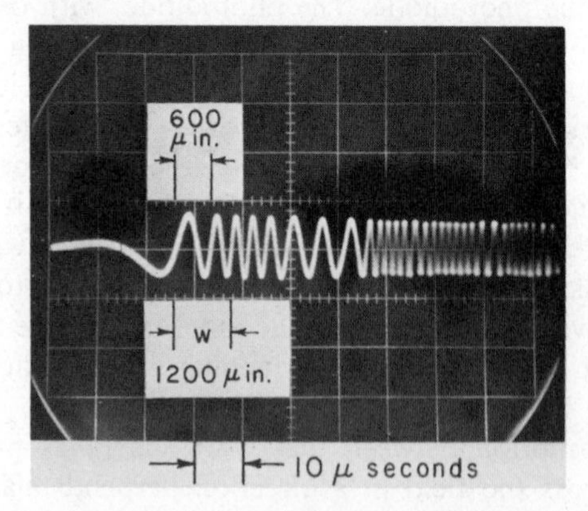

FIG. 6—*Output of optical grid system with corresponding linear displacements.*

the loading head produces a tensile pulse in the bolt, which is transmitted to the end of the bar.

The rise time achieved using this technique is approximately 20 to 25 μs as measured at the incident gage. However, due to dispersion of the pulse as it propagates down the bar, the rise time of the pulse when it reaches the fracture site is 35 to 40 μs. Since fracture of the specimen occurs within 20 to 25 μs, it is clear that fracture initiation occurs well within the rising portion of the pulse.

Analysis of Data

Construction of the Load-Displacement Curve

The data recorded from each dynamic test are in the form of photographs of oscilloscope traces. The transmitted load, as a function of time, is calculated directly from the photograph of the transmitted pulse. Figure 3 shows a trace of the transmitted pulse from a typical test with the corresponding load and time scales given. Crack-opening displacement as a function of time is calculated from the oscilloscope trace of the output from the optical extensometer, a typical example of which is shown in Fig. 6. As shown, one cycle equals 600 μin. in displacement. To construct the complete load-displacement curve for each test the load-time curve and the displacement-time curve are plotted using the same time scale as shown in Fig. 7.

A common zero time point is established between the two curves by considering the trigger times of the oscilloscopes and taking into account the time delays between the arrival of the pulse at the various data recording positions on the specimen. Once a common zero is established, time is eliminated between the two plots, resulting in a load-displacement curve for the dynamic fracture test. The load-displacement curve for specimen C-9 is shown in the upper portion of Fig. 10.

Calculation of Fracture Parameters

Having determined the load-displacement curve for a test, the various fracture initiation parameters of interest can be calculated. For a nominally brittle material the parameter of interest is K_{Ic}, the plane-strain fracture toughness. K_{Ic} is calculated according to Ref *11* as

$$K_I = \frac{P}{\pi R^2}\sqrt{\pi R}\, F\left(\frac{2R}{D}\right) \tag{2}$$

where

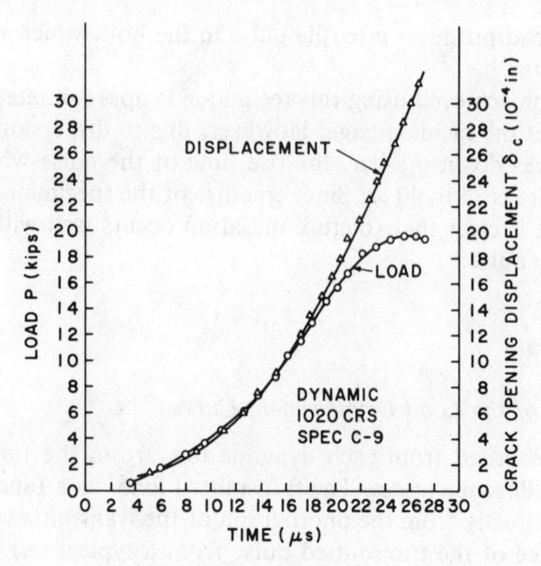

FIG. 7—*Load-time and displacement-time curves for typical test.*

R = radius of the remaining circular ligament after fatiguing,
P = applied load,
D = outer diameter of the bar,

$F\left(\frac{2R}{D}\right)$ = size function,

$$0 \leq F\left(\frac{2R}{D}\right) \leq ½$$

for

$$0 \leq \frac{2R}{D} \leq 1$$

$$F(½) \approx 0.48.$$

The load P used in calculating K_{Ic} from Eq 2 is determined from the load-displacement curve in accordance with the American Society for Testing and Materials' standards by using the 5 percent slope offset procedure.

In order to apply linear elastic fracture mechanics, the size of the crack-tip plastic zone must be small compared to the nominal dimensions of the specimen. As a criterion for a valid K_{Ic} test

$$R \geq 2.5 \left(\frac{K_{\mathrm{I}}}{\sigma_{yp}} \right)^2 \tag{3}$$

is used, where σ_{yp} is the yield stress of the material determined at a strain rate comparable to the strain rate achieved near the crack tip during the fracture test. For our dynamic fracture tests, the corresponding dynamic yield stress was determined using the method of Frantz and Duffy [16].

For the case of small-scale yielding where the plastic zone might be slightly larger than the given limit, a plastic zone correction can be applied [17]. Using an effective ligament radius of

$$R_{\mathrm{eff}} = R - \frac{1}{6\pi} \left(\frac{K_{\mathrm{I}}}{\sigma_{yp}} \right)^2 \tag{4}$$

instead of R in the calculation of K_{Ic} results in a better approximation of the plane-strain fracture toughness.

When testing more ductile materials such as mild steels, the specimen size used here may be insufficient to contain the plastic zone within the limits just described. Analysis of such tests is beyond the scope of linear elastic fracture mechanics, and thus one must use a fracture criterion which is valid in the elastic-plastic realm. For this purpose Rice's J-integral is used [18]. Begley and Landes [19] have shown that the J-integral provides a fracture initiation criterion for cracks under plane-strain conditions from essentially elastic to fully plastic behavior. Paris [20] has suggested that a possible criterion for a valid J-integral test is

$$R \geq 50 \frac{J_{\mathrm{Ic}}}{\sigma_{yp}} \tag{5}$$

This criterion was used in evaluating the validity of the results presented here.

Rice, Paris, and Merkle [21] have shown that the J-integral for a notched round bar can be expressed as

$$J = \frac{1}{2\pi R^2} \left[3 \int_0^{\delta_c} P \, d\delta_c - P \delta_c \right] \tag{6}$$

where δ_c is the load-point displacement due to the presence of the crack. For Eq 6 to be strictly valid, the displacement measure used must be the work conjugate of P. Using crack opening displacement from our experimental data is thus only an approximation of the load point displacement. However, as will be shown, this approximation does not cause a significant error. The key assumption made in deriving Eq 6 is that the radius R is the only specimen dimension of significance. This assumption is valid as long as the plastic zones do not extend to the surface of the bar. It should also be noted here that the J-integral is limited to problems where no unloading takes place and the deformation theory of plasticity is a realistic approximation of the elastic-plastic behavior. This, of course, rules out materials which exhibit significant subcritical crack growth prior to initiation of an unstable fracture, since crack growth implies unloading near the crack tip.

Using Eq 6, J can be evaluated directly as a function of displacement from the load-displacement record. A critical value of J, J_{Ic}, can be defined as that point on the J versus δ_c curve where crack growth is initiated.

A direct comparison can be made between the J-integral and the plane-strain fracture toughness by considering that for a specimen in the linear elastic region

$$J = \mathcal{G} = \frac{K_{\mathrm{I}}^2}{E}(1 - \nu^2) \tag{7}$$

where

E = elastic modulus,
ν = Poisson's ratio, and
$\mathcal{G}$ = Griffith energy release rate.

Once J_{Ic} is determined, an equivalent K_{Ic} can be calculated from

$$K_{\mathrm{Ic}}^{e} = \left[\frac{E\,J_{\mathrm{Ic}}}{(1 - \nu^2)}\right]^{1/2} \tag{8}$$

where K_{Ic}^{e} may be interpreted as the value of the plane-strain fracture toughness one would measure had a large enough specimen been used to achieve a valid test according to Eq 3.

The final parameter of interest in dynamic testing is $\dot{K}_{\mathrm{I}}$ which is defined usually as

$$\dot{K}_{\mathrm{I}} = \frac{K_{\mathrm{Ic}}}{t} \tag{9}$$

where t is some characteristic time of the test. Here t is taken as the time required to load the crack from the unstressed condition up to the critical value of K_{Ic}. Thus for a dynamic test t is approximately 25 μs, whereas for a static test t is usually on the order of 60 to 90 s.

Results for Two Steels

Tests on two quite different steels have been conducted using the dynamic fracture technique described. The first is SAE 4340 steel which, in the heat-treated condition, has a static yield strength of 205 ksi and fractures in a nominally brittle manner. The second is 1020 cold-rolled steel, which is both ductile and rate sensitive with a static yield strength of 66 ksi. The results presented demonstrate the full capability of the technique to test both brittle and ductile materials at high rates of loading. Also presented are results of static fracture tests conducted on the same specimen shape and materials so that a direct comparison between dynamic and static fracture initiation properties can be made. The static tests were performed using a 120 000-lb-capacity testing machine. The crack opening displacement was measured using a double-cantilever extensometer. The notched region of the static specimen was modified slightly from that of the dynamic specimens in order to accommodate the knife edges required for the extensometer.

SAE 4340 Steel

Dynamic and static fracture specimens of 4340 steel were heat treated in the following manner: normalized for 1 h at 1600°F, austenitized at 1550°F for 1 h and oil quenched, then tempered for 1 h at 600°F, resulting in a Rockwell C hardness of approximately 48. Typical load-displacement curves for the static and dynamic tests are shown in Fig. 8. The J-integral and K_{Ic} were calculated for each test as described previously. All tests satisfied the plane strain requirement given in Eq 3. In Fig. 9 the J-integral for both a static and a dynamic test is plotted as a function of crack opening displacement. Also shown in the figure is a plot of the energy release rate, $\mathcal{G}$, versus crack opening displacement. $\mathcal{G}$ is calculated from the load displacement curve at a given displacement using Eq 2 and the relation

$$\mathcal{G} = \frac{K_I^2}{E}(1 - \nu^2) \tag{10}$$

The good agreement between the curves of $\mathcal{G}$ and J for this material, as shown in Fig. 9, is entirely expected since in the linear elastic region $J = \mathcal{G}$. Because $\mathcal{G}$ is calculated independently of J, their agreement in the linear elastic region provides a basis for justification of the assumptions made in calculating J. A summary of the results of the tests on 4340 steel is presented in Table 1.

The results from the static tests agree with those of Kula and Anctil [*22*] who have done extensive testing on 4340 steel using a variety of specimen shapes. While the loading rates for the static and dynamic tests differ by six orders of magnitude, there is essentially no difference in the fracture initiation properties of the material under static and dynamic conditions. Cox and Low [*23*] suggest that fracture of 4340 steel occurs by

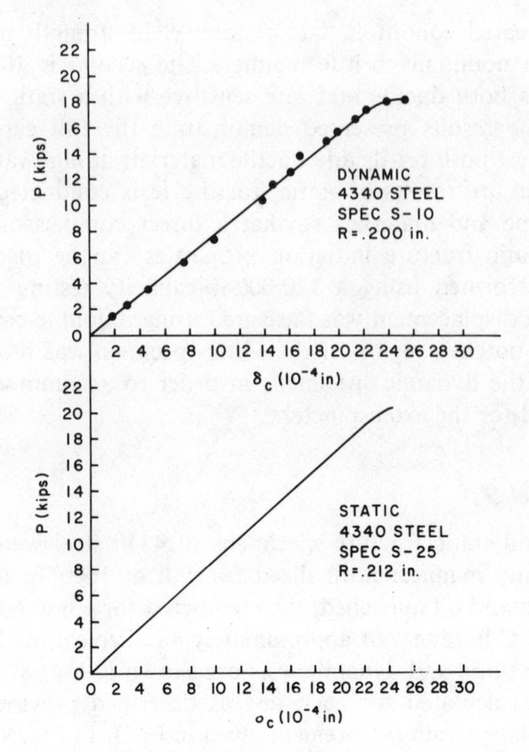

FIG. 8—*Typical static and dynamic load-displacement curves for 4340 steel.*

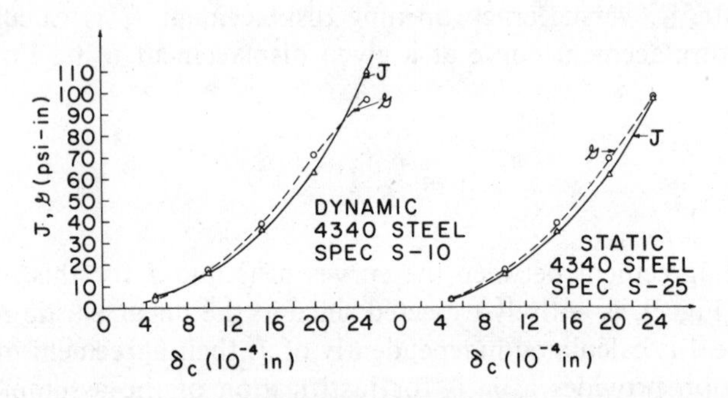

FIG. 9—*Static and dynamic J-integral for 4340 steel.*

nucleation of voids from manganese sulfide inclusions. However long before the voids coalesce by impingement they are connected by the rapid formation of void sheets composed of small voids nucleated by the cementite precipitates. This interruption of the void coalescence process at an early stage, suggests that the fracture process is nearly rate independent as confirmed by our results, since little plastic action is required to link the voids.

TABLE 1—*Summary of results for 4340 steel.*

	$\dot{K}_I$ psi$\sqrt{\text{in.}}$/s	K_{Ic} ksi$\sqrt{\text{in.}}$	J_{Ic} psi·in.	K_{Ic}^e ksi$\sqrt{\text{in.}}$
Dynamic	2×10^9	51	100	57
Static	1×10^3	57	95	56

TABLE 2—*Summary of results for 1020 cold-rolled steel.*

	$\dot{K}_I$ psi$\sqrt{\text{in.}}$/s	K_{Ic} ksi$\sqrt{\text{in.}}$	J_{Ic} psi·in.	K_{Ic}^e ksi$\sqrt{\text{in.}}$
Dynamic	2×10^9	64.2	124	63.9
Static	1×10^3	...	400	115

SAE 1020 Cold-Rolled Steel

Typical load-displacement curves for dynamic and static tests are shown in Fig. 10. In contrast to the results from 4340 steel, there is a considerable difference between the dynamic and static curves for 1020 cold-rolled steel (CRS). The two curves agree up to the point of fracture initiation on the dynamic curve. However, the static curve shows nearly a twofold increase in crack-opening displacement and appears to have nearly reached limit load at the onset of rapid crack propagation. The curves of J-integral and energy release rate versus crack opening displacement are shown in Fig. 11. For the static tests a valid K_{Ic} value could not be determined. However, for the dynamic tests, the plastic zone size is considerably smaller due to the elevation of the flow stress near the crack tip caused by the rapid loading, thus a K_{Ic} value was calculated with the aid of the plastic zone correction. All specimens satisfied the requirement for a valid J-integral test given by Eq 5.

For any materials where the load-displacement curves show that significant plastic deformation has taken place, one must raise the question as to whether any subcritical crack growth has taken place. Identifying the point during the test where crack growth initiates, whether subcritically or not, is important since the J-integral is not valid as a fracture parameter beyond this point. In order to determine this point, further static tests on 1020 CRS are currently being conducted and preliminary results indicate that no subcritical crack growth takes place until very near the point of rapid crack propagation. In Fig. 10 this would correspond to no crack growth up to the point of $\delta_c \approx 4500$ μin. Table 2 gives a summary of the results for 1020 CRS. For the static tests J_{Ic} is estimated based on the point where subcritical crack growth is believed to begin.

Under microscopic examination, the fracture surface of the dynamic 1020 CRS specimens appears quite similar to that of the static specimens, both indicating that transgranular cleavage is the primary mechanism of fracture. This implies that the large rate-sensitivity of fracture initiation

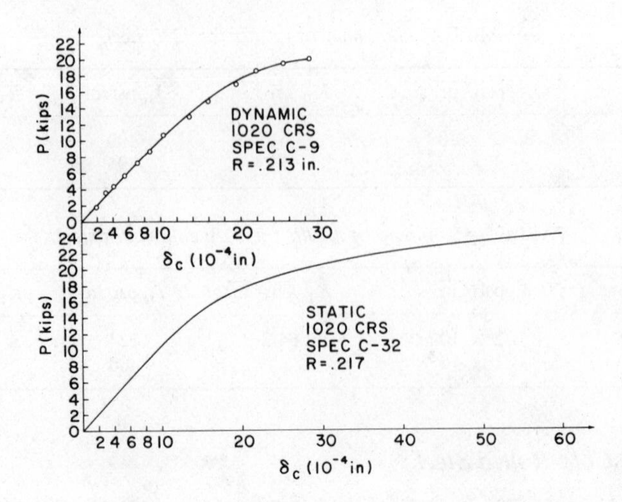

FIG. 10—*Typical static and dynamic load-displacement curves for 1020 CRS.*

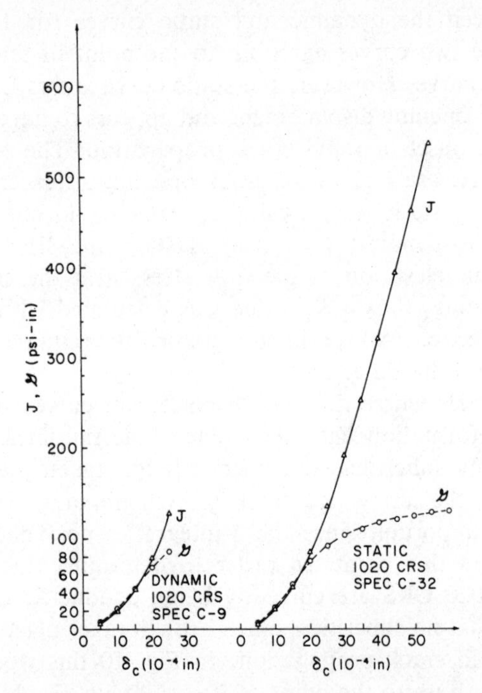

FIG. 11—*Static and dynamic J-integral for 1020 CRS.*

in this material arises from an inherent strain rate sensitivity and that the fracture initiation is governed by a critical stress criterion such as one proposed by Ritchie, Knott, and Rice [*24*].

Conclusions

The experimental technique described here is designed to determine the parameters usually used to characterize fracture initiation in structural metals under extremely high loading rates. The technique has the capability of accurately determining a load versus crack-opening displacement record for a specimen which is loaded to fracture in approximately 25 μs. This corresponds to a crack-tip loading rate in excess of 10^9 psi $\sqrt{\text{in.}}$/s, over two orders of magnitude faster than the loading rate achievable by a dynamic machine test. Data from this dynamic fracture apparatus, when compared to static data from similar specimens, provide a direct means of determining the sensitivity of fracture toughness to loading rate. Such sensitivity could arise from inherent strain rate effects, or from a conversion of fracture mechanism induced by the rapidly applied loads. It is also noteworthy that the loading rates achieved with this technique approach those which are presumed to exist in the vicinity of a rapidly propagating crack tip. Thus, the technique could also be employed to provide useful information on the effect of high local loading rate during crack propagation.

Acknowledgments

The authors gratefully acknowledge the assistance provided by Drs. J. R. Rice and P. C. Paris in the analysis and presentation of experimental data. They wish to thank also the National Science Foundation for the support provided under grant NSF ENG75-09612 and the Materials Research Laboratory at Brown University funded by the Advanced Research Projects Agency through the Office of Naval Research Grant No. N00014-75-C-1019.

References

[1] Krafft, J. M., *Applied Materials Research,* April 1964, pp. 88–101.
[2] Eftis, J. and Krafft, J. M., *Journal of Basic Engineering, Transactions,* American Society of Mechanical Engineers, March 1965, pp. 257–263.
[3] Paris, P. C., Bucci, R. J., and Loushin, L. L. in *Fracture Toughness and Slow-Stable Cracking, ASTM STP 559,* American Society for Testing and Materials, 1974, pp. 86–98.
[4] Crosley, P. B. and Ripling, E. J., *Journal of Basic Engineering, Transactions,* American Society of Mechanical Engineers, Sept. 1969, pp. 525–534.
[5] Shoemaker, A. K. and Rolfe, S. T., *Engineering Fracture Mechanics,* Vol. 2, 1971, pp. 319–339.
[6] Sailors, R. H. and Corten, H. T. in *Fracture Toughness, ASTM STP 514,* American Society for Testing and Materials, 1972, pp. 164–191.
[7] Barsom, J. M. and Rolfe, S. T. in *Impact Testing of Metals, ASTM STP 466,* American Society for Testing and Materials, 1970, pp. 281–302.
[8] Turner, C. E. in *Impact Testing of Metals, ASTM STP 466,* American Society for Testing and Materials, 1970, pp. 93–112.

[9] Mylonas, C. and Hermann, L., Report No. 40-002-080/16, Brown University, Providence, R.I., Aug. 1976.
[10] Kolsky, H., *Proceedings of the Physical Society,* B62, 1949, pp. 676–700.
[11] Tada, H., *The Stress Analysis of Cracks Handbook,* Del Research Corp., Hellertown, Pa., 1973.
[12] Tracey, D. M., "On the Fracture Mechanics Analysis of Elastic-Plastic Materials Using the Finite Element Method," NASA Report NGL 40-002-080/11, National Aeronautics and Space Administration, Washington, D.C., Feb. 1973.
[13] "An Introduction to Photofabrication Using Kodak Photosensitive Resists," Kodak Publication, P-79, Eastman Kodak Company, Rochester, N.Y., 1970.
[14] Guild, J., *The Interference Systems of Crossed Diffraction Gratings—Theory of Moiré Fringes,* Oxford University, London, 1960.
[15] Guild, J., *Diffraction Gratings as Measuring Scales,* Oxford University, London, 1960.
[16] Frantz, R. A. and Duffy, J., *Journal of Applied Mechanics, Transactions,* American Society of Mechanical Engineers, Vol. 39, 1972, pp. 939–945.
[17] Irwin, G. R., *Journal of Engineering for Power, Transactions,* American Society of Mechanical Engineers, Oct. 1964, pp. 444–450.
[18] Rice, J. R., *Journal of Applied Mechanics, Transactions,* American Society of Mechanical Engineers, Vol. 35, 1968, pp. 379–386.
[19] Begley, J. A. and Landes, J. D. in *Fracture Toughness, ASTM STP 514,* American Society for Testing and Materials, 1972, pp. 1–23.
[20] Paris, P. C., in written discussion to Ref *19*.
[21] Rice, J. R., Paris, P. C., and Merkle, J. G. in *Progress in Flaw Growth and Fracture Toughness Testing, ASTM STP 536,* American Society for Testing and Materials, 1973, pp. 231–245.
[22] Kula, E. B. and Anctil, A. A., *Journal of Materials,* Vol. 4, No. 4, Dec. 1969, pp. 817–841.
[23] Cox, T. B. and Low, J. R., *Metallurgical Transactions,* Vol. 5, June 1974, pp. 1457–1470.
[24] Ritchie, R. O., Knott, J. F., and Rice, J. R., *The Journal of Mechanics and Physics of Solids,* Vol. 21, 1973, pp. 395–410.

Experimental Methods for Fast Fracture and Crack Arrest

Hans Bergkvist[1]

An Investigation of Axisymmetric Crack Propagation

REFERENCE: Bergkvist, Hans, "**An Investigation of Axisymmetric Crack Propagation,**" *Fast Fracture and Crack Arrest, ASTM STP 627,* G. T. Hahn and M. F. Kanninen, Eds., American Society for Testing and Materials, 1977, pp. 321–335.

ABSTRACT: The strain energy released per unit of axisymmetric crack surface created statically can be expressed in terms of a J-integral related quantity. However, as soon as the crack starts to move only part of this energy will actually flow to the dissipative regions close to the crack tip and the rest will be distributed as kinetic and potential energy in the structure.

An energy balance at the crack tip requires that the flow of energy to the tip must be equal to the fracture energy, which for a given material is supposed to be a specific function of the crack-tip velocity. The energy flow is assumed to be expressible as the static strain energy release rate, times a dynamic screening function, which depends on the instantaneous crack-tip velocity only.

By using numerically calculated values for the strain energy release rate, an analytic expression for the dynamic screening function, and experimentally found data for the velocity dependence of the fracture energy, it has been possible to predict the motion of a penny-shaped crack in a bar of polymethylmethacrylate under uniaxial tension. The agreement with a small series of simple experiments is good.

KEY WORDS: axisymmetric, crack propagation, nonuniform velocity, penny shaped, polymethylmethacrylate, J-integral, quasi-dynamics, dynamics, fracture properties

The rigorous treatment of dynamic crack problems started in the 1950s, with the appearance of the classical paper by Yoffe [*1*].[2] Later the subject was treated by Craggs [*2*] and Broberg [*3,4*]. These works concentrated on plane problems and Kostrov [*5*] was the first to attack the axisymmetric problem of an expanding penny-shaped crack. Kostrov's work was followed by Craggs [*6*] and Atkinson [*7*]. What all these early contributions have in common is the assumption of a constant velocity of propagation. It is only recently that problems have been treated where the crack is expanding at a nonuniform velocity, notably by Eshelby [*8*] and Freund [*9*].

[1]Senior staff scientist, Institut CERAC S.A., Centre Europeen de Recherches, Atlas Copco, CH-1024 Ecublens, Switzerland.

[2]The italic numbers in brackets refer to the list of references appended to this paper.

Lately the writer has proposed ways of circumventing the restrictions in earlier papers when configurations of finite size are at hand, Bergkvist [*10,11*].

Following the same main lines in the present work, it is possible to make an approximate analysis of the propagation of an axisymmetric crack at nonuniform velocity in a finite body.

Dynamic Crack Problems in General

A basic assumption in the present analysis is that the crack can be considered as dominant, which rules out, for example, configurations where extensive crushing of the material takes place. Furthermore the material is assumed to behave linearly elastic.

In formulating the energy balance at the crack tip the notation from Bergkvist [*10*] is followed. Thus, the flow of energy to the tip of the crack is denoted by G, and the energy dissipation, which is assumed to take place in localized processes in the immediate neighborhood of the crack tip, per unit of crack extension, is denoted by $2\gamma_F$. Introducing as a fracture criterion the equivalence between these quantities, that is

$$G = 2\gamma_F \tag{1}$$

a relation will be obtained from which the crack motion can be determined. The quantity $2\gamma_F$ in Eq 1 should be thought of as a material property. There seems to be both experimental and theoretical support for the idea that $2\gamma_F$ should be a function of crack propagation velocity. This material property and its variation with crack-tip velocity thus has to be determined in a separate series of experiments, for example, along the guidelines described in Ref *20*.

The energy flow to the crack tip, G, on the other hand will depend on the loading situation, the dimensions of the configuration, and particularly so on crack size, crack-tip velocity, and, in a general case, possibly also on higher time derivatives of crack size, that is, the entire elastodynamic problem has to be investigated.

In cases where the crack is propagating at a constant velocity as well as in some special cases of nonuniform crack propagation, G can be shown to take the following general form

$$G(a,c) = G(a,0)\, w(c) \tag{2}$$

where a denotes a characteristic dimension of the crack and c the instantaneous crack-tip velocity, and where furthermore $G(a,0)$ is the strain energy release rate valid for the same crack size in the static case, G_{stat}.

Thus, the strain energy released from the field G_{stat} will not flow entirely to the crack tip in case of a moving crack, since a screening effect, expressed by the function w comes into play due to the changes in the near crack-tip stress and strain fields with crack-tip velocity [*10,11*]. The rest of the strain energy released is distributed as kinetic and potential energy in the structure.

For a given Poisson's ratio, the function w depends only on the instantaneous crack-tip velocity c. For the so called Broberg problem, that is, a crack of initial length zero, expanding at constant velocity in a large body under plane-strain conditions, w can be extracted from Ref *4* as done in Ref *10*. Denoting w by w^* the function is given in Fig. 1.

For the case of a semiinfinite crack extending at nonuniform velocity, the function w is given for the general Mode III case in Ref *8* and for the Mode I case in Ref *9*.

In the following section and in Appendix I the function w will be calculated for a penny-shaped crack expanding at constant velocity.

Axisymmetric Case

Consider a large body subjected to a uniaxial stress p_0 at infinity. When a penny-shaped crack of radius a is opened up statically and perpendicularly to the direction of the stress field, an amount W of strain energy will be released.

This quantity will be

$$W = \frac{8(1 - \nu^2)p_0^2a^3}{3E} \tag{3}$$

see for example, Sneddon and Lowengrub [*15*]. Here the elastic constants are denoted by E and ν for Young's modulus and Poisson's ratio, respectively.

The strain energy release per unit of area created will thus be

$$\frac{\partial W}{\partial A} = \frac{1}{2\pi a}\frac{\partial W}{\partial a} = \frac{4(1 - \nu^2)}{\pi E}\, p_0^2 a = G_{\text{stat}} \tag{4}$$

It could be noted that this expression differs by a factor of $(2/\pi)^2$ from the one valid for the plane-strain case.

In the dynamic case when a penny-shaped crack is expanding at constant velocity in a large body, the energy flow to the crack tip can be evaluated from the works by Kostrov [*5*], although numerous printing errors seem to exist in this reference. For the details of this analysis, refer to Appendix I.

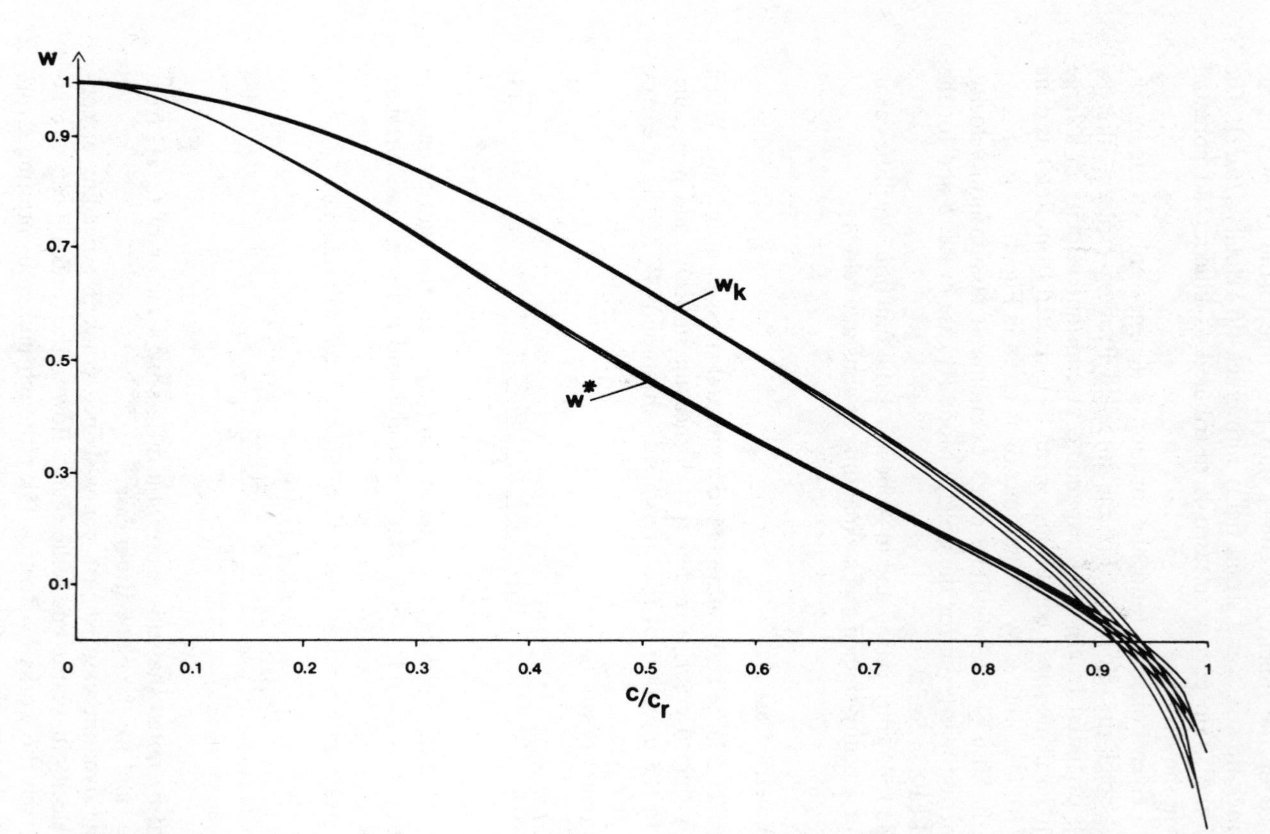

FIG. 1—*The dynamic functions* $w = w_K$ *(axisymmetric case) and* $w = w^*$ *(plane strain case) versus nondimensional crack-tip velocity,* c/c_r. c_r *is the velocity of equivoluminal waves. Poisson's ratio* ν = *0.25* (lower), *0.30, 0.35, 0.40* (upper).

The principal result can be expressed in the same way as was done in Eq 2. Here, $G(a,0) = G_{\text{stat}}$ is given in Eq 4, and the complicated expression for $w = w_K$ is given in Appendix I, Eqs 17 and 18.

In Fig. 1 $w = w_K$ for the axisymmetric case and the corresponding function $w = w^*$ for the plane case are given versus propagation velocity for different values of Poisson's ratio. It should be noted that in contrast to results by Tsai [*16*], which presumably are in error, both functions have the property of going to zero when the propagation velocity approaches the Rayleigh wave velocity c_s, thus indicating that c_s is a theoretical upper limit for the crack propagation velocity also in the axisymmetric case.

Quasi-Dynamic Approach

In Ref *14* is given a fully dynamic analysis of the acceleration phase of a crack of finite length extending under plane-strain conditions in a large body. In Ref *10* a quasi-dynamic analysis, that is, assuming G to be dependent on crack size and crack-tip velocity but not on higher time derivatives of crack length, has been carried out. A comparison indicates that the vastly simpler quasi-dynamic method gives results that deviate from those of the complete analysis only by 10 percent at the most.

Thus, in the quasi-dynamic approach it is assumed that in bodies of finite dimensions the energy flow G to the crack tip can be expressed as the static strain energy release rate G_{stat}, times an appropriate dynamic function, depending on the instantaneous crack-tip velocity only. In a plane case the static strain energy release rate, G_{stat}, can be computed by incorporating a J-integral calculation in a finite element procedure, since $G_{\text{stat}} = J$.

J-Integral in the Axisymmetric Case

The preceding approach to the analysis of penny-shaped cracks is complicated by the fact that the J-integral is not path independent in the general axisymmetric case as pointed up by Broberg [*17*]. Since, however, plane-strain conditions are present in a small region close to the tip of the crack, approximate path independence will hold for integration loops sufficiently near the crack tip.

Consider Fig. 2. Using an ordinary cylindrical coordinate system the J-integral counterpart takes the following form, where second order terms have been neglected in the derivation of the expression

$$J_R = \int_\Gamma \left\{ W dz - \left[\sigma_r \frac{\partial u_r}{\partial r} \cos\psi + \sigma_{rz} \left(- \frac{\partial u_r}{\partial r} \sin\psi \right. \right. \right.$$

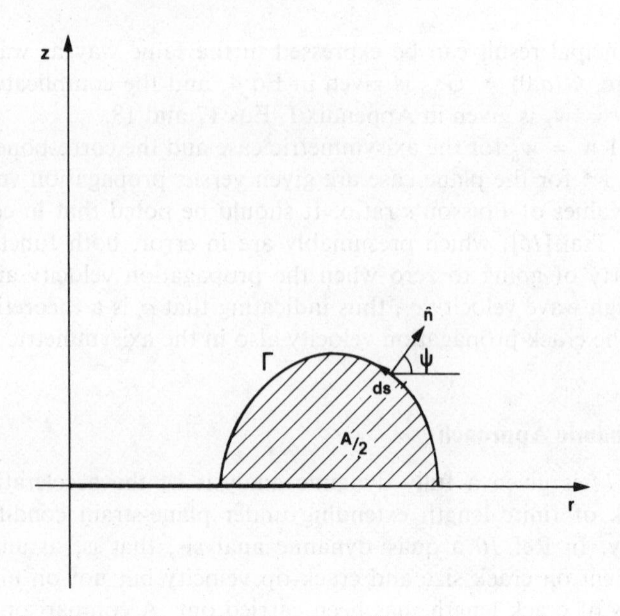

FIG. 2—*The integration path* (only upper half shown) *around the crack tip.*

$$+ \frac{\partial u_z}{\partial r} \cos \psi \bigg) - \sigma_z \frac{\partial u_z}{\partial r} \sin \psi \bigg] ds \bigg\} +$$

$$\int_A \frac{1}{r} \left(\sigma_\phi \epsilon_\phi - \sigma_r \epsilon_r - \sigma_{rz} \frac{\partial u_z}{\partial r} \right) dA \qquad (5)$$

Here standard notations, u, ϵ, and σ have been used for displacement, strain, and stress, respectively and W for the strain energy per unit volume. Other quantities are defined in Fig. 2.

Since the first integral is the J-integral valid in the plane-strain case

$$J_R = J + \int_A \frac{1}{r} \left(\sigma_\phi \epsilon_\phi - \sigma_r \epsilon_r - \sigma_{rz} \frac{\partial u_z}{\partial r} \right) dA \qquad (6)$$

Denoting a small distance from the crack tip by δ, then $\sigma \backsim \delta^{-1/2}$, $\epsilon \backsim \delta^{-1/2}$, and $dA \backsim \delta d\delta$. Thus, the second integral will be proportional to δ / r which tends to zero when δ is small with respect to r, that is, for integration loops close to the crack tip, and thus in the limit

$$J_R = \lim_{\Gamma \to \Gamma_0} J \tag{7}$$

where Γ_0 is a path infinitesimally close to the crack tip.

Numerical and Experimental Results

In a numerical and experimental verification of the foregoing analysis, a cylindrical specimen containing a penny-shaped crack having its plane perpendicular to the axis has been studied. The material chosen has been polymethylmethacrylate (PMMA) and two geometries, diameter 40 and 60 mm, have been investigated, each one at three different levels of axial load.

Before the experiment a 2-mm-diameter steel rod was pushed down a narrow hole drilled along the axis down to the prospective crack plane. After having put the specimen under the desired axial load, the crack propagation was triggered by letting a small gas gun driven projectile impact on the steel rod. A small penny-shaped crack was then formed, and the subsequent motion of the crack is determined by the applied tensile stress field.

The interception of a laser beam by the tapping projectile also triggered an image converter camera and a flash to give 10 frames, typically 5 μs apart, showing the crack growth, and thus giving a discrete crack size versus time record for the event. An example of such a record is given in Fig. 3, and in Fig. 4 a specimen in its fixtures is shown after a completed test. By changing the delays in the trigger circuits, different parts of the crack propagation event can be covered in subsequent experiments.

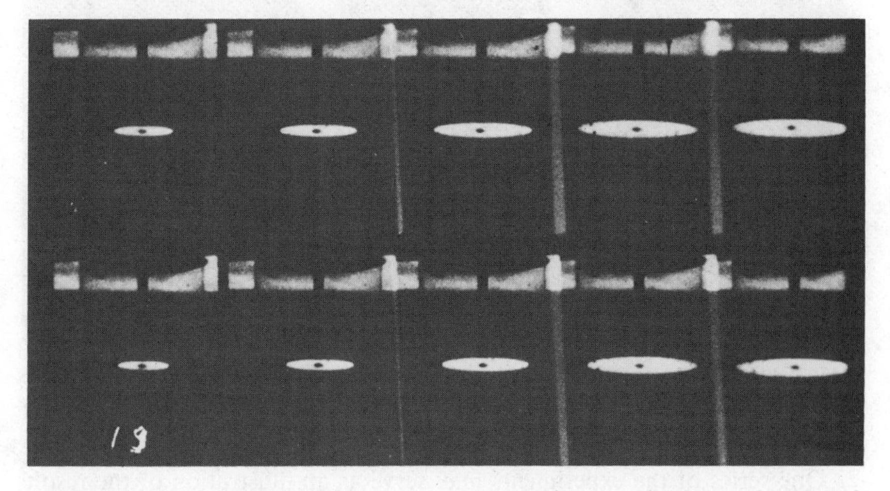

FIG. 3—*A set of 10 image converter camera pictures of an extending penny-shaped crack taken 5 μs apart. The camera axis is inclined with respect to the crack plane, which makes the crack show like an ellipse.*

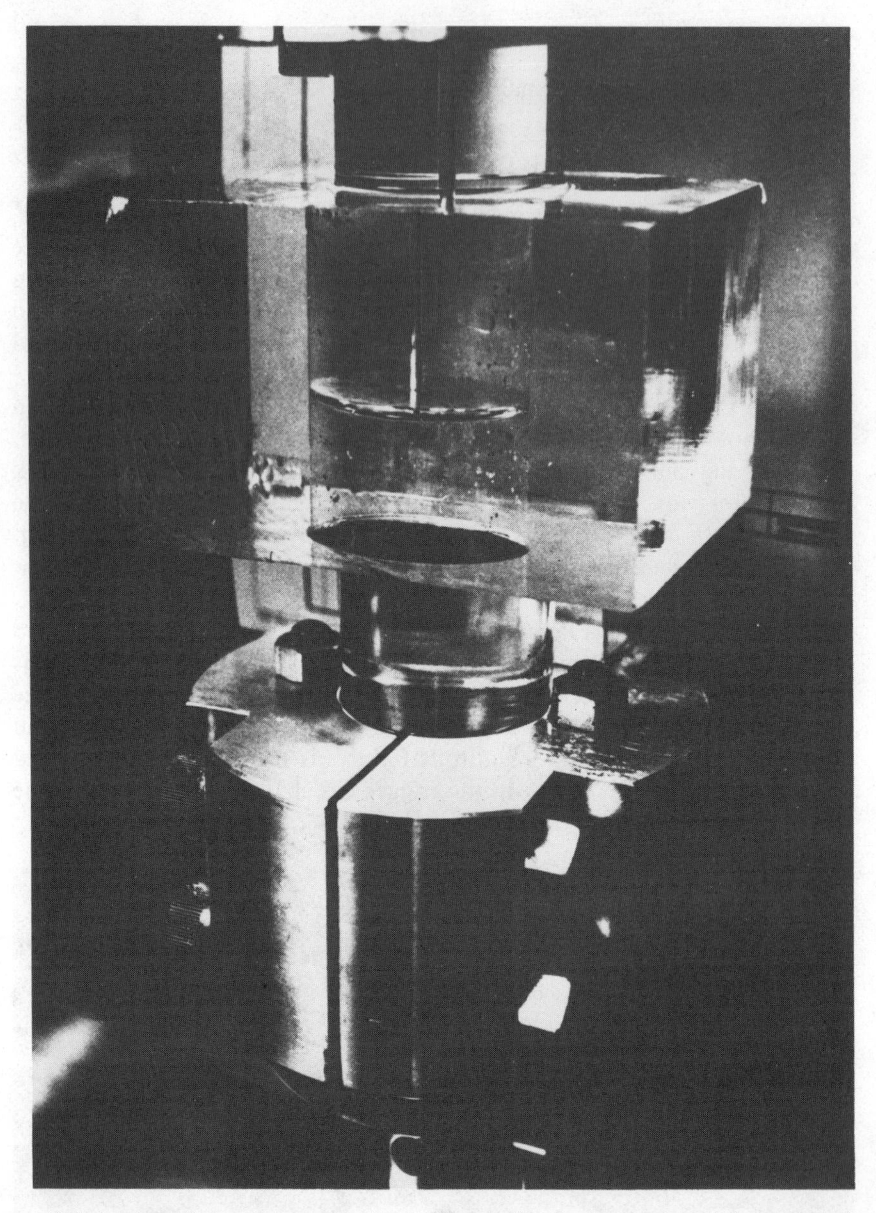

FIG. 4—*A specimen after completed test. Surrounding the central part of the specimen is a rectangular block of PMMA which is used to diminish the image distortion due to the cylindrical geometry of the specimen.*

One series of the experiments may serve as an illustration of the results obtained. In Fig. 5 the velocity versus crack size records for one series of experiments have been plotted. The velocity has simply been obtained

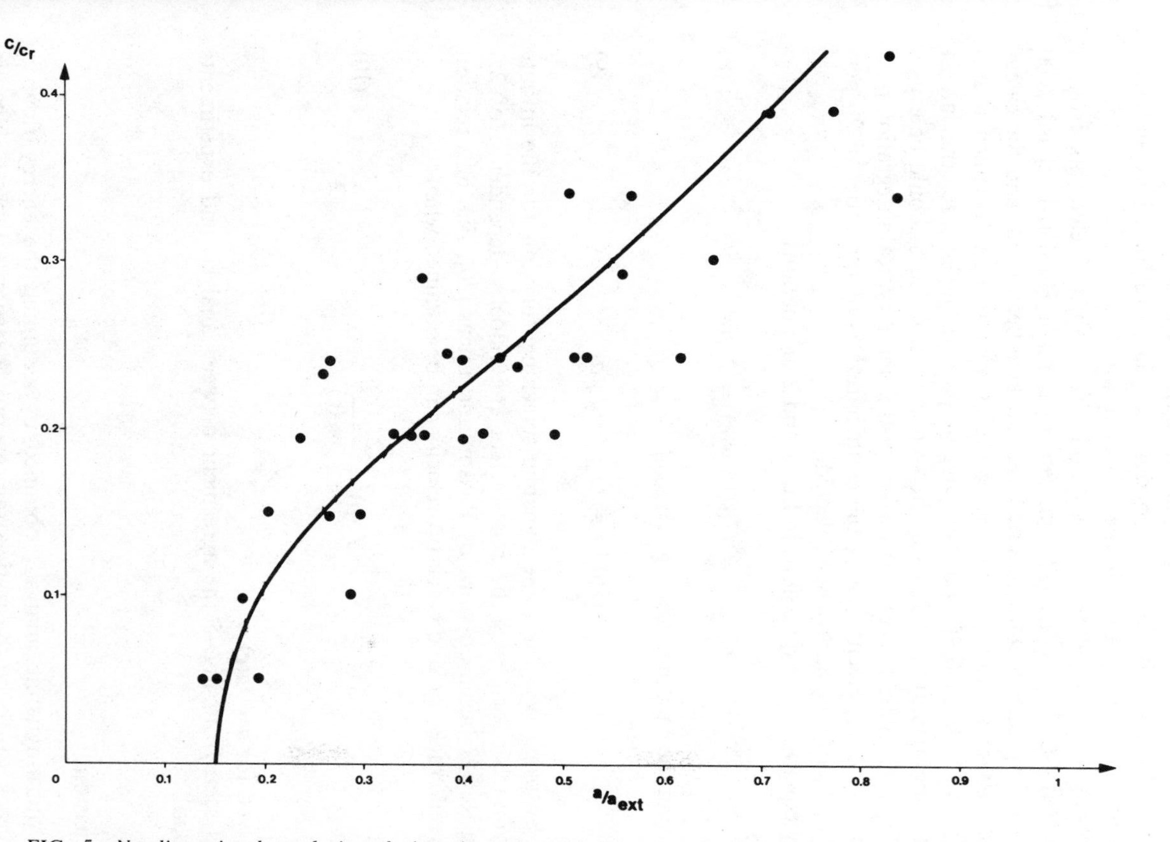

FIG. 5—*Nondimensional crack-tip velocity* c/c_r *versus nondimensional crack size,* a/a_{ext}*, taken from a series of pictures, an example of which is shown in Fig. 3. The curve represents the theoretically predicted relation. The velocity of equivoluminal waves* c_r *= 970 m/s, the external radius of the specimen* a_{ext} *= 30 mm.*

as the crack size difference between each two frames divided by the time difference. Although some scatter will be present in the individual results, the overall picture seems to give also quantitative data.

The solid curve is the corresponding calculated relation between crack velocity and size, obtained in the following way.

J_R has been calculated using 4-node isoparametric elements from a modified EUFEMI-code [*21*], implemented on a Hewlett-Packard 3000 system. Typically 500 degrees of freedom have been used, and the calculations cover a ratio between crack radius a and outer specimen radius a_{ext} from 0.10 to 0.95. For an integral path of given size, the largest relative contribution to J_R from the second term in Eq 6 should be expected for the smallest cracks. For $a/a_{\text{ext}} = 0.2$ and a typical integration path radius of 12.5 percent of a_{ext}, the contribution is of the order of 20 percent and can thus hardly be neglected.

By equating the expressions in Eqs 1 and 2 one obtains

$$G(a,c) = G(a,0)\, w(c) = 2\gamma_F(c) \tag{8}$$

By using the fact that, for a given load

$$G(a,0) = G_{\text{stat}} = J_R(a) \tag{9}$$

and by using $w = w_K$, the dynamic screening function for the infinite axisymmetric case and the relation for the velocity dependence of $2\gamma_F$ from Ref *11* based on work by Paxson and Lucas [*20*], Fig. 6, a relation between crack size and crack-tip velocity can be obtained when

$$J_R(a) = \frac{2\gamma_F(c)}{w_K(c)} \tag{10}$$

is solved for $a = a(c)$.

As seen from Fig. 5 the agreement between analysis and experiments is good.

Discussion

A quasi-dynamic analysis, obtained by assuming the energy flow to the crack tip to be the static strain energy release rate times a dynamic function depending on the instantaneous crack-tip velocity only, seems to be valid also in an axisymmetric configuration. Experimental results tend to support the use of the dynamic function $w = w_K$ for an infinite body also for configurations of finite size. The slight discrepancies for

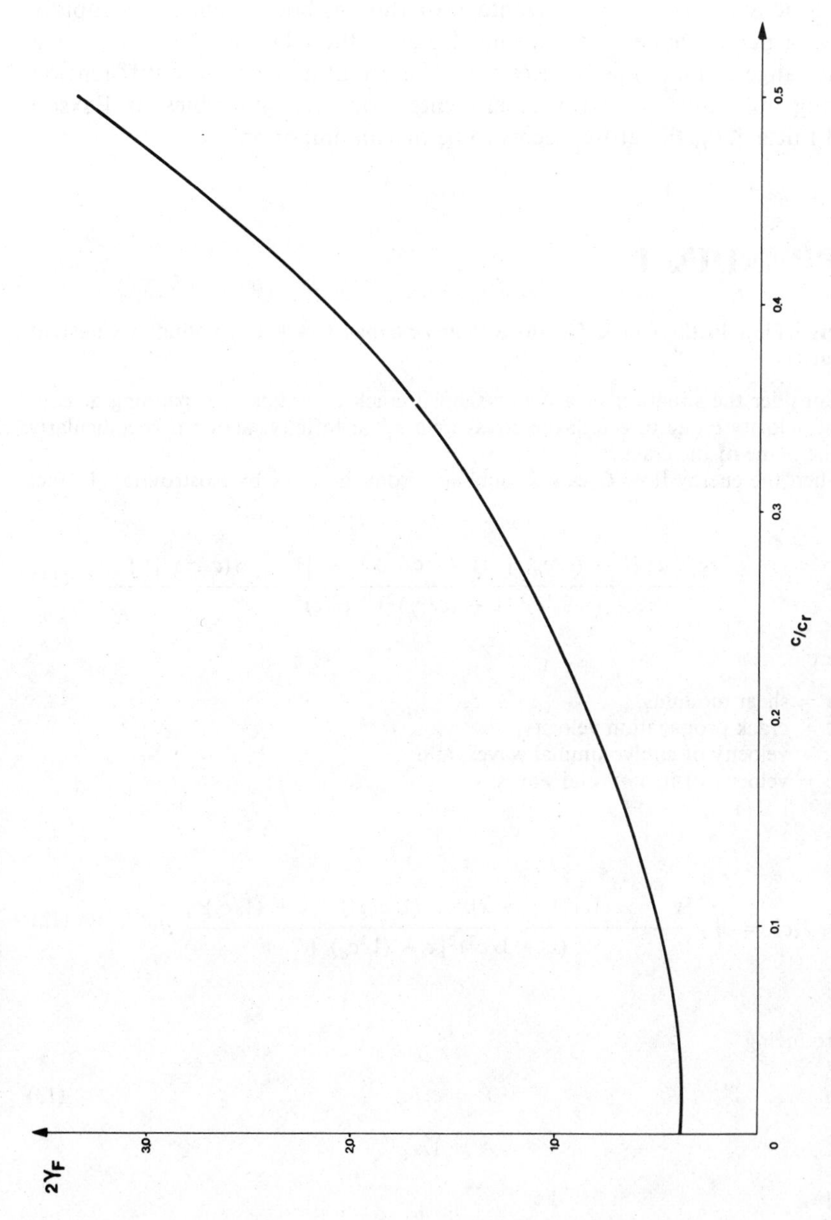

FIG. 6—*Fracture energy* $2\gamma_F$ *N/mm for polymethylmethacrylate from* Ref. 20, *versus nondimensional crack-tip velocity* c/c_r. *The velocity of equivoluminal waves* c_r = *970 m/s.*

large ratios of crack size to specimen diameter might indicate that the assumption of fixed load does not hold throughout the experiment.

To be able to take full advantage of this method of analyzing rapidly moving penny-shaped cracks, knowledge of the relation $\gamma_F = \gamma_F(c)$ for a wide range of materials is necessary. The use of an extremely stiff tension testing apparatus for strip experiments along the guidelines of Paxson and Lucas [*20*], therefore, seems to be of vital importance.

APPENDIX I

Energy Flow to the Crack-Tip for a Penny-Shaped Crack Expanding at Constant Velocity

Consider the situation of a penny-shaped crack of radius a, expanding at constant velocity c due to a uniaxial stress field σ_z^0 at infinity, acting perpendicularly to the plane of the crack.

Then the energy flow G can be obtained from the work by Kostrov [*5*]. In fact

$$G = \frac{\pi \sigma_z^{0^2} a\{[1 - (c/c_d)^2]^{1/2}[1 - (c/c_r)^2]^{1/2} - [1 - 1/2(c/c_r)^2]^2\}}{8\mu\, c_r^2 [1 - (c/c_d)^2]^{1/2} I^2(c)} \tag{11}$$

where

μ = shear modulus,
c = crack propagation velocity,
c_r = velocity of equivoluminal waves, and
c_d = velocity of irrotational waves.

and

$$I(c) = \int_0^\infty \frac{[x + 1/2(1/c_r)^2]^2 - x[x + (1/c_d)^2]^{1/2}[x + (1/c_r)^2]^{1/2}}{(x + 1/c^2)^2[x + (1/c_d)^2]^{1/2}} dx \tag{12}$$

Introducing

$$k = c_r/c_d \tag{13}$$

$$A = 1/c_d^2$$

and

$$\nu = c/c_d$$

Eq 11 reads

$$G = \frac{\pi\sigma_z^{0\,2} a}{E} \frac{3 - 4k^2}{8\,(1 - k^2)}$$

$$\times \frac{[(1 - v^2)^{1/2}\,(1 - (v/k)^2)^{1/2} - (1 - 1/2\,(v/k)^2)^2]}{(1 - v^2)^{1/2}\,F^2\,(k,v)} \tag{14}$$

where

$$F(k,v) = c_r\,I(c) = \frac{k}{\sqrt{A}}\,I(c)$$

Furthermore the relations

$$k^2 = \frac{1 - 2\nu}{2(1 - \nu)} \tag{15}$$

and

$$\mu = \frac{E}{2(1 + \nu)} \tag{16}$$

have been used.

To evaluate $I(c)$ the following procedure is made

$$I(c) = \lim_{N\to\infty} \{I_1 - I_2\}$$

where

$$I_1 = \int_0^N \frac{(x + A/2k^2)^2}{(x + A/v^2)^2\,(x + A)^{1/2}}\,dx$$

$$I_2 = \int_0^N \frac{x(x + A/k^2)^{1/2}}{(x + A/v^2)^2}\,dx$$

After suitable variable substitutions and integration by parts one arrives at the final result

$$F(k,v) = \frac{k}{\sqrt{A}}\,I(c) = k\left\{2\left(\frac{1}{k} - 1\right) + \frac{1}{\sqrt{d}}\left(\frac{\pi}{2} - \arctan\frac{1}{\sqrt{d}}\right)\left(4h + \frac{h^2}{d}\right)\right.$$

$$\left. - \frac{h^2}{d(1 + d)} - \frac{1}{\sqrt{f}}\left(\frac{\pi}{2} - \arctan\frac{1/k}{\sqrt{f}}\right)\left(2e + \frac{g}{f}\right) + \frac{g}{f}\,\frac{1/k}{1/k^2 + f}\right\} \tag{17}$$

where

$d = 1/v^2 - 1$
$e = 1/k^2 - 2/v^2$
$f = 1/v^2 - 1/k^2$

$$g = \frac{1}{v^2}(1/v^2 - 1/k^2)$$
$$h = 1/2k^2 - 1/v^2$$

As a check of the result obtained, the limiting value for G when the velocity tends to zero is sought.

$$G_{\text{stat}} = \lim_{\nu \to 0} G = \frac{\pi \sigma_z{}^{\text{O}2} a}{E} \frac{3 - 4k^2}{8(1 - k^2)}$$

$$\times \lim_{\nu \to 0} \left\{ \frac{[(1 - v^2)^{1/2}(1 - (v/k)^2)^{1/2} - (1 - \tfrac{1}{2}(v/k)^2)^2]}{(1 - v^2)^{1/2} F^2(k,v)} \right\}$$

One finds

$$\lim_{\nu \to 0} F(k,v) = \frac{\pi}{4}\left(\frac{1}{k^2} - 1\right) vk$$

and

$$\lim_{\nu \to 0} \left\{ \frac{[(1 - v^2)^{1/2}(1 - (v/k)^2)^{1/2} - (1 - \tfrac{1}{2}(v/k)^2)^2]}{(1 - v^2)^{1/2}} \right\} = \frac{v^2}{2}\left(\frac{1}{k^2} - 1\right)$$

And so

$$G_{\text{stat}} = \frac{\sigma_z{}^{\text{O}2} a}{\pi E} \frac{3 - 4k^2}{(1 - k^2)^2}$$

or using Eq 15

$$G_{\text{stat}} = \frac{\sigma_z{}^{\text{O}2} a}{\pi E} 4(1 - \nu^2)$$

which corresponds to the expression from Ref *15* for the static case.

Thus, in the dynamic case, Eq 11 could be written

$$G = G_{\text{stat}}\, w$$

where

$$w = w_K = \frac{\pi^2(1 - k^2)}{8} \frac{[(1 - v^2)^{1/2}(1 - (v/k)^2)^{1/2} - (1 - \tfrac{1}{2}(v/k)^2)^2]}{(1 - v^2)^{1/2} F^2(k,v)} \quad (18)$$

w_K is plotted for different values of k, that is, different values of Poisson's ratio in Fig. 1.

References

[*1*] Yoffe, E. H., *Philos Magazine,* Vol. 42, 1951, pp. 739–750.
[*2*] Craggs, J. W., *Journal of the Mechanics and Physics of Solids,* Vol. 8, 1960, pp. 66–75.
[*3*] Broberg, K. B., *Arkiv för Fysik,* Vol. 18, 1960, pp. 159–192.

[4] Broberg, K. B., *Journal of Applied Mechanics,* Vol. 31, 1964, pp. 546–547.
[5] Kostrov, B. V., *Prikladnaya Matematika i Mekhanika,* Vol. 24, 1964, pp. 644–652.
[6] Craggs, J. W., *International Journal of Engineering Science,* Vol. 4, 1966, pp. 113–124.
[7] Atkinson, C., *International Journal of Engineering Science,* Vol. 6, 1968, pp. 27–35.
[8] Eshelby, J. D., *Journal of the Mechanics and Physics of Solids,* Vol. 17, 1969, pp. 177–199.
[9] Freund, L. B., *Journal of the Mechanics and Physics of Solids,* Vol. 20, 1972, pp. 141–152.
[10] Bergkvist, H., *Journal of the Mechanics and Physics of Solids,* Vol. 21, 1973, pp. 229–239.
[11] Bergkvist, H., *Journal of the Mechanics and Physics of Solids,* Vol. 22, 1974, pp. 491–502.
[12] Erdogan, F. in *Fracture, Vol. 2—Mathematical Fundamentals,* H. Liebowitz, Ed., Academic Press, New York, 1968, Chapter 5, pp. 497–590.
[13] Rice, J. R., *Journal of Applied Mechanics,* Vol. 35, 1968, pp. 379–386.
[14] Bergkvist, H., "Numerical Treatment of a Brittle Crack Extending at Non-uniform Velocity," Report from Division of Solid Mechanics, Lund Institute of Technology, Lund, Sweden, 1974.
[15] Sneddon, I. N. and Lowengrub, M., *Crack Problems in the Classical Theory of Elasticity,* Wiley, New York, 1969, p. 138.
[16] Tsai, Y. M., *International Journal of Fracture,* Vol. 9, 1973, pp. 157–169.
[17] Broberg, K. B., "On Determination of the J-integral for Paths Close to a Crack-Tip in Cases of Axial Symmetry," Report SM 76-9, Graduate Aeronautical Laboratories, California Institute of Technology, Pasadena, Calif., 1976.
[18] Tada, H., Paris, P., and Irwin, G., *The Stress Analysis of Cracks Handbook,* Del Research Corporation, Hellertown, Pa., 1973, p. 28.1.
[19] Bergkvist, H., *Engineering Fracture Mechanics,* Vol. 6, 1974, pp. 621–626.
[20] Paxson, T. L. and Lucas, R. A. in *Dynamic Crack Propagation,* G. C. Sih, Ed., Noordhoff, Leyden, The Netherlands, 1973, pp. 415–426.
[21] Hernelind, J. and Pärletun, L.-G., *Programbibliotek till EUFEMI, komplement* (partially in Swedish), Division of Solid Mechanics, Lund Institute of Technology, Lund, Sweden, 1972.

John Congleton[1] *and B. K. Denton*[1]

Measurement of Fast Crack Growth in Metals and Nonmetals

REFERENCE: Congleton, John and Denton, B. K., **"Measurement of Fast Growth in Metals and Nonmetals,"** *Fast Fracture and Crack Arrest, ASTM STP 627*, G. T. Hahn and M. F. Kanninen, Eds., American Society for Testing and Materials, 1977, pp. 336–358.

ABSTRACT: The use of a surface deposited resistance grid technique for crack velocity measurements and the extension of its general applicability to brittle solids by the incorporation of a circular time base for single shot, open shutter oscilloscope recording is described. For metal specimens a more direct crack velocity measurement procedure was used, and it was found that the dynamic potential drop across the faces of the propagating crack obeyed an equation of the form $V_{dynamic} = A \cdot v \cdot c$, where v is the crack velocity, c the crack length, and A an empirical constant. Crack velocity profiles for three-point-bend tests on polymethylmethacrylate and a variously tempered tool steel are presented.

KEY WORDS: crack velocity, crack propagation, metals, nonmetals, bend tests, dynamics, fracture strength, fracture properties

Nomenclature

- c Crack length
- c_o Initial crack length
- c_m Crack length at velocity minimum in tension-impact tests
- E Elastic modulus
- K_{ID} Dynamic fracture toughness
- K_{Ic} Fracture toughness (static)
- K_q Equivalent stress intensity factor for blunt notched specimens
- K_t Stress concentration factor
- V Voltage
- v, $\bar{v}$ Crack velocity
- ρ Density

[1]Senior lecturer and senior research associate, respectively, Department of Metallurgy and Engineering Materials, University of Newcastle upon Tyne, Newcastle upon Tyne, England.

[2]The italic numbers in brackets refer to the list of references appended to this paper.

σ_{NF} Net section stress at fracture
σ_p Prestress used in tension-impact tests

A surface deposited resistance grid has been used previously [*1,2*][2] to measure crack velocities in electrically insulating solids that were in plate form with smooth, impervious surfaces. The basic assumption in the measurements was that the crack front spread through the plate normal to the plate surface so that monitoring fracture at the surface gave an adequate assessment of fracture propagation in the bulk material. The present paper describes the development of some velocity measurement techniques for ceramics and metals, and some velocity data are reported.

The details of the surface grid procedure have been published previously [*1*], and it was found that evaporated grid legs, either 0.25 mm wide spaced 1 mm apart or 1 mm legs spaced at 3 mm intervals, were satisfactory for a wide range of measurements. In making the resistance grid, the legs nearer to the fracture origin were made shorter to produce an almost equal change in potential across the grid as successive legs were broken by the moving crack.

In previous experiments [*1,3*] it was shown that the acceleration of a brittle crack, starting from an edge notch in a plate loaded monotonically to fracture in uniaxial tension, agrees with the theoretical predictions of Mott [*4*] and Berry [*5*]. In those experiments the measurements were performed mainly on polymethylmethacrylate (PMMA) using the surface deposited grid procedure. Such data could either be presented as the average crack velocities for the ligaments between adjacent grid legs or as the accurately obtained time and crack length measurements interpreted by an iterative procedure using the integrated form of the Berry equation [*3,5*]. The latter alternative allows an accurate assessment of terminal crack velocity and an indication of the ratio of actual stress to Griffith's fracture stress for the specimen.

Crack Velocity Measurements in Ceramics

The monitoring of fast moving cracks in PMMA and a soda-lime-silica glass was performed quite easily in both simple tension and combined tension-impact tests using the surface deposited grid [*1,2,3*]. However, attempts to extend the measurements to polycrystalline ceramics caused increased experimental difficulty on three accounts. First, crack velocities of the order of 3500 m/s were expected and were observed in the early experiments. Second, it was found impossible to evaporate satisfactory grids onto porous ceramic surfaces. Third, and most difficult to circumvent, it was observed that both in monotonically loaded and in tension-impact tests the crack sometimes propagated very slowly at first then accelerated rapidly. For instance, a crack might run at 200 m/s initially for an appreciable distance compared to the distance from the trigger leg in the grid to the crack tip, then rapidly accelerate to the terminal velocity for the material.

This wide range of velocities and the variability of the break out of fracture from specimen to specimen made single shot oscilloscope work virtually impossible. This was because the choice of a slow oscilloscope sweep rate would record the initial relatively slow crack growth, but in the range where the crack began to move very fast the horizontal time legs were too short to measure accurately. A faster sweep rate in some cases only recorded part of the time taken to break the first grid leg.

This variability of fracture behavior was experienced with reaction bonded silicon nitride, polycrystalline alumina, and polycrystalline magnesia, and it became evident that a modification in the experimental technique was required. The answer was to devise a means of obtaining an extended sweep time at fast sweep rate.

Oscilloscope Recording Using a Circular Time Base

An extended sweep time at a fast sweep rate for single shot oscilloscope work was achieved by manufacturing a circular time base and using the output from the resistance grid to modulate the radius of gyration of the oscilloscope beam. Single shot working was performed with the camera on open shutter using the trigger leg of the grid to activate a circuit that increased the beam intensity for an appropriate time. A block diagram of the circuit is shown in Fig. 1. The output from a frequency generator was fed into a pair of phase shift circuits to provide, respectively, an advance and a retard of 45 deg to a sinusoidal source. The resulting signals were then fed separately to integrated circuit networks capable of multiplication. That is, two inputs X and Y result in an output KXY, where K was an adjustable multiplication factor. Thus, if X was the processed signal from the signal generator and Y the output from the resistance grid, the multiplied signals could be used to drive the x and y amplifiers of the oscilloscope to yield a circular trace on the screen that would contract in radius in a stepwise manner as the crack spread and progressively broke the legs of the resistance grid.

For single shot work the trigger leg was used in a simple pulse generator circuit so that with the trigger leg intact a suitable blanking voltage was supplied to the Z (brightness) modulation of the oscilloscope. When fracture of the specimen caused the breaking of the trigger leg, a bright-up pulse was fed to the oscilloscope. The duration of the pulse could be varied by altering the capacitance C in the circuit presented in Fig. 2, and the magnitude of the blanking voltage could be varied by adjusting the relative values of the resistors R1 and R2.

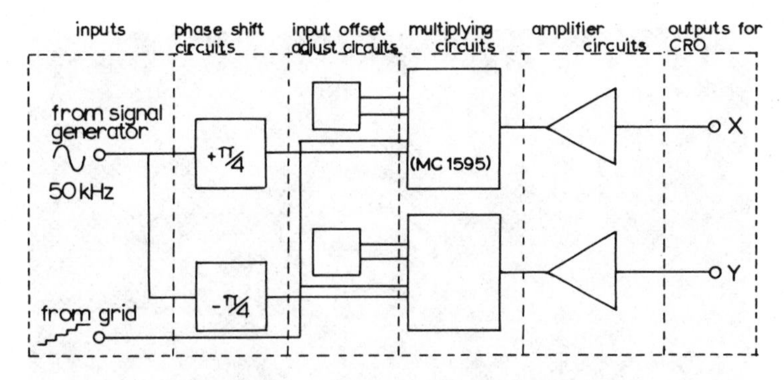

FIG. 1—*Circular time base circuit.*

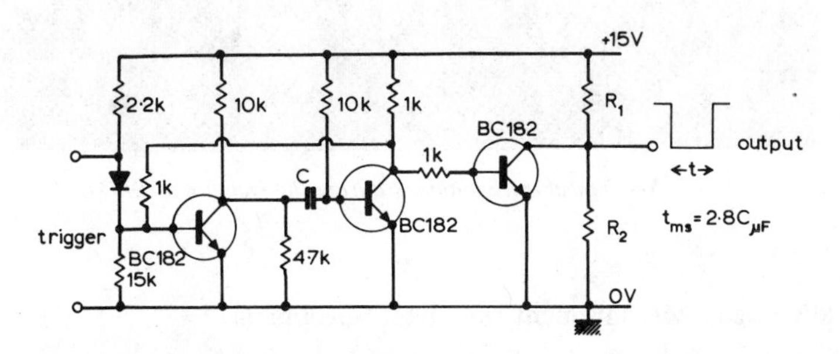

FIG. 2—*Circuit for triggering Z-modulation of cathode ray oscilloscope.*

The system was used with a 50-kHz sinusoidal source so that the oscilloscope spot rotated once every 20 μs. Photographs were interpreted with the aid of a standard rotating microscope stage that could measure angular rotations to an accuracy of 0.1 deg if the quality of the photograph allowed. The stage had translation controls independent of the center of rotation so that it was extremely easy to set up the photograph to rotate about the center of the circular trace. The recording arrangement allowed times of as short as 0.05 μs to be measured, but time intervals of up to 20 μs (1 revolution) could also be measured with ease. Thus, for grid legs spaced at 1 mm, crack velocities in the range 50 to 20 000 m/s could be coped with accurately on a single recording. The system is capable of easy modification to other speed ranges by altering the driving frequency and making minor adjustments to the phase shift circuits to maintain the 45-deg phase shifts. A typical photographic record for a tension-impact test on PMMA is shown in Fig. 3. The trace commences at maximum radius so that the greatest sensitivity of measurement is utilized in the initial stages of fracture where the grid legs were spaced at only 1 mm separation.

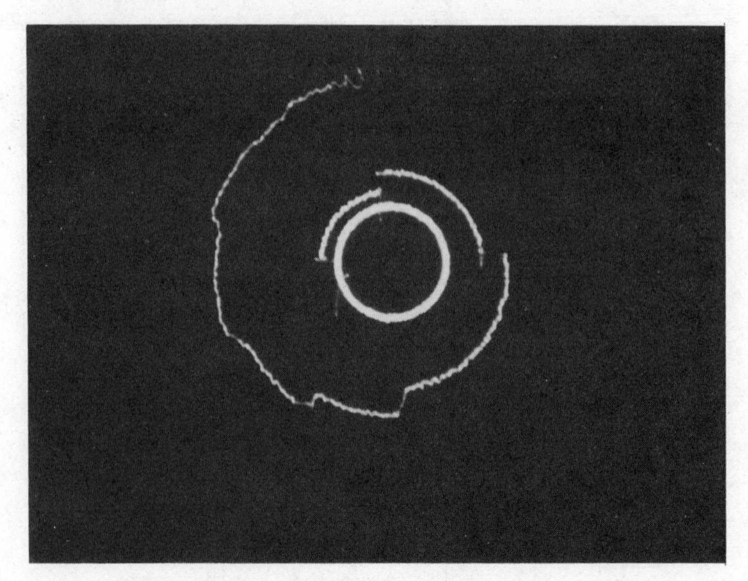

FIG. 3—*Typical trace obtained during the fracture of PMMA.*

Crack Velocity Measurement for Metal Specimens

The resistance grid procedure for crack velocity measurements is limited in its applicability. It is used most easily with those electrically insulating materials that can be prepared with smooth nonporous surfaces. For metal specimens and porous ceramics an insulating varnish layer was needed between the specimen and grid. However, even with an insulating lacquer, the technique relies on the cracking in the varnish paralleling that in the specimen; a somewhat unjustified assumption if the test material shows some ductility and develops shear lips. Thus, an attempt has been made to extend the well-established self-resistance technique for slow-crack velocity measurements to monitor fast-moving cracks. The electrical resistance of a cracked specimen depends upon crack length, and slow-moving cracks can be monitored by recording the potential drop across the crack faces. In many studies a constant 30-A current has been used giving a potential drop of the order of 1 to 10 mV as the crack traversed the specimen. We have monitored the changing potential drop across the crack faces in relatively thick specimens during fast-crack propagation, but two experimental difficulties were associated with the measurements. First, electrical noise had to be eliminated from the signal. Second, the interpretation of the signal was not straightforward. It was envisaged that interpretation of the output would be complicated because a fast-moving crack converts an applied direct current to the equivalent of an alternating current source because the cracking material experiences a step change in potential. The rise time of the pulse depends upon the crack velocity.

To ease the experimental problems, it was decided to use bend tests for the exploratory study. The specimens were insulated electrically from the test machine by inserting mica between the specimen and the knife edges.

Calibration Procedures for Metal Specimens

The autoresistance technique for monitoring crack growth has been quite widely used in stress corrosion and fatigue studies where crack growth rates are only of the order of 1 mm/h. Under such circumstances, calibration for the technique is relatively simple as it is possible to interrupt the crack growth at any stage and measure the length of the crack which corresponds to the potential drop across the crack faces at that time. However, in the present work it was generally not possible to stop the crack within the width of specimen used. Consequently, it was necessary to calibrate the specimens using thin notches to represent equivalent length cracks. Sometimes it was possible to obtain crack arrest in three-point-bend tests by using a hard loading system but usually only after the crack had traversed a major proportion of the specimen's width. In addition to the static calibration, a dynamic calibration was performed on specimens containing notches of various depth using a pulse generator to electrically simulate fast moving cracks.

Static Calibrations

If a constant direct current is passed through a specimen that contains a crack, the electric field within the specimen is perturbed by the discontinuity. As the crack lengthens, the resistive path between the current electrodes is increased, and the electrical potential measured across the crack faces is increased. For calibration purposes, the potential drop for various crack lengths was plotted by simulating a crack with a hacksawn notch.

The data obtained for a number of materials for three-point-bend and tension specimens are shown in Fig. 4. The compositions of the steels used are shown in Table 1. The as-quenched data were obtained from three separate specimens with different notch depths cut prior to heat treatment, and the electrical measurements were performed after hardening. The EN24 oil-quenched results were from a series of specimens heat treated and then fatigued to provide a range of crack lengths for measurement. The only factor affecting the calibration is specimen configuration and dimensions, and the minor differences in the full lines in Fig. 4 are due to this, as is the difference between those lines and the three-point-bend specimen curve shown dashed.

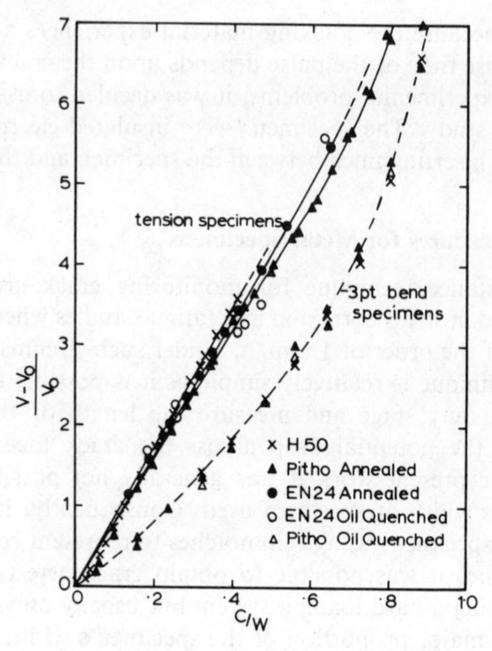

FIG. 4—*Normalized potential drop versus fractional crack depth for alloy steel specimens.*

Dynamic Calibrations

During fast fracture the static voltage distribution is no longer strictly applicable as the current path is altered under dynamic conditions. An indication of the effect of dynamic crack propagation on the output was obtained by using a high-power pulse generator in place of the constant-current power source. The resulting outputs from specimens of various configurations and chemical and metallurgical compositions were measured. An Advance Electronics high-power pulse generator, Type PG55A, capable of delivering 1-A square wave pulses of varying width, frequency, and rise times (approximately 6.5 to 80 ns) was connected across hack-sawn notches of various lengths in tensile and three-point-bend specimens of Pitho, EN24, and H50 steels in the annealed and oil-quenched conditions. The voltage difference across the notch was monitored continuously with an oscilloscope during the pulsing, and measurements were taken of the magnitude of the output on the leading edge of the square wave pulses. These were set at 100 μs duration recurring with a frequency of 1 kHz. The rise times of the leading edges were also measured. Typical results are shown in Fig. 5 for Pitho three-point-bend specimens. These show clearly that the output under dynamic conditions increased with increasing crack length and decreasing rise time. This suggested that any

TABLE 1—*Alloy steel compositions, percent.*

Material	C	Mn	P	S	Si	Ni	Cr	Mo	W	V
Pitho tool steel	0.9 to 1.0	1.1 to 1.3	...	...	...	...	0.45 to 0.65	...	0.45 to 0.8	0.15 max
EN24	0.35 to 0.45	0.45 to 0.7	0.05 max	0.05 max	0.1 to 0.35	1.3 to 1.8	0.9 to 1.4	0.2 to 0.35	...	...
H50	0.4	...	...	...	1.0	...	5.0	1.45	...	1.0

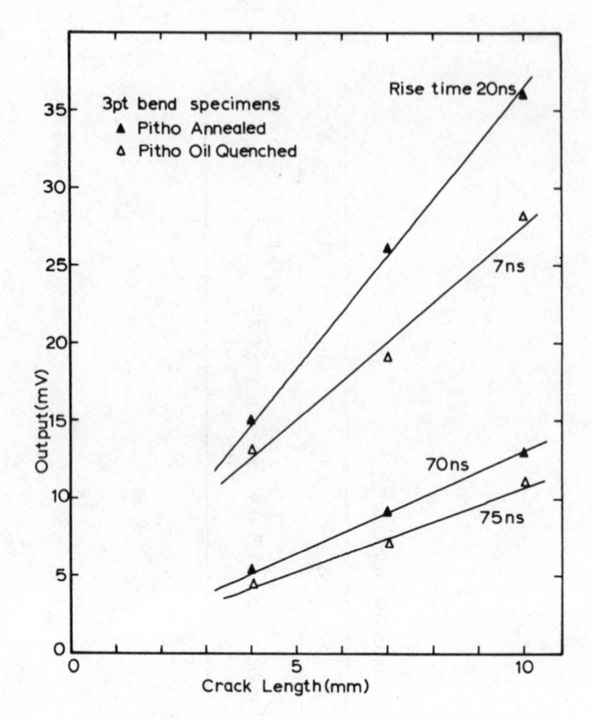

FIG. 5—*Output pulse height versus crack length for Pitho three-point-bend specimens.*

dynamic component would increase in magnitude as the crack length increased and as the crack velocity increased; two factors concomitant with a "skin" effect. That is, as the crack velocity increases the current path within the specimen follows successively narrower paths around the crack front. Thus, as the crack elongates the output increases due to the increased length of the current path, and as the velocity increases the output also increases due to the decreased thickness of material through which the current flows around the crack.

The output obtained during these dynamic calibrations may be expressed simply as

$$V_{\text{dynamic}} = f(\text{rise time}, c)$$

Figure 5 shows that for a given rise time

$$V_{\text{dynamic}} \, \alpha c$$

It was impossible to equate rise time to an equivalent crack velocity so an empirical relationship of the form

$$V_{dynamic} = A \cdot v \cdot c \text{ was assumed}$$

where

A = empirical constant,
v = crack velocity, and
c = crack length.

Thus, if the static and dynamic components were additive the output would be of the form

$$V_{total} = V_{static} + A \cdot v \cdot c$$

where V_{static} refers to the voltage obtained in the static calibrations described previously. Alternatively it was thought that for high-crack velocities the output would consist entirely of the dynamic component, so that the static calibration may only need consideration for slow moving cracks since the dynamic and static outputs relate to two different current paths which are essentially mutually exclusive. However, there was no way of determining the relative contributions from the two parts, and it was not possible to determine how velocity affected the relative contributions.

The simple empirical approach just described was adopted, but lengthy iterative calculations were required. Calculation of crack velocity from the recorded output was performed by first subtracting the calculated static contribution from the total output and then calculating the average crack velocity $\bar{v}$ for a small time interval (usually 0.2 or 1 μs)

$$\text{from } \bar{v} = (V_{output} - V_{static})/A \cdot c$$

The calculated $\bar{v}$ was then used to update the crack length to allow calculation of the static contribution relevant to the next data point, and the iterative procedure continued. The constant A was varied so that the data fitted the known boundary conditions of crack length. This was possible because c_o was known in all cases, and the recorded data allowed easy calculation of either the time and length at which the crack arrested or when complete fracture of the specimen occurred.

Crack Velocity Measurements in Steels Under Three-Point Bending

Bend tests were performed on a conventional screw driven testing machine. In most cases a 30-A constant current power pack was used for the tests, and the output was stored using a Datalab DL905 transient recorder. The pretrigger storage mode on the instrument allowed the use of the rising output signal as the trigger signal. The output from the

DL905 was displayed after the test on an oscilloscope, and both direct measurements and a polaroid photograph were taken.

The bend specimens were of dimensions 12.5 by 6.5 by 70 mm with notches of 0.8 mm width and 0.4 mm root radius, machined to a depth of 4 mm. The span of the test rig was 50 mm. The current input leads were of heavy gage copper, silver soldered into position 8 mm apart on either side of the notch. The silver soldering was accomplished using a spot welding gun as the heat source. Although the current passed through the copper leads and the specimen, the heating effect was localized sufficiently at the interface to leave the heat treatment of the specimen unaffected in the anticipated crack path. It was found that the use of brazing flux was only occasionally necessary. Short iron leads were spot welded to the specimen between the notch and the current input leads. These, in turn, were soldered to signal leads.

Initially, some problems were encountered with excessive amounts of electrical noise on the recorded signal. This was reduced sufficiently by using standard 50 Ω coaxial cable for the two potential leads. Ideally, these should have been connected via 50 Ω connectors to a differential amplifier to provide a measure of the potential difference across the crack, but it was found that a simple terminal box, wired to give a differential output, was adequate.

Figure 6 shows the result of a test in which arrest occurred. Such traces were reproduced consistently for similar specimens. The time scale for the

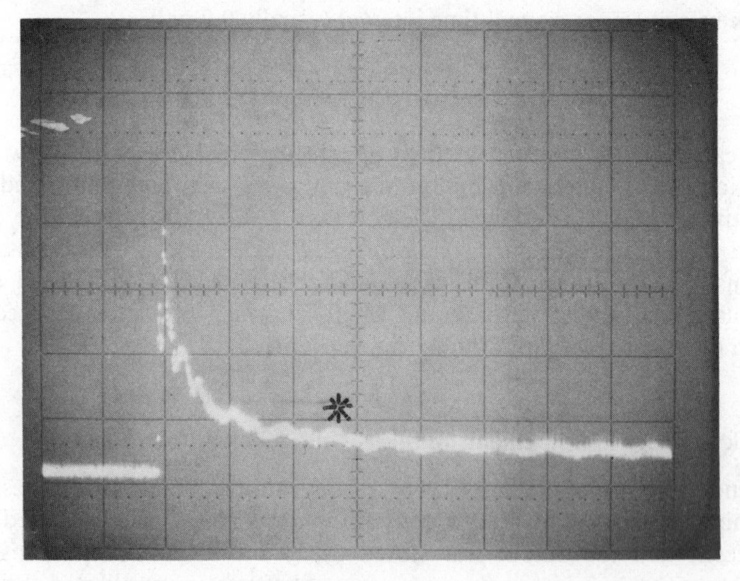

FIG. 6—*Oscilloscope trace, annealed Pitho, fracture load 4.9 kN, trace length 2.0 ms, final crack length 9.14 mm.*

fracture event was quite long, 200 to 500 μs, and the final electromotive force (EMF) was consistent with the final crack length. It was assumed that the slow drop in voltage after the point marked (*) in Fig. 6 was due to shorting across the crack faces as the crack closed up when the fracture effectively relaxed the stresses on the specimen. Two calculated velocity traces for annealed Pitho are shown in Fig. 7 that indicate that the output was consistent whether the power source was an electronically stabilized constant current device or a simple high-capacity storage battery.

The results obtained suggested that the static calibration was important in the bend tests where crack arrest had occurred and indicated that the crack velocities were relatively low. The static calibration was incorporated in the iterative procedure that has been described previously, and the value of the empirical constant A was chosen so that crack arrest occurred at a distance corresponding to the measured final crack length.

Bend tests have been performed on Pitho tool steel in the as-quenched condition, after tempering at 400 and 500°C and in the fully annealed condition. Typical crack velocity versus distance plots are shown in Fig. 8. In order that the calculated crack lengths fitted the boundary conditions of final crack length (either arrest at a known length and time or complete fracture in a known time) the constant A had to be determined iteratively for each specimen. This apparently unsatisfactory aspect of the calculations was rationalized when it was realized that the empirical factor A was linearly dependent upon the initial potential drop across the starting notch, as demonstrated in Fig. 9. The variations in initial potential drop from specimen to specimen resulted from minor differences in the positioning of the current and potential leads and the electrical resistivity of the specimens.

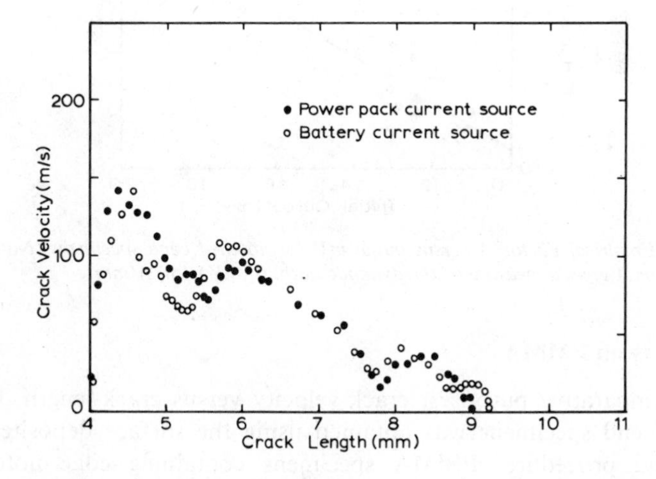

FIG. 7—*Crack velocity versus crack length, annealed Pitho three-point-bend tests.*

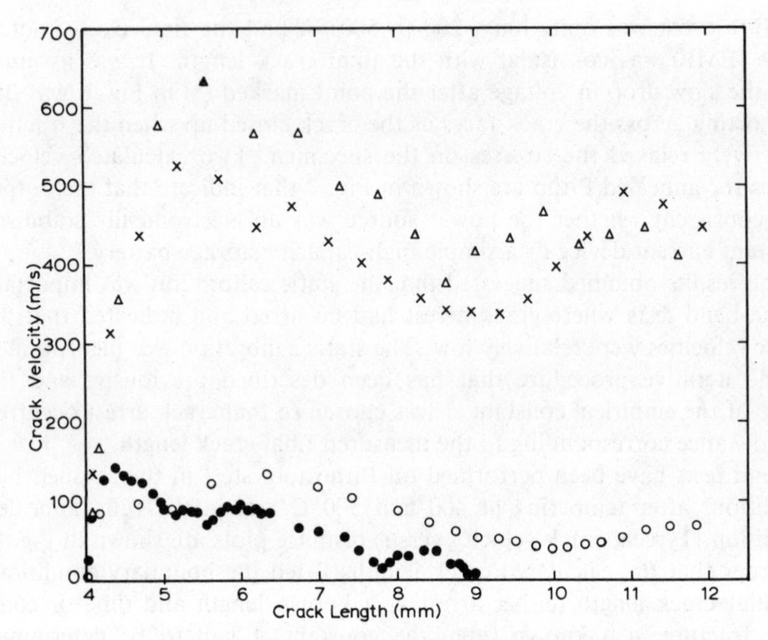

FIG. 8—*Crack velocity versus crack length, Pitho tool steel three-point-bend tests.* o *As quenched;* x *tempered at 400°C for 1h;* Δ *tempered at 500°C for 1 h;* • *annealed.*

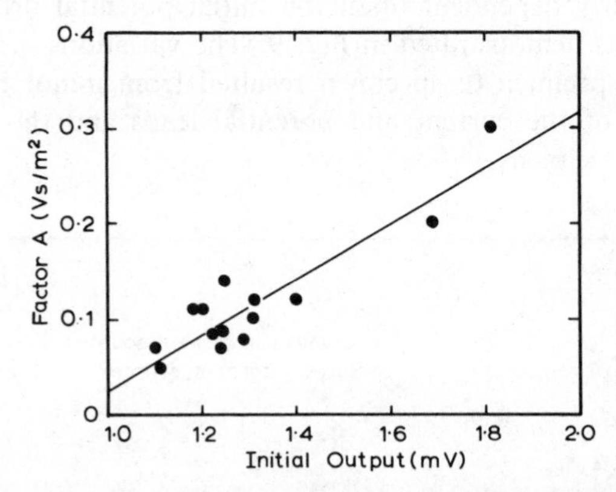

FIG. 9—*Empirical Factor A versus initial mV for notched bend specimens. Notch depth 4 mm. Factor A gives a measure of the dynamic output* [$(mV)/(m/s)/mm$].

Bend Tests on PMMA

For comparative purposes, crack-velocity versus crack-length data for PMMA bend specimens was obtained using the surface deposited resistance grid procedure. PMMA specimens containing edge notches of various depths were tested in three-point bending at a series of loading rates. The span to width ratio was 4:1. Velocities measured by the grid technique are shown in Figs. 10 to 12. In those diagrams the open symbols refer to the fastest loading rate, the closed symbols to an intermediate loading rate, and the crosses to a very slow crosshead speed of 0.1 μm/s. The crack-tip stress at fracture was calculated as the product of the net section stress at fracture, σ_{NF}, and the stress concentration factor K_t as calculated from Peterson [*6*]. This approach was used because the tests were performed on bend specimens with rather blunt edge notches. For the particular specimens referred to in Figs. 10, 11, and 12, the notch stress $\sigma_{NF}K_t$ can be converted to an effective stress intensity factor for an equal length sharp crack by dividing by 73. The error in the conversion would be less than 2 percent, and the units for the converted value would be MN $m^{-3/2}$.

The fracture velocities were in general independent of the loading rate but very dependent upon the fracture stress. The trend is best shown in Figs. 10 to 12 but existed for all of the data. Also, the crack velocity was initially quite large and decreased as the crack traversed the bend specimen. It was not possible to obtain velocity measurements very near to the crack tip because the grid legs were of appreciable thickness, so the

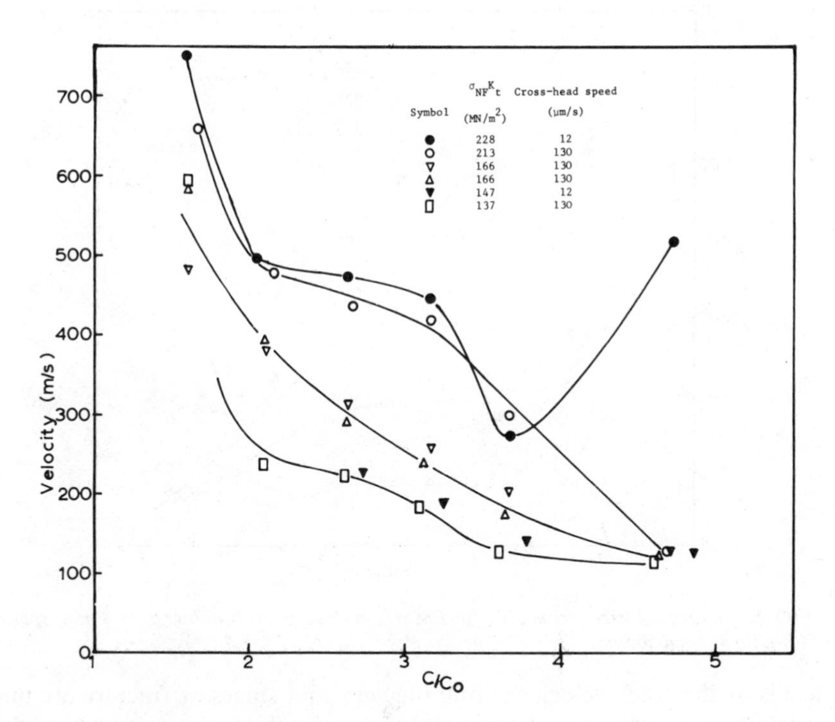

FIG. 10—*Crack velocity versus* c/c_0 *for PMMA in three-point bending.* c_0 = *2 mm; span/width ratio 4, span 50 mm.*

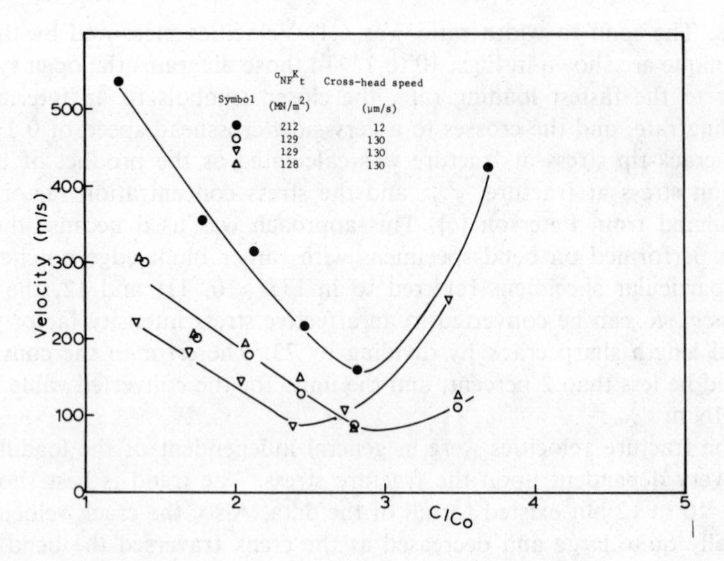

FIG. 11—*Crack velocity versus* c/c$_0$ *for PMMA in three-point bending.* c$_0$ = *3 mm; span/width ratio 4, span 50 mm.*

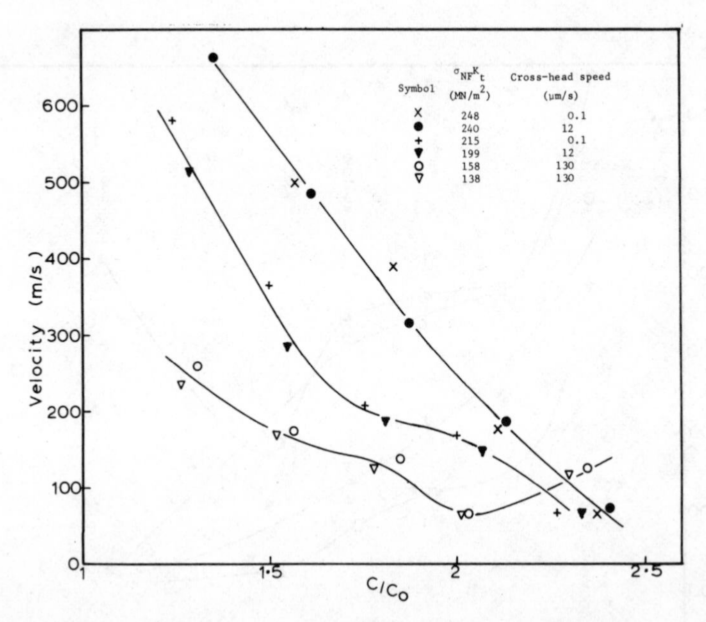

FIG. 12—*Crack velocity versus* c/c$_0$ *for PMMA in three-point bending.* c$_0$ = *4 mm; span/width ratio 4, span 50 mm.*

details of the crack velocity during the very first stages of fracture are uncertain. Crack velocities were greater the larger the fracture stress, and in all specimens, particularly for those in which the fracture stress was small, there was a tendency for the cracks to slow down then accelerate again as they traversed the specimen.

The variability in fracture stress from specimen to specimen for any single notch depth was found to correlate with the size and shape of the slow growth thumbnail crack that was apparent on all the fracture surfaces. Slow-crack growth at the root of a blunt notch will increase the local stress intensity factor significantly and therefore lower the applied load necessary for fracture, and a semicircular thumbnail will be less effective than an elliptical crack of the same depth [*7*]. However, although the low-fracture loads correlated with deep or wide thumbnails of slow growth or both, it was not possible to correlate the fracture loads quantitatively with the thumbnail sizes, and it seems more reasonable to refer to the notch stress at fracture for those tests than to refer to an equivalent stress intensity factor inadequately corrected for the thumbnail of slow-crack growth.

The fracture surfaces of the PMMA bend specimens showed a variety of features, but the presence of arrest marks was of particular interest to the velocity measurements. The grid technique allows only an average velocity between the grid legs to be evaluated, so if momentary crack arrest occurred it was recorded as an apparently very low velocity. It was observed consistently that very low apparent velocities correlated with arrest marks between the appropriate grid legs. The surface morphology in the arrest bands was extremely complicated as indicated by the interferogram in Fig. 13 where the lines in the photograph contour height differences of 0.533 μm. Presumably extensive crazing had occurred in these arrest bands.

Thus, the expected crack velocity profile for a brittle material tested in bending is an initial high-crack velocity that decreases as the crack traverses the specimen, but momentary crack arrest and renewed acceleration may occur. The detailed velocity profile will depend upon the loading arrangements, the specimen size, and the toughness of the material.

Dynamic Fracture Toughness Measurements

A single-edge-notched plate tested in uniaxial tension represents a very simple experimental system, and it has been postulated that dynamic fracture toughness data might be obtained by inducing fracture in a preloaded plate with an impactive blow at the root of the edge notch and monitoring the crack velocity during fracture [*2,8*]. In practice, it was found that loading conditions could be arranged that caused the crack to decelerate in the early part of its growth then accelerate after passing through a well-defined minimum velocity. By assuming that the stress pulse that initiated fracture was attenuated by the time that the crack reached the minimum velocity position and that the loading system was

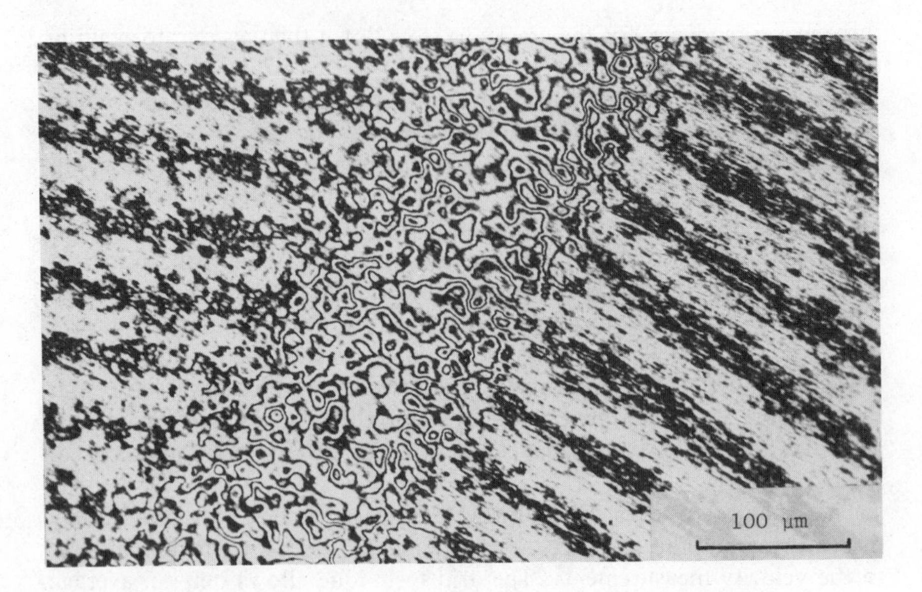

FIG. 13—*Interferogram of crack arrest mark in PMMA. Height difference/contour = 0.553 μm.*

soft enough to maintain the preload for a significant fraction of the fracture event, it was possible to calculate the dynamic crack-tip stress intensity factor from the preload stress and the crack length at minimum velocity. Briefly, it was assumed that the impulse load merely acted as a stress transient large enough to induce fracture initiation and that the main driving force for crack propagation was the preload. If the testing conditions produced rapid crack extension initially, the crack decelerated because the stress transient decayed and the preload was insufficient to maintain the initial high-crack velocity. However, the crack-tip stress intensity factor at constant load increases with crack length, and conditions could be arranged for the increase in crack-tip stress intensity factor to be sufficient to counteract the deceleration. Thus, at the minimum velocity position, the crack-tip stress intensity factor was just sufficiently large to accelerate the crack and is, by definition, a measure of the dynamic fracture toughness at that velocity.

The combined tension-impact procedure was used on ceramics by applying uniaxial tension to thin plates with a strap and roller loading system [*9*]. The specimens were generally edge notched by ultrasonic drilling, and fracture was initiated in preloaded specimens by driving a steel wedge into the root of the edge notch. In some cases it was appropriate to use unnotched specimens, and in those tests fracture was initiated by striking the edge of the plate with the wedge.

For each specimen, a crack-velocity versus crack-length profile was obtained and the minimum velocity position noted. Then, by assuming the original preload stress was operative at the minimum velocity position, a dynamic fracture toughness for the material was calculated from the product $\pi^{1/2}\sigma_p c_m^{1/2}$ which implies that the equivalent static stress intensity factor is an adequate estimate of the dynamic fracture toughness. Such data for reaction bonded silicon nitride are shown as the full circles in Fig. 14. In general, it will be necessary to correct both for finite specimen size and for inertia effects. In our experiments, the loading arrangements approximate most closely to tensile loading without end rotation, and the finite specimen size correction used was that due to Harris [*10*]. Also, in ceramics, very short starting cracks can be used because of the extreme brittleness of the material. Thus, the corrections were generally small. Additionally, we are of the opinion that as the finite specimen size correction applies to the fully relaxed elastic analysis, the equivalent static stress intensity factor at the minimum velocity position should be obtained by multiplying the equivalent static stress intensity factor for the starting notch, K_q, by a factor $[c_m/c_o]^{1/2}$.

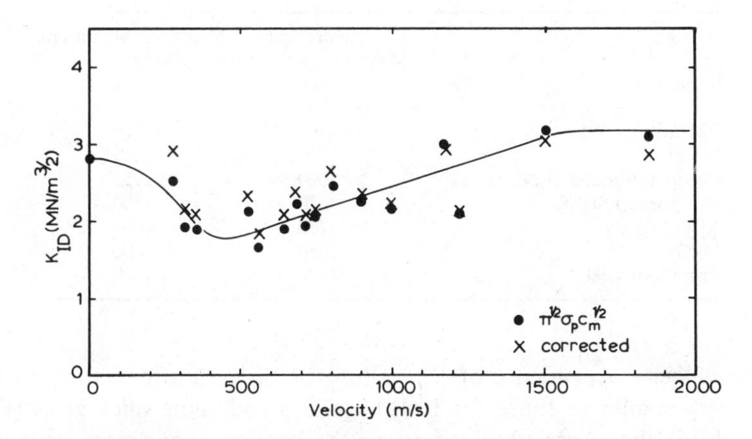

FIG. 14—K_{ID} *versus crack velocity for reaction bonded silicon nitride.*

A correction for inertia effects should also be made, and we have used the relationship

$$K_{ID} = K\left[1 - \frac{V}{C_R}\right]^{1/2}$$

as used by Hahn et al [*11*] to approximate to the Freund [*12*] and Broberg [*13*] analyses. Here, K is the equivalent static stress intensity factor and C_R the Rayleigh velocity.

The silicon nitride results corrected both for finite specimen size and crack velocity are shown as crosses in Fig. 14 and, as can be clearly seen, they lie quite close to the trend line drawn through the uncorrected data. However, the adequacy of the product $\pi^{1/2}\sigma_p c_m^{1/2}$ for describing the dynamic fracture toughness for the tests reported in the present paper arises because of the particular experimental conditions, and in general both static K and dynamic corrections will be necessary.

As can be seen in Fig. 14, K_{ID} for reaction bonded silicon nitride was less than the static K_{Ic} at low velocities of the order of 500 m/s but rose to slightly above the K_{Ic} value at higher velocities. The terminal velocity for the reaction bonded silicon nitride used should be of the order of 3500 m/s if calculated using the Roberts and Wells relationship [*14*] of 0.38 $(E/\rho)^{1/2}$. The expected terminal crack velocities for all of the materials tested are given in Table 2 along with the maximum velocities measured during the present series of experiments.

TABLE 2—*Comparison of theoretical terminal velocities with measured maximum velocities.*

Material	Theoretical Maximum Velocity, m/s	Measured Maximum Velocity, m/s
PMMA	764	770
Glass	1550	1600
Reaction bonded Si_3N_4	3000	2950
Hot pressed Si_3N_4	3550	3500
Al_2O_3	3750	2000
MgO	2650	1800
Pitho tool steel	1900	1700

The velocity dependence of K_{ID} values for silicon nitride shown in Fig. 14 is very similar to those for PMMA and a soda-lime-silica glass (Figs. 15 and 16) that were obtained using the tension-impact test procedure with resistance grid velocity measurement. The PMMA data agree well with that obtained by other workers using alternative procedures [*15–18*]. Again, in Figs. 15 and 16, the full circles refer to data calculated from the product $\pi^{1/2}\sigma_p c_m^{1/2}$ and the crosses to data corrected for finite specimen size and crack velocity. The full lines are the trend lines through the uncorrected data.

It might be argued that the crack-velocity versus crack-length results for the bend specimens should also be amenable to an interpretation that would yield dynamic fracture toughness data. This may be possible, but either a dynamic record of the load would be required in addition to the crack velocity data, or the experimental arrangement would need to

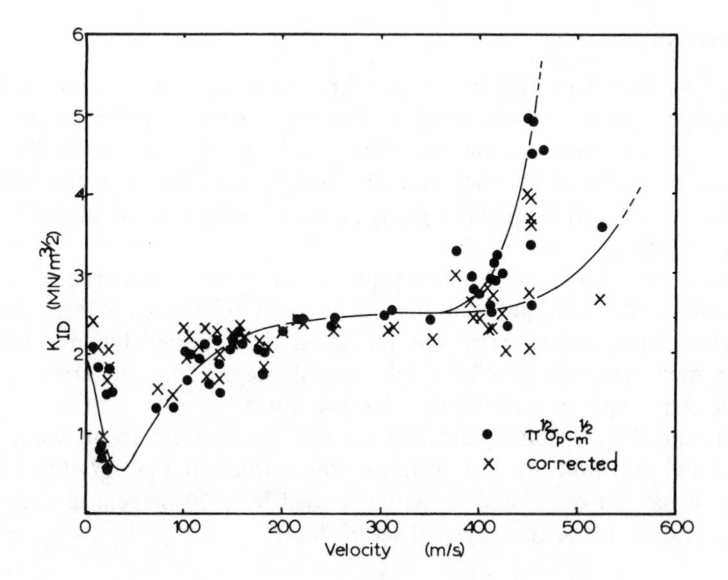

FIG. 15—K$_{ID}$ *versus crack velocity for PMMA.*

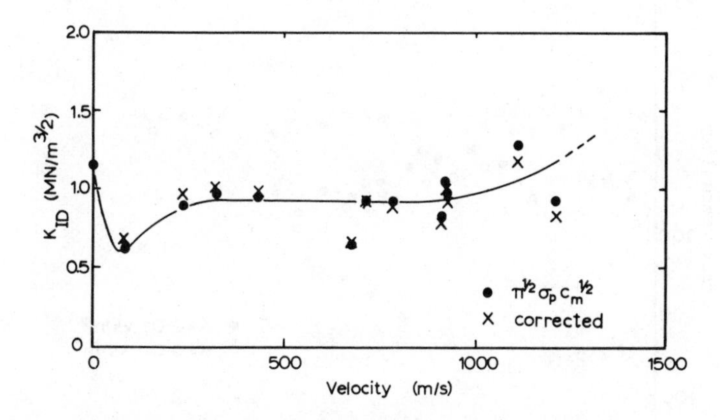

FIG. 16—K$_{ID}$ *versus crack velocity for soda-lime-silica glass.*

comply with a constant displacement fracture event as used by Hahn et al [*19*] in their double-cantilever-beam (DCB) work.

The aim of the present work was to explore techniques for velocity measurement, and the necessary additional load-resistance data were not obtained. In principle, with additional instrumentation, it is conceivable that K_{ID} versus crack velocity data could be obtained from three-point-bend tests by monitoring both crack velocity versus crack length and load versus time.

Discussion

The surface deposited grid procedure, especially when augmented with a circular time base to drive an oscilloscope, is extremely useful for monitoring crack velocities in materials that approximate to ideally brittle solids. In many cases, flat fronted cracks result, and the measurements at the surface are a reliable guide to crack propagation in the bulk of the material.

For metals, however, it is more satisfactory to use an alternative velocity measurement technique that should be both reliable and inexpensive to operate. The present work has indicated that simple dynamic potential drop measurements can be used to evaluate meaningful crack velocity data. An empirical relationship of the form $V_{\text{dynamic}} = A \cdot v \cdot c$ appears valid, and the calculated velocities are not too sensitive to the value of the empirical constant A. For instance, the curves in Fig. 17 illustrate the small effect on calculated velocities caused by a 10 percent change in the value chosen for A for a typical set of data.

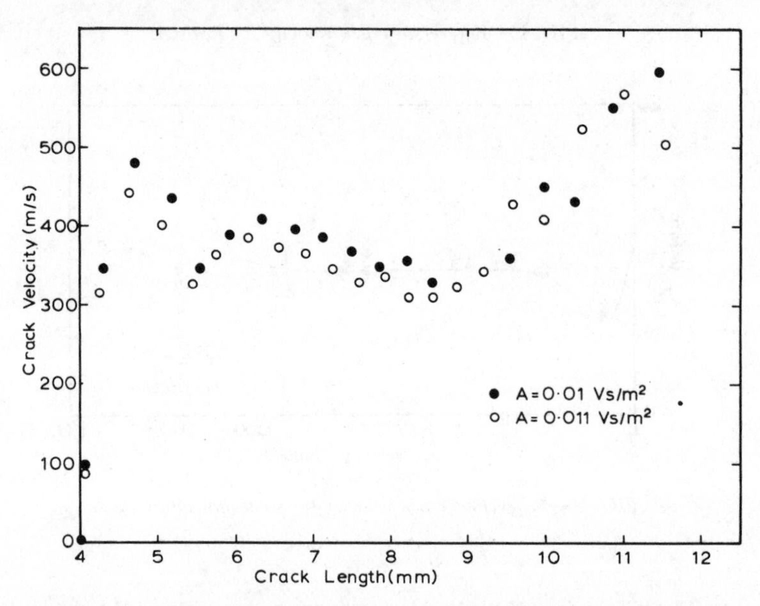

FIG. 17—*Effect of varying Parameter A on a bend test velocity profile.*

Although it would be desirable to confirm the velocity data obtained using the dynamic potential drop measurements by an alternative procedure, the values obtained are close to what would be expected intuitively and are reasonably convincing on that account. Also, alternative experimental techniques such as double exposure time lapse photography or high-speed photography are difficult to set up. The velocity profiles for bend tests on variously heat treated Pitho tool steel shown in Fig. 8 and the related fracture load data presented in Table 3 form a consistent set in that the larger fracture stresses are associated with faster moving cracks. In the case of the annealed tool steel with low fracture load, the high toughness of the material caused crack arrest within the width of the specimen, whereas the brittle as-quenched material with a lower fracture load exhibited a similar crack velocity but the crack propagated completely through the specimen.

TABLE 3—*Fracture load data for velocity profiles in Fig. 8 (three-point-bend test).*

Material	Fracture Load	K_{Ic}
As quenched	3.0 kN	16.5 $MN/m^{3/2}$
Pitho, tempered 400°C	9.4 kN	26 $MN/m^{3/2}$
Pitho, tempered 500°C	11.8 kN	34 $MN/m^{3/2}$
Annealed Pitho	6.7 kN	...

Also, although not fully documented in the text, many tests were performed that have indicated that the potential drop output for dynamic cracks was reproducible for similar specimens fractured under comparable conditions. Additionally, tension tests gave higher crack velocities as might be expected from the nature of the loading. Thus, the suggested empirical equation seems reasonable and may require no more than minor modifications in the light of further experimental data that will become available. Therefore, it is suggested that simple dynamic potential drop measurements may make a useful addition to the range of crack velocity measurement techniques currently available.

Acknowledgments

The authors wish to thank the European Research Office of the U.S. Army and the Science Research Council for their financial assistance during this work and Dr. L. Molyneux of the Department of Physics at the University of Newcastle upon Tyne for his help in the design and construction of the circular time base circuits.

References

[1] Anthony, S. R., Chubb, J. P., and Congleton, J., *Philosophical Magazine,* Vol. 22, 1970, pp. 1201–1216.
[2] Chubb, J. P. and Congleton, J., *Philosophical Magazine,* Vol. 28, 1973, pp. 1087–1097.
[3] Chubb, J. P. and Congleton, J., *Dynamic Crack Propagation,* G. C. Sih, Ed., Noordhoff International Publishing, Leyden, The Netherlands, 1973, pp. 439–448.
[4] Mott, N. F., *Engineering,* Vol. 165, 1948, pp. 16–18.

[5] Berry, J. P., *Journal of Mechanics and Physics of Solids,* Vol. 8, 1960, pp. 194–216.
[6] Peterson, R. E., *Stress Concentration Design Factors,* Wiley, New York, 1963.
[7] Sack, R. A., *Proceedings of the Physical Society,* London, Vol. 58, 1946, pp. 729–736.
[8] Chubb, J. P. and Congleton, J., *International Journal of Fracture Mechanics,* Vol. 8, 1972, pp. 227–230.
[9] Congleton, J. and Petch, N. J., *International Journal of Fracture Mechanics,* Vol. 1, 1965, pp. 14–19.
[10] Harris, D. O., *Journal of Basic Engineering,* Vol. 89D, 1967, pp. 49–53.
[11] Hahn, G. T., Gehlen, P. C., Hoagland, R. G., Kanninen, M. F., Popelar, C., Rosenfield, A. R., and de Campos, V. S., "Critical Experiments, Measurements and Analyses to Establish a Crack Arrest Methodology for Nuclear Pressure Vessel Steels," Battelle Report MB1-1937, Battelle Columbus Laboratories, Columbus, Ohio, Aug. 1975.
[12] Freund, L. B., *Journal of Mechanics and Physics of Solids,* Vol. 21, 1973, p. 47.
[13] Broberg, K. B., *Arkiv för Fysik,* Vol. 18, 1960, pp. 159–192.
[14] Roberts, D. K. and Wells, A. A., *Engineering,* Vol. 178, 1957, pp. 820–821.
[15] Carlsson, J., Dahlberg, L., and Nilsson, F., *Dynamic Crack Propagation,* G. C. Sih, Ed., Noordhoff International Publishing, Leyden, The Netherlands, 1973, pp. 165–181.
[16] Vincent, P. I. and Gotham, K. V., *Nature,* Vol. 210, 1966, p. 1254.
[17] Marshall, G. P., Culver, L. E., and Williams, J. G., *Plastics and Polymers,* Vol. 37, 1969, p. 75.
[18] Johnson, F. A. and Radon, J. C., *Materialprufung,* Vol. 12, 1970, pp. 307–310.
[19] Hahn, G. T., Hoagland, R. G., Kanninen, M. F., and Rosenfield, A. R., *Dynamic Crack Propagation,* G. C. Sih, Ed., Noordhoff International Publishing, Leyden, The Netherlands, 1973, pp. 649–662.

R. J. Weimer[1] *and H. C. Rogers*[2]

A High-Speed Digital Technique for Precision Measurement of Crack Velocities

REFERENCE: Weimer, R. J. and Rogers, H. C., "**A High-Speed Digital Technique for Precision Measurement of Crack Velocities,**" *Fast Fracture and Crack Arrest, ASTM STP 627,* G. T. Hahn and M. F. Kanninen, Eds., American Society for Testing and Materials, 1977, pp. 359–371.

ABSTRACT: The control of propagating cracks in structures first requires an understanding of the interrelationships of microstructure, fractographic features, dynamic stress intensity factor, and crack velocity in materials. Conventional techniques for measuring crack velocity suffer in varying degrees from imprecision, excessively stringent synchronization requirements or poor resolution due to data compression on a single oscilloscope sweep. A new instrumentation concept has evolved from consideration of the advantages and limitations of earlier techniques. High-speed digital data processing techniques are used to measure time of sequential events 300 ns apart to an accuracy of ±50 ns. Temporary storage, high-speed sampling, and a 3:1 multiplexing scheme have been combined with a random access memory structure to enable recording times of as many as three simultaneous events per microsecond. Special templates have been designed to vapor deposit on sample metallic propagation grid configurations that take full advantage of the electronic capabilities of the system. These have 250-μm slits precisely spaced 5 deg apart in radial arrays and 1 mm apart in parallel arrays. Applications to fast fracture, crack branching, fatigue cracking, and stress-corrosion cracking are discussed.

KEY WORDS: crack propagation, dynamic fracture, crack velocity, time measurement, digital instrumentation, fatigue (materials), stress corrosion, fracture properties

At present the micromechanical sources of dynamic toughness are not well understood; eventually they should be characterized in terms of interrelationships between microstructural properties, fractographic features, dynamic stress intensity factor, and crack velocity. From this viewpoint, quantitative studies demand, above all, a reliable technique for

[1]Physicist, Pitman-Dunn Laboratory, Frankford Arsenal, Philadelphia, Pa. 19137.
[2]Professor, Department of Materials Engineering, Drexel University, Philadelphia, Pa. 19104.

precisely determining crack velocity as a function of position on the fracture surface. The numerous methods developed to accomplish this may be divided into two general classes: (*a*) surface measurement of the trace velocity of a fracture, and (*b*) bulk measurement of the actual crack-tip velocity. Some of the more common techniques are reviewed briefly both to compile a list of the various useful approaches and to analyze the advantages and disadvantages of each. This will aid in establishing design goals for an improved system.

Surface Velocity Measurements

Surface measurement of the trace velocity of a running crack is by far the most common method of determining crack speed. In general, this approach is reasonably accurate for constant speed cracks, but the results are suspect for accelerating cracks [*1*].[3]

Ultrahigh-Speed Photography

Photoinstrumentation is ideally suited to explosive-loading experiments, particularly in ductile materials which tend to form shear lips [*2,3*]. There are many commercially available systems, which are reviewed elsewhere [*4*]. Unfortunately, the synchronization requirements are quite critical for the high-speed fractures encountered in brittle metals. The difficulties may be overcome by explosive initiation of fracture and by simply designing appropriate time delays into the initiation, exposure, and illumination functions. However, the problems appear insurmountable for high-velocity fracture from a blunt notch under quasistatic loading, and this type of failure is of the highest engineering interest. It must be also noted that this is the only currently available technique for observing multiple fractures (branch cracks) and for experimentally determining dynamic stress intensities (photoelasticity) with any precision [*5–7*].

Resistive Propagation Grids

In this widely used technique, a parallel array of resistive strips is vacuum deposited in the anticipated fracture path. The resistance of this network increases incrementally as an advancing crack ruptures successive legs, so that connection into a voltage divider produces a voltage that changes incrementally with crack advance. Some investigators adjust the lengths of successive legs to produce approximately equal voltage increments as the crack advances [*8*]. Oscilloscopic photographs are used to measure the time between successive grid breaks and can record behavior of the

[3]The italic numbers in brackets refer to the list of references appended to this paper.

fastest cracks. However, the oscilloscope sweeps only at a fixed rate; therefore, the choice must be made between either detailed information during initial crack growth or good velocity data throughout the fracture process, or else the grid spacings must be inconveniently altered. One resolution of this dilemma is to record the grid ruptures on a high-speed, wideband, multichannel tape recorder [9]. An instant replay feature is used to play back selected portions of the recording, and oscilloscope records can be made at any desired sweep speed. The long playing time of the tape recorder averts any problems with synchronization.

Capacitive Propagation Grid

A series of small parallel-plate capacitors is constructed in the fracture path by metal vapor deposition [10]. Driven by a high-frequency current, each capacitor in the array retains its charge when its source is opened by grid rupture. A relationship is established between drive frequency and crack velocity. Although this method utilizes simple inexpensive equipment, it requires advance knowledge of crack velocity and suffers from poor resolution.

Radio-Frequency Skin Effect

The tendency of high-frequency currents to travel within a few micrometres of the surface of a conductor is used to produce a fracture specimen with impedance that varies almost linearly with crack length [11]. Good records of instantaneous crack velocity may be obtained this way, but the technique requires a moderate degree of electronic expertise on the part of the user.

Bulk Velocity Measurements

In practice, bulk measurements of crack velocity are limited to ultrasonic fractography and autoresistance (electric potential) methods for which precision and resolution are quite good. Flash radiography and acoustic holography, however, seem to be good candidates for further development in this area.

Ultrasonic Fractography

By introducing ultrasonic waves into a tension fracture specimen, the maximum principal stresses that govern the direction of crack propagation are made to vary periodically in space and time [12–14]. As a consequence, the fracture surface topography exhibits waviness. The wavelength is related precisely to crack speed and the frequency of the ultrasonic modulator. Very precise local determinations of crack speed are possible using simple optical microscopy. However, the method seems to work well only for smooth noncrystallographic fractures. This seriously limits its usefulness for study of typical structural materials.

Autoresistance

This technique makes use of the fact that the electric potential between two field points in the fracture specimen varies predictably as a function of crack length. Very accurate specimen calibrations are possible using one-dimensional current paths [*15*]. Symmetric two-dimensional geometries can also be calibrated analytically using conformal mapping and conjugate function techniques [*16*]. Quite complicated two-dimensional configurations can be calibrated empirically using resistance paper for simulation of cracked specimens.

Digital Approach

The vast array of mutually compatible integrated circuits now available off-the-shelf makes it possible to conceive many specialized, low-cost measurement and control instruments. Precision measurement of crack velocity is particularly challenging because of the dynamic range required by the instrument. After reviewing the previously used methods, the following design criteria were established:

1. The operating range must cover the spectrum of crack behavior from the threshold fatigue or stress-corrosion crack to the fastest terminal velocity crack.
2. The instrument must not require synchronization.
3. The system must be user-oriented, that is, simple to operate and capable of self-testing.

Functional Description

The instrumentation system finally developed is illustrated in Fig. 1. The basic device is a 64-channel time interval meter that precisely records the time at which the crack passes 64 selected positions on the fracture specimen. Event signals are simply voltage level changes and may be transients due to rupture of fine grid wires or changes in specimen resistance as desired. A simplified functional diagram is presented in Fig. 2 to clarify data flow in the system.

Because some of the expected crack speeds approach 2 mm/μs and because it was desired to determine velocity at positions 2 mm or less apart, the clock for the timer was designed to operate at 10 mHz. This yields a

FIG. 1—*Sixty-four channel time interval meter.*

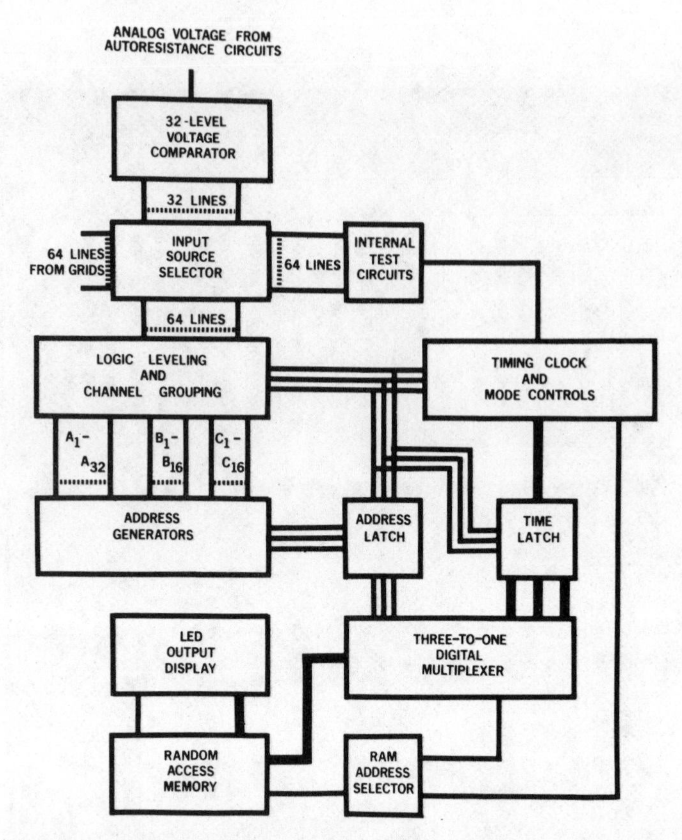

FIG. 2—*Simplified functional diagram of time interval measurement system.*

time uncertainty of ±50 ns. In addition, the condition that no synchronization be required demands that the time counter be started prior to the test and not overflow before the test is complete. This was satisfied by providing ten stages of binary-coded-decimal counting, which will not overflow for almost 17 min at 10 mHz. In addition, the clock frequency is counted down by tens to as low as 1 kHz before driving the time counter for long duration tests such as stress corrosion. At its lowest rate, the time counter will not overflow for nearly four months and records time to a precision of ±500 μs.

The 64 event signals are completely independent, but they are internally segregated for data flow into subgroups of 32 A-channels, 16 B-channels, and 16 C-channels. These events may occur at random within a subgroup but not closer than about 250 ns. Simultaneity is acceptable between subgroups. Each event signal is conditioned for logic compatibility and assigned a unique memory address that is stored temporarily in data latches in addition to the precise time of its occurrence. A readout heirarchy established in system control directs the multiplexer to transfer time and address data from the *A, B,* or *C* latches to the permanent random access memory. This feature enables three simultaneous events to be recorded. Memory is organized to store 64 words of 40 bits with a 45 ns access time. Readout is provided by a light-emitting-diode (LED) display of channel (event) number and ten digits of time data. The entire memory is interrogated simply by advancing the channel number with a front panel switch.

Another property of the system is the ability to provide voltage/time records of events characterized by monotonically changing voltages. That is the purpose of the bank of comparators. As the event signal passes a preset voltage threshold, the appropriate comparator generates an event signal which precipitates a time record in the normal fashion. The type of signal used to characterize events depends entirely on the nature of the test to be performed; some of these are discussed in the applications section.

Applications

In general the electronic capabilities of this instrument can best be exploited using precision propagation grids to generate crack position data. Many of the structural materials of interest are metal and, therefore, require electrical isolation from the grid networks. After experimenting with a variety of coatings, a phenolic varnish (MIL-V-12276) was selected because of its good adherency, craze-resistance, and fidelity to the fracture path in the base metal. It can be easily thinned with xylene or toluene to provide uniform, nonporous, dielectric substrates less than 5 μm thick.

The design philosophy of this system relies upon conductive grids rather than the more usual highly resistive grids. Vapor-deposited aluminum is suitable for this purpose; a grid 5 cm long by 250 μm wide by 500 Å thick has a resistance of approximately 90 Ω, in contrast with 30 to 50 kΩ for carbon-platinum grids. Special grid configurations have been developed for each application.

High-Velocity Cracks and Branch Cracks

A blunt-notched single-edge-notched (SEN) specimen used for investigating crack branching behavior is illustrated in Fig. 3. The parallel grid array is used to analyze main crack speed at 32 positions spaced 1 mm apart. The radial array is divided symmetrically into two groups of 16 grids to analyze upper and lower half-plane branch cracks separately. It must be emphasized that these grids do not act in concert as variable resistors, but they are completely independent position markers. Therefore, only those grid positions useful to the experiment are selected. Connection to the time interval meter is accomplished by attaching very fine

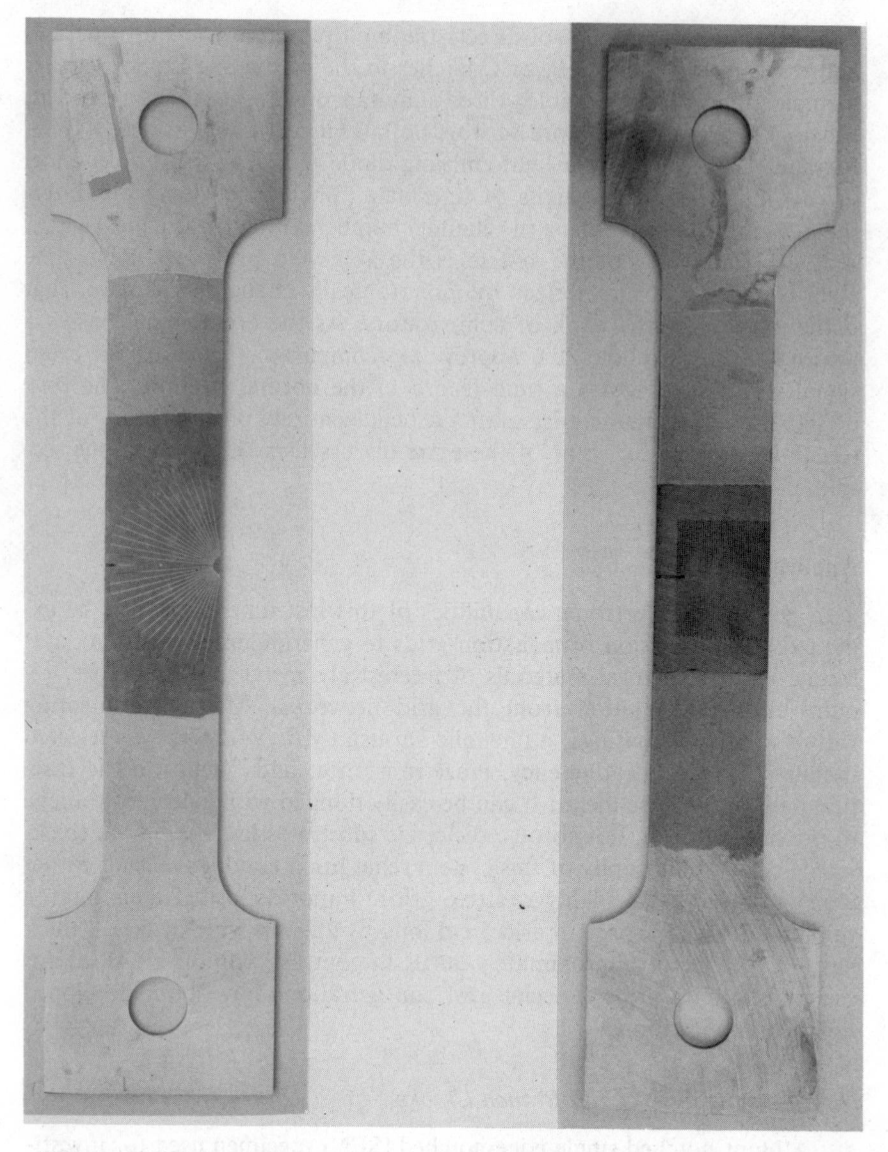

FIG. 3—*Fracture specimen showing radial and parallel grid configurations for crack velocity measurements.*

(30 AWG) kynar-insulated wire to the grids with a highly conductive silver epoxy resin, for example, Epo-Tek Type H-31. This test configuration generates an accurate profile of crack velocity over the entire velocity spectrum. In addition, the radial grid array makes it possible to analyze the dynamics of both branches of a bifurcated crack, not just the fastest.

Autoresistance

This technique takes advantage of the fact that resistance of a fracture specimen increases as the crack extends, depending entirely upon an accurate calibration of voltage as a function of crack length. Conventionally, voltage changes are recorded on an oscilloscope with time as the linear factor. Interpretation of a small photographic trace is subject to considerable error, particularly in view of the severe data compression. Considerably more precision is possible by linearizing the voltage scale of the specimen response and recording the exact time at which selected levels are reached. These thresholds can be set very accurately to correspond to particular crack lengths. With the present instrumentation, up to 32 comparators are driven in parallel by the specimen output voltage. Figure 4 illustrates two typical fracture specimen configurations and the method

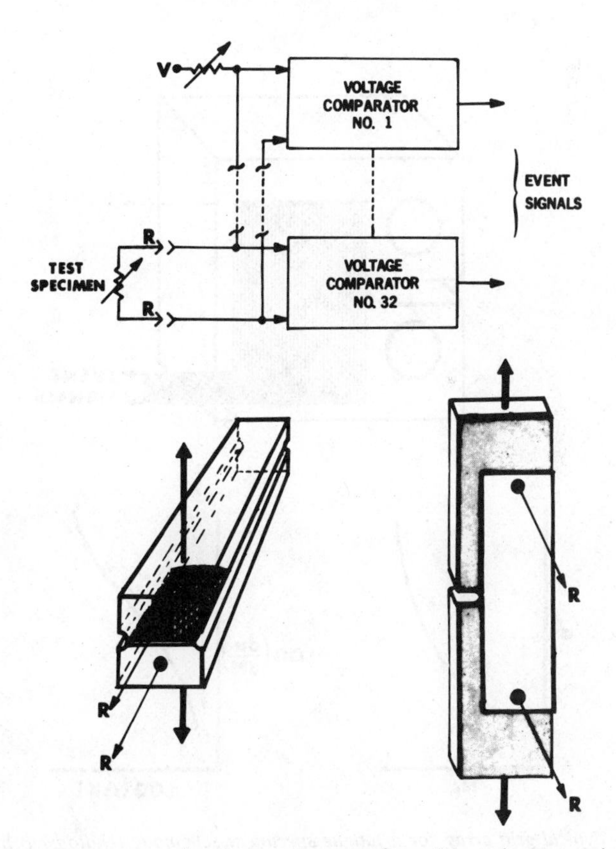

FIG. 4—*Comparator array and typical specimen configurations using autoresistance technique.*

of connection to the comparator array. As the crack advances and the voltage increases, the comparators sequentially generate event signals at present crack lengths. The time interval meter then records the elapsed time exactly as in the case of grid rupture. For conducting specimens, the autoresistance of the specimen itself may be used. For nonconducting specimens, it is necessary to vapor deposit a conducting metal film having a convenient resistivity. Even for conducting specimens, this approach is somewhat better because a uniform calibration can be developed for all specimens by depositing a sheet of the same geometry.

Fatigue Cracking Rates

The growth of a fatigue crack is monitored by vapor-depositing a parallel grid array in the anticipated fracture path as shown in Fig. 5.

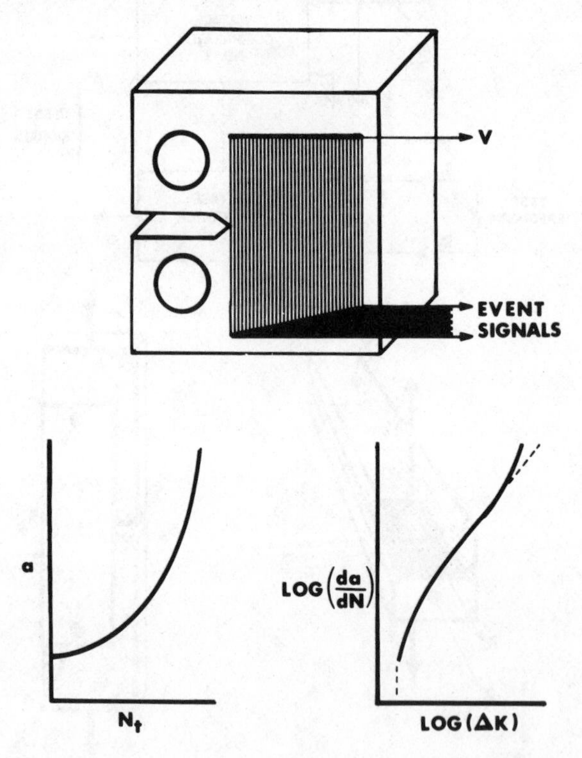

FIG. 5—*Typical grid array for a fatigue specimen; schematic relationship between crack length,* a, *and total number of cycles,* N, *and crack growth rate,* da/dN, *and stress intensity range,* ΔK.

For random loading tests, a separate load-time record must be cross-correlated with the instrument's time record of crack position. For the more common constant-load type test, it is far more practical to use the cyclic load frequency as the clock for the instrument. The memory then records the number of load cycles at grid rupture points rather than time of rupture. These data are differentiated easily to provide conventional crack growth rates as a function of stress intensity factor. The usual techniques for monitoring fatigue crack length are optical microscopy, change in specimen compliance, or automated ultrasonics [17]. The present approach has two advantages over these methods: a propagation grid can be placed on a specimen of any geometry, and the instrument will record crack progress through the entire low-cycle fatigue regime with no danger of the unstable crack outrunning the ability to record its position.

Stress Corrosion Cracking

Crack velocity data for materials in corrosive environments are obtained easily using parallel array propagation grids and the slow clock of the instrument. The multiplexing feature presently allows three simultaneous tests but is expandable if desired. In this method, specimens are prepared by applying a thin dielectric substrate to the surface being monitored. A conductive metal sheet is vapor-deposited over this, and an electrode is connected to the sheet. Another thin dielectric layer is applied over this, and the propagation grid is applied. After connecting wires to the grid lines, the entire array is coated with dielectric to insulate the grid from the environmental solution. As the corrosion crack advances, the solution itself makes electrical contact between the grid line and the vapor-deposited metal sheet, thereby generating event signals for the time interval meter. An expanded schematic view of the fracture process zone is presented in Fig. 6. Total displacement of the grid plane from the specimen surface is about 10 μm.

Simulation Testing

The applications cited subject the timer to extreme conditions in monitoring dynamic fracture behavior. Internal test circuits have been designed and utilized to assess the performance of the timer under a variety of test conditions simulating these extremes. One test circuit simulates grid rupture by a fast crack by sequentially activating the 64 event inputs precisely at 1-μs intervals with 50-ns pulses. In mutiplex testing, the first 16 A-channels are tested sequentially as before, but the last 16 A-channels are activated simultaneously with corresponding B- and C-channels. This simulates the recording of three simultaneous events per microsecond. In both test modes the entire system performed exactly as designed.

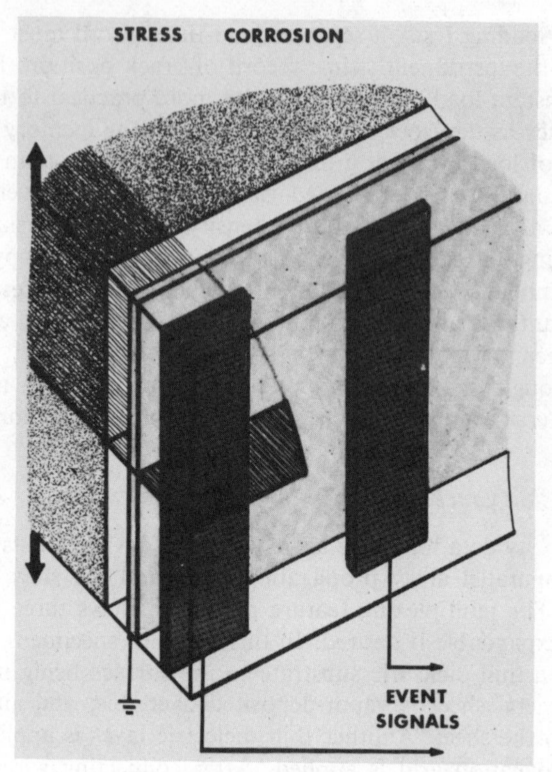

FIG. 6—*Fracture process zone showing schematically relative positions of grid components and stress corrosion crack.*

The signal generated when the autoresistance technique is employed was simulated by using an external saw-tooth generator with excellent results. If, as has been suggested, electrical noise in the actual fracture specimen may become a problem, preamplification and filtering of the input signal will be required.

This multichannel timing system was developed for utilization in a broad program on dynamic fracture and crack arrest phenomena in a variety of engineering structures. Several of the measurement techniques discussed may be required. The excellent response of the timer in the simulation tests, then, generates considerable confidence about its expected performance in the applications described, especially since the range of conditions is normally not as wide as those created by the test circuitry.

Summary

The versatility of high-speed digital techniques has been exploited to improve the precision of a number of experimental techniques for monitoring crack velocity. The ease with which complicated logical functions may be devised using standard commercial integrated circuits makes this an extremely powerful approach whenever custom instrumentation is required at modest cost. The present system costs approximately $1200 for parts and took less than 150 h to assemble. Parts lists and wiring diagrams will be available from the authors.

References

[*1*] Kerkhof, F. in *Dynamic Crack Propagation,* G. C. Sih, Ed., Noordhoff International Publishing, Leyden, The Netherlands, 1973, pp. 3–35.

[*2*] Van Elst, H. C., *Transactions,* American Institute of Mining, Metallurgical, and Petroleum Engineers, Vol. 230, 1964, pp. 460–468.

[*3*] DeGraaf, J. G. A., *Applied Optics,* Vol. 3, Nov. 1964, pp. 1223–1229.

[*4*] Hyzer, W. G., *Engineering and Scientific High-Speed Photography,* MacMillan, New York, 1963.

[*5*] Sommer, E. and Soltesz, V., *Engineering Fracture Mechanics,* Vol. 2, 1971, pp. 235–241.

[*6*] Bradley, W. B. and Kobayashi, A. S., *Experimental Mechanics,* Vol. 10, 1970, pp. 106–113.

[*7*] Bradley, W. B. and Kobayashi, A. S., *Engineering Fracture Mechanics,* Vol. 3, 1971, pp. 317–332.

[*8*] Anthony, S. R., Chubb, J. P., and Congleton, J., *Philosophical Magazine,* Vol. 22, 1970, pp. 1201–1216.

[*9*] Hahn, G. T., Hoagland, R. G., Kanninen, M. F., Rosenfield, A. R., and Sejhoha, R., "Fast Fracture and Crack Arrest in Structural Steels," Ship Structure Committee Report SSC-242, U.S. Coast Guard Headquarters, Washington, D.C., 1973.

[*10*] Carlsson, A. J. in *Recent Progress in Applied Mechanics,* Wiley, New York, 1967, pp. 153–160.

[*11*] Carlsson, J., *Transactions of the Royal Institute of Technology,* Stockholm, No. 189, *Mechanical Engineering,* Vol. 6, 1962, pp. 2–55.

[*12*] Kerkhof, F. in *Dynamic Crack Propagation,* G. C. Sih, Ed., Noordhoff International Publishing, Leyden, The Netherlands, 1973, pp. 3–35.

[*13*] Greenwood, J. H., *Journal of Material Science,* Vol. 6, 1971, pp. 390–394.

[*14*] Greenwood, J. H., *International Journal of Fracture Mechanics,* Vol. 8, June 1972, pp. 183–193.

[*15*] Burns, S. J. and Bilek, Z. J., *Metallurgical Transactions,* Vol. 4, pp. 975–984.

[*16*] Johnson, H. H. in *The Stress Analysis of Crack Handbook*, by Tada, Paris, and Irwin, Del Research Corp., Hellertown, Pa., 1973, p. 2.34.

[*17*] Weimer, R. J. and Carman, C. M., "Automated Ultrasonic Crack Follower for Fatigue Studies," Frankford Arsenal Report M73-2-1, Philadelphia, Pa., Feb. 1973.

P. B. Crosley[1] *and E. J. Ripling*[1]

Towards Development of a Standard Test for Measuring K_{Ia}

REFERENCE: Crosley, P. B. and Ripling, E. J., "**Towards Development of a Standard Test for Measuring K_{Ia},**" *Fast Fracture and Crack Arrest, ASTM STP 627,* G. T. Hahn and M. F. Kanninen, Eds., American Society for Testing and Materials, 1977, pp. 372–391.

ABSTRACT: Measurement of K_{Ia} requires the production of a run-arrest segment of crack extension in a laboratory specimen and evaluation of the stress intensity factor a short time after the crack has arrested. The crack should propagate under conditions which simulate propagation in a thick section. Progress towards meeting these requirements with tests on tapered-double-cantilever-beam specimens is described. Aspects which require further clarification are discussed.

KEY WORDS: crack propagation, stress intensity, crack arrest, measurements, crack initiation, fracture properties

- a Crack length, measured from common centerline of loading holes in a double-cantilever-beam (DCB) specimen
- a_o Initial crack length
- B Specimen thickness
- B_N Net thickness, distance between roots of face grooves
- C Specimen compliance, loading point displacement per unit load, Δ/P
- C_o Specimen compliance when $a = a_o$
- C_M Test frame or test machine compliance
- C' $= dC/da$, rate of change of specimen compliance with crack length
- C'_o C' at $a = a_o$
- Δ Displacement of loading points of specimen
- Δ_M Crosshead displacement of test machine
- E Young's modulus
- $\mathcal{G}$ Strain energy release rate
- H Beam height of DCB specimen
- K Stress intensity factor

[1]Principal scientist and director of research, respectively, Materials Research Laboratory, Inc., Glenwood, Ill. 60425.

K_{Ic} Plane-strain crack toughness
K_q Crack initiation toughness, not necessarily K_{Ic}
K_{Ia} Crack arrest toughness
m' Calibration constant of tapered DCB specimen
ξ $= a/H$
P Applied load
P_q Load at onset of fracture
P_a Crack arrest load
σ_Y Yield stress
W Distance from the common centerline of loading holes to the back end of a compact specimen

A complete methodology of crack arrest characterization would involve knowledge of the fracture resistance of a material as a function of crack velocity, and a dynamic analysis capability to permit application of this knowledge to structures of interest. A realistic consideration of the difficulties of this approach suggests the desirability of a simpler characterization of crack arrest. While a simpler approach may be less rigorous, it may well have practical engineering usefulness. The meaningfulness of crack arrest toughness, K_{Ia}, has been challenged on the basis that it does not explicitly incorporate dynamic effects—inertial loads, kinetic energy, reflected stress waves. And yet measurements of K_{Ia} have resulted in remarkably consistent values under conditions where different dynamic effects could be anticipated. These data have been reviewed elsewhere [*1*].[2] The viewpoint taken here is that K_{Ia} has sufficient promise as a meaningful and useful engineering parameter to justify further efforts to define and measure it.

Crack arrest toughness, K_{Ia}, has been tentatively defined as the value of the stress intensity factor determined a short time after a run-arrest segment of crack extension. The short time, of the order of a millisecond, is the time required for the setting up of a static condition which allows a calculation of K. To proceed from this definition to a method of K_{Ia} measurement requires consideration of a number of questions. What type of specimen should be used and how should it be loaded? What measured quantities should be used to calculate K_{Ia}? What size specimen is required to simulate a run-arrest event in a thick section? What restrictions should be imposed on crack jump length, crack front straightness, and other fracture surface features? Answers to these questions may be influenced by the type of materials to be tested. In pressure vessel steels the greatest interest in K_{Ia} is at temperatures extending upwards from the nil-ductility-transition (NDT) temperature where K_{Ia} appears to become progressively

[2]The italic numbers in brackets refer to the list of references appended to this paper.

lower relative to K_{Ic} and to initiation toughness values obtained with rapid loading rates [2]. The ability to measure K_{Ia} at higher temperatures appears to be limited, not by the greater K_{Ia} values, but by the difficulty of initiating a crack at a small enough value of K so that it can be arrested in a specimen of reasonable size.

Development of a standard method for K_{Ia} will undoubtedly involve compromises between what is most desirable and what is practical. This paper cannot give final answers to the questions just posed; hopefully, it can call attention to some of the choices which must be made and offer some guidance based on testing experience at Materials Research Laboratory, Inc. (MRL).

Current Practice

Tapered DCB Specimen

Crack arrest studies at MRL have employed contoured or tapered double cantilever beam (DCB) specimens, specimens designed so that the proportionality between applied load, P, and the stress intensity factor, K, is independent of crack length over a significant crack length range. Different individual specimen designs have been used; the most recent is shown in Fig. 1.

Compliance calibrations were carried out on specimens of 2024-T351 aluminum alloy machined in accordance with Fig. 1. It was found that the compliance, C, increased linearly with crack length for 40 mm $\leqslant a \leqslant$ 120 mm where a is the crack length measured from the common centerline of the loading holes. The experimentally derived value of dC/da gave

$$m' = \frac{EB}{8}\frac{dC}{da} = 0.728 \text{ mm}^{-1} = 1.85 \text{ in.}^{-1} \tag{1}$$

where

E = Young's modulus and
B = specimen thickness.

If the strain energy release rate, $\mathcal{G}$, is computed using the equation

$$\mathcal{G} = \frac{P^2}{2B_N}\frac{dC}{da} \tag{2}$$

application of the plane-stress relation between $\mathcal{G}$ and K,

$$K = \sqrt{\mathcal{G}E} \tag{3}$$

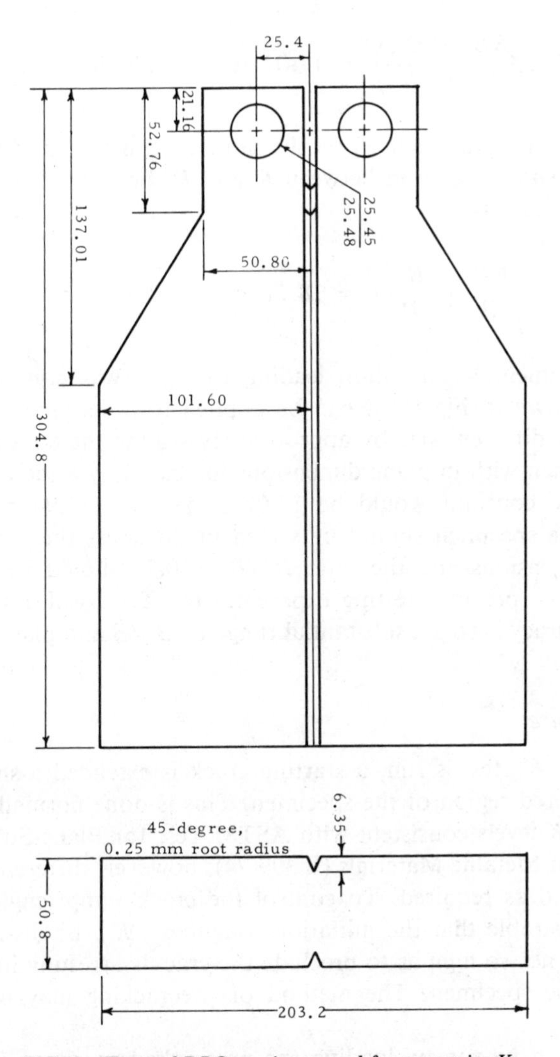

FIG. 1—*Tapered DBC specimen used for measuring* K_{Ia}.

results in the following expression for K

$$K = \frac{P}{\sqrt{B\,B_N}}\sqrt{4\,m'} \tag{4}$$

where B_N is the net specimen thickness, that is, the thickness at the crack plane between the roots of the face grooves. From the experimentally determined value of dC/da

$$\frac{KB}{P}\left(\frac{B_N}{B}\right)^{1/2} = 17.07\ \text{m}^{-1/2} = 2.72\ \text{in.}^{-1/2} \quad (5)$$

An analysis by Kanninen [*3*] on the same specimen also showed a crack length independent relation between K and P, but gave a somewhat different value, namely

$$\frac{KB}{P}\left(\frac{B_N}{B}\right)^{1/2} = 18.71\ \text{m}^{-1/2} = 2.98\ \text{in.}^{-1/2} \quad (6)$$

The experimental calibration leading to Eq 5 was conducted on the specimen shown in Fig. 1; it can be applied to a specimen of the same shape but of different size by appropriately scaling the constant in Eq 5. For a specimen with in-plane dimensions increased by a factor of 1.5, for example, the constant would be $17.07\ (1.5)^{-1/2} = 13.94\ \text{m}^{-1/2}$. Strictly speaking, the specimen should be scaled in thickness the same as in the in-plane dimensions and the ratio $B_N/B = 0.75$ should be maintained; however, from previous testing experience [*4*], Eq 5 will apply with reasonable accuracy across a substantial range of B_N/B and plate thicknesses.

Test Procedure

Before the K_{Ia} test is run, a starting crack is extended a short distance into the tapered region of the specimen. This is done normally by fatigue cracking at K levels consistent with ASTM Test for Plane-Strain Fracture Toughness of Metallic Materials (E 399-74); however, different procedures could be used as required. To control the crack jump length in the K_{Ia} test, it is desirable that the initiation toughness, K_q, be distinctly higher than K_{Ia} but not so high as to preclude the crack's arresting in the tapered region of the specimen. The method of precracking may be altered to influence K_q.

The test can be run by loading the precracked specimen in a conventional tension test machine until the first segment of unstable crack extension occurs. When possible, the test is interrupted before further crack extension occurs so that the arrested crack front can be marked by heat tinting or by some additional fatigue cracking before the specimen is broken completely in two. Because of the crack length independence feature, the crack front position (provided that the crack arrests in the tapered portion of the specimen) need not be known to calculate a value of K from a load value; however, inspection of the arrested crack front may provide information on which to base acceptance of a particular test in the same way that inspection of the fatigue crack is required to establish validity of a K_{Ic} test.

One test variable to be considered is the loading rate, which again has bearing on the K_q value. At MRL, loading rates varying from conventional slow testing speeds to rates at which a specimen is loaded to fracture in about 10 ms have been used. The general experience with pressure vessel steels has been that slower rates give values which are generally higher and more variable than are the initiation values of K_q for high loading rates [2]. Over some temperature range above NDT, static toughness increases more rapidly with temperature than does dynamic toughness, and here the use of high loading rates may be necessary to measure K_{Ia}. A major disadvantage of high testing rates is loss of the ability to interrupt the test to mark the arrested crack. Otherwise, testing at high and low rates is generally the same; similar test records interpreted in the same way are obtained.

Test Record Interpretation

In the course of the test two records are obtained: load versus displacement and load versus time. The load signal is obtained from a load cell in series with the specimen. The displacement signal is obtained from a clip gage located between knife edges mounted on the front end of the specimen. Schematic load-displacement and load-time records which might be obtained on an oscilloscope are shown in Fig. 2. They exhibit the same basic features: a linear increase in load up to the onset of unstable cracking; an abrupt decrease in load (and increase in displacement) as the crack runs; and a reloading of the specimen after the crack has arrested. The record represents a test which is stopped during this reloading. The portion of the test records corresponding with the crack propagation interval is shown as a dashed line in Fig. 2; even if a trace is obtained in this interval, it is not readily interpretable. What the test records can define is the equilibrium situation preceding rapid crack propagation and the equilibrium situation following the run-arrest seg-

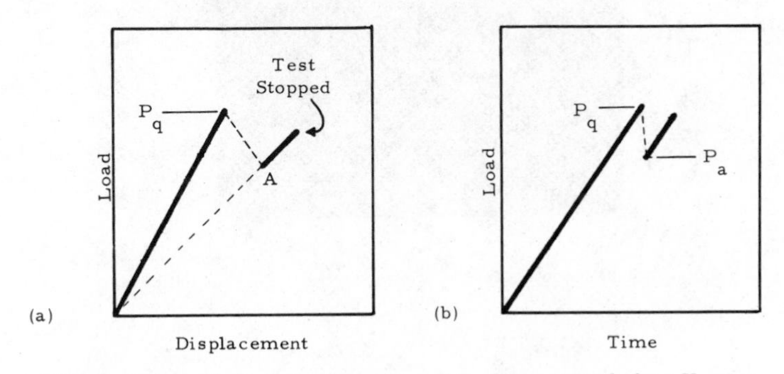

FIG. 2—*Schematic load-displacement and load-time records for a* K_{Ia} *test.*

ment of crack extension. The load P_q identified with crack initiation can be used to calculate K_q. The load P_a is used to calculate the crack arrest toughness, K_{Ia}.

The test records shown in Fig. 2 are somewhat idealized. As the crack propagates, vibrations are set up in the load cell and in the clip gage measuring specimen displacement. The clip gage vibrations are commonly of high enough amplitude to prevent close definition of point *A* in Fig. 2*a*; consequently, the load-time rather than the load-deflection curve is used to determine a value of P_a from which to calculate K_{Ia}. Load-time records from slow and fast tests are shown in Fig. 3. The load-time record from the slower test, Fig. 3*a*, is much like the idealized record, Fig. 2*b*. Some vibration in the load cell is evident, but it does not interfere with reading the crack arrest load. The test was stopped during the reloading following the single run-arrest segment. The oscilloscope record of the faster test, Fig. 3*b*, has two traces; a load-deflection trace starting from

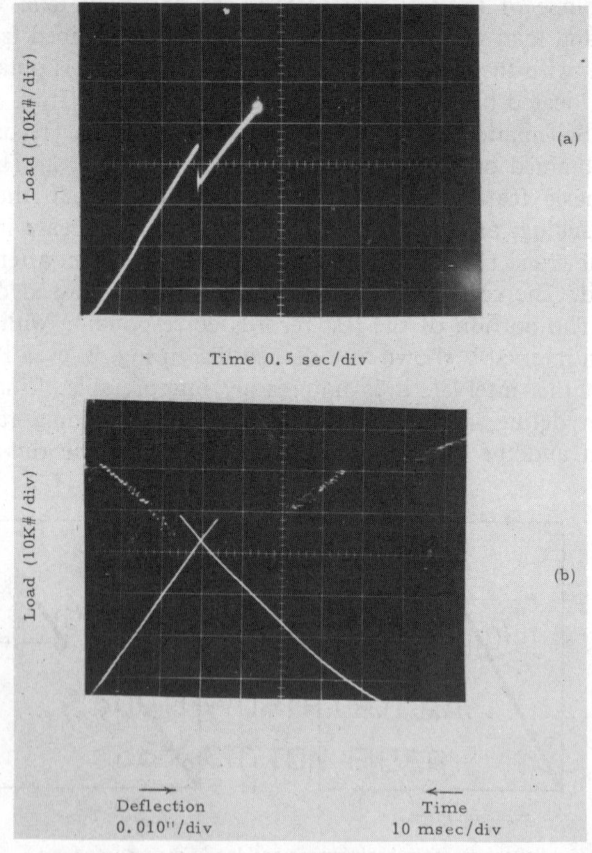

FIG. 3—*Test records from* K_{Ia} *tests of A533B. Tests conducted at two different loading rates.*

the lower left, and a load-time trace starting from the lower right. Two run-arrest segments occurred in this test, and two reloading load-displacement traces can be seen in the upper right hand quarter of the photograph. In the load-time record, which proceeds from right to left, the crack arrest load following the first run-arrest segment is not defined as clearly as in the slower test because of load cell vibrations; however, a crack arrest load can be obtained by extrapolating the reloading trace back to a point on the time axis corresponding with the run-arrest event. It might be noted that this method of extrapolation which ignores the load cell vibrations leads to a test record interpretation of the fast test which is consistent with that of the slower test. The vibrations are not necessarily less in the slower test; they are simply less apparent because of the compressed time scale.

Some justification for ignoring the load cell vibrations in reading an arrest load is furnished by an auxiliary experiment in which a strain gage was mounted on the specimen arm in a position where the output was insensitive to the crack length. This is equivalent to using the specimen itself as a load cell. Figure 4 shows a record from such a strain gage, along with a record from the in-line load cell, obtained in the course of a crack arrest test. It is evident that the vibrations from the load cell are much more pronounced than those from the strain gage mounted on the specimen. It is considered that a mean value of load cell output provides an appropriate estimate of crack arrest load.

The test record in Fig. 3*b* illustrates a phenomenon which we have observed regularly in tests on pressure vessel steels but not on some other materials, for example, not with adhesively bonded specimens. When the crack advances in successive run-arrest segments, initiation loads and arrest loads have been observed to increase progressively. Because of the crack length independence feature of the test specimen, this indicates that K_q and K_{Ia} are increasing likewise. While it is not surprising that K_q measured on a rough arrested crack would be greater than the value measured with a smooth fatigue crack, the continued increase in K_q on successive initiations and the progressive increase in arrest toughness is not well understood. There is a tendency with increasing crack length for the crack surfaces to become rougher and for the crack plane to deviate from the minimum section defined by the side grooves. Whether this is a sufficient explanation is not clear. As a practical expedient and in order to define K_{Ia} in a conservative fashion, evaluations have been limited to the first run-arrest segment in a test, that is, to the arrest of a crack initiated from a fatigue crack.

Controlling Crack Direction

A serious problem with DCB specimens, whether uniform or tapered, is a tendency for the crack to veer out of the plane of symmetry and break

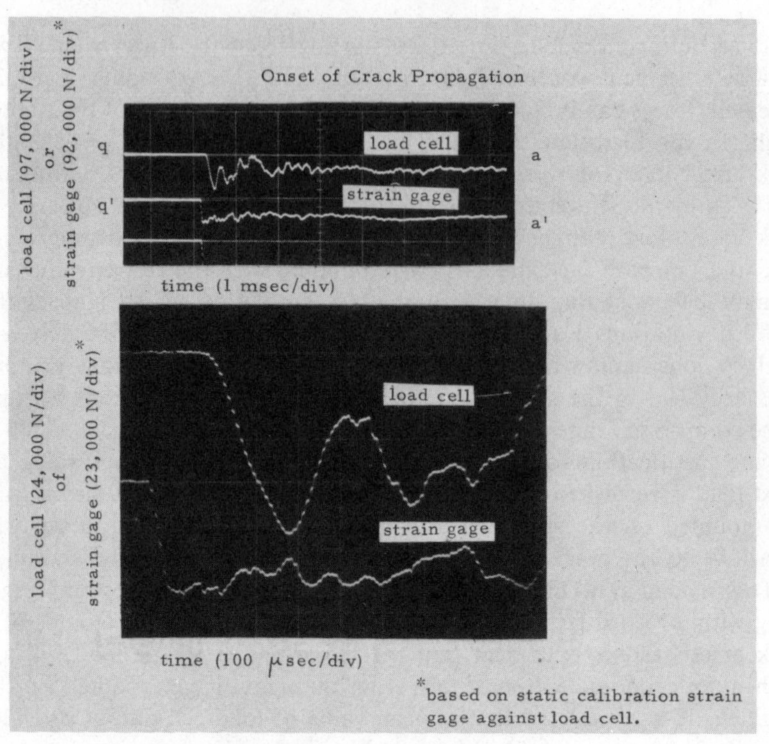

FIG. 4—*Output of load cell and strain gage mounted on specimen arm over a run-arrest segment of crack extension. The levels* q *and* q' *define arrest levels. Bottom photograph is the same as top one with expanded scales.*

off an arm of the specimen. Face grooves may be used with either specimen to help direct the crack, but there are objections to using deep grooves. The first of these is that face grooves may produce a crack tip stress state which varies through the thickness; and the greater the face groove depth, the greater is the uncertainty arising from this cause. The second concern, which must be ultimately answered by experiment, is the criterion for adequate plane-strain constraint in a face grooved specimen; that is, whether the gross thickness, the net thickness, or a combination of the two, should be used in establishing the thickness required for measuring plane-strain toughness values. Since net thickness is expected to be important to this criterion, deep face grooves are expected to require larger specimens.

In light of the complexities associated with the use of deep face grooves, it is preferable to control crack direction by modifying the in-plane dimensions of the specimen. A feature of crack line loaded specimens not present in tension loaded specimens is a large bending stress parallel to the crack plane. It is reasonable to attribute the tendency of the crack not to extend straight in the former specimen type to the presence of this bending stress, and, hence, to seek better crack direction control through a design which reduces the bending stress. This consideration led to the specimen design shown in Fig. 1, a specimen more steeply tapered than the ones used previously. The specimen worked well; that is, cracks propagated straight, with A533B steel from one source; however, with material from another source crack branching occurred in a majority of specimens. Whether the crack branching was peculiar to the material or traceable to the specimen design has not yet been ascertained. Also, whether or not the material which exhibited crack branching will be typical of pressure vessel steels to which the method is to be applied is not yet known. There is evidence that the crack branching can be avoided by the use of deeper face grooves [5], but, for reasons discussed previously, it would be desirable to find another solution, if possible.

Specimen Measurement Capacity

Investigation of specimen measurement capacity involves consideration of the quantities: K_{Ia}, K_q, and the ratio K_q/K_{Ia}. In order that K_{Ia} be acceptable as a thick section (plane-strain) toughness parameter a requirement of the type

$$B \geq \alpha \left(\frac{K_{Ia}}{\sigma_Y}\right)^2 \tag{7}$$

must ultimately be established. If different face groove depths are used, the value of α may also depend on B_N or B_N/B. The equation assumes that the in-plane dimensions of the specimen are large enough that the thickness, B, is the limiting critical dimension. The yield stress, σ_Y, may be a static value or a corrected value reflecting the strain rate at the plastic zone boundary of a running crack. Following ASTM Method E 399 the value of α would be 2.5; some evidence has been presented that a value $\alpha = 1.0$ may be adequate. For a 50.8-mm-thick specimen, with $\sigma_Y = 550$ MN/m^2, the two criteria give maximum values of about 80 and 125 MN/m$^{3/2}$, respectively. The comprehensive testing required to establish a value of α experimentally has not been carried out.

In order to measure K_{Ia}, it is necessary to initiate cracking at some level of toughness, K_q. For the specimen shown in Fig. 1, a limitation on the value of K_q is imposed by plastic bending of the specimen arms which occurs first at the start of the taper. The criterion for plastic bending based on Eq 5 and a strength-of-materials calculation of bending stress is

$$\left(\frac{K_q}{\sigma_Y}\right) \geq 53.6 \text{ mm} \tag{8}$$

As long as an appropriate criterion for K_{Ia}, Eq 7, is met, there may not be a fundamental objection to some plastic bending prior to initiation; however, there is some physical limit to the amount by which K_q can exceed the condition of Eq 8. Moreover, if a fast loading rate is employed for the purpose of lowering K_q, the intervention of plastic bending will diminish $\dot{K}$ and, thus, nullify the fast loading rate. Lastly, the material which showed crack branching also had high initiation toughness values, so there is at least a possibility that high K_q values may promote the tendency for cracks to branch.

For a given specimen design, the ratio K_q/K_{Ia} along with the testing machine stiffness determines how far the crack will jump before arresting. With a pin loaded specimen there is a practical limit below which the test machine compliance cannot be reduced. For the test set up at MRL, it was found that with K_q/K_{Ia} greater than about 1¼ the crack would not arrest in the tapered section of the specimen.

These considerations illustrate the desirability, if not the necessity, of lowering the K_q value in order to measure K_{Ia} above the NDT temperature. One method, already alluded to, is to employ fast loading rates where the specimen is loaded to fracture in 1 to 10 ms. A second device, which was employed by MRL [2], is to impose a temperature gradient along the length of the specimen so that a crack is initiated in a colder region and propagates into a warmer one. Perhaps the most promising method is to use a brittle crack starter, either initiate the crack from a brittle weld or from a welded-on starter section of a material of lower toughness than the test section. Experiments along these lines are being carried out at MRL.

General Considerations

Experimental study of crack arrest, either through measurement of K_{Ia} or by means of some other analysis scheme, requires that a run-arrest segment of crack extension be produced in a laboratory specimen. Service conditions may involve crack initiation in a region of low toughness followed by propagation under increasing K until the crack arrests in a region of increasing toughness. This sequence of events could be set up in a laboratory test, and, in fact, a limited number of crack arrest tests have been run on single-edge-notched (SEN) specimens in which electron beam welds were used to produce a low-toughness crack starter material [6]. A more suitable laboratory test, however, is one in which crack arrest occurs as a result of decreasing K with crack length as the crack propagates. The tapered DCB specimen discussed previously works in this way, but other specimens could also be used. For some specimen types a very stiff loading system, for example, wedge loading, may be needed to produce a sufficiently rapid decrease in K. For evaluating K_{Ia} the loading system must be such as to accomodate instrumentation which allows determination of K a short time after the run arrest segment of crack extension. Before discussing alternative specimens for measuring K_{Ia}, it is appropriate to call attention to some features required of any specimen which is to be used. In order that crack arrest occur under conditions which simulate thick section behavior, edge effects must be minimized. This requirement is met by the use of face grooves.

Face Grooves

In considering face grooves it is convenient to think of the stress factor intensity factor, K, as a quantity which may vary along the crack front and the material's resistance to crack propagation as also varying along the crack front. Even if K is constant across the crack front in a smooth sided specimen, fracture resistance is not. Material near the specimen edges where plane-stress conditions govern plastic zone formation is more resistant to fracture than the central region where, if the specimen is thick enough, plane strain prevails. Thus, there is an inherent three dimensional problem even in the absence of face grooves. In measuring K_{Ic} this three-dimensional aspect is circumvented by making the specimen thick enough so that crack motion in the central plane strain position of the crack front can be detected in the absence of significant crack extension near the edges of the specimen. This situation is not acceptable for K_{Ia} evaluation. Were the arrested crack front to reveal that crack motion occurred only in the center region of the specimen while the crack remained pinned at the edges, it would be natural to conclude that the more resistant plane-stress portion of the crack front, not the plane-strain portion, dominated the crack arrest.

The principal purpose of face grooves is to eliminate undue edge influence. A simple way of viewing their effect is as follows: stress intensification at the root of the face grooves enhances K in this region, and stress triaxiality induced by the side grooves may locally reduce the fracture resistance. With an appropriate face groove configuration, therefore, edge material could be made to fracture with about the same ease as material in the central portion of the specimen. The term "ease" here does not have a precise definition; nonetheless, it should be possible to assess the efficacy of the face grooves by examination of the arrested crack front. The face grooves would be judged too severe if the arrested crack front showed that the crack at the surface (that is, at the root of the face grooves) extended ahead of the center portion, and inadequate if the crack lagged at the surface. Experience at MRL has shown that relatively shallow (B_N/B = ¾) but fairly sharp (0.25 mm root radius) face grooves produce a reasonably straight crack front in pressure vessel steels. Figure 5 shows the configuration of some arrested cracks as revealed by heat tinting or fatigue cracking.

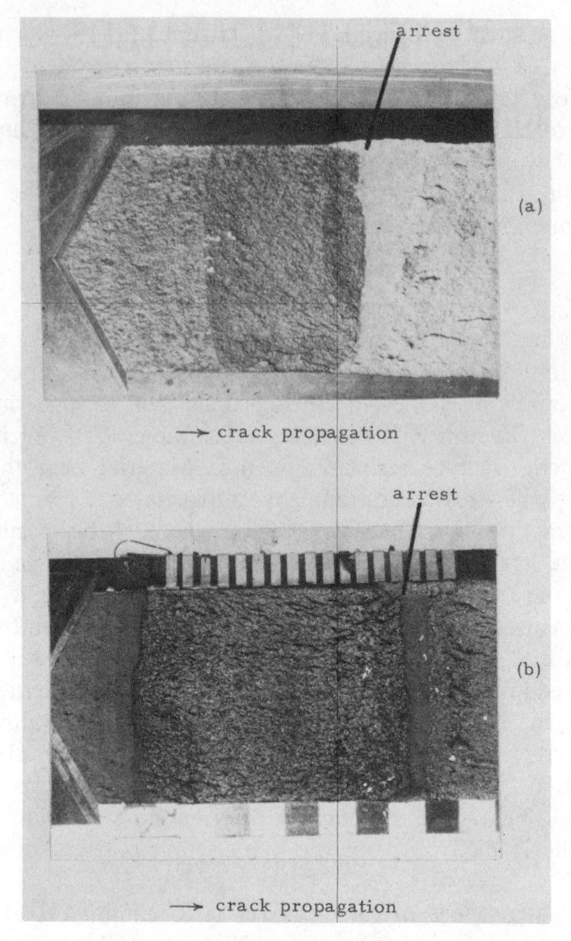

FIG. 5—*Fracture surface of two specimens of A533B steel tested at 10°F (NDT). In* (a) *the arrested crack was marked by heat tinting, in* (b) *by fatigue cracking.*

The use of face grooves introduces some analysis uncertainty, but, if the grooves are shallow, the uncertainty is not objectionably large. Two extremes may be considered. First, the effect of the face grooves in increasing K may be confined to a small region near the root of the grooves, so that K in the central portion is the same as it would be in an ungrooved specimen. The other extreme is that K is elevated uniformly across the crack front in which case the K for the face grooved specimen would be $(B/B_N)^{1/2}$ times the value for an ungrooved specimen. The practice of MRL (which is reflected by using B_N rather than B in Eq 2) has been to use the average K across the net section, which, for $B_N/B = 3/4$ can result in over estimate of no more than 15 percent. The potential error with deeper grooves is, of course, greater.

The function of face grooves is to eliminate plane-stress fracture influence of material near the edges of the specimen. This by no means implies that face grooves reduce the specimen thickness required to obtain plane-strain fracture conditions. A net thickness which is large relative to a calculated plastic zone should be a formal requirement, exactly how large must be ascertained experimentally.

Controlling Crack Jump Length

One concern in selecting a specimen for measuring K_{Ia} is the ratio K_{Ia}/K_q as a function of crack jump length. If K_{Ia}/K_q does not drop sufficiently rapidly as the crack extends, the possibility of a crack's arresting is diminished. The ratio, K_{Ia}/K_q is evaluated readily. For any specimen

$$K \alpha P \sqrt{C'} \tag{9}$$

where $C' = dC/da$, the rate of change of specimen compliance with crack length. The load may be considered to be applied by a crosshead displacement Δ_M operating across a load train with compliance C_M and the specimen with compliance C. Then, $P = \Delta_M/(C + C_M)$ and

$$K \alpha \Delta_M \frac{\sqrt{C'}}{C + C_M} \tag{10}$$

Assuming that the value of Δ_M after crack arrest is equal to the value at the onset of crack propagation

$$\frac{K_{Ia}}{K_q} = \sqrt{\frac{C'}{C'_0}} \left(\frac{C_0 + C_M}{C + C_M} \right) \tag{11}$$

where C_0 and C'_0 are evaluated for the initial crack position, a_0, and C and C' are calculated for a hypothetical arrest crack position, a. Fixed-grip loading conditions are associated with $C_M = 0$, fixed-load with $C_M \rightarrow \infty$. Actual test conditions would fall somewhere in between. Testing experience at MRL suggests that a value of $C_M = 1.5 \times 10^{-8}$ m/N is a reasonable test machine compliance with a pin-loaded specimen.

Figure 6 shows three specimens with comparable dimensions, the tapered DCB specimen, a uniform DCB specimen, and a compact specimen. The specimens are taken to be 50.4 mm thick and assumed to be made of steel, $E = 2.07 \times 10^5$ MN/m^2. For the tapered DCB specimen with $a_0 = 40$ mm, the initial compliance is $C_0 = 1.81 \times 10^{-9}$ m/N; and the rate of compliance change, which is independent of crack length, is $C' =$

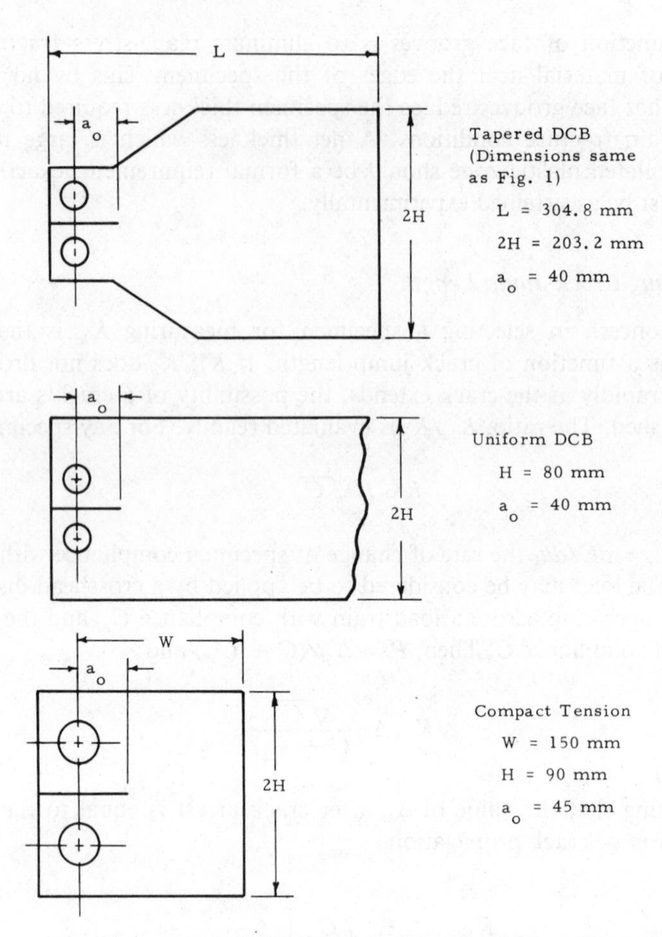

FIG. 6—*Candidate specimens for* K_{Ia} *measurement evaluated for crack arresting ability.*

5.55×10^{-8} N^{-1}. The values lead to the curves for K_{Ia}/K_q shown in Fig. 7. For fixed-load loading conditions K_{Ia}/K_q is, of course, constant. For any finite machine compliance, the curve lies between constant K_{Ia}/K_q and the fixed-grip curve. For $C_M = 1.5 \times 10^{-8}$ m/N, K_{Ia}/K_q drops to about 0.73 over the tapered region of the specimen, in reasonable agreement with the observed measurement ability of the specimen in MRL's test setup.

For the uniform DCB specimen compliance calibration results of Mostovoy et al [4] were used. These can be written

$$C = \frac{8}{EB} [(\xi + 0.6)^3 + \xi] \tag{12}$$

and

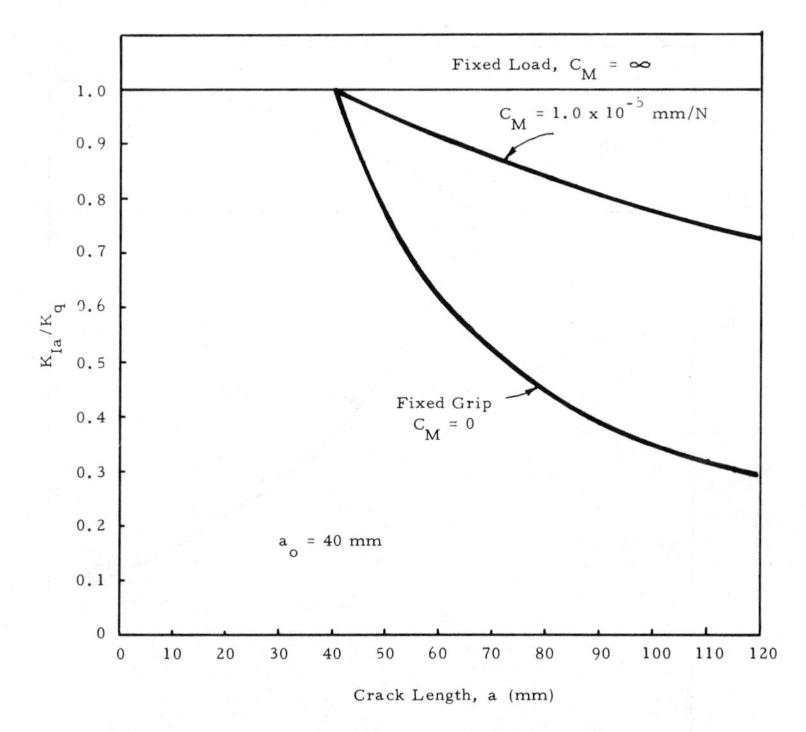

FIG. 7—*Decrease in* K *with crack length in tapered DCB specimen of Fig. 6.*

$$C' = \frac{8}{EBH}[3(\xi + 0.6)^2 + 1] \tag{13}$$

where $\xi = a/H$, the crack length divided by the specimen height. Taking $a_0 = 40$ mm in a specimen with $H = 80$ mm, the curves plotted in Fig. 8 were obtained. Under fixed-grip conditions the drop in K_{Ia}/K_q is comparable to that in the tapered DCB specimen. Under fixed-load conditions, K_{Ia}/K_q (which is not shown) increases continuously. For $C_M = 1.5 \times 10^{-8}$ m/N, it increases somewhat over the first 120 mm of crack extension. This indicates that particular attention to test machine stiffness, and possibly the use of wedge loading, may be required to measure K_{Ia} with this specimen.

For the compact specimen, the calibration

$$K = \frac{P}{B\sqrt{W}} f(a/W) \tag{14}$$

where

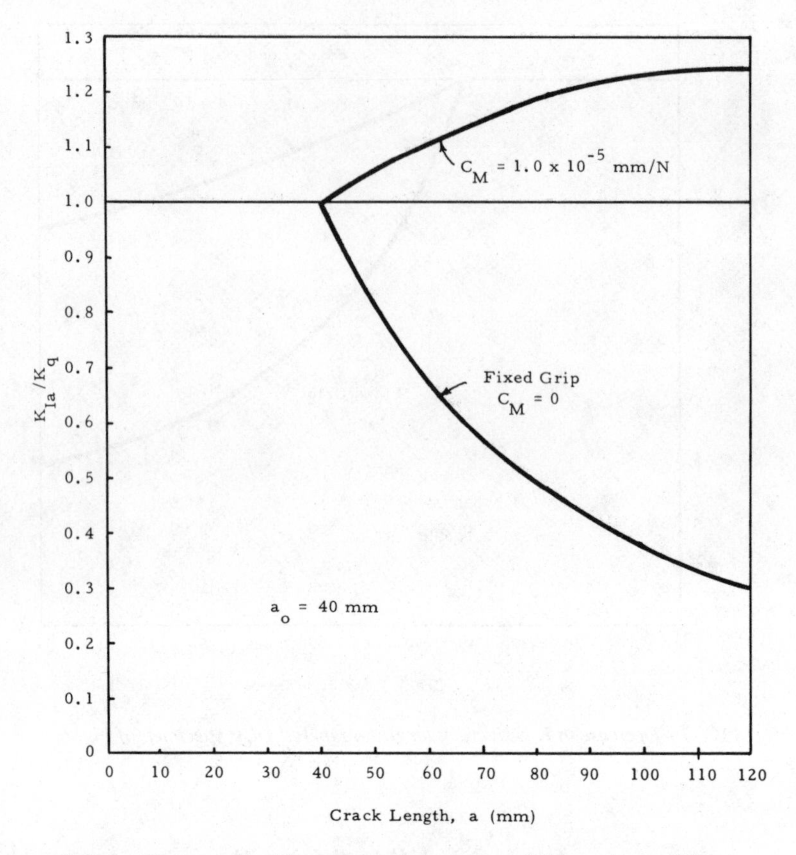

FIG. 8—*Change in* K *with crack length in uniform DCB specimen of Fig. 6.*

$$f\left(\frac{a}{W}\right) = 29.6\left(\frac{a}{W}\right)^{1/2} - 185.5\left(\frac{a}{W}\right)^{3/2} + 655.7\left(\frac{a}{W}\right)^{5/2}$$

$$- 1017.0\left(\frac{a}{W}\right)^{7/2} + 638.9\left(\frac{a}{W}\right)^{9/2}$$

was used. Based on this equation

$$\sqrt{C'} = \left(\frac{2}{BWE}\right)^{1/2} f(a/W), \tag{15}$$

and

$$C - C_0 = \frac{2}{BE}\int_{a_0/W}^{a/W} f^2(\theta)d\theta \tag{16}$$

The dimensions chosen were $W = 150$ mm, $H = 90$ mm, and $a_0 = 45$ mm corresponding to $a_0/W = 0.3$. The initial compliance C_0 was estimated from Eq 12. Curves of K_{Ia}/K_q are shown in Fig. 9. Under fixed-grip conditions K_{Ia}/K_q drops fairly rapidly with crack length; but for an assumed machine compliance, $C_M = 1.5 \times 10^{-8}$ m/N, K_{Ia}/K_q increases faster with crack length than for the uniform DCB specimen.

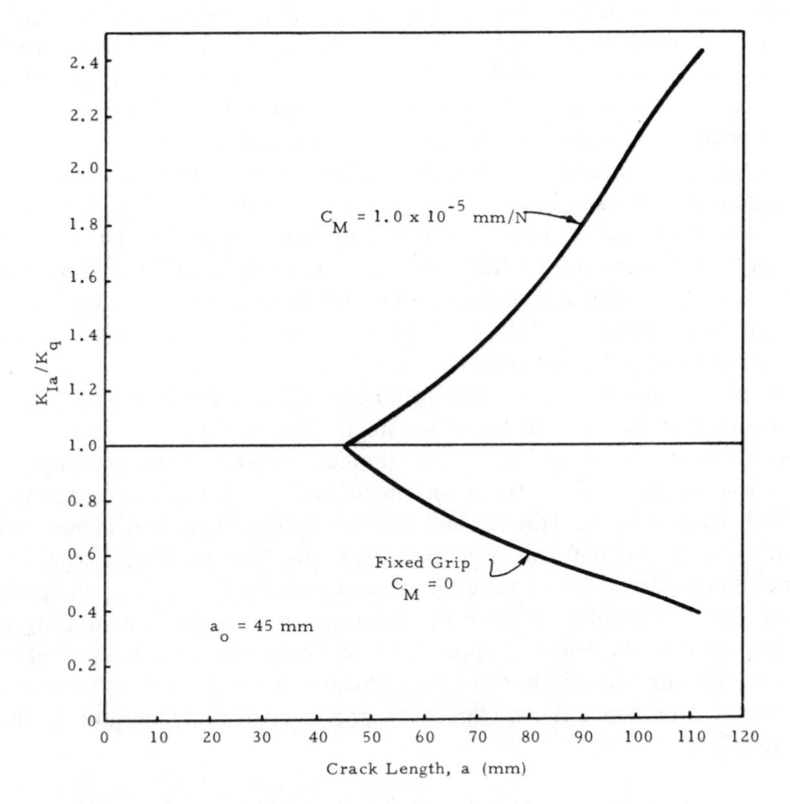

FIG. 9—*Change in* K *with crack length for compact specimen of Fig. 6.*

Summary

The study of the fracture behavior of pressure vessel steels at MRL has led, over the years, to the development of procedures for measuring crack arrest toughness, K_{Ia}. The measurements are normally made with contoured or tapered DCB specimens, having sharp but shallow face grooves. The face grooves are required to produce a reasonably straight arrested crack front. The latest tapered DCB design is an improvement over earlier ones, in controlling crack direction; however, it cannot be guaranteed that the arrested crack will always be flat and confined to the minimum section defined by the face grooves. The K_{Ia} calculation is based on the static condition a short time after a run-arrest segment of crack extension; and the load corresponding to this time is inferred readily from a load-time record obtained during the course of the test. Other specimen types should be usable for measuring K_{Ia}. Two types considered—the uniform DCB specimen and the compact specimen—appear to have the disadvantage of a lower capability for crack arrest under pin loading. Increased stiffness in the loading train achieved by wedge loading could avoid this disadvantage, but whether or not wedge loading lends itself to instrumentation for defining the crack arrest load remains an open question. In order to make K_{Ia} measurements above the NDT temperature, the temperature range of greatest interest, the major problem is to initiate cracking. Some means for reducing the crack initiation toughness have been described in early reports [*1–3, 7*]. These include the use of fast loading rates, or thermal and metallurgical gradients or both. The latter might be done by welding on a brittle front end, by electron beam melting and quenching of the metal where crack initiation is to occur, or by depositing an embrittled bead as is done by NDT testing. The latter two require the use of sharply machined notches.

In spite of the fact that some problems still remain in K_{Ia} testing, a variety of materials can be tested satisfactorily using the specimen whose dimensions are shown in Fig. 1. The simpliest method for suppressing the initiation toughness for low- or intermediate-strength steels is by the use of high loading rates. This method has the disadvantage that it may not be possible to permanently stop the crack after the run-arrest segment. A permanent arrest is not necessary for evaluating K_{Ia} on tapered specimens, but it is helpful to mark the position of arrest by heat tinting or fatigue so that the fracture appearance at arrest can be examined after testing. The arrest position can be approximated for a fast test, however, by use of compliance if the clipgage is prevented from flying out during the test.

Acknowledgments

This paper describes work done for the Electric Power Research Institute (EPRI) on Contract No. RP 303-1. Comments by Dr. K. E. Stahlkopf and, more recently, Dr. T. U. Marston, of EPRI, were helpful. The many discussions the authors had with Professor G. R. Irwin and Dr. S. Mostovoy are gratefully acknowledged.

References

[*1*] Crosley, P. B. and Ripling, E. J., *Journal of Pressure Vessel Technology, Transactions*, American Society of Mechanical Engineers, Vol. 97, Series J, No. 3, Nov. 1975, pp. 291–298.

[2] Crosley, P. B. and Ripling, E. J., *Nuclear Engineering and Design,* Vol. 17, No. 1, pp. 32–45.
[3] Hahn, G. T., Gehlen, P. C., Hoagland, R. G., Kanninen, M. F., Popelar, C., and Rosenfield, A. R., "Critical Experiments, Measurements and Analyses to Establish a Crack Arrest Methodology for Nuclear Pressure Vessel Steels," BMI-1939, Battelle-Columbus Laboratories, Columbus, Ohio.
[4] Mostovoy, S., Crosley, P. B., and Ripling, E. J., *Journal of Materials,* Vol. 2, No. 3, Sept. 1967, pp. 661–681.
[5] Rosenfield, A. R., private communication.
[6] Crosley, P. B. and Ripling, E. J., "Crack Arrest in an Increasing K-Field," *Proceedings of the Third International Conference on Pressure Vessel Technology, Part II, Materials, Fabrication and Inspection,* 1973.

G. C. Angelino [1]

Influence of the Geometry on Unstable Crack Extension and Determination of Dynamic Fracture Mechanics Parameters

REFERENCE: Angelino, G. C., **"Influence of the Geometry on Unstable Crack Extension and Determination of Dynamic Fracture Mechanics Parameters,"** *Fast Fracture and Crack Arrest, ASTM STP 627,* G. T. Hahn and M. F. Kanninen, Eds., American Society for Testing and Materials, 1977, pp. 392–407.

ABSTRACT: The dynamic fracture toughness of the high-strength steel VCN-100 (UNI 38 NiCrMo4) is derived from tests on TPB 9 (three-point-bend) specimens. A wide range of crack velocities was obtained by changing the ER (energy ratio) of the specimen at crack instability; the crack velocity was evaluated from load versus time records during crack propagation. The results show a dependence of K_{ID} on crack velocity in good agreement with literature data.

KEY WORDS: crack propagation, dynamic properties, fracture strength, fractures (materials), fast fracture, energy ratio (geometry), velocity, bending, high strength steels, fracture properties

The length L of a notched specimen can be changed to vary the specimen energy ratio (ER) at load instability. Changes in ER, associated with the elastic energy (w_s) available to produce fracture work with respect to the fracture work (w_f) to be done, can be used, as shown in detail in Appendix I, to induce small or large crack propagations in a specimen. The effectiveness of the method was tested on aluminum alloy (AA6351-T6), both via the experimental determination of the specimen length L_c, at which corresponds the just complete fracture of the specimen, and via the experimental determination of the materials dynamic toughness [*1,2*];[2] the test technique proved also to be an interesting alternative to Battelle

[1]Head, Materials Engineering Section, Mechanics Division, Centro Informazioni Studi Esperienze, Segrate Milano, Italy

[2]The italic numbers in brackets refer to the list of references appended to this paper.

double-cantilever-beam (DCB) testing [3,5] for the dynamic characterization of a material.

This paper describes the testing procedure and the dynamic toughness results for the high-strength steel VCN-100 (UNI 38 NiCrMo4), very similar, in chemical composition and mechanical properties, to the more well-known SAE 4340 (Table 1 and Fig. 1). The results of the work suggests the idea of an intimate relationship between the ER of the specimen and the crack velocity and confirm the usefulness of the method for the dynamic characterization of a material.

Experimental Procedure

Material

Measurements of dynamic fracture toughness, K_{ID}, are performed on VCN-100 in two heat-treatment conditions: (1) annealed (as received, σ_{ys} = 390 MN m^{-2}) and (2) quenched and tempered (Q&T): oil quenched at 860°C and tempered at 380°C for 1 h (σ_{ys} = 1360 MN m^{-2}).

Specimens

Specimens are machined to a thickness B = 5 mm, width W = 10 mm and lengths L between 50 and 150 mm; longer specimens are obtained by welding two extensions of the same material. The crack length a is varied between 1 and 5.5 mm; all the cracks are fatigued according to the rules of the American Society for Testing and Materials (ASTM).

Loading Procedure and Test Equipment

The specimens are tested in three-point-bend (TPB) on a 0.1 MN test machine; the compliance of the test system, with respect to the specimen one, allows to neglect the energy released by the loading system during the crack propagation. The specimens are slowly loaded, at different velocities, to keep constant, irrespective of their length, the derivative of bending moment versus time ($\dot{M}$ = 1.2 Nm/s), the load-midspan displacement is recorded through the main load cell and through a flexometer on a X-Y recorder. The load versus time evolution during crack propagation is measured by an high-frequency load cell (cutoff frequency $\leqq$ 0.5 MHz) and a transient recorder (Fig. 2). After the crack propagation the specimen is unloaded to record its final compliance.

Post-Fracture Examinations

The specimens are heat tinted and completely fractured, the crack propagation area is measured on a toolmakers optical microscope with X-Y

TABLE 1—*Chemical composition of VCN-100 and SAE 4340.*

Material	C, %	Mn, %	Cr, %	Mo, %	Ni, %	Si, %	P, %	S, %	Fe, %
VCN 100 (UNI 38NiCrMo4)	0.32 to 0.34	0.50 to 0.80	0.70 to 1.00	0.15 to 0.25	0.70 to 1.00	≤0.40	≤0.035	≤0.035	balance
SAE 4340	0.38 to 0.43	0.60 to 0.80	0.70 to 0.90	0.20 to 0.30	1.65 to 2.00	0.20 to 0.35	≤0.040	≤0.040	balance

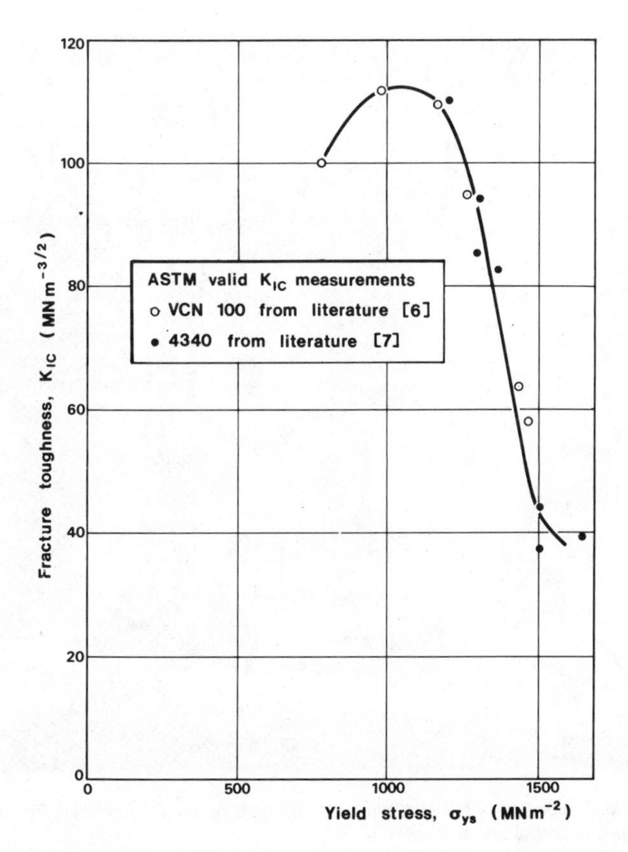

FIG. 1—*Fracture toughness of high-strength steels VCN-100 and SAE 4340, ASTM valid measurements from literature.*

displacements (0.01 mm accuracy). The fracture surface characteristics of some specimens are also examined at the scanning electron microscope (SEM).

Analysis of Measurements

Dynamic Toughness

The dynamic toughness K_{ID} is derived through

$$K_{ID} = \sqrt{E' G_D} \tag{1}$$

where

$E' = E/(1 - \nu^2)$ = Young's modulus corrected for plane strain,
ν = Poisson's ratio of the material, and

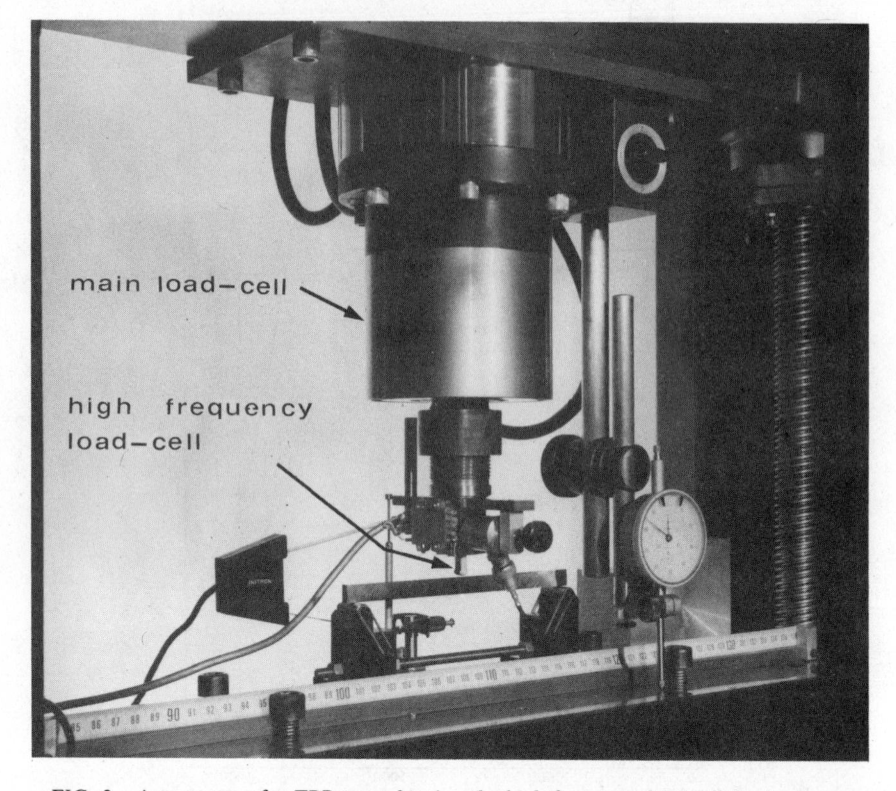

FIG. 2—*Arrangement for TPB tests showing the high-frequency load-cell for load versus time records during fast crack propagation.*

G_D = energy per unit area released during the crack propagation

$$G_D = \frac{\Delta w}{\Delta s} \tag{2}$$

where

Δw = total energy released from the specimen during crack propagation and

Δs = associated crack area.

Δw is calculated from the load-midspan displacement record as the difference between the potential elastic energy before crack instability (*ABC* triangle area, Fig. 3) and the residual elastic energy at crack arrest (*ACD* area). The use of Eq 2 is based on the assumption, suggested by the dynamic load versus time records, that the energy spent as damping energy in the specimen after the crack arrest, is small in comparison with the

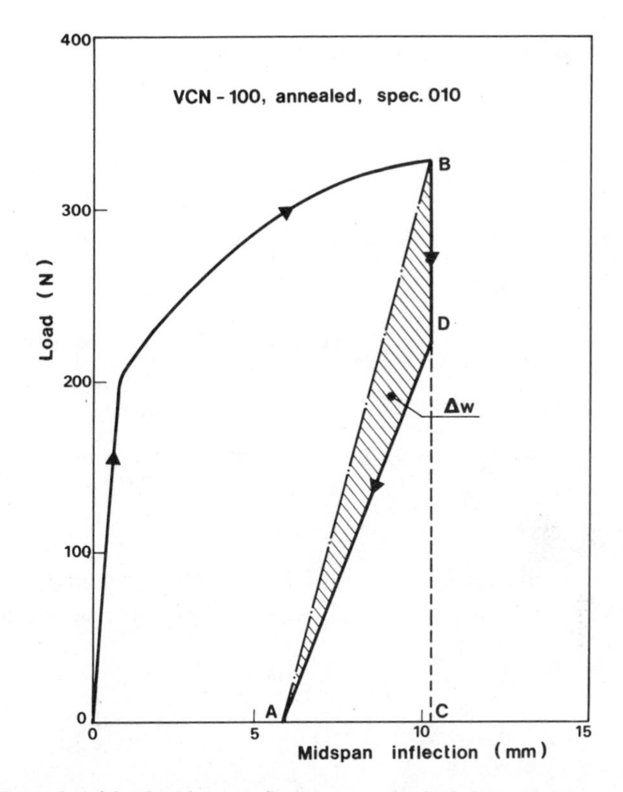

FIG. 3—*Example of load-midspan inflection record, shaded area represents the elastic energy released during crack propagation.*

energy involved in the fracture process; moreover, Δw is evaluated as a difference between two static energy levels: all the problems connected with the kinetic energy recovery, as fracture energy during crack propagation or elastic energy after the crack arrest, therefore are circumvented. ΔS in Eq 2 is evaluated from the graphic presentation of fracture results; only the area which actually corresponds to the fast crack propagation is taken into account.

Crack Velocity

The average crack velocity is evaluated from the crack propagation length divided by the crack propagation time; the first determined from post-fracture examinations, the second from load versus time records.

The propagation time is assumed to correspond to the linear unloading of the specimen, as indicated by t in Fig. 4; after the crack propagation time the records show the onset of superimposed transverse and longitudinal oscillations into the specimen.

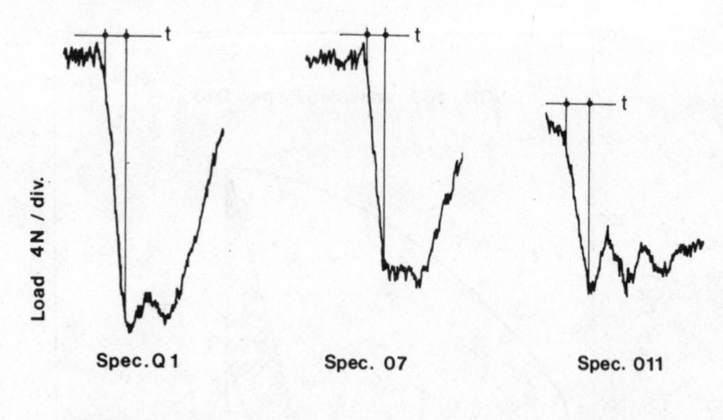

FIG. 4—*Examples of dynamic load versus time records.*

Static Toughness

The static toughness K_{Ic} at fracture initiation is calculated, for the specimens which satisfy the rule $B \geqslant 2.5\ (K_{Ic}/\sigma_{ys})^2$, from the equation

$$K_{Ic} = Y \frac{6M\sqrt{a}}{BW^2} \tag{3}$$

where

M = bending moment at load instability and
Y = dimensionless function of (a/w) and (L/W) [8].

Since the test procedure slightly deviates from ASTM rules and Y values are interpolated for (L/W) ratios corresponding to pure bending, 8 and 4, the measurements cannot be considered, strictly speaking, true K_{Ic} values. The toughness K_{IA} at crack arrest is determined, on specimens which develop a sufficiently straight crack line, with the use of the same procedure.

Results and Discussion

Toughness Measurements

A summary of data is listed in Table 2 for the annealed material; the crack velocity v, calculated from crack propagation time, Fig. 4, is plotted in Fig. 5 versus the specimen ER. In the same diagram are also reported the velocities v' calculated on the basis of a supposedly constant propagation time (average value on all tests $t \leqq 7\ \mu s$); in fact the best fit of v' with respect to v supports the idea of a constant propagation time in the tested

TABLE 2—*VCN-100 annealed* (σ_{ys} = *390 MN* m^{-2}), *5 × 10 mm TPB specimens,* L = *150 to 300 mm,* (a/w) = *0.55.*

Specimen No.	ER	Δw, J × 10^{-3}	Δs, mm^2	K_{ID}, MN m$^{-3/2}$	t, μs	v, m/s	v', m/s	v^*, m/s
M 1	0.02	11.6	0.46	76.4	...	...	22	21
O 11	0.02	11.0	0.40	79.8	8.7	21	19	21
O 17	0.025	15.0	0.54	80.3	...	...	25	26
Q 7	0.02	10.6	0.50	70.2	7.9	22	24	21
Q 11	0.025	13.2	0.56	74.1	6.9	28	27	26
Q 2	0.06	30.9	1.40	71.4	8.7	54	67	63
M 4	0.08	38.7	1.84	69.9	5.1	120	87	84
O 7	0.09	45.6	1.90	74.5	6.0	105	90	95
Q 13	0.08	47.5	1.78	78.6	7.1	83	84	84
O 10	0.10	43.9	2.16	68.6	6.3	114	103	105
O 14	0.095	53.6	2.06	77.6	7.7	88	97	100
Q 8	0.095	49.4	2.16	72.7	6.6	109	103	100
O 16	0.105	50.0	2.32	70.8	7.6	101	110	110
Q 1	0.12	63.3	2.72	73.3	6.3	144	130	126
Q 14	0.125	51.2	2.68	66.5	6.7	133	127	131
E 10	0.16	69.7	3.54	67.7	...	...	169	168

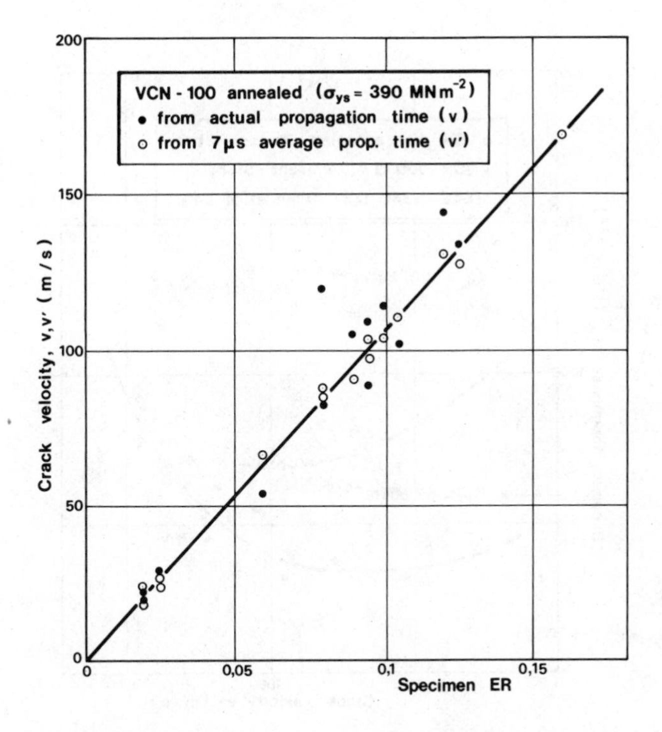

FIG. 5—*Dependence of crack velocity on specimen energy ratio.*

geometry. The direct proportionality between crack velocity and ER (v^* = 1050 ER) is assumed as a basis for the velocity determinations.

In Table 3 the summary of data is listed for the Q&T material; during this set of tests the electronics, used for the dynamic loading recording, failed and crack velocities reported are extrapolated on the basis of the relationship $v^* = 1050$ ER.

The K_{ID} measurements for both annealed and Q&T material are reported in Fig. 6 as a function of crack velocity v^*, in the same figure are reported for comparison the Battelle data [4], the good agreement supports the extrapolation procedure just mentioned. The logarithmic abscissa is used in Fig. 6 because of the wide range of velocities experienced, and to evidence the points in the minimum K_{ID} zone. The trend reported in Fig. 6 suggests a negative slope at low velocities for both the annealed and Q&T material. For the annealed material the K_{Ic} is unknown, but a tentative value around 130 MN m$^{-3/2}$ can be assessed on the basis of J-integral measurements [9] and crack tip opening displacement (CTOD) measurements [7]; for the Q&T material the measured value of about 57 MN m$^{-3/2}$ (see Table 3) seems slightly lower than literature data (see Fig. 1), but reasonable; the K_{Ic} data of the two materials are both distinctly higher than the minimum K_{ID} values measured. In Table 3 some K_{IA} data

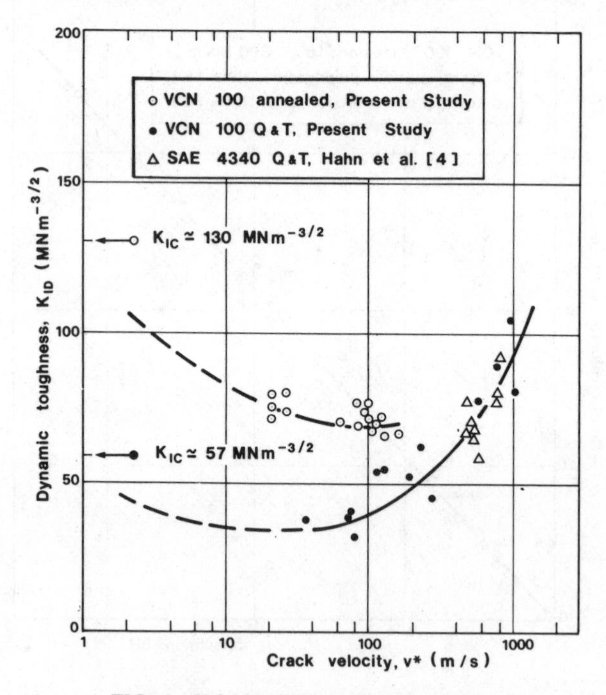

FIG. 6—*Velocity dependence of* K_{ID} *values.*

TABLE 3—*VCN-100 Q&T* (σ_{ys} = *1360 MN* m^{-2}), *5 × 10 mm TPB specimens,* *L = 60 to 150 mm,* (a/W) = *0.1 to 0.3.*

Specimen No.	ER	Δw, J × 10^{-3}	Δs, mm^2	K_{ID}, MN $m^{-3/2}$	v^*, m/s	K_{Ic} MN $m^{-3/2}$	K_{IA}, MN $m^{-3/2}$
5 D2 bis	0.035	7.5	1.16	38.2	37	70.2	...
2 D2 bis	0.075	12.9	2.70	32.9	79	47.5	...
5 D1 bis	0.07	18.1	2.60	40.1	74	50.6	...
10 D2 bis	0.07	17.5	2.48	40.4	74	60.6	...
2 D1 bis	0.11	54.9	4.20	54.7	116	54.3	63.5
4 D2 bis	0.125	61.8	4.60	55.9	131	57.5	64.7
1 D1 bis	0.185	82.4	6.80	53.1	194	52.5	...
4 D1 bis	0.22	137.0	7.90	63.4	231	64.0	...
1 D2 bis	0.26	102.0	10.90	46.6	273	54.7	78.2
1 D	0.53	607	22.60	78.9	557	51.7	54.4
4 D	0.73	1142	32.40	90.4	767	53.7	...
11 D	0.93	1991.0	41.00	105.9	977	64.0	...
2 D	0.97	1245.0	43.00	82.0	1019	50.9	...
5 D	> 1	6896	complete fracture	...	> 1050	70.2	...
8 D	> 1	2266	complete fracture	...	> 1050	50.1	...
10 D	> 1	1962	complete fracture	...	> 1050	60.6	...

are also listed for the Q&T material; the value of 54.5 MN $m^{-3/2}$ is found for Specimen 1*D*, the only one showing a nearly straight crack propagation front line, and a rather large fracture involving the whole specimen thickness. In the other specimens, which showed thumbnail propagations, confined within the specimen thickness, the use of Eq 3 is highly questionable.

Fractographic Measurements

Two examples of graphic presentation of fracture results are shown in Fig. 7. All the annealed specimens show a stable crack extension (SCE) before the fast crack propagation. The SCE fracture, substantially ductile, extends to the whole specimen thickness and exhibits, at SEM, dimples (Fig. 8*a*) produced by void coalescence. The fast crack propagation, confined in the specimen thickness induces brittle fracture: the cleavage facets are shown in Fig. 8*c*; the transition between the two fracture modes develops a "secondary" stretch zone (Fig. 8*b*).

In the case of the Q&T material, no SCE is observed, as shown in Fig. 7*b* and the SEM reveals the predominantly intergranular fracture with secondary cracks at low-crack velocities (Fig. 9*a*). In specimens fractured at relatively high velocity, the fracture is intergranular, with more pronounced secondary cracks (Fig. 9*b*); however, some well-developed cleaved areas are present (Fig. 9*c*), and the transition between intergranular and cleaved areas is often marked by narrow dimpled zones (Fig. 9*d*).

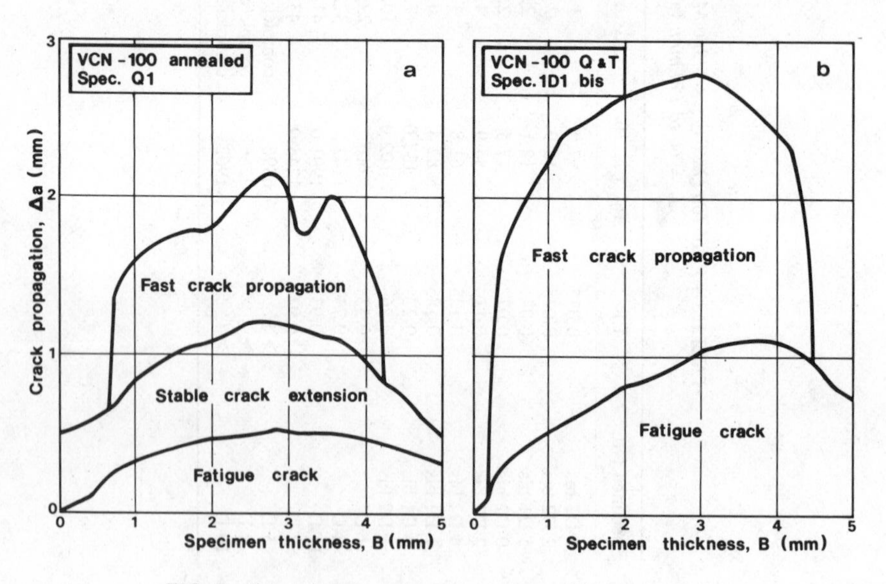

FIG. 7—*Examples of graphic presentation of fractures results.*

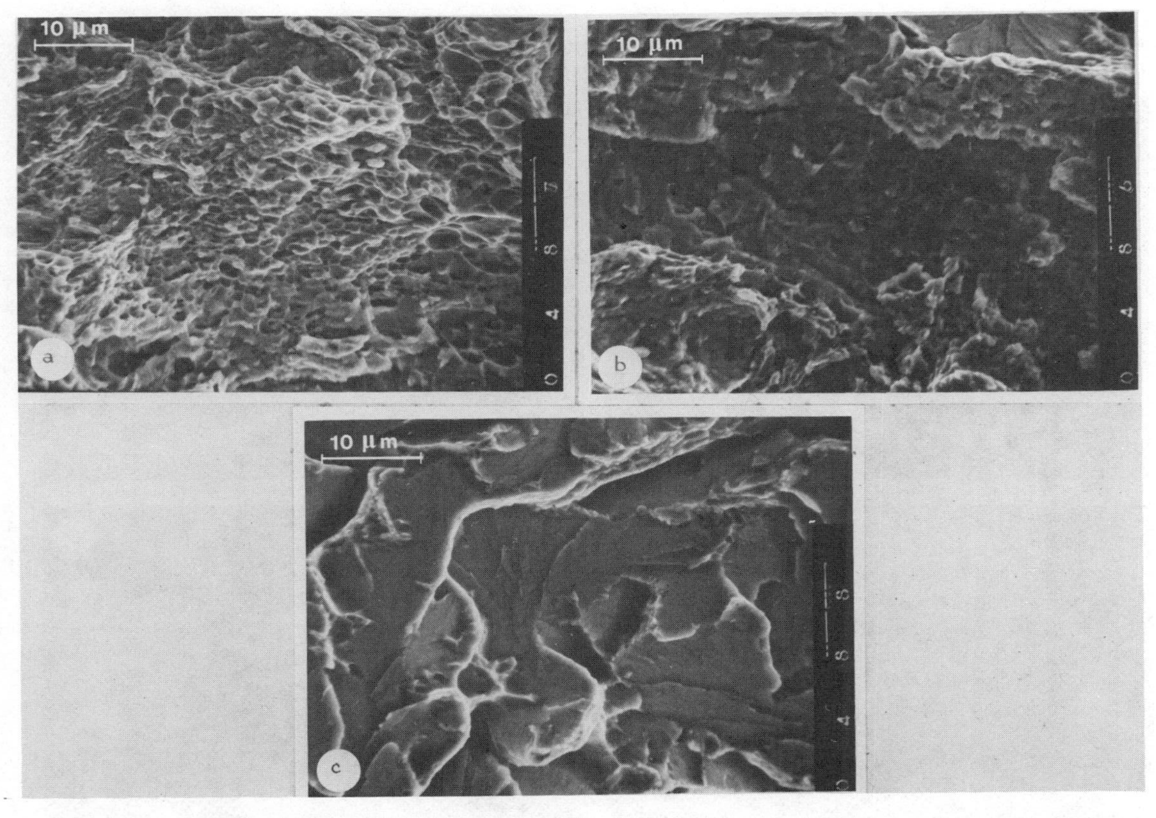

FIG. 8—*Annealed material, specimen 07* (v = *90/ms*), (a) *dimpled fracture in the SCE zone,* (b) *transition between SCE and fast crack extension and* (c) *cleavage facets and small dimpled areas in the fast crack extension zone.*

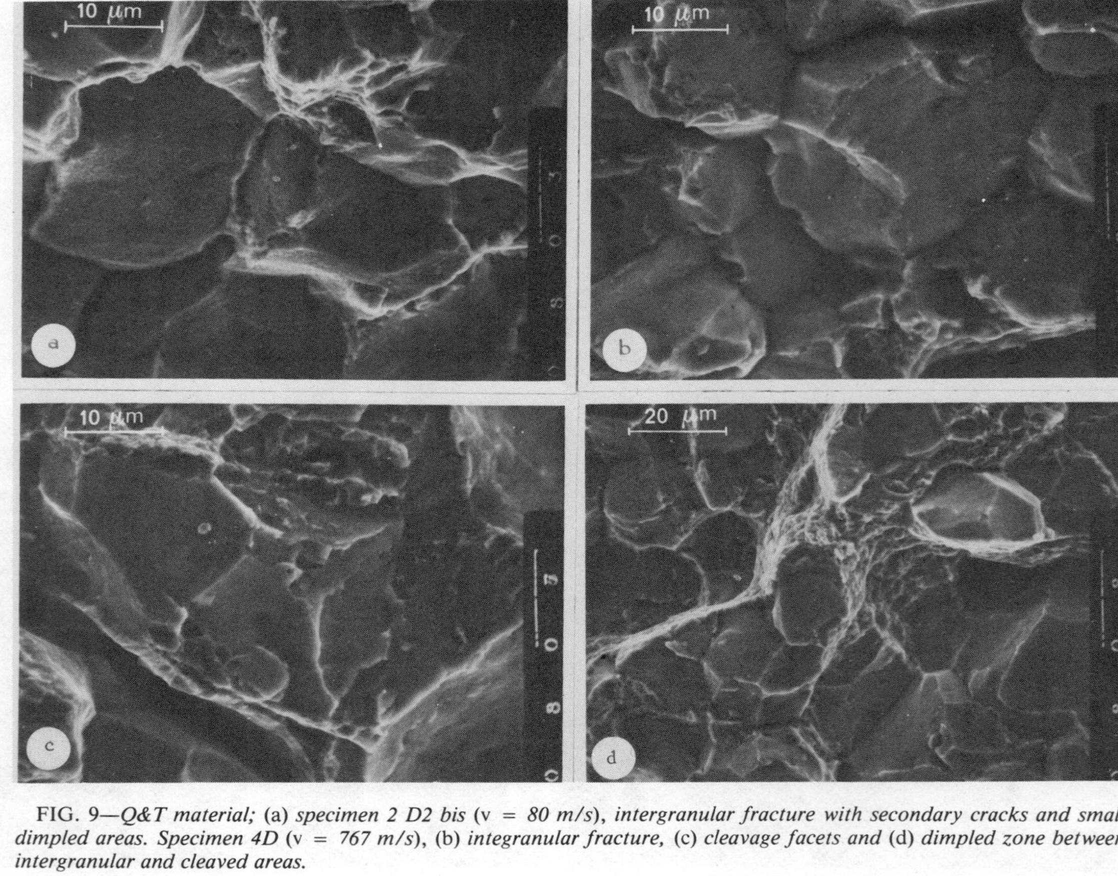

FIG. 9—*Q&T material;* (a) *specimen 2 D2 bis* (v = *80 m/s*), *intergranular fracture with secondary cracks and small dimpled areas. Specimen 4D* (v = *767 m/s*), (b) *integranular fracture,* (c) *cleavage facets and* (d) *dimpled zone between intergranular and cleaved areas.*

Conclusion

The concept of the TPB specimen tested at different lengths, to vary the specimen ER, has proven to be an useful tool for dynamic toughness measurements. The main advantages are the following:

1. A very wide velocity range can be explored.
2. In the case of the annealed material the size requirements for a K_{Ic} value are not fulfilled; however, both the fast crack propagation well confined in the specimen thickness and the observed cleavage fracture in this zone suggest the assumption that the crack propagates with a fairly good regime of lateral constraint and support the use of small coupons of material to determine correct K_{ID} measurements.
3. The test procedure is rather simple.
4. The relationship between crack velocity and ER, to be further tested on different materials and geometrical shapes could prove useful for an estimate of velocity. An analytical model of crack propagation, in the tested geometry, is in progress; anyway, the data presented in this work are self consistent and the agreement with literature is good.

Acknowledgments

The work described in this paper has been supported by CISE/ENEL contract MAT-2; the author is grateful to Ente Nazionale dell'Energia Elettrica for the permission to publish the data. Author thanks are due G. Caglioti for the helpful discussions during the work and A. Aguzzi, F. Barbesino, F. Bondesan, C. Fossati, and A. Uggè for the contribution to the experimental work.

APPENDIX I

The ER (energy ratio) of a specimen, defined as

$$\mathrm{ER} = w_s/w_f \tag{4}$$

where w_s and w_f are the stored elastic energy at load instability, and the fracture energy of the specimen, respectively, can be modified for a given material through changes in specimen geometry.

The stored elastic energy which in its general form is

$$w_s = \int_v S\,dV \tag{5}$$

where S is the strain energy density in a body of volume V and can be written for a cracked specimen at load instability as

$$w_s = \alpha \frac{\sigma_f^2}{2E} BWL \tag{6}$$

where

α = dimensionless function of geometry and loading which accounts for the actual stress distribution in the specimen,
E = Young modulus of the material,
σ_f = applied stress at load instability, and
B, W, L = dimensions of the specimen.

The maximum applied stress σ_f is related to the crack length a and to the critical stress intensity factor, when linear elastic fracture mechanics (LEFM) can be applied through

$$\sigma_f = \frac{K_{\text{Ic}}}{Y\sqrt{a}} \tag{7}$$

where Y is the well known dimensionless function of geometry and loading.

On the other hand the fracture energy of the specimen is

$$w_f = G_c\left(1 - \frac{a}{W}\right) BW \tag{8}$$

where $G_c = 2\ (\gamma_s + \gamma_p)$, is the specific fracture energy which takes into account both the surface energy γ_s and the plastic work γ_p, and $(1 - a/w)BW$ is the area of the specimen ligament.

Introducing Eqs 6 and 8 into 4, it follows

$$\text{ER} = \chi \frac{\sigma_f^2}{EG_c} L \tag{9}$$

where $\chi = \alpha/2(1 - a/W)$ is again a dimensionless function of geometry and loading.

Equation 9 shows that the ER can be modified, for a given material and loading geometry, through changes of geometrical parameters; namely, the specimen length L, or more generally the length in the direction orthogonal to the fracture plane, and the crack length or shape; in this second case the maximum ER is limited by the yield stress σ_{ys} of the material. As the value of ER reflects the energy available to produce fracture work with respect to the fracture work to be done, two ER levels seems to deserve particular interest:

1. ER < 1—crack arrests within the specimen.
2. ER = 1—stored elastic energy is just sufficient to propagate the crack on the whole specimen ligament area.

The length of a specimen corresponding to the near complete fracture of a tested specimen: $\Delta s \leqq (1 - a/W)BW$ and ER $\leqq 1$, has been called L_c (critical length) [1,2]. Introducing into Eq 9 $K_{\text{Ic}} = \sqrt{EG_c}$ and resolving for L_c, it follows

$$L_c = \frac{1}{\chi}\left(\frac{K_{\text{Ic}}}{\sigma_f}\right)^2 \tag{10}$$

which shows a noticeable formal similarity with Eq 7 rewritten as

$$a_c = \frac{1}{Y^2}\left(\frac{K_{\text{Ic}}}{\sigma_f}\right)^2 \tag{11}$$

When tests are performed on materials which show velocity dependent mechanical properties, the use of Eqs 9 and 10 is not straightforward; however, the critical length of the specimen can be experimentally determined and the ER of the specimen, at $L < L_c$, can be measured *a posteriori* as the ratio between the fracture area actually produced and the specimen ligament area.

References

[1] Angelino, G. C., "Proposta Preliminare per una Nuova Metodologia di Misura dei Parametri Caratteristici Della Meccanica Della Frattura Relativi al modo I," CISE Technical Note 73.047, Centro Informazioni Studi Esperienze, Milano, Italy, Nov. 1973.

[2] Angelino, G. C., "New Approaches to the Experimental Determination of Fracture Mechanics Parameters," Enrico Fermi International School of Varenna, July 1974.

[3] Hahn, G. T., Hoagland, R. G., Kanninen, M. F., and Rosenfield, A. R., "A Preliminary Study of Fast Fracture and Arrest in the DCB Test Specimen," International Conference on Dynamic Crack Propagation, Lehigh University, Bethlehem, Pa., July 1972, pp. 646–662.

[4] Hahn, G. T., Gehlen, P. G., Hoagland, R. G., Kanninen, M. F., Popelar, C., Rosenfield, A. R., and de Campos, V. S., "Critical Experiments, Measurements, and Analyses to Establish a Crack Arrest Methodology for Nuclear Vessel Steels," BMI Report 1937, Battelle-Columbus Laboratories, Columbus, Ohio, Aug. 1975.

[5] Hahn, G. T., Gehlen, P. G., Hoagland, R. G., Kanninen, M. F., Popelar, C., Rosenfield, A. R., "Critical Experiments, Measurements and Analyses to Establish a Crack Arrest Methodology for Nuclear Pressure Vessel Steels," BMI-NUREG Report 1944, Battelle-Columbus Laboratories,—U.S. Nuclear Regulatory Commission, Office of Nuclear Regulatory Research, March 1976.

[6] Erra, A., Valeriani, G., and Venzi, S., *La Metallurgia Italiana,* Vol. LXIV, No. 9, Sept. 1972, pp. 421–426.

[7] Robinson, J. N. and Tetelman, A. S., "The Crack-Tip Opening Displacement and Microscopic and Macroscopic Fracture Criteria for Metals," UCLA-ENG Report No. 7360, University of California, Los Angeles, Aug. 1973.

[8] Brown, W. F., Jr., and Srawley, J. E., *Plane Strain Crack Toughness Testing of High Strength Metallic Materials, ASTM STP 410,* American Society for Testing and Materials, p. 13.

[9] Barbesino, F., Fossati, C., "Integrale J: Risultati sull'Acciaio 38 NiCrMo4," CISE-SSR-MAT 2 Report No. 22, Centro Informazioni Studi Esperienze, Milano, Italy, April 1976.

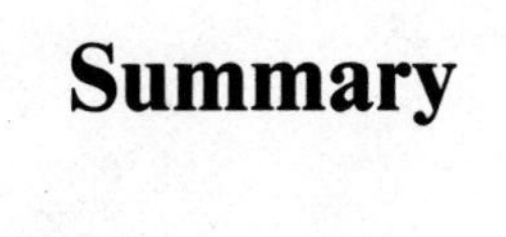

Summary

Summary

There is now general agreement that the arrest of a rapidly propagating crack, from a fundamental point of view, can occur only when the conditions for its continued propagation can no longer be satisfied. Consequently, precise treatments of crack arrest must start from an analysis of a propagation event. There is less agreement on the extent to which the considerable mathematical and experimental complexity required for a fundamentally correct analysis is necessary. Many practical applications in which the prevention of extended unstable crack propagation is an important consideration undoubtedly can be adequately treated in much simpler ways. The problem is that such instances cannot always be identified without the help of a more complete treatment.

Broadly speaking, the papers contained in this volume tacitly reflect the schism that now exists. Some papers take a fundamental point of view, while others are more pragmatic. In the former category, with the exception of small crack jumps, account generally must be taken of dynamic effects in the body (for example, inertia forces, stress wave interactions with free boundaries, kinetic energy) and a possible dependence of the crack propagation criterion on the crack speed. There can be a substantial difference between this, a "dynamic fracture mechanics" approach, and a quasi-static interpretation of a run-arrest event. This is clearly shown in one of the most significant papers in this volume—the paper by Kalthoff, Beinert, and Winkler—which describes experimental results using the popular double-cantilever-beam (DCB) test specimen.

As reflected by the bulk of the work contained in this volume, current efforts in dynamic fracture mechanics are essentially dynamic generalizations of conventional linear elastic fracture mechanics. A basic premise involved in such an approach is that the critical value of a crack-tip characterizing parameter, either K or $\mathcal{G}$, be a geometry-independent material property. Thus, the systematic experimental evidence reported by T. Kobayashi and Dally showing that the dynamic fracture toughness parameter K_{ID} is at most a function of crack speed is of great importance. At the same time, it must be recognized that the exact shape of the $K_{ID} = K_{ID}(V)$ curve is not known precisely for any material. Indeed, as Broberg points up in his paper, our fundamental understanding of this function is far from complete. Perhaps the micromechanical picture proposed in the paper of Shockey et al has the potential to resolve these difficulties.

However, as indicated by Irwin, the effects of material damping away from the crack tip may also be important.

The papers in this volume that attempt to analyze fast crack propagation do so entirely within the confines of the linear elasticity theory. For special conditions, closed form techniques can be applied. Two such instances are reported in the papers by Freund and Achenbach and Tolikas. However, most work requires numerical solution techniques. Papers in this volume based on the finite-element method are those by Yagawa et al, A. Kobayashi et al, Emery et al, Shockey et al, and Aberson et al. Finite difference based analyses are given by Kanazawa et al, Shmuely and Peretz, and Kanninen et al. The latter also offers a way in which the particular geometry in a problem of interest can be exploited to simplify the analysis.

In view of its complexities, any simplifications that can be made in the application of fast fracture and crack arrest theory to engineering problems are welcome. The proposal by Professor G. Irwin, that the K_{ID} crack velocity curve can be represented by a speed-independent value equal to K_{Im} is in this category. This idealization has several virtues. It is conservative, it can simplify computations, and it reduces the number of measurements needed to characterize the material.

Methods of measuring K_{Im} are currently under development in a number of laboratories.[1] Different approaches are described in the papers by Angelino, Crosley and Ripling, Hoagland et al, Bergkvist, and Burns and Chow contained in this volume. The first three of these papers are based on essentially static measurements of load or displacement or both and the crack length at arrest. The last two methods depend on measurements of crack speed. Because crack-speed measurements are difficult to obtain, they can benefit from the improved instrumentation and recording techniques reported here by Weimer and Rogers and Congleton and Denton.

Actually, the complexity of the instrumentation is only one of the factors to be considered in weighing the different methods. Both the specimen size and load requirements needed to measure the K_{Im} values of practical interest—150 $\text{MPa}\cdot\text{m}^{1/2} \lesssim K_{Im} \lesssim 200\ \text{MPa}\cdot\text{m}^{1/2}$ in the case of nuclear pressure vessels—and the extent to which the underlying analysis applies under actual test conditions are exceedingly important. As already noted, the analyses for all the different methods described in this volume are based on linear elastic behavior and are subject to the same awesome size requirements that are contained in ASTM Method E 399-74. But, a substantial relaxation of specimen thickness requirements appears possible

[1]It should be noted that a number of authors in this volume use the symbol K_{Im} to represent the actual minimum in the K_{ID} velocity curve, and the symbol K_{Ia} to represent estimates of K_{Im} derived from static analyses of post arrest measurements.

because of the exceedingly high strain rates and higher effective yield stress associated with the plastic zone of a rapidly propagating crack. Very significant size economics can also be achieved through the use of duplex specimens as discussed by Hoagland et al. Deep side grooves represent another device both for reducing specimen size and conferring greater crack path stability to the DCB specimens, but this approach is still being questioned.

The evolution of a well-defined crack-arrest toughness property is beginning to generate interest both in the relation between K_{Im} and other toughness properties, notably K_{Id} (the toughness of a stationary crack loaded dynamically), and microstructural properties at arrest. The new technique for measuring K_{Id}, reported by Costin et al can facilitate comparison between these two dynamic toughness properties. The work of Bullock and Smith is a forerunner of studies that will examine metallurgical variables.

An important part of this conference was the culminating agenda discussion session. The session was addressed to critical issues and unresolved problems in developing an engineering approach to crack arrest. To start the session, individuals representing different technological areas in which fast fracture arrest knowledge plays a crucial role were invited to give their view of the problem and, on the basis of the papers presented during the conference, their feelings on how current research efforts are coping with them. These individuals were J. Darlaston (Berkley Nuclear Laboratory, U.K.), S. Yukawa (General Electric Company), W. A. Maxey (Battelle), G. C. Smith (Oak Ridge National Laboratory), and E. A. Chazel, Jr., (U.S. Coast Guard). Their short presentations were of great value in focusing the discussions in accord with the theme of the session.

The chairmen for the concluding discussion session were E. K. Lynn (Nuclear Regulatory Commission) and T. U. Marston (Electric Power Research Institute). In addition to their very capable handling of the session, they have evolved a set of conclusions and recommendations based upon discussions during the session and written comments submitted subsequently. With their kind permission, the conclusions representing consensus opinions are given here as follows.

1. The complete relation between crack speed and the fast fracture toughness K_{ID} should be known and used as input to an exact dynamic analysis of crack propagation and arrest in a structure.[2] This contains the particular value, K_{Im} defined as the minimum value of K_{ID} on a graph of crack speed versus K_{ID}. Crack arrest will always occur when $K < K_{Im}$.

2. It is difficult to obtain the crack speed versus K_{ID} relation and to perform a complete dynamic analysis in an ideal fashion. Therefore, it would be useful to study methods for predicting crack arrest in a structure

[2]Testing conditions corresponding to plane strain near the crack tip are assumed.

which would be less complex, less expensive, and sufficiently accurate for engineering purposes.

3. Since the results of a dynamic analysis clearly depend upon the structural configuration, future studies should focus attention on configurations and loadings which are of practical interest, for example, a two-dimensional approximation of a crack penetrating the wall of a pressure vessel.

4. The goal of a single property measurement technique is measurement of K_{Im}. From available information, methods used previously for K_{ID} and K_{Ia} evaluation deserve consideration.[3] The conditions under which such results differ significantly from K_{Im} require further study.

5. High values of $(K/\sigma_y)^2$ at crack initiation are undesirable both in the static K_{Ia} and dynamic K_{ID} approaches to the determination of K_{Im}. Therefore, the use of either temperature (toughness) gradients or the use of duplex specimens may be necessary when $K_{Im} > 100$ ksi $\sqrt{\text{in.}}$ (109 $\text{MNm}^{3/2}$).

6. Large specimen tests, $B > 6$ in. (150 mm), are needed to validate the test results obtained with smaller specimens.

The recommendation for further research evolving from the discussions in the concluding session, as collected by Lynn and Marston, are as follows.

1. The behavior of the crack-tip stress intensity, K, as a function of time following the arrest of the crack needs to be explored.

2. The development of simplified K_{Im} techniques such as Battelle's technique based on the crack jump length in a DCB specimen with a blunted initial crack tip (or K_{Ia}, if applicable) needs to be pursued.

3. Further studies into the effect of energy damping on fast fracture and crack arrest need to be made.

4. The K_{ID} versus crack velocity relationship should be measured in the same structural metal using at least two independent testing techniques to establish the reproducibility and experimental accuracy of the relationships.

5. The sensitivity of the results of current (and future) dynamic analyses on the nature of the K_{ID} crack velocity dependence needs to be assessed.

6. Dynamic fracture analyses of some engineering structures are needed. Effort should be directed to apply the existing dynamic analyses and develop simplified approximate analyses for practical applications.

7. Frequently, the volume of material available for characterization is insufficient for conventional specimens. Therefore, compound or composite specimens must be developed in order to evaluate the initiation, propagation, and arrest properties of such a material.

8. Component verification tests of the extant theories of crack arrest should be expanded.

[3] K_{Ia} is a measure of the stress intensity immediately after static equilibrium has been achieved following the arrest of a rapidly propagating crack.

9. Three-dimensional dynamic analyses of crack propagation should be developed to test the validity of the two-dimensional dynamic analyses and analyze geometries too complex for two-dimensional analyses.

It might be noted that these recommendations are confined to research directions within the context of linear elastic material behavior. This is the focus of current research. Fast fracture and arrest attended by inelastic material behavior also offer significant research opportunities.

In conclusion, perhaps the most remarkable aspect of fast fracture propagation and arrest research is its timeliness. The advances described in this volume could not have been made before the availability of large-scale computers, and the advances in experimental capabilities that are enabling researchers all over the world to address the problem in a fundamentally correct manner. The new analytical capabilities will make it easier to meet the critical needs for energy, material conservation, and improvements in reliability and structural safety.

G. T. Hahn
M. F. Kanninen
Battelle Columbus Laboratories, Columbus, Ohio; editors.

Index

K

L

M

N

O

P

R

S

T